HOUGHTON MIFFLIN
MATHEMATICS
PROGRAM

MODERN

INTRODUCTORY

ANALYSIS

COVER

The design on the cover is a motion-study photograph of the painted aluminum sculpture of José de Rivera entitled "Construction in Blue and Black," 1951. It is used by permission of the Whitney Museum of American Art, New York. Here the photographer has been interested in describing photographically the path of the sculpture through space over a brief interval of time. In a similar manner, mathematicians are interested in describing with equations the change in position of objects as a function of time.

MODERN

INTRODUCTORY

ANALYSIS

Mary P. Dolciani

Edwin F. Beckenbach

Alfred J. Donnelly

Ray C. Jurgensen

William Wooton

EDITORIAL ADVISER

ALBERT E. MEDER, JR.

Houghton Mifflin Company • *Boston*

ATLANTA • DALLAS • GENEVA, ILL. • HOPEWELL, NEW JERSEY • PALO ALTO • TORONTO

ABOUT THE AUTHORS

Mary P. Dolciani, Associate Dean for Academic Services and Professor, Department of Mathematics, Hunter College of the City University of New York. Dr. Dolciani has been a director and teacher in numerous National Science Foundation and New York State Education Department institutes for mathematics teachers, and Visiting Secondary School Lecturer for the Mathematical Association of America.

Edwin F. Beckenbach, Professor of Mathematics, University of California, Los Angeles. Dr. Beckenbach has been a team member of National Council of Teachers of Mathematics summer writing projects. He is Chairman of the Committee on Publications of the Mathematical Association of America.

Alfred J. Donnelly, Master Instructor and holder of the William Pitt Oakes Chair of Mathematics, Culver Military Academy and Culver Academy for Girls. Mr. Donnelly brings a rich background of both mathematics study and teaching to his authorship.

Ray C. Jurgensen, Chairman of Mathematics Department and holder of the Eppley Chair of Mathematics, Culver Military Academy and Culver Academy for Girls, Culver, Indiana. Mr. Jurgensen is a regular reader for the Advanced Placement Examinations of the College Entrance Examination Board.

William Wooton, Mathematics Consultant, Vista, California, Unified School District. Mr. Wooton was formerly Professor of Mathematics at Los Angeles Pierce College and has been a teacher at the junior and senior high school levels.

EDITORIAL ADVISER

Albert E. Meder, Jr., Professor of Mathematics and Dean of the University, Emeritus, Rutgers University, the State University of New Jersey.

CONTENTS

4 The Algebra of Vectors 121

5 Plane Analytic Geometry of Points and Lines 167

6 Functions 215

10 The Circular Functions and Trigonometry 373

11 Properties of Circular and Trigonometric Functions 415

15 Probability 599

ACKNOWLEDGMENTS

The authors of *Modern Introductory Analysis* wish to thank their colleagues for their assistance and inspiration in the development of this book. They particularly wish to express appreciation to the following persons for their valuable comments on the manuscript: Professor Jewell Hughes Bushey, Hunter College; Professor William C. Doyle, S. J., Rockhurst College; Professor Burton W. Jones, The University of Colorado; Mrs. Marion Pressel, Bedford, Massachusetts.

Special thanks are due Professor Robert M. Walter of Rutgers University for major contributions to the chapter on Probability, and Professor O. Lexton Buchanan, Jr. of the University of South Carolina for the appendix on Area under a Curve.

Photograph Credits

PAGE

Cover | José de Rivera: *Construction "Blue and Black."* 1951. Painted aluminum. Collection of the Whitney Museum of American Art, New York. (Photographed in motion.)

31 | Courtesy of University College, Cork

67 | Courtesy of J. R. Goldstein

117 | Courtesy of Inter Nationes, Bonn

165, 213, 251, 281, 321, 371 | Courtesy of Columbia University Library, D. E. Smith Collection

413 | Courtesy of Harvard University

457 | Courtesy of the Department of Mathematics, The University of Chicago

458 | Lissajous figures from Cundy and Rollett's *Mathematical Models*, 2nd edition, 1961, Oxford University Press, with the permission of the publishers.

505 | United Press International, Inc.

563 | Courtesy of Trinity College Library, Cambridge

597 | The Bettman Archive

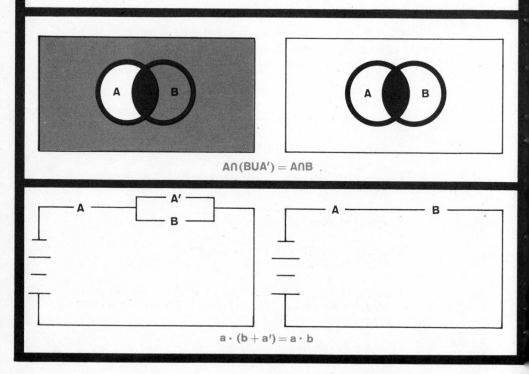

p	q	p′	q∨p′	p∧(q∨p′)	p∧q
T	T	F	T	T	T
T	F	F	F	F	F
F	T	T	T	F	F
F	F	T	T	F	F

p∧(q∨p′) = p∧q

A∩(B∪A′) = A∩B

a · (b + a′) = a · b

Above, the same theorem is stated in terms of logic, set theory, and an abstract mathematical system called Boolean algebra. In logic the theorem is proved by means of a truth table. In set theory it is illustrated by Venn diagrams and in Boolean algebra by circuit diagrams.

Statements and Sets

in Mathematics

One way to view mathematics is to think of it as a study of patterns. In this book, you will learn to work with a wide variety of patterns, some familiar to you, such as $x^2 - y^2 = (x + y)(x - y)$, and others quite new. In order to learn the mathematics you will encounter, you will need to understand the logical machinery used to discuss mathematical statements; this is what you will study in the present chapter.

SIMPLE STATEMENTS AND SETS

1-1 Logical Statements; Sets

In studying algebra and geometry you have discovered many logical connections between mathematical statements. But do you know what constitutes a statement in logic?

A **statement** or **proposition** is a set of symbols (and *words* are symbols, of course) which forms a meaningful assertion that is either true or false, but not both true and false.

The following assertions are examples of statements:

True Statements	*False Statements*
(1) $2 + 3 = 5$.	(1) $0 > 1$.
(2) Shakespeare wrote *Hamlet*.	(2) Plato was a Chinese philosopher.
(3) Ottawa is not a province of Canada.	(3) $\sqrt[3]{125} \neq 5$.

On the other hand, none of the following sentences is a statement because none can be said to be definitely true or definitely false.

(1) Give me liberty or give me death.

(2) $x^2 + 1 = 5$.

(3) This sentence is false.

1

Logical statements in mathematics frequently involve the use of symbols of equality and inequality. You should recall that the symbol "=" represents the word "equals" or the phrase "is equal to," and is used between expressions to show that they represent the same object. Similarly, the inequality symbols ">," "<," "≥," and "≤" represent "is greater than," "is less than," "is greater than or equal to," and "is less than or equal to," respectively. These symbols are used in sentences and statements comparing numbers. A bar, / or |, is used in conjunction with certain symbols to denote negation. For example, the symbol "≠" placed between two expressions asserts that the expressions do not represent the same object, and the symbol ≮ stands for "is not less than."

Some mathematical statements concern *membership* in a *set*. You should recall from your earlier study of mathematics that the objects in a set are called **members** or **elements** of the set, and are said to *belong to* or to be *contained in* the set. The symbol ∈ is used to denote "is an element of," while ∉ means "is not an element of." For example, if J is the set of integers, then $3 \in J$ is a true statement, whereas $4 \notin J$ is a false statement.

A statement that two sets are equal is an assertion that they contain the same elements. Thus, the statement $A = B$ means that A and B name the same set. This definition of the equality of sets implies that to *specify* a set, you must be able to identify its elements. You can sometimes specify a set by listing the names of its elements within braces, { }. For example, $\{-1, 0, 1\}$, read "the set whose members are -1, 0, and 1," is a *roster* (list) of the numbers -1, 0, and 1. Quite frequently, however, a set has so many elements that it is inconvenient or impossible to list them all. Thus, we may write $\{1, 2, 3, \ldots, 50\}$ and expect the reader to understand that the set specified contains the integers from 1 to 50, inclusive. Similarly, $\{1, 2, 3, \ldots\}$ specifies the set of all positive integers.

The members of a set can, themselves, be sets. $\{\{1, 3\}, \{5, 7\}, \{9, 11\}\}$, for example, is the set whose members are $\{1, 3\}$, $\{5, 7\}$, and $\{9, 11\}$. Observe that the set $\{\{a, b\}\}$ is not the same as the set $\{a, b\}$. The first contains just one element, $\{a, b\}$, while the second contains two elements, a and b.

Another way to specify a set consists in giving a rule or condition that enables you to decide whether or not any given object belongs to the set. For example, {the teachers of mathematics}, read "the set of the teachers of mathematics," specifies a set whose roster contains many thousands of names. Of course, you certainly recognize that every mathematics teacher you know belongs to

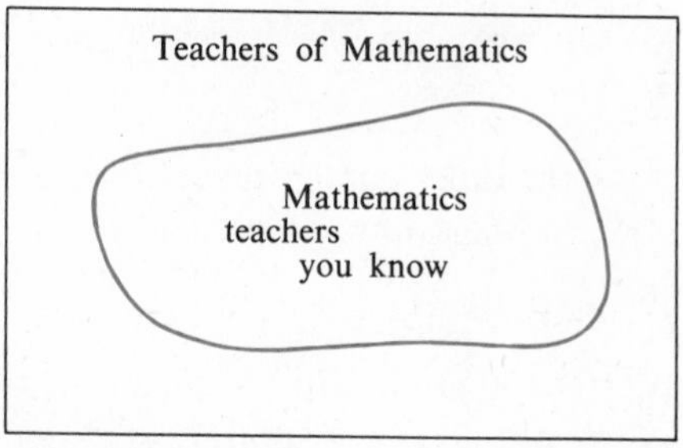

Figure 1–1

Teachers of Mathematics

Mathematics
teachers
you know

{the teachers of mathematics}. Whenever each element of a set R is also an element of a set S, we say that R is a **subset** of S, in symbols "$R \subset S$." Thus, {mathematics teachers you know} $\subset$ {teachers of mathematics}. Diagrams such as the one shown are used to illustrate a set and a subset; they are called **Venn diagrams.**

Since every positive integer is a member of the set of positive integers, it is certainly true that the set of positive integers is a subset of itself. Each set is said to be the **improper subset** of itself; every other subset is called a **proper subset** of the set.

Can you list the members of the set of integers between $\frac{1}{2}$ and $\frac{2}{3}$? This set contains no elements at all and is therefore called the **empty set** or **null set.** We use the symbol $\emptyset$, written without braces, to designate the empty set. Because of our agreement on the meaning of equality of sets, there is only one empty set, $\emptyset$. Furthermore, $\emptyset$ is taken to be a *proper* subset of every set except itself.

Exercises

Which of the sentences in Exercises 1–16 are statements? Of the statements, which are true? Give a reason for each answer.

1. $5 \cdot 4 = 20$
2. $5 - 4 = 2$
3. $3 + 7(2) = 2 + 15$
4. $7(4 + 2) = 7 \cdot 4 + 7 \cdot 2$
5. $\dfrac{6 + 2}{2} = 6 + 1$

6. $(-2)^3 \geq (-2)^4$
7. $1 + 3 \neq 1 + 6$
8. $2 + 3 > 0$
9. Man the lifeboats!
10. Help!

In Exercises 11–16, let $J = $ {integers} $ = \{\ldots, -3, -2, -1, 0, 1, 2, 3, \ldots\}$.

11. $\{1, 2, 7\} \subset J$
12. $0 \in J$
13. $\{0\} \in J$

14. $\emptyset$ is not a subset of J.
15. $-1 \subset J$
16. $\{-1, 0, 2\} \notin J$

Copy each sentence, making it a true statement by replacing each question mark with a numeral or with one of the symbols $=, \neq, \in, \notin, \subset$. (Note: There may be more than one correct answer.)

17. $-3 \times ? = -3$
18. $? \times 7 = 0$
19. $5(? - 3) = 20$
20. $\dfrac{24 - 6}{6} \ ? \ 4 - 6$

21. $\dfrac{10 \times 4}{2} \ ? \ 5 \times 2$
22. $\dfrac{21 + ?}{3} \neq 7 + 1$
23. $\{0 \cdot 2\} \subset \{1, 3, ?\}$
24. $\{1, \frac{6}{2}, -1\} = \{-2 \div 2, 3, ? \times 4\}$

B   **25.** $\{0, 2, 4\}$? {the even integers}

26. $5 + ? \notin$ {the positive and negative numbers}

27. $\dfrac{8 \times ?}{4} \in \{8\}$ **29.** $0 \ ? \ \{0\}$ **31.** $\{1, \{2\}\}$? $\{\{2\}, 1\}$

28. $\emptyset \ ? \ \{7 - 7\}$ **30.** $\{\emptyset\} \ ? \ \emptyset$ **32.** $\{1, \{2\}\}$? $\{\{1\}, 2\}$

Let $U = \{-4, 0, 8\}$. List all the subsets of U that

33.   Have exactly one element.   **35.**   Have at least two elements.

34.   Have no elements.   **36.**   Have no more than 2 elements.

Which of the following rosters or rules (Exercises 37–40) specify sets? Justify your answer by explaining whether or not it can be decided that an arbitrary object is or is not a member.

37.   {the authors of this textbook}

38.   {bell, book, candle}

39.   {the digits appearing in the decimal numeral for $\frac{1}{7}$}

40. $\{3, 1, 4, 5, 9, 2, 6, \ldots\}$

C   **41.**   Make a list of all subsets of $\{\emptyset, \{\emptyset\}\}$.

42.   A set contains $n > 0$ elements. How many subsets does it have?

43.   A set containing $k + 1$ elements has 8 more subsets than a set containing k elements. Find k.

44.   Argue that if $A \subset B$ and $B \subset A$, then $A = B$.

45.   Argue that if $A \subset B$ and $B \subset C$, then $A \subset C$.

46.   Can an element of a set be a subset of the set? Justify your answer.

1–2 Variables and Quantifiers

In logic and mathematics you encounter sentences, such as "He is an elected official" or "$x + 1 > 0$," which cannot be described as true or as false. To work with such sentences, you must understand the role of the pronoun *He* and the letter *x*. Each is a symbol, called a **variable**, and is used to represent any element of a specified set. The set whose elements may serve as replacements for the variable is called the **domain**, or **replacement set**, or **universe** of the variable. The members of the domain are called the **values** of the variable. A variable with just one value is called a **constant**. If the domain of the pronoun *He* in the sentence "He is an elected official" is {the public officeholders in New York City}, you obtain a true statement when you replace *He* by the name of the mayor, because in New York City the mayor is elected. On the other hand, when you write the name of the superintendent of schools in place of *He*, a false statement results, because his is an appointive office. Do you see that if the domain of x is {positive integers}, then the sentence $x + 1 > 0$ yields a true statement for any replacement of x by one of its values?

Sentences containing variables are called **open sentences**. Because an open sentence serves as a pattern for the various statements, each either true or false, which you obtain by replacing the variable with names for the different values of the variable, you can use an open sentence to specify a set. The subset of the domain consisting of the values of the variable for which the open sentence is true is called the **solution set** or **truth set** of the open sentence over that domain. Each element of the solution set is said to **satisfy** and to be a **solution** or **root** of the open sentence. For example, suppose $S = \{0, 1, 2, 3\}$. Then

$$\{y\colon\ y \in S \text{ and } y + 3 = 4\},$$

read "the set of all y, such that y belongs to S and $y + 3 = 4$," is the set consisting of those members of S for which the open sentence $y + 3 = 4$ is true. Do you see that the solution set of this open sentence is {1}? To **solve** an open sentence over a given domain means to determine its solution set in that domain.

In the preceding examples we have converted open sentences into statements by replacing variables by particular values. The use of such key words as *each, all, every,* and *any* enables you to convert an open sentence into a general statement. For example, the general statement

For all positive integers x, $x + 1 > 0$

asserts the following truth: Whenever you replace x with a numeral for a positive integer, the sentence $x + 1 > 0$ becomes a true statement. Other ways of stating the same general assertion are the following:

For each positive integer x, $x + 1 > 0$.

For every positive integer x, $x + 1 > 0$.

For any positive integer x, $x + 1 > 0$.

On the other hand, the general statement, "Every public officeholder in New York City is an elected official," is certainly false, because many such officeholders are appointed.

Combining a variable with such words as *there is, there exists, there are, for some, for at least one* provides another way of forming statements from open sentences. The assertion,

There is a positive integer x such that $x + 1 > 0$,

is certainly true. It states that, in the set of positive integers, there is a replacement for x for which the sentence $x + 1 > 0$ becomes a true statement. Of course, there are many such replacements, but the existence of at least one is enough to ensure the truth of the given assertion. Other forms of this statement are these:

> **There exists a positive integer x such that $x + 1 > 0$.**
>
> **For some positive integer x, $x + 1 > 0$.**
>
> **For at least one positive integer x, $x + 1 > 0$.**

Such key words as *all*, *every*, *some*, *there exists*, and so on, involve the idea of "how many," or of "quantity." For this reason, we call such a word, when used in combination with a variable in an open sentence, a **quantifier.**

Many of the statements you have used in geometry and algebra have involved quantifiers, often implied rather than openly stated. For example, the assertion

> **The base angles of an isosceles triangle have equal measure**

is a brief form of the proposition

> **For each isosceles triangle t, the base angles of t have equal measure.**

Similarly, the algebraic statement

$$a^2 - b^2 = (a - b)(a + b)$$

really means

> **For every number a and every number b,**
>
> $a^2 - b^2 = (a + b)(a - b).$

Also, you might write $u^2 = 49$ when, in fact, you mean

> **For some numbers u, $u^2 = 49$.**

Exercises

Solve the open sentence over the given set.

1. $y + 2 = 9$; {integers} 7

2. $x - 3 = 4$; {positive integers}

3. $r + 2 = 0$; {integers} -2

4. $2 - s = 0$; {integers}

5. $5k = 0$; {odd integers} ∅

6. $t + 3 = t$; {odd integers}

7. $v - 1 \leq 0$; {nonnegative integers} {0,1}

8. $2m \geq 0$; {nonpositive integers}

Determine which of the following statements are true.

9. $\{3, 1, 4\} \subset \{k: k$ is a digit in the decimal numeral for $\pi\}$ ~~true~~

10. A square $\notin \{u: u$ is a parallelogram$\}$

11. $\{7\} \subset \{t: t$ is an integer and $-7 + t = 0\}$ ~~true~~

12. $\{1, 3\} \subset \{m: m$ is an integer and $5 \times m = m \times 5\}$

Specify each of the following sets by roster.

13. $\{y: y$ is a negative odd integer greater than $-10\}$ $\{-9, -7, -5, -3, -1\}$

14. $\{x: x$ is a digit in the decimal for $\frac{1}{4}\}$

15. $\{z: z$ is a letter appearing at least once in the word *mathematics*$\}$

16. $\{l: l$ is a positive integer less than 20 and 1 less than a multiple of 3$\}$

B **17.** $\{A: A$ is a subset of $\{2\}\}$

18. $\{B: B$ is a subset of $\{1, 2\}\}$

19. $\{v: v = \{0\}\}$

20. $\{u: u \in \{1, 2, \emptyset\}\}$

21. $\{C: C \subset \{y: y$ is an integer and $3 \times y \neq y \times 3\}\}$

22. $\{D: D$ is a proper subset of $\{w: w$ is an integer such that $2(w + 1) = 6 + 2\}\}$

Convert the following sentences into true statements by using quantifiers.

23. $y^2 - 3y - 4 = 0$

24. $5t - (t - 1) = 2(2t + \frac{1}{2})$

25. $\frac{m}{3} + \frac{m}{4} \neq \frac{m}{7}$

26. $\sqrt{a^2 + 25} \neq a + 5$

27. $(x^2 - 1)^2 = x^4 + 1$

28. A is a subset of A.

29. $a(b + c) = ab + ac$

30. $\frac{u + v}{t} = \frac{u}{t} + \frac{v}{t}$

31. $-(x + y) = (-x) + (-y)$

32. $\frac{ab}{cd} = \frac{a}{c} \cdot \frac{b}{d}$

33. $\sqrt{x^2} = x$

34. $|x| = x$

COMBINING STATEMENTS AND SETS

1–3 Operations on Sets and Statements

In mathematics you often use sets formed by operations on two sets. Suppose, for example, that you are given the combination of open sentences $x^2 = 4$, $x(x - 2) = 0$, and are asked to determine the solution set of this combination over the set of integers. To solve this problem, you must decide whether you want only the numbers belonging to the solution sets of *both* of the sentences or whether you want the numbers belonging to the solution set of *at least one* of the sentences. You can use the language and symbolism of sets to describe these situations. The **intersection** of two sets R and S (in symbols, $R \cap S$) is the set consisting of the elements belonging to both R and S, while the **union** of R and S (in symbols, $R \cup S$) is the set consisting of the elements belonging to at least one of the given sets.

The Venn diagrams in the following figure illustrate these operations on sets. The regions within or on the indicated circles represent the sets R and S. The shaded regions represent $R \cap S$ and $R \cup S$, as shown.

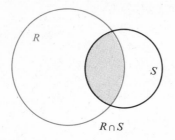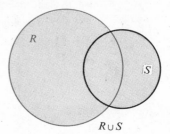

Figure 1–2

Given the open sentences $x^2 = 4$, $x(x - 2) = 0$ over the set of integers, you may therefore seek the intersection of their solution sets or the union of these sets. In the first instance,

$$\{x: \ x^2 = 4\} \cap \{x: \ x(x - 2) = 0\} \ = \ \{-2, 2\} \cap \{0, 2\} \ = \ \{2\},$$

and $\{2\}$ is the set of integers for which both $x^2 = 4$ and $x(x - 2) = 0$ are true. In the second instance,

$$\{x: \ x^2 = 4\} \cup \{x: \ x(x - 2) = 0\} \ = \ \{-2, 2\} \cup \{0, 2\} \ = \ \{-2, 0, 2\},$$

and $\{-2, 0, 2\}$ is the set of integers for which either $x^2 = 4$ is true or $x(x - 2) = 0$ is true. Notice that this set contains 2, the integer for which both open sentences are true.

The operations of union and intersection of sets are closely related to combining statements by means of the words *or* and *and*. To help us explore this idea, let us agree to represent a statement by a single letter, such as p or q. For example, we might use p to represent the statement "3 is an integer."

The word *and* placed between two statements p, q produces a new statement p **and** q, called the **conjunction** of p and q. For example, the conjunction of the statements "Mathematics is the Queen of the sciences," "Mars is not a planet," is

Mathematics is the Queen of the sciences and Mars is not a planet.

The truth of a conjunction is determined by the following agreement:

> The conjunction p and q is true provided *both* p and q are true; otherwise it is false.

Thus, the conjunction printed in red above is false because its second component statement, namely, "Mars is not a planet," is false. A true conjunction is the statement, "Mathematics is the Queen of the sciences and Mars is a planet."

Placing the word *or* between two statements p, q yields a new statement p **or** q, called the **disjunction** of p and q. We agree that:

> The disjunction p or q is true provided *at least one* of the statements p, q is true; otherwise it is false.

Thus, the only case in which p *or* q is false occurs when both p and q are false. Can you explain why each of the following disjunctions is true?

Mathematics is the Queen of the sciences or Mars is not a planet.
2 is an even integer or 2 is greater than zero.

Notice that in ordinary English the word *or* sometimes means that just one of two alternatives occurs. It is used in this sense in the statement, "At 2:00 P.M. I will be in Toronto or in Ottawa." In mathematical usage, however, the word *or* generally means that one or both of two alternatives occur. For example, in the disjunction "3 is less than 7 or 3 is positive," both component statements are true, as is the disjunction.

Exercises

Specify by roster (a) the intersection (if not empty) and (b) the union of the given sets.

A

1. $\{1, 3, 5, 9\}$; $\{3, 6, 9, 12\}$
2. $\{4, 3, 2, 1\}$; $\{-1, 0, -2, 4\}$
3. $\{8, 4, 2\}$; $\{2, 8, 4\}$
4. $\{1, 2, 5\}$; $\{3, 5, 4\}$
5. {even integers} ; {odd integers}
6. {odd integers} ; {negative integers}
7. {nonnegative integers} ; {integral multiples of 5}
8. $\emptyset$; {integers}

In Exercises 9–20, determine which of the statements are true. Give a reason for each answer.

9. 1 is a positive integer and Lincoln's birthday is next month.

10. 0 is not an integer or 5 is an odd number.

11. −1 is less than 1 or the sum of −1 and 1 is 0.

12. 3 is a subset of the integers and −5 belongs to the set of integers.

13. Every subset of a set contains one or more elements of the set. *false*

14. Some subsets of a set contain all or none of the elements of the set.

In Exercises 15–20, let the domain of x be the set of integers.

15. $5 \in \{x: 2x + 1 = 12\}$ or $5 \notin \{t: t$ is a negative integer$\}$

16. $5 \notin \{x: 2x + 1 = 12\}$ and $5 \notin \{t: t$ is a negative integer$\}$

17. $\{-1, -2\} \subset \{x: x^2 - 1 = 3 \text{ or } x^2 - x - 2 = 0\}$

18. $2 \in \left\{x: \dfrac{x^2 - 4}{x - 2} = x + 2 \text{ or } x + 2 = 0\right\}$

19. $-3 \notin \left\{x: \dfrac{x^2 - 9}{x + 3} = x - 3 \text{ and } x + 3 = 0\right\}$

20. $\emptyset = \left\{x: \dfrac{x + 1}{x} = 1 + 1 \text{ or } x \neq x\right\}$

Specify by roster the following subsets of the set of integers.

21. $\{h: h + 2 = 4\} \cap \{k: k^2 + 1 = 5\}$

22. $\{g: 2g + 1 = 9\} \cup \{v: -3 + v = 4\}$

23. $\{t: t^2 - 1 = 8\} \cup \{s: s + 5 > 6\}$

24. $\{a: a^2 + a = 0\} \cap \{b: 2b + 3 < 9\}$

Let the region within or on the indicated rectangles in the adjoining Venn diagram represent the subsets A, B, and C of a set U. In Exercises 25–34, redraw the diagram and shade the region representing the subset of U specified in each exercise.

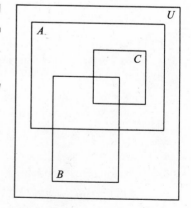

25. $A \cup C$

26. $B \cap A$

27. $\{y: y \in B \text{ and } y \notin A\}$

28. $\{t: t \notin A, t \notin B, \text{ and } t \notin C\}$

29. $\{g: g \in A, g \in B, \text{ or } g \in C\}$

30. $\{h: h \in A \text{ and } h \notin (B \cup C)\}$

Exs. 25–34

C **31.** $\{u: u \in (A \cap B) \text{ and } u \in (A \cap C)\}$

32. $\{q: q \in (A \cap B) \text{ or } q \in (A \cap C)\}$

33. **a.** $A \cup (B \cap C)$ ·   **b.** $(A \cup B) \cap (A \cup C)$

   c. Compare the shaded regions obtained for **(a)** and **(b)**, and use your observation to formulate a guess about the set operations $\cup$ and $\cap$. Try to justify your guess.

34. **a.** $A \cap (B \cup C)$ **b.** $(A \cap B) \cup (A \cap C)$

   c. Compare the shaded regions obtained for **(a)** and **(b)**, and use your observation to formulate a guess about the set operations $\cap$ and $\cup$. Try to justify your guess.

35. Let R and S be nonempty sets such that $R \cap S = R$. Which, if any, of the following statements must be true? Justify your answers.

   a. $R \subset S$ **c.** $R \cup S = S$

   b. $S \subset R$ **d.** $R \cup S = R$

36. Let T and V be nonempty sets such that $T \cup V = V$. Which, if any, of the following statements must be true? Justify your answers.

   a. $V \subset T$ **c.** $T \cap V = T$

   b. $T \subset V$ **d.** $T \cap V = V$

1–4 Conditional Statements and Converses

The words "if" and "then" are often used in mathematics to combine two statements, p and q, into the new statement, **If p, then q,** which is called the **conditional** of p and q. Some examples of conditional statements are the following assertions:

> **If x is an integer, then $2x$ is an even integer.**
>
> **If two triangles are congruent, then the triangles are similar.**

The truth of the conditional of p and q is determined as follows:

> The conditional of p and q is true whenever
>   (a) p is true and q is true.
>   (b) p is false and q is true.
>   (c) p is false and q is false.

This definition implies that the conditional of p and q is false only when p is true and q is false.

EXAMPLE 1. Determine which of the following conditional statements are true. Give a reason for each answer.

    a. If $4 + (-4) = 0$, then Magellan was an explorer.
    b. If $4 + (-4) = 0$, then $7(4 + (-4)) = 1$.
    c. If $4 + (-4) \neq 0$, then $5 \cdot 1 = 5$.
    d. If $4 + (-4) \neq 0$, then $5 \cdot 1 = 6$.

Solution: **a.** True, because "$4 + (-4) = 0$" and "Magellan was an explorer" are both true statements.

    b. False, because "$4 + (-4) = 0$" is true whereas "$7(4 + (-4)) = 1$" is false.

    c. and **d.** True, because "$4 + (-4) \neq 0$" is a false statement.

Notice that, in case p is a false statement, the conditional "If p, then q" is true whether q happens to be true or false. In case p is a true statement, and the conditional is true, you may conclude that q is also true. But asserting the truth of the conditional of p and q does not mean that p is a true statement.

A conditional may be worded in a variety of ways. Consider the statement,

> **If two triangles are congruent, then the triangles are similar.**

Another way to express this assertion is:

> **A sufficient condition for two triangles to be similar is that the triangles be congruent.**

On the other hand, two triangles cannot be congruent unless they are similar. Other ways of stating this latter fact are these:

> **(1) A necessary condition for two triangles to be congruent is that the triangles be similar.**

> **(2) Two triangles are congruent only if they are similar.**

Table 1 shows various wordings for the conditional of p and q. Familiarity with these different phrasings is essential in reading mathematics.

Table 1

If p, then q.
p is sufficient for q.
q is necessary for p.
p, only if q.
q, if p.
p implies q.
q follows from p.

If you interchange the statements p and q in the conditional "If p, then q," you obtain the new statement, "If q, then p," called the **converse** of the given conditional. Confusing a statement with its converse is a serious error. The following examples should convince you that a conditional and its converse are very different statements, and that the converse of a true conditional may be true or it may be false.

(1) Conditional. If two triangles are congruent, then they are similar. True.

Converse. If two triangles are similar, then they are congruent. False.

(2) Conditional. If a and b are numbers such that $a = 0$, then $ab = 0$. True.

Converse. If $ab = 0$, then a and b are numbers such that $a = 0$. False.

(3) Conditional. If a triangle is isosceles, then the measures of the base angles of the triangle are equal. True.

Converse. If the measures of the base angles of a triangle are equal, then the triangle is isosceles. True.

Example (3) illustrates a situation in which both a conditional and its converse are true. Whenever both of the statements, "If p, then q" and "If q, then p," are true, we say that p and q are equivalent statements. This means that p and q are both true or both false statements. By referring to Table 1 you can discover the different ways shown in Table 2 of stating that p and q are equivalent. Each of these statements is called an **equivalence statement**, or **equivalence**.

If p, then q, and if q, then p.
If p, then q, and conversely.
If q, then p, and conversely.
p is necessary and sufficient for q.
q is necessary and sufficient for p.
q, if and only if p.
p, if and only if q.

Table 2

EXAMPLE 2. Reword the following equivalence statement as a conjunction of conditionals, and tell whether the equivalence is true: "For each integer a, $a > 0$ if and only if $a^2 > 0$."

Solution: "For each integer a, if $a > 0$, then $a^2 > 0$; and if $a^2 > 0$, then $a > 0$." (*continued on page 14*)

The equivalence is false because although the conditional "For each integer a, if $a > 0$, then $a^2 > 0$" is true, there exist cases for which the converse statement "For each integer a, if $a^2 > 0$, then $a > 0$" is false. To show one such case, you can replace a with -5, and obtain $(-5)^2 = 25 > 0$, which is true, but it is not true that $-5 > 0$.

Notice that the statement in Example 2 made an assertion about *all* integers. Therefore, to show that the statement is false it was enough to find a *single* permissible value of the variable for which the statement is false. Such a value of the variable is called a **counterexample** to the statement.

Exercises

State a converse of each of the following conditionals, and tell whether the converse is always, sometimes, or never true.

A

1. If a man lives in London, then he lives in England.
2. If an animal is a normal cat, it has four legs.
3. If a triangle is equilateral, it is isosceles.
4. If two triangles are congruent, their corresponding angles have equal measure.
5. If 2 is a factor of an integer, then 2 is a factor of the square of the integer.
6. If 6 is a factor of an integer, then 6 is a factor of the square of the integer.

B

7-12. Using (**a**) the "sufficient" condition wording, (**b**) the "necessary" or the "only if" wording, restate each of the conditionals in Exercises 1-6.

In Exercises 13-18, write the given equivalence in the "necessary and sufficient" wording.

13. x is an odd integer if and only if x^2 is an odd integer.
14. In any isosceles triangle the bisectors of the base angles are of equal length, and conversely.
15. For all sets A and B, $A \subset B$ if and only if $A \cup B = B$.
16. For all sets R and S, $R \subset S$ if and only if $R \cap S = R$.
17. For all integers b and c, $x^2 + bx + c = 0$ has integral roots if and only if $b^2 - 4c$ is the square of an integer.
18. Let a and b denote real numbers; $ab = 0$ if and only if either $a = 0$ or $b = 0$.
19. A salesman signed a contract according to the terms of which he was required to work six days a week only if he received a stock option in addition to his commission. His employer honored the contract, but the salesman loafed 3 days a week. Did the salesman fail to live up to his contract?
20. "A $50.00 deposit is sufficient to reserve your living-room suite," advertises the furniture merchant. You have only $20.00 in cash, and the merchant always keeps his word. Must he reject your request for credit?

1-5 Negations

Is it true that $4 + 5 = 8$? The statement "$4 + 5 = 8$" is certainly false. But from this false statement you can obtain true assertions, such as:

(1) It is false that $4 + 5 = 8$

or

(2) It is not the case that $4 + 5 = 8$

or, more simply,

(3) $4 + 5 \neq 8$.

Each of the statements (1), (2), (3) is called the *negation* of the statement of "$4 + 5 = 8$." In general, if p is any statement, then **not** p (the **negation** of p) is the denial of p and is true when p is false and false when p is true.

When p is a simple statement, the meaning of *not* p is clear. To decide the meaning of the negation of a compound statement may require careful thought.

EXAMPLE 1. State the negation of: "$a = 0$ or $b = 0$."

Solution: "$a = 0$ or $b = 0$" asserts that *at least* one of the statements "$a = 0$," "$b = 0$" is true. To deny this assertion is to declare that neither of the statements is true; that is, that both are false. Hence, the negation is: "$a \neq 0$ *and* $b \neq 0$."

In general,

> The negation of p or q is not p and not q.

EXAMPLE 2. State the negation of: "John is tall and Tom is short."

Solution: The given statement asserts that "John is tall" and "Tom is short" are *both* true statements. Its negation denies that both are true and, hence, affirms that *at least one* is false. Therefore, the negation is "John is not tall *or* Tom is not short."

In general,

> The negation of p and q is not p or not q.

EXAMPLE 3. State the negation of: "If he is a citizen, then he may vote."

Solution: "If he is a citizen, then he may vote" affirms that whenever "he is a citizen" is a true statement, then "he may vote" is also a true statement. The negation of the given statement,

$N(\forall p)$
negations of for all p
16
CHAPTER ONE

therefore, declares that even though "he is a citizen" is true, "he may vote" is false. Hence the negation is: "He is a citizen *and* he may not vote."

In general,

> **The negation of** If p, then q **is** p and not q.

Mathematical discourse often involves the negation of a statement involving a quantifier.

EXAMPLE 4. State the negation of: "Some people are men."

Solution: "Some people are men" states that there exists *at least one* person who is a man. To deny this assertion is to declare: "*All* people are *not* men." Another way of wording this negation is, "Every person is not a man," or "No person is a man."

$\forall$ in place of "for all or forever"

$\exists$ in place of "there exist"

In general,

> **The negation of** For some, p **is** For all, not p.

EXAMPLE 5. State the negation of: For all numbers x, $x^2 + 1 \neq 0$."

Solution: The given statement affirms that for *every* replacement of x by a numeral, the statement "$x^2 + 1 \neq 0$" is true. Hence, its negation asserts that for *at least one* value of x, "$x^2 + 1 \neq 0$" is a false statement. Thus, the negation is: "For some number x, $x^2 + 1 = 0$."

In general,

$N(\forall p) \quad \exists \sim p$

> **The negation of** For all, p **is** For some, not p.

Exercises

State the negation of each of the following assertions. Do not merely preface the statements with the word "not" or with the words "it is false that" or "it is not the case that." Tell whether the given statement or its negation is the true assertion.

1. Algebra is a branch of mathematics.
2. Geology involves the study of the earth.
3. Scientists are not uneducated.
4. Geometry is not worthless.

5. $7 + 1 = 8$ and $8 > 2$.   **7.** $5 \geq 7$.

6. $0 < 1$ or $4 - 1 = 3$.   **8.** $12 \leq 9$.

9. 1 belongs to the set of integers and to the set of positive numbers.

10. 1 belongs to the set of integers or to the set of negative numbers.

11. Some equations have real roots.

12. All equations have at least one real root.

13. All integers cannot be expressed as a product of prime factors.

14. Some numbers are integers.

15. Not all numbers are prime numbers.

16. There exist even integers.

17. If a number is an integer, then it is greater than 0.

18. If a number is a negative integer, then it is less than 0.

Convert each open sentence into a true statement by inserting a quantifier, and then state the negation of the statement.

B   **19.** $\dfrac{5}{y} + \dfrac{3}{y} = \dfrac{8}{y}$ **22.** If $x \in \{0, 1\}$, then $x = x^2$.

20. $\dfrac{y}{5} + \dfrac{y}{3} = \dfrac{y}{8}$ **23.** If $a^2 - b^2 = 0$, then $a = b$ or $a = -b$.

21. If $x \in \{0, 1\}$, then x is not 0.   **24.** If $a^2 - b^2 = 0$, then $a = b$.

$\exists y \ni \frac{5}{y} + \frac{3}{y} \neq \frac{8}{y}$ there exist.

$\ni = $ such that

1-6 Complements

Closely related to the notion of negation of a statement is the concept of *complement* of a set. In connection with any specific problem the elements of the sets you discuss usually all belong to some given set or *universe*. For example, in elementary algebra the universe is likely to be the set of all real numbers, whereas in geometry you might be concerned with a universe of triangles. Figure 1–3 illustrates a set A as a subset of a universe U. The points outside the circular region picturing A represent the elements of U that *do not belong* to A. We call the set of all such elements the **complement of A in U,** or simply the **complement** of A (in symbols, A'). Thus,

$$A' = \{x \colon x \notin A\}.$$

In Figure 1–3, A' is shown as the hatched region. Notice that the complement of a set A depends on the universe of which A is considered to be a subset.

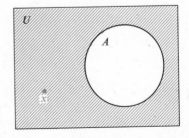

Figure 1–3

Figures 1–4 and 1–5 on the following page picture the complements of the union and of the intersection, respectively, of two sets R and S. See Exercises 19 and 20 on page 18.

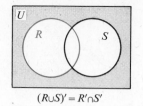

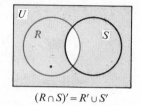

$R \cup S$

$(R \cup S)' = R' \cap S'$

Figure 1–4

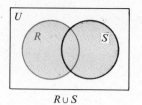

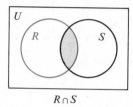

$R \cap S$

$(R \cap S)' = R' \cup S'$

Figure 1–5

Exercises

Let $U = \{1, 2, 3, 4, 5, 6, 7, 8\}$. Specify each of the following sets by roster.

A

1. $\{1, 3, 5\}'$

2. U'

3. $\emptyset'$

4. $\{1, 2, 4, 8\}'$

5. $(\{1, 2, 6\} \cup \{1, 2, 3, 4\})'$

6. $(\{1, 2, 6\} \cap \{1, 2, 3, 4\})'$

7. $(\{3, 5, 1, 4\} \cap U)'$

8. $(\{3, 5, 1, 4\} \cup \emptyset)'$

Let the regions within or on the adjoining rectangles represent the subsets R, S, and T of a universe U. In Exercises 9–18 redraw the Venn diagram and shade the region representing the subset of U specified in each exercise.

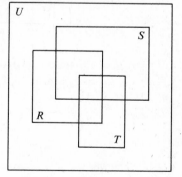

9. $R' \cup S$

10. $S' \cap T$

11. $T' \cap S'$

12. $R' \cap T'$

B

13. $(R' \cup T')'$

14. $(R' \cap S')'$

15. $(R \cup (S \cap T))'$

16. $(R \cap (S \cup T))'$

17. $(R \cap (S \cup T)')'$

18. $(R' \cap (S \cup T))'$

Use the facts that $R = \{x: x \in R\}$, $S = \{x: x \in S\}$, $R \cap S = \{x: x \in R$ and $x \in S\}$, and $R \cup S = \{x: x \in R$ or $x \in S\}$ to prove:

C

19. $(R \cup S)' = R' \cap S'$

20. $(R \cap S)' = R' \cup S'$

1–7 Evaluating Compound Statements; Truth Tables

In Sections 1–3 and 1–4 four basic types of compound statements were described: conjunction, disjunction, conditional, and equivalence. Rules were stated in words for the *truth value* (truth or falsity) of each type of compound statement in terms of the truth values of the statements being combined. Expressing corresponding rules in words for elaborate compound statements would be cumbersome. By adopting symbols, such as those shown in the following table, the work of evaluating all forms of compound statements can be greatly simplified.

BASIC SYMBOLISM		
Symbolism	*How Read*	*Denote(s)*
$p, q, r, s, \ldots$		statements (propositions)
$p \wedge q$	p and q	a conjunction
$p \vee q$	p or q	a disjunction
$p \rightarrow q$	if p, then q	a conditional
$p \leftrightarrow q$	p if and only if q	an equivalence
p'	not p	a negation

Our previously accepted rules for the truth value of each type of compound statement, as well as of the negation of a statement, can now be conveniently expressed in a compact form known as a *truth table*. In such tables T designates that the corresponding statement is true, F that it is false. Here are five examples of truth tables incorporating the definitions of conjunction, disjunction, conditional, equivalence, and negation.

CONJUNCTION

p	q	$p \wedge q$
T	T	T
T	F	F
F	T	F
F	F	F

DISJUNCTION

p	q	$p \vee q$
T	T	T
T	F	T
F	T	T
F	F	F

CONDITIONAL

p	q	$p \rightarrow q$
T	T	T
T	F	F
F	T	T
F	F	T

EQUIVALENCE

p	q	$p \leftrightarrow q$
T	T	T
T	F	F
F	T	F
F	F	T

NEGATION

p	p'
T	F
F	T

By means of a truth table containing auxiliary columns you can determine the truth value of a compound statement. Such a truth table for the statement $(p \wedge q) \rightarrow (p \vee q)$ is shown below. The first, second, and last columns give the essential information. The third and fourth columns merely help in arriving at the truth values shown in the last column.

p	q	p ∧ q	p ∨ q	(p ∧ q) → (p ∨ q)
T	T	T	T	T
T	F	F	T	T
F	T	F	T	T
F	F	F	F	T

By comparing the first, second, and last columns you can see that the statement $(p \wedge q) \rightarrow (p \vee q)$ is true no matter what truth values are assigned to the statements p and q. A compound statement having this characteristic is called a **tautology**. Tautologies represent basic laws of logic.

Consider the truth tables for the two statements:

(1) $p \vee q$

(2) $p' \rightarrow q$

(1)

p	q	p ∨ q
T	T	T
T	F	T
F	T	T
F	F	F

(2)

p	q	p'	p' → q
T	T	F	T
T	F	F	T
F	T	T	T
F	F	T	F

You will note that the truth values of the two statements agree with each other for each particular assignment of truth values to the statements p and q. Any two compound statements which have this characteristic are said to be **logically equivalent**, and it follows that $(p \vee q) \leftrightarrow (p' \rightarrow q)$ is a tautology. A statement can be replaced by a logically equivalent statement in a compound statement without affecting the truth value of the original compound statement.

Exercises

In Exercises 1–9, assume that p and q are true statements and that r is a false statement. Determine the truth value of each statement.

1. $p \rightarrow r$　　　　　　**4.** $r \rightarrow p$　　　　　　**7.** $p' \rightarrow (q' \vee r)$

2. $p' \wedge q$　　　　　　**5.** $p \wedge (q \vee r)$　　　**8.** $p \rightarrow (q \rightarrow r)$

3. $(p \wedge q) \vee r$　　　**6.** $(p \vee r) \rightarrow q$　　　**9.** $p \rightarrow (q \vee r)$

thru 19 all
20-25 a few

If p represents the statement "Eric plays golf" and q the statement "Oscar plays tennis," write the statement represented by each of the following.

10. $p \rightarrow q$ **12.** $p \wedge q'$ **14.** $p' \vee q$

11. $q' \rightarrow p$ **13.** $p \leftrightarrow q$ **15.** $p' \leftrightarrow q$

In Exercises 16–19, classify each statement as true or false. Give a reason for your answer.

16. 6 is a prime number if and only if 8 is a prime number.

17. If $3 = 5$, then $6 + 2 = 8$.

18. If $5 > 3$ or $5 < 3$, then $6 > 7$.

19. $\frac{5}{0}$ is a real number only if $5 \cdot 0 = 5$.

Given: $p \rightarrow q$ is a false statement. Give the truth value of each of the following statements and a reason to support your answer.

20. $p \wedge q$ **22.** $p' \rightarrow q'$ **24.** $p' \leftrightarrow q'$

21. $q \rightarrow p$ **23.** $(p' \wedge q) \leftrightarrow (p \vee q)$ **25.** $(p \vee q) \wedge p$

26. By means of truth tables show that $p \wedge q$ and $p' \vee q'$ have opposite truth values for all combinations of truth values assigned to p and to q. Are the statements negations of each other?

Construct truth tables for each of the following statements. Indicate whether or not the statement is a tautology.

27. $(p \vee q) \rightarrow p$ **29.** $(p \rightarrow q) \leftrightarrow (q' \rightarrow p')$

28. $(p \wedge p') \rightarrow q$ **30.** $(p \rightarrow q) \leftrightarrow (p \vee q)$

31. By means of a truth table show that $[(p \rightarrow q) \wedge (q \rightarrow r)] \rightarrow (p \rightarrow r)$ is a tautology. (*Hint:* There are 8 combinations of truth values for p, q, and r.)

Using only the connectives $\vee$, $\wedge$, and $'$ form a statement equivalent to:

32. $p \rightarrow q$ **33.** $(p \rightarrow q)'$ **34.** $p \leftrightarrow q$

1–8 Patterns of Inference

In studying mathematics you have proved many theorems. A **theorem** is a statement which is true in a given context. To *prove* a theorem, you must show that its truth follows by *logical inference* from other statements accepted or previously proved to be true.

In making logical inferences, we will use the following principles.

1. **Principle of Inference or Detachment.** If the conditional "$p \rightarrow q$" is true and "p" is true, then "q" is true.

Thus, assuming the "given" statements in Example 1 to be true, the

Principle of Inference guarantees the truth of the statement labeled "Conclusion."

EXAMPLE 1. *Given:* (1) If Dale lives in Canada, then Dale is a resident of North America.

(2) Dale lives in Canada.

Conclusion: ∴ Dale is a resident of North America.

In logic, statements that are given as true are usually called **premises**; in mathematics, we frequently call them **hypotheses** (sing. *hypothesis*).

The adjoining truth table indicates the validity of the Principle of Detachment. Notice that the column giving the truth value of $[(p \to q) \land p] \to q$ always has the entry T, regardless of the entries for p and q. Do you see that this means that the statement $[(p \to q) \land p)] \to q$ is a tautology?

p	q	p → q	[(p → q) ∧ p] → q	
T	T	T	T	T
T	F	F	F	T
F	T	T	F	T
F	F	T	F	T

2. **Principle of Contraposition or Negative Inference.** If "$p \to q$" is true and "q" is false, then "p" is false.

EXAMPLE 2. *Given:* (1) If Dale lives in Canada, then Dale is a resident of North America.

(2) Dale is *not* a resident of North America.

Conclusion: ∴ Dale does *not* live in Canada.

Using truth tables to verify this principle and the three following ones will be left to you (page 26).

3. **Principle of Disjunctive Inference.** If "p or q" is true and "p" is false, then "q" is true.

EXAMPLE 3. *Given:* (1) a is a real number less than or equal to 5.

(2) a is not less than 5.

Conclusion: ∴ a equals 5.

4. **Principle of Equivalence Inference.** If "$p \leftrightarrow q$" is true and "p" is true, then "q" is true.

EXAMPLE 4. *Given:* (1) The set A equals the set B if and only if $A \subset B$ and $B \subset A$.

(2) $A = B$.

Conclusion: ∴ $A \subset B$ and $B \subset A$.

By means of a truth table, you can verify that "$p \rightarrow q$" and "$q' \rightarrow p'$" are logically equivalent. (Exercise 29, page 21.) We call "$q' \rightarrow p'$" the **contrapositive** of "$p \rightarrow q$." Thus, the Principle of Equivalence Inference lets you replace a conditional by its contrapositive.

5. **Principle of the Syllogism.** If "$p \rightarrow q$" is true and "$q \rightarrow r$" is true, then "$p \rightarrow r$" is true.

EXAMPLE 5. *Given:* (1) If x is a real number such that $x^2 - 9 = 0$, then $(x + 3)(x - 3) = 0$.

(2) If $(x + 3)(x - 3) = 0$, then $x = -3$ or $x = 3$.

Conclusion: ∴ If x is a real number such that $x^2 - 9 = 0$, then $x = -3$ or $x = 3$.

6. **Principle of Substitution for Variables.** Substituting throughout an open sentence a specific value for a variable with given domain produces a true statement whenever the open sentence is true for all values of the variable.

EXAMPLE 6. *Given:* (1) All men are mortal.

(2) Socrates is a man.

Conclusion: ∴ Socrates is mortal.

7. **Principle of Substitution for Statements.** If "$p \leftrightarrow q$" is true, then from any true (false) statement involving "p" a true (false) statement results when "q" is substituted throughout for "p."

EXAMPLE 7. *Given:* (1) Nonvertical lines in a plane are parallel if and only if the lines have the same slope.

(2) In a plane, parallel lines either coincide or have no point in common.

Conclusion: In a plane, nonvertical lines having the same slope either coincide or have no point in common.

For brevity, we will refer to each of the principles of substitution simply as "Substitution."

To illustrate the concept of proof, let us first accept the following assertions as **axioms** or **postulates**, that is, as statements assumed to be true as the basis of a given discussion.

Axiom 1. All college graduates are industrious.

Axiom 2. Industrious people are successful.

Axiom 3. If a person is successful, he is not in debt.

Axiom 4. If a man is foolish, he is in debt.

Notice that these axioms are not "eternal truths"; they are merely statements from which other statements (theorems) are to be derived. One such theorem is the assertion

If Jack is a college graduate, he is not foolish.

Outline of Proof

STATEMENT	REASON
1. Jack is a college graduate.	Hypothesis.
2. ∴ Jack is industrious.	Substitution (for variables) in Axiom 1.
3. ∴ Jack is successful.	Substitution and the Principle of Detachment in Axiom 2.
4. ∴ Jack is not in debt.	Substitution and the Principle of Detachment in Axiom 3.
5. ∴ Jack is not foolish.	Substitution and the Principle of Contraposition in Axiom 4.

Thus, by a succession of logical inferences based on Axioms 1–4, we can reason from the hypothesis "Jack is a college student" to the conclusion "Jack is not foolish." This chain of reasoning proves the theorem.

In practice, the form in which proofs are written is usually not even as detailed as the skeletal outline of the preceding argument. In particular, the specific rules of logic involved in each step are not identified. Moreover, in all but the simplest arguments, many details are often omitted. For example, an abridged proof of the theorem, "If a man is in debt, then he is not a college graduate," might run as follows: "Since the man is in debt, Axiom 3 implies that he is not successful. Therefore, by Axiom 2, he is not industrious. Hence, by Axiom 1, he is not a college graduate."

There are two errors in reasoning that commonly occur in false proofs. The first employs the following invalid argument, known as *asserting the conclusion:* If "$p \rightarrow q$" is true and "q" is true, then "p" is true. Referring to the truth table on page 22, you can see that in the third row "$p \rightarrow q$" and "q" have truth value T, but "p" has F as its truth value. An example of this faulty reasoning is the following argument.

Given: (1) If $x = 2$, then $x^2 = 4$.
(2) $x^2 = 4$.

Conclusion: Therefore, $x = 2$.

Another error in reasoning is the argument called *denying the premise:* If "$p \rightarrow q$" is true and "p" is false, then "q" is false. Can you explain why this argument is invalid? The following example uses it to draw an erroneous conclusion.

Given: (1) All animals die.

(2) No plant is an animal.

Conclusion: Therefore, no plant dies.

Exercises

Name the principle(s) of inference used in each argument.

A

1. *Given:* (1) If roses are black, then violets are green.

(2) Violets are not green.

Conclusion: Therefore, roses are not black.

2. *Given:* (1) If Henry is tall, then Henry is a good basketball player.

(2) Henry is tall.

Conclusion: Therefore, Henry is a good basketball player.

3. *Given:* (1) If Roger is honest, then William is a good judge of character.

(2) If William is a good judge of character, then William should be elected leader.

Conclusion: Therefore, if Roger is honest, then William should be elected leader.

4. *Given:* (1) All dogs have four legs.

(2) John's pet is a dog.

Conclusion: Therefore, John's pet has four legs.

5. *Given:* (1) Either Smith or Brown will be promoted.

(2) Brown will not be promoted.

Conclusion: Therefore, Smith will be promoted.

6. *Given:* (1) a is even if and only if a is divisible by 2.

(2) a is divisible by 2.

Conclusion: Therefore, a is even.

7. *Given:* If a triangle is isosceles, at least two of its angles have the same measure.

Conclusion: If no pair of angles in a triangle have the same measure, the triangle is not isosceles.

8. *Given:* (1) The decimal for an irrational number does not terminate or repeat.

    (2) The decimal for $\frac{3}{4}$ terminates.

    Conclusion: Therefore, $\frac{3}{4}$ is not an irrational number.

Use a truth table to verify the validity of the indicated principle and to show that the given statement is a tautology.

9. Principle of contraposition; $[(p \rightarrow q) \wedge q'] \rightarrow p'$.

10. Principle of disjunctive inference; $[(p \vee q) \wedge p'] \rightarrow q$.

11. Principle of equivalence inference; $[(p \leftrightarrow q) \wedge p] \rightarrow q$.

12. Principle of the syllogism; $[(p \rightarrow q) \wedge (q \rightarrow r)] \rightarrow (p \rightarrow r)$.

In Exercises 13–18 discuss the validity of the reasoning.

13. *Given:* (1) All cats eat fish.

    (2) No whale is a cat.

    Conclusion: Therefore, no whale eats fish.

14. *Given:* (1) Only elected officials are governors.

    (2) Mr. X is not the governor of his State.

    Conclusion: Therefore, Mr. X is not an elected official.

15. *Given:* (1) A man is happy if and only if he is contented.

    (2) Happy men are good husbands.

    Conclusion: Therefore, a man is a good husband if and only if he is contented.

16. *Given:* (1) If $a = 3$, then a is a factor of 15.

    (2) a is a factor of 15.

    Conclusion: Therefore, $a = 3$.

17. *Given:* (1) I will pay the bill if I am wrong.

    (2) I will not pay the bill.

    Conclusion: Therefore, I am not wrong.

18. *Given:* (1) I will pay the bill only if I am wrong.

    (2) I will pay the bill.

    Conclusion: Therefore, I am wrong.

On the basis of the given set of axioms, prove each theorem in Exs. 19–22.

Axiom 1. Each line is a set of points.

Axiom 2. There exist at least two points.

Axiom 3. If $\mathcal{L}$ is a line, there is a point not on $\mathcal{L}$.

Axiom 4. If P and Q are distinct points, there is one and only one line containing P and Q.

B

19. If P is a point, there exists a point Q different from P.

20. If P is a point, there is at least one line containing P.

21. If P is a point, there are at least two lines containing P.

22. There are at least three lines.

Use the following axioms to prove the statements in Exercises 23 and 24.

Axiom 1. If a man lives in village X, he belongs to at least one club.

Axiom 2. Not all men in X belong to the same club.

Axiom 3. Every club in X has at least two men as members.

Axiom 4. There are exactly four men in X.

Axiom 5. Every two clubs in X have at least one member in common.

23. There are at least two clubs in X.

24. If no club has more than two members, there must be at least three clubs in X.

Chapter Summary

1. In mathematics, expressions involving the use of symbols such as $=$, $<$, $\in$, $\subset$, and $\geq$ are called **sentences**. If a sentence contains a variable, it is called an **open sentence**. **Statements** are meaningful assertions that are definitely true or definitely false, but not both true and false.

2. An open sentence serves as a pattern for statements which are formed by replacing each variable in the sentence with a value from the domain of the variable. A value of the variable for which the resulting statement is true is called a **solution** of the sentence.

3. When words or phrases such as *each, all, some,* and *there exists* are used in conjunction with variables, these words are **quantifiers**, and tell you whether a given assertion is intended to hold for every value in the domain of the variable or simply for values in some nonempty subset of the domain.

4. The combination **p and q** $(p \land q)$ of two statements is called the **conjunction** of p and q, and is true whenever both p and q are true. The combination **p or q** $(p \lor q)$ of two statements is called the **disjunction** of p and q and is true whenever p or q or both are true.

5. Compound statements of the form **if p, then q** $(p \to q)$ are called **conditionals**, and are true whenever p is true and q is true, p is false and q is true, or both p and q are false. If the component statements of a conditional are interchanged, the resulting conditional is called the **converse** of the original one.

6. The negation, **not** p (p'), of statement p is the statement that is true whenever p is false and false whenever p is true. The negation of a conjunction, p *and* q, is the disjunction of the negations of p and q, **not** p **or not** q $[(p \wedge q)' = p' \vee q']$. The negation of a disjunction, p *or* q, is the conjunction of the negations of p and q, **not** p **and not** q $[(p \vee q)' = p' \wedge q']$. The negation of a conditional, *if* p, *then* q, is the conjunction of p and the negation of q, p **and not** q $[(p \rightarrow q)' = p \wedge q']$.

7. **Truth tables** can be used to find the truth values of compound statements. A compound statement that is true for every truth value of every statement involved in the compound statement is called a **tautology**. Any two compound statements that agree with each other for all truth values of the statements involved are **logically equivalent**. The conditional $p \rightarrow q$ is logically equivalent to its **contrapositive** $q' \rightarrow p'$.

8. A **theorem** is a statement which is true in a given context. You prove theorems by means of logical inference. For this, you use the principles of *detachment, contraposition, disjunction, equivalence, substitution,* and *syllogism.*

Chapter Test

1–1 Given $A = \{0, 3, 5\}$. Which of the following are true statements?

1. $3 \in A$ **3.** $5 \subset A$ **5.** $\{3\} \subset A$

2. $\{5\} \in A$ **4.** $0 \in \emptyset$ **6.** $A \subset A$

1–2 Assuming that the domain of x is the set of real numbers, convert each sentence into a true statement by using one of the three quantifiers: (1) for all x, (2) for some x, (3) for no x.

7. $\sqrt{x^2} = x$ **10.** $x^2 > x$

8. $(x - 3)(x + 3) = 9$ **11.** $|x| \geq x$

9. $x + 2 = x - 3$ **12.** $x^2 + 9 = 0$

1–3 Given: $A = \{x: x^2 - 2x - 8 = 0\}$, $B = \{x: x^2 + 2x = 0\}$, $C = \{x: x > 0\}$, specify each of the following sets by roster.

13. $A \cap B$ **14.** $A \cup B$ **15.** $B \cup \emptyset$ **16.** $(A \cup B) \cap C$

17. If "p and q" is a false statement, does it follow that "p or q" is also a false statement?

1–4 Express each of the following in *if, then* form:

18. p, only if q. **20.** t is necessary for p.

19. r implies s. **21.** q is sufficient for s.

Form the converse and tell whether it is necessarily true.

22. If $x = 3$, then $x^2 = 9$. **23.** If $A \cup \emptyset = \emptyset$, then $A = \emptyset$.

1-5 **24.** Which of the following is the negation of: If $x = y$, then $x^2 = y^2$?

  a. If $x^2 = y^2$, then $x = y$.   **c.** If $x^2 \neq y^2$, then $x \neq y$.

  b. $x = y$ and $x^2 \neq y^2$.   **d.** $x \neq y$ and $x^2 = y^2$.

1-6 Make a Venn diagram similar to that shown and indicate by shading:

  25. $A \cap B$

  26. $A' \cup B'$

  27. $A \cup B$

  28. $A' \cap B$

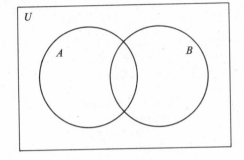

1-7 Given: statement p is true and statement q is false. Classify each of the following compound statements as true or false.

  29. $p \rightarrow q$ **30.** $q \rightarrow p$ **31.** $p \wedge q$ **32.** $(p \vee q) \wedge p$

1-8 **33.** The first two statements of a syllogism are:
  If studying mathematics is useful, then studying mathematics is important.
  If studying mathematics is important, then people should study mathematics. Therefore: __?__

  34. Discuss the validity of the following argument.
  The car is blue, or it is old and green.
  If it is old, then it needs to be inspected and repaired.
  It need not be inspected.
  Therefore, the car is blue.

If you failed on a test exercise, you may need to review the section listed at the left margin.

Reading List

ALLENDOERFER, C. B., and CLETUS O. OAKLEY. *Principles of Mathematics*, 2nd ed. New York: McGraw-Hill Book Co., Inc., 1963.

ANDRÉE, RICHARD V. *Selections from Modern Abstract Algebra*. New York: Holt, Rinehart and Winston, Inc., 1958.

CHACHERE, MARVIN L. *The Logic of Absolute Value Inequalities*. The Mathematics Teacher, vol. 57, pp. 73–74, 1964.

EXNER, ROBERT M., and MYRON S. ROSSKOPF. *Logic in Elementary Mathematics*. New York: McGraw-Hill Book Co., Inc., 1959.

Félix, Lucienne. *The Modern Aspect of Mathematics.* Translated by Julius H. Hlavaty and Fancille H. Hlavaty. New York: Basic Books Inc., 1960.

Hamilton, Norman T., and Joseph Landin. *Set Theory: The Structure of Arithmetic.* Boston: Allyn and Bacon, Inc., 1961.

Kattsoff, Louis O. *Symbolic Logic and the Structure of Elementary Mathematics.* The Mathematics Teacher, vol, 55, pp. 269–275, 1962.

Kemeny, John G., and others. *Finite Mathematical Structures.* Englewood Cliffs, New Jersey: Prentice-Hall, Inc., 1959.

Lewis, C. I. *A Survey of Symbolic Logic.* Berkeley, Calif.: University of California Press, 1918.

Mac Lane, S. *Symbolic Logic.* American Mathematical Monthly, vol. 46, pp. 289–296, 1940.

May, Kenneth O. *Elements of Modern Mathematics.* Reading, Mass.: Addison-Wesley Publishing Co., Inc., 1959.

National Council of Teachers of Mathematics. *Topics in Mathematics for Elementary-School Teachers. Booklet No. 1: Sets.* Washington, D.C.: National Council of Teachers of Mathematics, 1964.

Oehmke, Robert H. *Fundamentals of College Mathematics.* Boston: Allyn and Bacon, Inc., 1963.

Stabler, E. R. *An Introduction to Mathematical Thought.* Reading, Mass.: Addison-Wesley Publishing Co., Inc. 1953.

Stephanie, Sister M. *Venn Diagrams.* The Mathematics Teacher, vol. 56, pp. 98–101, 1963.

Stoll, Robert R. *Sets, Logic, and Axiomatic Theories.* San Francisco: W. H. Freeman and Co., 1961.

Swain, Robert L. *The Equation.* The Mathematics Teacher, vol. 55, pp. 226–236, 1962.

Western, Donald W., and Vincent H. Haag. *An Introduction to Mathematics.* New York: Holt, Rinehart and Winston, Inc., 1959.

Weyl, H. *Mathematics and Logic.* American Mathematical Monthly, vol. 53, pp. 2–13, 1946.

Whitesitt, John E. *Boolean Algebra and Its Applications.* Reading, Mass.: Addison-Wesley Publishing Co., Inc. 1961.

Wiseman, John D. Jr. *The Exclusive Disjunction.* The Mathematics Teacher, vol. 55, pp. 356–359, 1962.

Zehna, Peter W., and Robert L. Johnson. *Elements of Set Theory.* Boston: Allyn and Bacon, Inc., 1962.

George Boole

One day a logician was handed a sheet of paper which read, "The statement on the other side of this sheet is false." Turning the paper over, he found the assertion, "The statement on the other side of this sheet is false." Was the statement on the front side of the paper true or false? Can you determine?

Puzzles such as this have intrigued philosophers and logicians since ancient times, but it was not until the early 20th century that logic was considered to be within the domain of mathematics. The man whose work provided the foundation for this change in attitude was the English mathematician George Boole (1815–1864).

Boole's best-known work, usually referred to as *Laws of Thought*, appeared in 1854. In this book he developed logic from the standpoint of an abstract mathematical system consisting of undefined elements and binary operations, along with a set of postulates defining the way in which operations could be performed upon the elements. You are now quite familiar with the elements (propositions) and operations (conjunction, disjunction, negation) of this system.

With this approach Boole was able to reduce logic to a special kind of algebra. There were many advantages in this. In the first place, representing logical problems in symbols avoided the ambiguities of language and revealed relationships which might otherwise have been hidden in a tangle of words. As a consequence, later mathematicians were able to discover and solve problems that would have been extremely difficult without Boole's symbolic notation. Secondly, errors in reasoning were reduced, for in many instances, once a problem was translated into symbolic language, its solution became largely mechanical. Most important, though, was the great generality of Boole's system, for it could be validly applied to many specific problems in mathematics and the sciences.

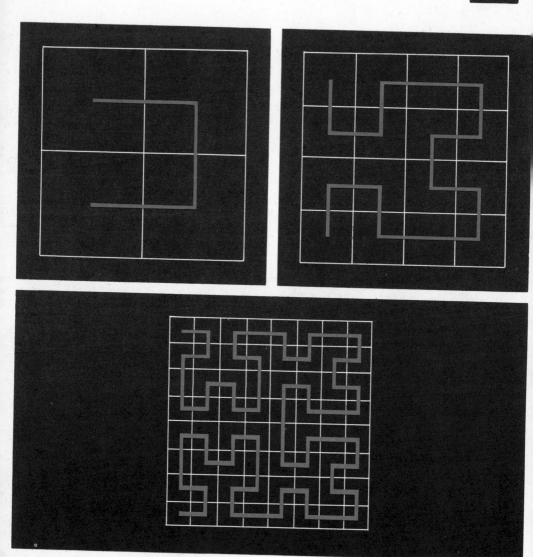

The diagrams show the first three stages of an unusual "curve." In every stage the curve passes through the center of each of the smaller squares; it will occupy the entire interior of the given square if the process is repeated without end. That is, given any point in the square, it can be shown that the curve passes through that point.

Ordered Fields

Any branch of mathematics begins with a set of statements accepted as the basis of the discussion. From these basic statements, valid conclusions are drawn by the use of logic. In this chapter, you will use the rules of logic discussed in Chapter 1 to deduce properties of the system of real numbers.

FIELD PROPERTIES

2–1 Axioms for Fields

The basis of most of the work in this book is the set of axioms for the system $\mathfrak{R}$ of real numbers. You are familiar with the geometric representation of real numbers by the points of a uniformly scaled line (Figure 2–1).

Figure 2–1

However, this picturing of real numbers is a device to help you to think about numbers, not a definition of the meaning of the numbers. In fact, we shall take the real numbers to be undefined objects.

You are also familiar with the binary* operations of addition (denoted by $+$) and of multiplication (denoted by $\times$ or $\cdot$) of pairs of real numbers and with the use of the symbol $=$. These concepts will also be accepted without definition. Thus, the undefined terms *real number, addition,* and *multiplication* and the symbols $+$, $\times$, $\cdot$, and $=$, together with the language of logic and the nontechnical words of ordinary English discourse, form the basic vocabulary of $\mathfrak{R}$.

The axioms that we state first govern the use of the symbol $=$.

---

* The adjective "binary" emphasizes the fact that each operation assigns a real number to every *pair* of real numbers.

Axioms of Equality

For all a, b, and c in $\Re$:

REFLEXIVE PROPERTY	1. $a = a$.
SYMMETRIC PROPERTY	2. If $a = b$, then $b = a$.
TRANSITIVE PROPERTY	3. If $a = b$ and $b = c$, then $a = c$.

The next two sets of axioms are formal statements of the following familiar properties of addition and multiplication in $\Re$.

1. When you add and when you multiply two real numbers a and b, you obtain in $\Re$ a unique (one and only one) *sum* $a + b$ and a unique *product* $a \cdot b$. The expressions $a \times b$, $a(b)$, $(a)b$, and ab also denote the product.

2. In a sum such as $(3 + 11) + 99$, you may pair any *term* with an adjacent term: $(3 + 11) + 99 = 3 + (11 + 99)$. Similarly, in a product such as $(3 \cdot 11) \cdot 99$, you may pair any *factor* with an adjacent factor: $(3 \cdot 11) \cdot 99 = 3 \cdot (11 \cdot 99)$. Note the use of parentheses to indicate the order of operations. Thus, $(3 + 11) + 99$ is the sum of $(3 + 11)$ and 99, but $3 + (11 + 99)$ is the sum of 3 and $(11 + 99)$; $(3 \cdot 11) \cdot 99$ is the product of $(3 \cdot 11)$ and 99, but $3 \cdot (11 \cdot 99)$ is the product of 3 and $(11 \cdot 99)$.

3. When you add the real number 0 to a given real number, the sum is identical with the given number: $0 + 7 = 7 + 0 = 7$.
Similarly, when you multiply the real number 1 by a given real number, the product is identical with the given number: $1 \cdot 7 = 7 \cdot 1 = 7$.

4. Each real number has a *negative* such that the sum of the number and its negative is 0: $3 + (-3) = (-3) + 3 = 0$.
Each nonzero real number has a *reciprocal* such that the product of the number and its reciprocal is 1: $3 \cdot \frac{1}{3} = \frac{1}{3} \cdot 3 = 1$.

5. You may add or multiply two real numbers in either order: $2 + 4 = 4 + 2$ and $2 \cdot 4 = 4 \cdot 2$.

The following axioms are precise statements of these properties.

Axioms of Addition

CLOSURE	For all a and b in $\mathcal{R}$, $(a + b) \in \mathcal{R}$ and $a + b$ is unique.
ASSOCIATIVITY	For all a, b, and c in $\mathcal{R}$, $(a + b) + c = a + (b + c)$.
EXISTENCE OF IDENTITY	There exists in $\mathcal{R}$ a unique element 0 having the property that for every a in $\mathcal{R}$, $0 + a = a$ and $a + 0 = a$.
EXISTENCE OF INVERSES	For each a in $\mathcal{R}$, there exists an element $-a$ in $\mathcal{R}$ such that $a + (-a) = 0$ and $(-a) + a = 0$.
COMMUTATIVITY	For all a and b in $\mathcal{R}$, $a + b = b + a$.

Note that the number $-a$ is called the **additive inverse**, or the **negative**, of a. Thus, the additive inverse of 3 is -3, and the additive inverse of -3 is 3. It can be shown that the additive inverse of a number is unique (p. 41).

Axioms of Multiplication

CLOSURE	For all a and b in $\mathcal{R}$, $ab \in \mathcal{R}$ and ab is unique.
ASSOCIATIVITY	For all a, b, and c in $\mathcal{R}$, $(ab)c = a(bc)$.
EXISTENCE OF IDENTITY	There exists in $\mathcal{R}$ a unique element $1(1 \neq 0)$ having the property that for every a in $\mathcal{R}$, $1 \cdot a = a$ and $a \cdot 1 = a$.
EXISTENCE OF INVERSES	For each a except 0 in $\mathcal{R}$, there exists an element $\dfrac{1}{a}$ in $\mathcal{R}$ such that $a \cdot \dfrac{1}{a} = 1$ and $\dfrac{1}{a} \cdot a = 1$.
COMMUTATIVITY	For all a and b in $\mathcal{R}$, $ab = ba$.

Note that $\dfrac{1}{a}$ is called the **multiplicative inverse**, or the **reciprocal**, of a. You can show that the multiplicative inverse of a number is unique. (Corollary 2, page 42.)

Any set of elements together with a binary operation satisfying the axioms of closure, associativity, existence of identity, and existence of inverses is called a **group** with respect to the given operation. In case the axiom of commutativity is also satisfied, the set is called a **commutative group**. Thus, $\mathcal{R}$ is a commutative group with respect to addition. The set of real numbers excluding 0 is a commutative group with respect to multiplication.

Do you see that the set J of integers, $\{\ldots, -3, -2, -1, 0, 1, 2, 3, \ldots\}$, is also a commutative group with respect to addition? However, the set of integers excluding 0 is not a group with respect to multiplication because it does not contain the reciprocal of each of its elements.

The following assumption, called the *Distributive Axiom*, establishes a link between addition and multiplication.

Distributive Axiom of Multiplication with Respect to Addition

For all a, b, and c in $\Re$:

1. $a(b + c) = (ab) + (ac)$.
2. $(b + c)a = (ba) + (ca)$.

The expression $(ab) + (ac)$ is usually written without parentheses: $ab + ac$. Thus, the Distributive Axiom permits you to assert: $7(9 + 2) = 7 \cdot 9 + 7 \cdot 2$ and $7 \cdot \frac{1}{2} + 5 \cdot \frac{1}{2} = (7 + 5)\frac{1}{2}$.

The last axiom to be stated in this section ensures that a sum or product of numbers does not depend on the numerals used to denote the numbers.

Axiom of Equality of Sums and Products

For all $a, b, c,$ and d in $\Re$ such that $a = c$ and $b = d, a + b = c + d$ and $ab = cd$.

Thus, given that $5 + 95 = 100$ and $4 \cdot 25 = 100$, this axiom lets you conclude that

$$(5 + 95) + (4 \cdot 25) = 100 + 100.$$

Because it appears that 100 has been "substituted" for both $(5 + 95)$ and $(4 \cdot 25)$, the axiom used is often referred to as the **Substitution Axiom**.

A set of numbers, together with operations of addition and multiplication, satisfying all the axioms of equality, addition, and multiplication, and the distributive axiom, is said to be a **number field**, or simply a **field**. Do you see that $\Re$ is a field?

Because addition and multiplication in a field are binary operations, you must define expressions such as $a + b + c$ and abc, where more than two numbers are to be added or multiplied. We agree on the following pattern for defining sums and products of three or more numbers:

$a + b + c$	$= (a + b) + c$	abc	$= (ab)c,$
$a + b + c + d$	$= (a + b + c) + d,$	$abcd$	$= (abc)d,$
$a + b + c + d + e$	$= (a + b + c + d) + e,$	$abcde$	$= (abcd)e,$
	and so on.		and so on.

For example, $5 + 62 + 95 + 36 = [(5 + 62) + 95] + 36$
$$3 \cdot 8 \cdot 4 \cdot 2 = [(3 \cdot 8) \cdot 4] \cdot 2.$$

From the axioms listed in this section you can derive numerous statements true in any field, not only in $\mathcal{R}$.

   EXAMPLE   **a.** By using quantifiers, convert the following sentence into a true statement: $x(y + z) = y$.

   b. Indicate why the axioms guarantee the truth of the resulting statement.

   Solution: **a.** For some numbers x and z in a field and for all numbers y in the field, $x(y + z) = y$.

   b. Replace x by 1 and
   z by 0. Then:
   $y + 0$ is a number
   in the field.   Closure axiom of addition.

   $1(y + 0) = y + 0.$ Existence of identity for
                              multiplication.

   $y + 0 = y.$ Existence of identity for addition.

   $\therefore 1(y + 0) = y.$ Transitive property of equality.

Exercises

By using quantifiers where needed, convert each of the following sentences into a true statement. Name the axioms which ensure the truth of the statements.

   1. $1 \cdot d = 1 \cdot d.$

   2. $(v + t) + (r + s)$ is a real number.

   3. $(m + r)k$ is a real number.

   4. $b + 1 = 1 + b.$

   5. $(t + 1)(a + b) = (t + 1)a + (t + 1)b.$

   6. $x(y + z) = xy + x.$

   7. $0 + t = 0.$ **11.** $a(b + c) = ba + ca.$

   8. $x + 1 = 1.$ **12.** $0 \cdot n = (0 + 0)n.$

   9. $a \cdot \dfrac{1}{b} = 1.$ **13.** $1 \cdot d = d.$

   10. $a + (-b) = 0.$ **14.** If $u = 1$, then $ut = 1.$

Name the axiom or definition that justifies each step in each of the following sequences of statements. Assume that the domain of each variable is the set of real numbers. In Exercise 15 you may use the fact that $2 = 1 + 1$.

15.
$$2a = (1 + 1)a$$
$$(1 + 1)a = 1a + 1a$$
$$1 \cdot a = a$$
$$1 \cdot a + 1 \cdot a = a + a$$
$$(1 + 1)a = a + a$$
$$\therefore 2a = a + a$$

16. $b + c$ denotes a real number.
$$a + (b + c) = (b + c) + a$$
$$b + c = c + b$$
$$(b + c) + a = (c + b) + a$$
$$a + (b + c) = (c + b) + a$$
$$(c + b) + a = c + (b + a)$$
$$\therefore a + (b + c) = c + (b + a)$$

Which of the following sets are closed under (a) addition and (b) multiplication? When a set is not closed, give an example which shows this.

17. $\{0\}$

18. $\{1\}$

19. $\{1, 2\}$

20. $\{0, 3\}$

21. {natural numbers}

22. {0 and natural numbers}

In Exercises 23–26 an operation $*$ has been defined over the set of natural numbers. In each case, (a) find $2 * 3$; (b) determine whether or not the set of natural numbers is closed under $*$; (c) state whether $*$ is (1) commutative, (2) associative.

[handwritten: 26. 9, closed, not commny not assoc]

B

23. $x * y = (1 + x) + y$

24. $x * y = x(2y)$
[handwritten: 12, 13 closed, is commy is assoc]

25. $x * y = xy^2$

26. $x * y = (1 + x)y$

In Exercises 27 and 28, state (a) whether the operations $\oplus$ and $\otimes$ defined for natural numbers a, b as indicated are (1) associative, (2) commutative; (b) whether (1) $\oplus$ is distributive with respect to $\otimes$, (2) $\otimes$ is distributive with respect to $\oplus$.

[handwritten: ⊕ not assoc, comm ⊗ assoc, comm ⊕ a not dist]

27. $a \oplus b = 2(a + b)$
$$a \otimes b = 3ab$$

28. $a \oplus b = (a + 1)(b + 1)$
$$a \otimes b = 1$$

29. Let S be a set with two members denoted by the symbols 0 and 1. Let $\oplus$ and $\otimes$ be two operations defined over S by the following tables:

$\oplus$	0	1
0	1	0
1	0	1

$\otimes$	0	1
0	0	1
1	1	1

(a) Determine whether or not these operations are (1) commutative, (2) associative. (b) Does S contain an identity element for (1) $\oplus$, (2) $\otimes$? (c) Show that $\otimes$ is distributive with respect to $\oplus$.

30. Let T be the set of all subsets of a universe U. State whether **(a)** T is closed with respect to the operation (1) $\cup$, (2) $\cap$; **(b)** the operations $\cup$ and $\cap$ are (1) commutative, (2) associative; **(c)** T contains an identity element for (1) $\cup$, (2) $\cap$; **(d)** $\cup$ is distributive with respect to $\cap$; **(e)** $\cap$ is distributive with respect to $\cup$.

31. Let $K = \{p, q, r, s\}$, and let the following table with respect to a binary operation $\circ$ apply in K.

$\circ$	p	q	r	s
p	p	q	r	s
q	q	p	s	r
r	r	s	p	q
s	s	r	q	p

a. Is K closed with respect to the operation $\circ$?

b. Is $\circ$ an associative operation?

c. Is there an identity element for $\circ$ in K?

d. Does each element in K have an inverse with respect to $\circ$?

e. Is K a group under $\circ$?

f. Is K a commutative group under $\circ$?

32. Let $L = \{p, q, r\}$, and let the following table with respect to a binary operation $*$ apply in L.

$*$	p	q	r
p	p	q	r
q	q	r	p
r	r	p	q

a. Is L a group with respect to $*$? Why or why not?

b. Is L a commutative group with respect to $*$? Why or why not?

33. A set S with binary operation $\circ$ is called a **semigroup** if and only if S is closed with respect to $\circ$ and $\circ$ is an associative operation in S. Let $S = \{p, q\}$, and let the following table with respect to $\circ$ apply in S.

$\circ$	p	q
p	p	q
q	q	p

a. Is S a semigroup?

b. Is S a group?

c. Is S a commutative group?

d. Is every group a semigroup?

34. Let $S = \{p, q, r\}$, and let the following table with respect to the binary operation $\circ$ apply in S.

$\circ$	p	q	r
p	p	q	r
q	p	q	r
r	p	q	r

a. Is S a semigroup with respect to $\circ$?

b. Is S a group with respect to $\circ$?

2–2 Proving Theorems

As a result of your earlier work in mathematics, you should be familiar with many of the properties of $\Re$ which are consequences of the axioms discussed in the preceding section. In order to have the most important of those consequences available for future reference, we shall state them in this and the following section and in the exercises on pages 44, 45, and 46. Proofs of a few of these results will be outlined to increase your familiarity with proof in algebra. Other proofs will be left for you to supply in the exercises.

The first theorem to be stated and proved is the one that allows you to conclude that the equations $x + 3 = 5 + 3$ and $x = 5$ are equivalent in $\Re$, that is, have the same solution set in $\Re$. The theorem is often called the **Cancellation Law for Addition**.

THEOREM	For all a, b, and c in $\Re$, $a + b = c + b$ if and only if $a = c$.

Proof: 1. The "if" part of the theorem follows easily from the substitution axiom. By hypothesis, a, b, and c belong to $\Re$, and $a = c$. By the reflexive property of equality, $b = b$. Hence, the substitution axiom lets you conclude that $a + b = c + b$.

2. To prove the "only if" part, suppose that $a + b = c + b$. Because $b \in \Re$, $-b \in \Re$. (Why?) Hence, from part (1), it follows that $(a + b) + (-b) = (c + b) + (-b)$. But because addition is associative $(a + b) + (-b) = a + [b + (-b)]$. Also, $b + (-b) = 0$ (Why?), so that $a + [b + (-b)] = a + 0$ (Why?). Now, $a + 0 = a$. (Why?) Hence, by the transitive property of equality, $(a + b) + (-b) = a$. Similarly, $(c + b) + (-b) = c$. From the equations printed in red, the conclusion, $a = c$, now follows by reason of the symmetric and transitive properties of equality. (See Exercise 2, page 44.)

From one theorem you are sometimes able to deduce quickly another closely related theorem, called a **corollary**. Because addition in $\Re$ is commutative, you can easily prove the following corollary of the preceding theorem.

COROLLARY. For all a, b, and c in $\mathfrak{R}$, $b + a = b + c$ if and only if $a = c$.

You know that the equation $x + 3 = 7$ has a single root in $\mathfrak{R}$, namely, $7 + (-3)$, or 4. The following theorem generalizes this observation.

THEOREM For all a and b in $\mathfrak{R}$, the equation $x + a = b$ has the unique solution $b + (-a)$ in $\mathfrak{R}$.

Proof: 1. First, we must verify that $[b + (-a)] \in \mathfrak{R}$ and is a root of the equation. Because $a \in \mathfrak{R}$ and $b \in \mathfrak{R}$, $-a \in \mathfrak{R}$ and $[b + (-a)] \in \mathfrak{R}$. (Why?) Also, $[b + (-a)] + a = b + [(-a) + a]$. (Why?) Moreover, $(-a) + a = 0$ (Why?); therefore, by the substitution axiom, $b + [(-a) + a] = b + 0$. But $b + 0 = b$. (Why?) Hence, by repeated use of the transitive property of equality, you find that $[b + (-a)] + a = b$; this means that $b + (-a)$ is a root of $x + a = b$.

2. Secondly, to prove that the equation has no more than one root, suppose r_1 and r_2 both denote roots. Then

$$r_1 + a = b \quad \text{and} \quad r_2 + a = b.$$

Hence, by the symmetric and transitive properties of equality, $r_1 + a = r_2 + a$. The Cancellation Law for Addition now enables you to conclude that $r_1 = r_2$. Thus, the equation cannot have more than one root. Together, arguments (1) and (2) prove the theorem.

COROLLARY 1. For all a and b in $\mathfrak{R}$, the equation $a + x = b$ has the unique solution $b + (-a)$ in $\mathfrak{R}$.

Proof: By the commutative axiom, for all a and x in $\mathfrak{R}$, $a + x = x + a$. Therefore, the equations $a + x = b$ and $x + a = b$ are equivalent in $\mathfrak{R}$.

COROLLARY 2. Each number in $\mathfrak{R}$ has a unique additive inverse.

Proof: The additive inverse of a in $\mathfrak{R}$ is the unique solution of $a + x = 0$.

COROLLARY 3. For all a in $\mathfrak{R}$, $-(-a) = a$; that is, the negative of the negative of a is a.

Proof: $-(-a)$ is the unique solution of $x + (-a) = 0$. But a satisfies this equation. (Why?) Hence, $-(-a) = a$. (Why?)

COROLLARY 4. For all a and b in $\Re$, $-(a + b) = (-a) + (-b)$.

Proof: *Plan:* Verify that the solution of $x + (a + b) = 0$ is $(-a) + (-b)$. Writing the proof constitutes Exercise 11, page 45.

We usually write $b - a$ in place of $b + (-a)$ and call $b - a$ the **difference** between a and b, or the result of **subtracting** a from b. Thus, $b - a$ is the unique solution of $x + a = b$.

The preceding theorems and corollaries have been deduced from the axioms of equality and addition. Using also the axioms of multiplication, you can similarly deduce the following **Cancellation Law for Multiplication** and the related assertions stated after it. Proofs are left as exercises.

THEOREM For all a, c, and nonzero b in $\Re$, $ab = cb$ if and only if $a = c$.

COROLLARY. For all a, c, and nonzero b in $\Re$, $ba = bc$ if and only if $a = c$.

THEOREM For all b and nonzero a in $\Re$, $xa = b$ has the unique solution $b \cdot \dfrac{1}{a}$.

COROLLARY 1. For all b and nonzero a in $\Re$, $ax = b$ has the unique solution $b \cdot \dfrac{1}{a}$.

COROLLARY 2. Each nonzero number in $\Re$ has a unique multiplicative inverse.

COROLLARY 3. For all nonzero a in $\Re$, $\dfrac{1}{\frac{1}{a}} = a$; that is, the reciprocal of the reciprocal of a is a.

COROLLARY 4. For all nonzero a and nonzero c in $\Re$, $\dfrac{1}{ac} = \dfrac{1}{a} \cdot \dfrac{1}{c}$.

We usually write the **fraction** $\dfrac{b}{a}$ ($a \neq 0$) in place of $b \cdot \dfrac{1}{a}$ and call $\dfrac{b}{a}$ (also written, b/a) the **quotient** of b and a, or the result of **dividing*** b by a. Thus, $\dfrac{b}{a}$ is the unique solution of $xa = b$. The theorems in Exercises 33–40, page 46, state the properties of fractions. (See also Exercise 42, page 46.)

---

* The notation $b \div a$ (read, b *divided by* a) is often used in elementary mathematics.

By using the distributive axiom along with the other assumptions, you can prove the following **Multiplication Property of Zero**.

THEOREM   For all a in $\Re$, $a \cdot 0 = 0$ and $0 \cdot a = 0$.

Proof: (Providing the reason for each step is left to you.)

1.	$a \in \Re$	6.	$a \cdot 0 = 0 + a \cdot 0$
2.	$0 + 0 = 0$	7.	$\therefore a \cdot 0 + a \cdot 0 = 0 + a \cdot 0$
3.	$a = a$	8.	$\therefore a \cdot 0 = 0$
4.	$\therefore a(0 + 0) = a \cdot 0$	9.	$0 \cdot a = a \cdot 0$
5.	$a(0 + 0) = a \cdot 0 + a \cdot 0$	10.	$\therefore 0 \cdot a = 0$

The familiar "rules" for multiplying additive inverses of numbers are by-products of the next theorem.

THEOREM   For all a in $\Re$, $(-1)a = -a$ and $a(-1) = -a$.

Proof: Plan: Verify that $(-1)a$ satisfies $x + a = 0$; because $-a$ is the unique solution of this equation, the conclusion $(-1)a = -a$ will follow.

1.	$a \in \Re$	6.	$\therefore (-1 + 1)a = 0 \cdot a$
2.	$a = 1 \cdot a$	7.	$\therefore (-1)a + 1 \cdot a = 0 \cdot a$
3.	$\therefore (-1)a + a = (-1)a + 1 \cdot a$	8.	$0 \cdot a = 0$
4.	$(-1)a + 1 \cdot a = (-1 + 1)a$	9.	$\therefore (-1)a + 1 \cdot a = 0$
5.	$-1 + 1 = 0$	10.	$\therefore (-1)a + a = 0$

(You should supply a reason for each step of the proof.) Hence $(-1)a$ satisfies $x + a = 0$, and must, therefore, equal $-a$. Because multiplication in $\Re$ is commutative, $a(-1) = (-1)a$, so that it is also true that $a(-1) = -a$.

COROLLARY 1. $(-1)(-1) = 1$.

Proof: Replace a by -1 in the statement of the theorem and use Corollary 3, page 41.

COROLLARY 2. For all a and b in $\mathcal{R}$:

1. $(-a)b = -ab$;
2. $a(-b) = -ab$;
3. $(-a)(-b) = ab$.

Proof of 1: Since $-a = -1 \cdot a$, you have $(-a)b = (-1 \cdot a)b$. Because multiplication is associative, $(-1 \cdot a)b = (-1)(ab)$. By the theorem just proved, $(-1)(ab) = -(ab) = -ab$. Hence, the transitive property of equality permits the conclusion $(-a)b = -ab$.

Proofs of the other parts of the corollary are required in Exercises 5 and 6, page 45.

Notice that the proofs of theorems stated in this section depend on axioms assumed in any field. Consequently, similar theorems are valid in every field.

The following agreement regarding the meaning of expressions involving several operations should be noted. In the absence of parentheses to indicate the order of operations, perform in order from left to right, first, multiplications and divisions, and then, additions and subtractions. Thus, $a - b - c = (a - b) - c$, and $a - b/c + d = a - (b/c) + d$.

Exercises

Name the axiom, theorem, or definition justifying each step in the following proofs. Variables denote any real numbers with the exceptions, if any, indicated.

A

1. *Prove:* If $x = y$ and $x = z$, then $y = z$.

Proof

$\{x, y, z\} \subset \mathcal{R}$

$\quad x = y$ and $x = z$

$\quad y = x$

$\therefore\ y = z$

2. *Prove:* If $x = y$, $x = z$, and $y = t$, then $z = t$.

Proof

$\{x, y, z, t\} \subset \mathcal{R}$

$\quad x = y$, $x = z$, and $y = t$

$\quad x = t$

$\quad z = x$

$\therefore\ z = t$

3. *Prove:* $(x + y) - y = x$.

Proof

$x \in \mathcal{R}, y \in \mathcal{R}$

$(x + y) - y = (x + y) + (-y)$

$(x + y) + (-y) = x + [y + (-y)]$

$(x + y) + (-y) = x + 0$

$(x + y) + (-y) = x$

4. *Prove:* If $a = b$, then $a^2 = b^2$.

Proof

$a \in \mathcal{R}, b \in \mathcal{R}$

$\quad a = b$

$\quad b = a$

$\quad ab = a \cdot a$

$\therefore\ ab = a^2$

$\quad ab = b \cdot b$

$\therefore\ ab = b^2$

$\therefore\ a^2 = b^2$

5. *Prove:* $a(-b) = -ab$.

Proof

$a \in \Re, b \in \Re$

$-b = b \cdot (-1)$

$a(-b) = a[b(-1)]$

$a(-b) = (ab)(-1)$

$\therefore a(-b) = -ab$

6. *Prove:* $(-a)(-b) = ab$.

Proof

$a \in \Re, b \in \Re$

$(-a)(-b) = (-1 \cdot a)(-1 \cdot b)$

$= -1 \cdot [a \cdot (-1 \cdot b)]$

$= -1 \cdot [[(a \cdot (-1)]b]$

$= -1 \cdot [(-1 \cdot a) \cdot b]$

$= (-1)[-1 \cdot (ab)]$

$= [(-1) \cdot (-1)](ab)$

$= 1(ab)$

$= ab$

$\therefore (-a)(-b) = ab$

7. *Prove:* $x(y - z) = xy - xz$.

Proof

$\{x, y, z\} \subset \Re$

$y - z = y + (-z)$

$x(y - z) = x[y + (-z)]$

$= xy + x(-z)$

$= xy + [-(xz)]$

$= xy - xz$

$\therefore x(y - z) = xy - xz$

8. *Prove:* $-(x - y) = -x + y$.

Proof

$x \in \Re, y \in \Re$ *hyp*

$x - y = x + (-y)$ *def of sub*

$\therefore -(x - y) = -[x + (-y)]$ *2 thiodgr*

$-[x + (-y)] = -x + [-(-y)]$ *corally 4*

$= -x + y$ *corally 3*

$\therefore -(x - y) = -x + y$ *transitive*

9. *Prove:* If $u \neq 0$, $\dfrac{x + y}{u} = \dfrac{x}{u} + \dfrac{y}{u}$.

Proof

$\{x, y, u\} \subset \Re; u \neq 0$

$x + y \in \Re$

$\dfrac{x + y}{u} = (x + y)\dfrac{1}{u}$

$= x \cdot \dfrac{1}{u} + y \cdot \dfrac{1}{u}$

$= \dfrac{x}{u} + \dfrac{y}{u}$

$\therefore \dfrac{x + y}{u} = \dfrac{x}{u} + \dfrac{y}{u}$

10. *Prove:* $z - (x - y) = (z - x) + y$.

Proof

$\{x, y, z\} \subset \Re$ *hyp*

$z - (x - y) = z + [-(x - y)]$ *def of su*

$= z + (-x + y)$ *exercise 8*

(Ex. 8)

$= [z + (-x)] + y$ *assoc*

$= (z - x) + y$ *def of sub*

$\therefore z - (x - y) = (z - x) + y$ *trans.*

Prove the indicated theorem or corollary.

B   **11.** Corollary 4, top of page 42.

12. Cancellation Law for Multiplication and its corollary (page 42).

13. The second theorem stated on page 42 and Corollary 1, page 42.

14. Corollary 2, page 42.

15. Corollary 3, page 42.

16. Corollary 4, bottom of page 42.

Prove each of the following results. Except as indicated, the domain of each variable is $\Re$.

17. $(x + y) + (z + v) = z + [x + (y + v)]$

18. $(3x + 2y) + (5x + 4y) = 8x + 6y$

19. $(x^2 + 3) + (3x + x) = (x + 1)(x + 3)$

20. $(y^2 + 5y) + (10 + 2y) = (y + 2)(y + 5)$

21. $(4x - 2y) - (2x + 3y) = 2x - 5y$

22. $(-4y + 3x + 11) - (-2x + 3y + 11) = 5x - 7y$

23. If $x \neq 0$, then $\dfrac{0}{x} = 0$.

25. If $x = y$, then $-x = -y$.

24. If $y \neq 0$, then $(xy)\dfrac{1}{y} = x$.

26. If $x \neq 0$ and $x = y$, then $\dfrac{1}{x} = \dfrac{1}{y}$.

27. If $x = z$ and $y = u$, then $x - y = z - u$.

28. If $x = z$, $y = u$, and $y \neq 0$, then $\dfrac{x}{y} = \dfrac{z}{u}$.

C **29.** Prove that the converse of the theorem stated in Exercise 27 is false.

30. Prove that the converse of the theorem stated in Exercise 28 is false.

31. For $a \neq 0$: $ax + b = c$ if and only if $x = \dfrac{c - b}{a}$.

32. For $uv \neq 0$: $\dfrac{x}{u} = \dfrac{y}{v}$ if and only if $xv = uy$.

In Exercises 33–40, assume $u \neq 0$ and $v \neq 0$.

33. $\dfrac{x}{u} \cdot \dfrac{y}{v} = \dfrac{xy}{uv}$.

37. $\dfrac{x}{u} + \dfrac{y}{v} = \dfrac{xv + uy}{uv}$.

$\left(Hint: \dfrac{x}{u} = \dfrac{xv}{uv}; \dfrac{y}{v} = \dfrac{uy}{uv}. \right)$

34. $\dfrac{xv}{uv} = \dfrac{x}{u}$.

38. $\dfrac{x}{u} - \dfrac{y}{v} = \dfrac{xv - uy}{uv}$.

(*Hint:* See Exercise 37.)

35. If $y \neq 0$, $\dfrac{1}{y/v} = \dfrac{v}{y}$.

39. $\dfrac{-x}{u} = \dfrac{x}{-u} = -\dfrac{x}{u}$.

36. If $y \neq 0$, $\dfrac{x}{u} \div \dfrac{y}{v} = \dfrac{xv}{uy}$.

40. $\dfrac{-x}{-u} = \dfrac{x}{u}$.

41. a. Show that the operation of subtraction in $\Re$ is neither commutative nor associative.

b. Is there an identity element for subtraction in $\Re$?

42. a. Show that the operation of division in $\Re$ is neither commutative nor associative.

b. Is there an identity element for division in $\Re$?

2-3 Indirect Proof

The proofs discussed in the last section are called *direct proofs*. A direct proof begins with the hypothesis "*p*" of a theorem: "*p* → *q*." From "*p*" the proof deduces a succession of statements, each derived by logical inference based on axioms, definitions, or previously proved theorems. The last statement deduced in the proof is "*q*," the conclusion of the theorem.

Another type of argument is known as *indirect proof* or *proof by contradiction*. An indirect proof begins with the hypothesis "*p*" of a theorem, "*p* → *q*," and with the *assumption that the conclusion "q" of the theorem is false;* that is, with the assumption that "*q′* " is true. From "*p* and *q′*," the proof derives by a succession of logically valid steps a contradictory statement, that is, a denial of "*p*" or "*q′*," or of an axiom, or of a previously proved theorem. The truth of the theorem is then inferred on the basis of the following principle. (See Exercise 13, page 49.)

Principle of Indirect Inference. If a contradiction can be derived from the statement "*p* ∧ *q′*," then the statement "*p* → *q*" is true.

You can use an indirect argument to establish the converse of the multiplication property of 0 (page 43).

THEOREM If $a \in \mathcal{R}$, $b \in \mathcal{R}$, and $ab = 0$, then $a = 0$ or $b = 0$.

You begin the proof with the hypothesis *and* the negation of the conclusion: "$a \in \mathcal{R}$, $b \in \mathcal{R}$, and $ab = 0$; *and* it is not the case that $a = 0$ or $b = 0$." (Recall that the negation of "$a = 0$ or $b = 0$" is "$a \neq 0$ *and* $b \neq 0$.") Then, you deduce logically valid statements leading to a contradiction.

Indirect Proof

$a \in \mathcal{R}$, $b \in \mathcal{R}$, and $ab = 0$	Hypothesis.
Suppose $a \neq 0$ and $b \neq 0$.	Negation of conclusion.
$\dfrac{1}{a} \in \mathcal{R}$ and $\dfrac{1}{a} \cdot a = 1$	Existence of inverses for multiplication.
$\dfrac{1}{a} = \dfrac{1}{a}$	Reflexive property of equality.
$\dfrac{1}{a}(ab) = \dfrac{1}{a} \cdot 0$	Cancellation law for multiplication.
$\dfrac{1}{a} \cdot 0 = 0$	Multiplication property of 0.
$\therefore \dfrac{1}{a}(ab) = 0$, and $0 = \dfrac{1}{a}(ab)$	Transitive and symmetric properties of equality.

(continued on page 48)

Also $\dfrac{1}{a}(ab) = \left(\dfrac{1}{a}\cdot a\right)b$ Associativity for multiplication.

$\therefore \left(\dfrac{1}{a}\cdot a\right)b = 1\cdot b$ Substitution axiom.

But $1\cdot b = b$ Identity for multiplication.

$\therefore \dfrac{1}{a}(ab) = b$ Transitive property of equality.

$\therefore 0 = b$ Transitive property of equality.

Thus, the hypothesis and the assumption "$a \neq 0$ and $b \neq 0$" lead to the contradictory statement, "$0 = b$." Because the assumption that the conclusion of the theorem is false when the hypothesis is true implies a contradiction, you know that the theorem must be true.

The multiplication property of 0 and its converse are often jointly stated in the following form, called the **Zero-Product Theorem**.

> **THEOREM**   A product of real numbers is 0 if and only if at least one of its factors is 0.

This theorem implies that over any subset of $\Re$, the solution set of the equation

$$(x + 3)(x - 7) = 0$$

equals the solution set of the sentence $x + 3 = 0$ *or* $x - 7 = 0$.

Thus, over the set of integers the solution set of $(x + 3)(x - 7) = 0$ is $\{-3, 7\}$.

Exercises

Give the axioms, definitions, or theorems justifying the steps in the following indirect proofs. Assume variables denote real numbers.

1. *Prove:* $-1 \neq 0$.

Indirect proof

Suppose: $-1 = 0$
Then: $-1 + 1 = 0 + 1$
Also $-1 + 1 = 0$
$0 + 1 = 1$
$\therefore 0 = 1$
But $0 \neq 1$
$\therefore$ "$-1 = 0$" is false,
so that   "$-1 \neq 0$" is true.

2. *Prove:* $\frac{1}{2} \neq 0$.

Indirect proof

Suppose: $\frac{1}{2} = 0$
Then: $2(\frac{1}{2}) = 2\cdot 0$
$2(\frac{1}{2}) = 1$
$2\cdot 0 = 0$
$\therefore 1 = 0$
But $1 \neq 0$
$\therefore$ "$\frac{1}{2} = 0$" is false,
so that   "$\frac{1}{2} \neq 0$" is true.

3. *Prove:* If $x \neq 0$, $y \neq 0$, and $x \neq y$, then $\dfrac{1}{x} \neq \dfrac{1}{y}$.

Indirect proof

x, $y \in \mathcal{R}$, and x, $y \neq 0$, $x \neq y$.

$\dfrac{1}{x}$ and $\dfrac{1}{y}$ are real numbers.

Suppose $\dfrac{1}{x} = \dfrac{1}{y}$.

$$\therefore xy\left(\frac{1}{x}\right) = xy\left(\frac{1}{y}\right)$$

$$(xy)\frac{1}{x} = y$$

$$(xy)\frac{1}{y} = x$$

$$\therefore y = x$$

But   "$y = x$"

contradicts "$x \neq y$."

$\therefore$ "$1/x = 1/y$" is false,

so that "$1/x \neq 1/y$" is true.

4. *Prove:* If $x \neq y$, then $x + 1 \neq y + 1$.

Indirect proof

x, $y \in \mathcal{R}$, and $x \neq y$.

1 is a real number.

Suppose: $x + 1 = y + 1$

$$\therefore x = y$$

But   "$x = y$"

contradicts "$x \neq y$."

$\therefore$ "$x + 1 = y + 1$"

is false, so that

"$x + 1 \neq y + 1$"

is true.

Prove each theorem. Use an indirect argument in each case. Assume $x, y, z \in \mathcal{R}$.

B

5. $1 \neq 2$

6. $\frac{1}{2} \neq 1$.

7. If $x \neq 0$, then $-x \neq 0$.

8. If $x \neq 0$, then $\dfrac{1}{x} \neq 0$.

9. If $x^2 \neq y^2$, then $x \neq y$.

10. If $x \neq y$, then $-x \neq -y$.

11. If $xz \neq yz$, and $z \neq 0$, then $x \neq y$.

12. If $x + z \neq y + z$, then $x \neq y$.

Use a truth table to prove that $p \rightarrow q$ is equivalent to:

13. $(p \wedge q')'$

14. $p' \vee q$

ORDER PROPERTIES

2–4 Axioms of Order

Pairing the real numbers with the points of a line (Figure 2–1, page 33) enables you to visualize another fundamental property of the set of real numbers: the existence of an *ordering* denoted by the symbol $<$ (read "is less than"). For example, the *inequality* $-2 < 3$ stands for "-2 is less than 3" and is pictured on the number line by showing the point corresponding to -2 (the *graph* of -2) to the left of the graph of 3 (Figure 2–2).

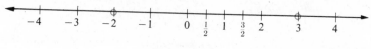

Figure 2–2

Figure 2–2 suggests that such statements as the following are true: $0 < 1$, $1 < 2$, $\frac{1}{2} < 3$, $-1 < 0$, $-3 < -1$. These facts can be proved on the basis of the following **axioms of order**.

Axiom of Comparison

For all a and b in $\Re$, one and only one of the following statements is true:

$$a < b, a = b, b < a.$$

Transitive Property of Order

For all a, b, and c in $\Re$, if $a < b$ and $b < c$, then $a < c$.

The conjunction "$a < b$ and $b < c$" is often written in the form $a < b < c$, read "a is less than b, which is less than c."

The next axiom ensures that adding the same real number to each member of a true inequality produces a true inequality.

Addition Property of Order

For all a, b, and c in $\Re$, if $a < b$, then $a + c < b + c$ and $c + a < c + b$.

A real number c for which the statement "$0 < c$" is true is called a **positive** number. If $c < 0$, c is called a **negative** number. The following axiom guarantees that multiplying each member of a valid inequality by the same *positive* number yields a true inequality.

Multiplication Property of Order

For all a and b in $\Re$ and all positive numbers c in $\Re$, if $a < b$, then $ac < bc$ and $ca < cb$.

The substitution axiom and transitive property of equality permit you, in an equation, to denote a number by any of its numerals. The following theorem implies that substitution is also permissible in an inequality.

THEOREM   If x, y, and u are real numbers such that $x < y$ and $x = u$, then $u < y$.

Indirect proof

To show that $u < y$, you must prove that assuming that u is *not* less than y (in symbols, $u \not< y$) leads to a contradiction. If $u \not< y$, then by the axiom of comparison there are two cases to consider:

Case 1: Assume that $u = y$.
　　But $x = u$.
　　$\therefore x = y$.

Case 2: Assume that $y < u$.
　　But $x < y$.
　　$\therefore x < u$.

Be sure to give the reasons for each step.

In each case the final assertion contradicts the hypothesis: $x < y$ *and* $x = u$. (Why?) Therefore, the assumption that $u \not< y$ must be false, and the conclusion "$u < y$" must be true.

From this theorem you can deduce the following corollary.

Substitution Property of Order

Let x, y, u, and v denote real numbers. If $x < y$, and if $x = u$ and $y = v$, then $u < v$.

Can you suggest how to prove that $0 < 1$? Using the axiom of comparison, you know that if 0 is not less than 1, then either $0 = 1$ or $1 < 0$. But $0 = 1$ is false because the multiplicative identity axiom asserts that 0 and 1 are different numbers. The statement $1 < 0$ is also false, because assuming it to be true, you have:

$1 < 0$	Assumption.
$1 + (-1) < 0 + (-1)$	Addition property of order.
$1 + (-1) = 0$	Existence of additive inverse.
$0 + (-1) = -1$	Additive identity.
$\therefore 0 < -1$	Substitution property of order.
$\therefore 0(-1) < -1(-1)$	Multiplication property of order.
But $0(-1) = 0$ and	Multiplication properties of 0
$-1(-1) = 1$	and -1.
$\therefore 0 < 1$	Substitution property of order.

Thus, the assumption "$1 < 0$" leads to the contradictory statement "$0 < 1$." Since neither "$0 = 1$" nor "$1 < 0$" can be true, the axiom of comparison implies that "$0 < 1$" must be true.

Knowing that $0 < 1$, you can deduce that $0 + 1 < 1 + 1$ or $1 < 2$. (Why?) Similarly, you show that $1 + 1 < 2 + 1$, or $2 < 3$, that $3 < 4$, and so on.

Also from $0 < 1$, you obtain $0 + (-1) < 1 + (-1)$, or $-1 < 0$. This fact in turn enables you to deduce that $-2 < -1$, $-3 < -2$, and so on.

These results together with the transitive property of order confirm the ordering of the integers used on the number line in Figure 2–2, page 50:

$$\ldots -4 < -3 < -2 < -1 < 0 < 1 < 2 < 3 < 4 \ldots$$

This ordering suggests the following theorem, asserting that 0 is between each nonzero number and its additive inverse. (See Exercise 21, page 55.)

THEOREM   For every b in $\Re$, $0 < b$ if and only if $-b < 0$.

By an indirect argument, you can also deduce that every nonzero number and its reciprocal are both positive or both negative numbers. (Exercises 27 and 28, page 56.)

THEOREM   For every nonzero a in $\Re$, $0 < a$ if and only if $0 < \dfrac{1}{a}$.

Other *inequality symbols* often used are: $>$, $\leq$, $\geq$ and their "negations" $\not>$, $\not\leq$, $\not\geq$. The statement "$a > b$," read "a is greater than b," is defined to mean $b < a$. (To avoid confusing the symbols $<$ and $>$, think of them as arrowheads always pointing to the numeral for the lesser number.) The disjunction "$a < b$ or $a = b$" is usually written $a \leq b$ and read, "a is less than or equal to *b*." Similarly, $a \geq b$ stands for "*a* is greater than or equal to *b*." It is easy to see that restating the transitive, addition, multiplication, and substitution properties of order in terms of the symbols, $>$, $\geq$, and $\leq$ yields true statements. (Exercises 17, 18, 19, and 20, page 55.)

On a number line you often picture a subset of the set of real numbers as a set of points, called the **graph of the subset**.

EXAMPLE 1. Graph the following subsets of the set of real numbers.

a. $\{r: \ r = -2 \text{ or } r = 2\}$ **c.** $\{k: \ k < 3\}$

b. $\{y: \ y \geq -3\}$ **d.** $\{m: \ -1 < m \leq 2\}$

Solution: **a.**

b.

c.

d.

Note: A red or heavy dot • denotes a point corresponding to a number in the set. A red or heavily marked portion of a line ——— indicates that all points on it belong to the graph. Open dots ∘ or lightly marked portions of lines show points not belonging to the graph. A red or heavy arrowhead implies the graph continues unendingly in the indicated direction.

EXAMPLE 2. Solve $3y + 1 \geq y - 5$ over $\mathfrak{R}$.

Solution: The field and order properties imply that the following inequalities are equivalent to each other:

1. $3y + 1 \geq y - 5$ 5. $2y \geq -6$
2. $3y + 1 - 1 \geq y - 5 - 1$
3. $3y \geq y - 6$ 6. $\dfrac{2y}{2} \geq \dfrac{-6}{2}$
4. $3y - y \geq y - 6 - y$ 7. $y \geq -3$

∴ the solution set over $\mathfrak{R}$ of $3y + 1 \geq y - 5$ is
$\{y: y \geq -3\}$, **Answer**.
The graph of the solution set is shown in Example 1(b).

The multiplication property of order (page 51) states the effect of multiplying an inequality by a *positive* number. The following theorem establishes the result of multiplication by a negative number.

> **THEOREM** For all a and b in $\mathcal{R}$ and all negative numbers c in $\mathcal{R}$, if $a < b$, then $ac > bc$ and $ca > cb$.

For example, If $x < 2$, then $-3 \cdot x > -3 \cdot 2$, or $-3x > -6$.

If $-3y > 15$, then $-\frac{1}{3}(-3y) < -\frac{1}{3} \cdot 15$, or $y < -5$.

Proof: By hypothesis, $c < 0$. Therefore, $-c > 0$. (Why?) But the hypothesis also states that $a < b$. Therefore, the multiplication property of order implies that $a(-c) < b(-c)$. (Why?) Because $a(-c) = -ac$ and $b(-c) = -bc$ (Why?), you have $-ac < -bc$. Thus, adding $ac + bc$ to each member of the latter inequality you obtain, by the addition and substitution properties of order:

$$-ac + (ac + bc) < -bc + (ac + bc),$$

or $\qquad\qquad bc < ac;$

that is, $\qquad\quad ac > bc.$

Because $ca = ac$ and $cb = bc$, the conclusion $ca > cb$ also follows. (Why?)

From the preceding theorem, the multiplication property of order and the order property of a number and its reciprocal, you can deduce the following assertion. (Exercises 33 and 34, page 56.)

> **THEOREM** For all a and c in $\mathcal{R}$:
>
> 1. $ac > 0$ if and only if either $a > 0$ and $c > 0$, or $a < 0$ and $c < 0$.
> 2. $ac < 0$ if and only if either $a > 0$ and $c < 0$, or $a < 0$ and $c > 0$.

EXAMPLE 3. Solve $x^2 - 3x < 0$ over $\mathcal{R}$.

Solution: Since $x^2 - 3x = x(x - 3)$ (Why?), the inequality

$$x^2 - 3x < 0$$

is equivalent to

$$x(x - 3) < 0.$$

It will therefore be satisfied if and only if either

$$x > 0 \text{ and } x - 3 < 0 \quad or \quad x < 0 \text{ and } x - 3 > 0.$$

$$\therefore x > 0 \text{ and } x < 3 \qquad \therefore x < 0 \text{ and } x > 3$$

| The intersection of the solution sets of these inequalities is $\{x: 0 < x < 3\}$. | The intersection of the solution sets of these inequalities is $\emptyset$. |

$$\therefore \{x: x^2 - 3x < 0\} = \{x: 0 < x < 3\} \cup \emptyset = \{x: 0 < x < 3\}, \textbf{ Answer.}$$

Exercises

Solve each open sentence over $\mathcal{R}$, and graph each nonempty solution set.

1. $3y + 9 \le 5y - 3$

2. $6 + 5x \ge x - 2$

3. $r + 5 - 5r > -16 + 2r$

4. $3m + 25 < m + 5 - 4m$

5. $9 - z < 7 - (z - 2)$

6. $3 - (u + 3) < 5 - u$

7. $-4 \le x - 5 \le 4$

8. $-1 < y + 2 < 1$

9. $v^2 - 3v \le 0$

10. $u^2 + 2u \le 0$

11. $(x + 1)(x - 3) > 0$

12. $(y - 1)(y - 2) \ge 0$

13. $m^2 > 2m$

14. $n \le -6n$

Prove the following theorems. Assume variables denote real numbers with restrictions, if any, as indicated.

15. No real number x exists such that $x < x$.

16. If $a \le b$ and $b \le a$, then $a = b$.

17. If $x \ge y$ and $y \ge z$, then $x \ge z$.

18. If $x \ge y$ and $z > 0$, then $xz \ge yz$.

19. If $x > y$, then $x + z > y + z$.

20. If $x \ge y$ and $x = u$, then $u \ge y$.

21. $a \le b$ if and only if $a - b \le 0$.

   Corollary 1. $0 \le b$ if and only if $-b \le 0$.

   Corollary 2. $b \le 0$ if and only if $-b \ge 0$.

22. $a > b$ if and only if $a - b > 0$.

   Corollary 1. $b < 0$ if and only if $-b > 0$.

   Corollary 2. $0 < b$ if and only if $-b < 0$.

23. If $0 < x < 1$, then $x^2 < x$; if $x > 1$, then $x^2 > x$.

24. If $x \ne 0$, then $x^2 > 0$.

25. If $x \le y$ and $z < 0$, then $xz \ge yz$.

26. If $x > y$ and $z < 0$, then $xz < yz$.

C **27.** If $a > 0$, then $\dfrac{1}{a} > 0$. (*Hint:* Use an indirect argument.)

28. If $a < 0$, then $\dfrac{1}{a} < 0$. (*Hint:* Use an indirect argument.)

29. If $x > 1$, then $(x - 1)(x^2 + 3x + 1) > 0$.

30. If $x < 2$, then $(x - 2)(x^2 + 1) < 0$.

31. $x^2 + y^2 \geq 0$.   **32.** $x^2 + y^2 \geq 2xy$.

33. $ac > 0$ if and only if either $a > 0$ and $c > 0$, or $a < 0$ and $c < 0$.

34. $ac < 0$ if and only if either $a > 0$ and $c < 0$, or $a < 0$ and $c > 0$.

35. Given $x > 0$ and $y > 0$: $x < y$ if and only if $\dfrac{1}{x} > \dfrac{1}{y}$.

36. Given $y > 0$ and $z > 0$: $\dfrac{x}{y} < \dfrac{w}{z}$ if and only if $xz < wy$.

37. Given $x > 0$ and $y > 0$: $x^2 > y^2$ if and only if $x > y$. (*Hint:* $x^2 - y^2 = (x + y)(x - y)$.)

38. If $x < y$, then $x < \dfrac{x + y}{2} < y$.

39. If $x < u$ and $y < v$, then $x + y < u + v$.

Prove that the set of positive numbers is closed under the indicated operation.

40. Addition   **41.** Multiplication

Prove by counterexample that the following assertions are false.

42. For all x and y in $\mathfrak{R}$, $x^2 > y^2$ only if $x > y$.

43. For all x, u, y, and v in $\mathfrak{R}$: if $x < u$ and $y < v$, then $xy < uv$.

44. The converse of the theorem stated in Exercise 39.

2–5 Absolute Value

For every nonzero real number x, its **absolute value**, denoted by $|x|$, is the positive number of the pair x and $-x$. For example, $|4| = 4$, $|-3| = 3$, $|-\frac{1}{2}| = \frac{1}{2}$. The **absolute value of 0** is 0 itself. Notice that the absolute value of a number is never a negative number: for every x, $|x| \geq \mathbf{0}$. It is also easy to see that $|7| = |-7| = 7$ and, in general, $|x| = |-x|$.

You recall (page 52) that the additive inverse of a real number is negative, 0, or positive according as the number is positive, 0, or negative. This fact means that you can restate the definition of absolute value as follows:

$$|x| = \begin{cases} x \text{ if } x \geq 0. \\ -x \text{ if } x < 0. \end{cases}$$

When you represent numbers as points on a number line, $|x|$ is the *distance* of the graph of x from the **origin** or graph of 0. Can you describe the graph of the subset of real numbers, $\{x: |x| < 2\}$? It consists of those points whose distance from the origin is less than 2 (Figure 2–3).

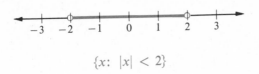

$$\{x: |x| < 2\}$$

Figure 2–3

This suggests that the inequality $|x| < 2$ is satisfied if and only if the sentence $-2 < x < 2$ is true, and illustrates the following assertion.

THEOREM   Let x and a denote real numbers such that $a > 0$. Then $|x| < a$ if and only if $-a < x < a$.

There are two statements to prove:

1. If $|x| < a$, then $-a < x < a$.
2. If $-a < x < a$, then $|x| < a$.

In proving these statements, recall that $-a < x < a$ means $-a < x$ *and* $x < a$.

Proof of 1: For every $x \in \mathcal{R}$, $|x| \geq 0$. Since $a > 0$, you know $-a < 0$. Therefore, for every x, $-a < |x|$. (Why?)

Now, first consider those x's for which $x \geq 0$. For these, $|x| = x$, and you have

$-a < |x|, |x| = x, |x| < a$, or, by substitution, $-a < x < a$, the desired result.

Now consider those x's for which $x < 0$. In these cases, $|x| = -x$, and you have

$-a < |x|, |x| = -x, |x| < a$, or, by substitution, $-a < -x < a$. Multiplying by -1, you obtain $a > x > -a$, or $-a < x < a$, the desired result.

Proof of 2: Since $-a < x < a$, then $-a < x$ and $x < a$.

Consider first those x's for which $x \geq 0$. You have $|x| = x$ and $x < a$, or $|x| < a$, as desired.

Now consider those x's for which $x < 0$. In this situation, you have $|x| = -x$, or equivalently, $x = -|x|$.

From $x = -|x|$ and $-a < x$ you have $-a < -|x|$. Multiplication by -1 yields $|x| < a$, as desired.

Can you solve the inequality $|t - 1| < 2$ over $\mathcal{R}$? The theorem just proved implies that $|t - 1| < 2$ if and only if $-2 < t - 1 < 2$. Adding 1 to each member of this pair of inequalities, you have

$$-2 + 1 < t - 1 + 1 < 2 + 1, \quad \text{or} \quad -1 < t < 3.$$

Thus, $\{t: |t - 1| < 2\} = \{t: -1 < t < 3\}$. Notice that on the number line (Figure 2–4), the graph of this set is the set of points each of which is *less than 2 units from 1.*

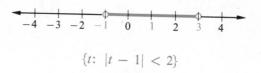

$$\{t: |t - 1| < 2\}$$

Figure 2–4

Figures 2–4 and 2–5 suggest a useful interpretation of the absolute value of the difference of two real numbers, a and b: $|a - b|$ is the distance between the graphs of a and b.

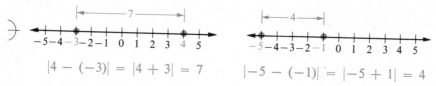

$$|4 - (-3)| = |4 + 3| = 7 \qquad |-5 - (-1)| = |-5 + 1| = 4$$

Figure 2–5

Figure 2–6 shows the graph of the solution set of the open sentence $|t - 1| \geq 2$. Can you explain why the given

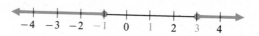

Figure 2–6

inequality is equivalent to the following disjunction?

$$t - 1 \leq -2 \quad or \quad t - 1 \geq 2;$$

that is,

$$t \leq -1 \quad or \quad t \geq 3.$$

This example uses the following theorem. (See Exercises 21 and 22, page 60.)

THEOREM   If $x \in \Re$, $a \in \Re$, and $a > 0$, then $|x| \geq a$ if and only if $x \leq -a$ or $x \geq a$.

Can you see why the two theorems stated in this section are still true if we remove the condition that $a > 0$? The extensions of the theorems might seem unimportant, but you use both of the extended theorems to solve inequalities like the following ones.

EXAMPLE 1. *Solve:* $|2x - 1| < 5 - x$.

Solution: $|2x - 1| < 5 - x$ if and only if

$$-(5 - x) < 2x - 1$$
$$-5 + x < 2x - 1$$
$$-5 + x - x + 1 < 2x - 1 - x + 1$$
$$-4 < x$$

and

$$2x - 1 < 5 - x$$
$$2x - 1 + x + 1 < 5 - x + x + 1$$
$$3x < 6$$
$$x < 2$$

$\therefore \{x: |2x - 1| < 5 - x\} = \{x: -4 < x < 2\}$, **Answer.**

EXAMPLE 2. *Solve:* $|2x - 1| \geq 5 - x$.

Solution: $|2x - 1| \geq 5 - x$ if and only if

$$2x - 1 \leq -(5 - x) \quad or \quad 2x - 1 \geq 5 - x$$
$$2x - 1 \leq -5 + x \quad | \qquad 3x \geq 6$$
$$x \leq -4 \qquad or \qquad x \geq 2$$

$\therefore \{x: |2x - 1| \geq 5 - x\} = \{x: x \leq -4\} \cup \{x: x \geq 2\}$,

Answer.

Figure 2–7 shows the graphs of the solution sets of the inequalities in Examples 1 and 2.

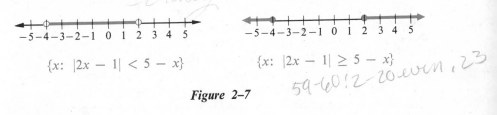

$\{x: |2x - 1| < 5 - x\}$ $\{x: |2x - 1| \geq 5 - x\}$

Figure 2–7   59-60:2-20 even, 23

Exercises

Specify and graph the solution set of each open sentence over $\mathcal{R}$.

A

1. $\|r\| \leq 3$	**5.** $\|1 - 4y\| = 13$	**9.** $\|3 - 5g\| \geq 7$
2. $\|s\| \leq 4$	**6.** $\|2 - 3k\| = 17$	**10.** $\|5 - 2h\| > 3$
3. $\|y + 1\| > 6$	**7.** $\|2x - 9\| \leq 1$	**11.** $\|1 - (2 - x)\| < 4$
4. $\|u - 1\| \geq 4$	**8.** $\|3t - 7\| < 2$	**12.** $\|6 - (y - 3)\| \leq 9$

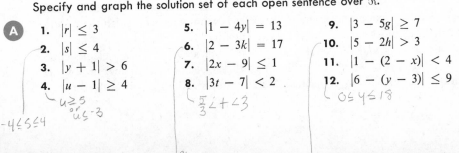

Specify and graph the solution set of each open sentence over $\mathfrak{R}$.

B 13. $|2y + 1| = y - 4$ 17. $|5s - 3| \geq 1 + 3s$

14. $|3t + 2| = t + 5$ $p > 7/2$ 18. $|2p + 6| < 4p - 1$

15. $|1 + 2(x - 1)| = |3x + 7|$ 19. $\left|\dfrac{v}{2} + 9\right| - v + 3 < 0$

16. $|5w - 9| = |4 - 3(2 - w)|$ 20. $|r - 3| - \dfrac{r}{4} \geq 2$

                               $r \geq 20/2 \text{ or } r \leq 4/5$

Prove each theorem. Variables denote real numbers restricted as indicated.

C 21. If $|x| \geq a > 0$, then $x \geq a$ or $x \leq -a$.

22. If $a > 0$ and $x \leq -a$ or $x \geq a$, then $|x| \geq a$.

23. $|a|^2 = a^2$.   25. $|xy| = |x| \cdot |y|$.

24. $xy \leq |xy|$.   26. If $y \neq 0$, $\left|\dfrac{x}{y}\right| = \dfrac{|x|}{|y|}$.

27. $|x + y| \leq |x| + |y|$. (*Hint:* Since $|x + y|$ and $|x| + |y|$ denote nonnegative numbers, note that the theorem is equivalent to $|x + y|^2 \leq (|x| + |y|)^2$. Then, use Exercises 23 and 24.)

28. $|x| - |y| \leq |x + y|$.

2-6 Subsets of $\mathfrak{R}$

Among the important subsets of the field $\mathfrak{R}$ of real numbers are:

1. The set N of natural numbers, or positive integers: $\{1, 2, 3, \ldots\}$.

2. The set J of integers: $\{\ldots, -3, -2, -1, 0, 1, 2, 3, \ldots\}$.

3. The set R of rational numbers: $\{x: \ x = \dfrac{p}{q}, p \in J \text{ and } q \in N\}$.

The order axioms are satisfied in each of the sets N, J, and R. However, although N and J are closed with respect to addition and multiplication, and satisfy the commutative, associative, and distributive laws for these operations, neither of these sets fulfils *all* the requirements of a field. N fails to contain not only 0, the additive identity element, but also the additive and multiplicative inverses of its members. J, on the other hand, satisfies all the field axioms with the exception of the existence of multiplicative inverses. Because R consists of those real numbers that are quotients of integers, the properties of fractions (Exercises 33–40, page 46) ensure that R is a field. In Chapter 3 you will study the last axiom characterizing the real number system: the axiom of completeness. This axiom will distinguish the ordered field $\mathfrak{R}$ from its subset, the ordered field R.

Because N and J do not contain the reciprocals of all their elements, the concept of *divisibility* is significant in these sets. For instance, in J we say that 6 is *divisible* by 3 because the equation $3x = 6$ can be solved over J.

On the other hand, 6 is *not divisible* by 4 in J because $4x = 6$ is not satisfied by any number x in J. In general, if $a \in J$, $b \in J$, and $b \neq 0$, then a is said to be **divisible** by b in J if and only if there exists an integer q in J such that $a = bq$. In this case, we write $\frac{a}{b} = a \div b = q$; we call b a **factor** or **divisor** of a and we denote these facts by the symbol $b|a$ (read "b is a factor of a," "b divides a," or "a is divisible by b.") For example, $3|6$, $15|-195$, and $7|0$. On the other hand, the symbol $b \nmid a$ means that b is *not* a factor of a. Thus, $4 \nmid 6$, $15 \nmid -175$, and $0 \nmid 7$.

If an integer is the product of other integers, say $a = bcd$, then the expression bcd is called a **factorization** of a. By the multiplicative identity axiom every integer a has the *trivial factorization:* $a = 1 \cdot a$. Thus, for every a in J, $1|a$ and $a|a$.

From the factorization $12 = 2 \cdot 2 \cdot 3$, you obtain at once such associated factorizations as $12 = (-2)(-2)3$; $12 = (-2)2(-3)$, $-12 = -1 \cdot 2 \cdot 2 \cdot 3$, $-12 = 2 \cdot 2 \cdot (-3)$. Thus, to determine whether an integer a is factorable in J, you need only discover whether $|a|$ is factorable in N. Therefore, we shall restrict our attention to *positive factors of positive integers*.

The following theorem indicates that every divisor of a positive integer a must either equal a or be less than a.

THEOREM   For all a and b in N, if $b|a$, then $b \leq a$.

Proof: By hypothesis, there exists an integer q in N such that $a = bq$. In case $q = 1$, $a = b$ and the indicated factorization of a is trivial. In case $q > 1$, it must be true that $b < a$. For if $b \geq a$, then $bq \geq aq > a$ (Why?). Thus, $b \geq a$ would imply that $bq > a$ in contradiction to the hypothesis $a = bq$. Therefore, if $q > 1$, then $b < a$. Thus, in both cases the theorem is true.

Because 15 is a factor of 150 and also of 60, we call 15 a *common factor* of these integers. In general, if a, b, and c are integers and c is a factor of both a and b, then c is a **common factor** or **common divisor** of a and b. The largest common factor of a and b is called their **greatest common factor** (G.C.F.). For example, the G.C.F. of 150 and 60 is 30.

If the G.C.F. of two integers a and b is 1, then a and b are said to be **relatively prime**. Thus, 28 and 15 are relatively prime. An important theorem concerning relatively prime integers is the following assertion which we state without proof.

THEOREM   For all integers a, b, and c, if a and b are relatively prime and $b|ac$, then $b|c$.

For example, if c is an integer such that $28|15c$, then $28|c$. Thus, if an integer is a factor of the product of two integers and is relatively prime to one of the integers, then it must be a factor of the other.

If an integer greater than 1 has only a trivial factorization, then the integer is called a **prime number**, or simply a **prime**. The first few primes are 2, 3, 5, 7, 11, 13. Any integer greater than 1 that is not a prime is a **composite number**. Thus, 195 is composite because $195 = 3 \cdot 5 \cdot 13$. The following proposition, to be stated without proof, is called the **Fundamental Theorem of Arithmetic**, and is probably the most useful of all theorems concerning the factorization of positive integers.

> **THEOREM** Every integer greater than 1 can be expressed as a product $b_1 \cdot b_2 \cdots b_k$ of prime numbers in one and only one way, except for the order of the factors.

Knowing the prime factorizations of two integers, you can easily determine their G.C.F. For example, suppose the integers are 360 and 588. Factoring, you have:

$$360 = 2 \cdot 2 \cdot 2 \cdot 3 \cdot 3 \cdot 5, \qquad 588 = 2 \cdot 2 \cdot 3 \cdot 7 \cdot 7.$$

∴ the G.C.F. of 360 and 588 is $2 \cdot 2 \cdot 3$, or 12.

Given the numbers 28 and 10, can you determine integers q and r such that $28 = 10q + r$ when $0 \le r < 10$? The statement $28 = 10 \cdot 2 + 8$ indicates the solution of this simple problem and illustrates the following theorem on which many properties of the integers depend.

> **THEOREM** If a and b are integers ($b \ne 0$), then there exist unique integers q and r such that $a = bq + r$ where $0 \le r < |b|$.

Although we will not prove this proposition, we shall make use of it. Do you see that the assertion that every integer is of the form $2n$ or $2n + 1$ for some n in J depends on this theorem?

Exercises

In Exercises 1–10 let $E = \{\text{even integers}\}$ and $O = \{\text{odd integers}\}$.

1. Is E closed with respect to addition? multiplication?
2. Is addition commutative in E? multiplication?
3. Is addition associative in E? multiplication?
4. Is there an additive identity element in E? a multiplicative identity element?
5. Is there an additive inverse for every element in E? a multiplicative inverse?

Handwritten in left margin: For Monday 63. 11–18, 33, 35, 38, 41 + Chapter Test

6. Is the distributive law obeyed in E?

7. Is E a group with respect to addition? Why or why not?

8. Is E a group with respect to multiplication? Why or why not?

9. Is O a group with respect to addition? Why or why not?

10. Is O a group with respect to multiplication? Why or why not?

In Exercises 11–18 replace the comma with $|$ or $\nmid$ so that the resulting statement is true.

11. 4, 8   13. 5, 7   15. 11, 143   17. 8, 78

12. 3, 29 no   14. 6, 144 yes   16. 15, 60 yes   18. 9, 74 no

Determine the prime factorization of each integer.

19. 256   21. 1260   23. 57   25. 15,288

20. 343   22. 468   24. 101   26. 469

Determine the G.C.F. of the given integers.

27. 256; 1260   28. 343; 468   29. 57; 15,288   30. 101; 469

B 31. Let p be a *prime other than 5*. List the positive factors of $5p$ and show that their sum is $6(p + 1)$.

32. Let p be an *odd prime*. List the positive factors of $4p$ and show that their sum is $7(p + 1)$.

Prove each theorem given that a, b, c, and x denote elements of N.

C 33. If $b|a$ and $a|c$, then $b|c$.

(*Hint:* By hypothesis, there exist integers q_1 and q_2 such that $a = bq_1$ and $c = aq_2$.)

34. If $b|a$ and $a|b$, then $a = b$.

35. If $b|a$ and $b|c$, then $b|(a + c)$.

36. If $b|a$ and $b|c$, then $b|(a - c)$.

37. If p is a prime and $p|a^2$, then $p|a$.

38. If b and p are primes, $b|pa$ and $b \nmid a$, then $b = p$.

39. Observe that 6 is a divisor of 36, and $36 = 9 \cdot 4$. But 6 is not a divisor of either 9 or 4. Explain why these facts do not contradict the second theorem stated on page 61.

40. If $a \neq 0$, the equation $ax - b = 0$ is solvable if and only if $a|b$.

41. $a(a + 1)(2a + 1)$ is divisible by 6.

42. If a is odd, $a(a^2 - 1)$ is divisible by 24.

Chapter Summary

1. In a **direct proof** one or more principles of inference are invoked to deduce a chain of statements from given **facts**, **definitions**, **axioms** (statements accepted as true), or **theorems** (statements previously shown to be true). The first statement in the chain is the hypothesis and the last is the conclusion of the theorem being proved. In an **indirect proof** you show that assuming the hypothesis and the negation of the conclusion of a theorem leads to a contradiction.

2. The system $\Re$ of real numbers is a logical structure whose properties are derived from undefined terms and axioms through the use of logic. **Equality** in $\Re$ is governed by four axioms. Because the binary operations of addition and multiplication in $\Re$ are governed by the eleven **field axioms**, $\Re$ is a field.

3. $\Re$ is an **ordered field** because its elements satisfy the **order axioms** with respect to the **ordering** *less than* ($<$), or equivalently, *greater than* ($>$).

4. The **absolute value**, $|x|$, of x in $\Re$ is the nonnegative member of the pair x and $-x$.

   $|x| = a$ is equivalent to: $\quad x = a$ or $x = -a$

   $|x| < a$ is equivalent to: $\quad -a < x$ and $x < a$; i.e., $-a < x < a$

   $|x| > a$ is equivalent to: $\quad -a > x$ or $x > a$

5. The set J of integers satisfies all the ordered-field axioms except the axiom requiring the existence of multiplicative inverses. If a and b are integers and the equation $bx = a$ is solvable over J, then b is a **factor** or **divisor** of a, and this is denoted by $b|a$. The **greatest common factor** (G.C.F.) of two integers a and b is the greatest integer c such that $c|a$ and $c|b$. The **Fundamental Theorem of Arithmetic** asserts that an integer can be expressed as a product of prime numbers in one and essentially only one way.

Chapter Test

2–1 Name the axiom justifying each statement.

  1. If $3 + 2 = 5$, then $5 = 3 + 2$. _sym_

  2. If $x \in \Re$, then $x^2 + x = x(x + 1)$. _dist._

2–2 **3.** Prove that if $a, b \in \Re$, then $(ab)^2 = a^2 b^2$.

  4. Prove that if $a, b \in \Re$ and $a = \dfrac{1}{b}$, then $ab = 1$.

2–3 **5.** Prove that if $x \in \Re$ and $|x| \neq 1$, then $x^2 \neq 1$.

  6. Prove that if $x, y, z \in \Re$ and $x \neq y$, then $x + z \neq y + z$. _Assume Addition_
  Add Inv.

2–4 **7.** State the axiom of comparison. _50_

  8. Is $<$ a symmetric relation? Why or why not? _No._

  9. Solve $x^2 + 3x < 0$ over $\Re$. _−3 < x < 0_

2–5 **10.** In which of the following cases must x be positive for every $a \in \Re$?

  _no_ _no_ _no_ _yes_
  a. $|x| < a$ **b.** $x < |a|$ **c.** $|x| > a$ **d.** $x > |a|$

  11. Solve $|x - 2| \leq 3x$ over $\Re$. _—absolute x ≥ x ≥ ½_

2–6 **12.** Determine the G.C.F. of 576 and 336. _48_

Reading List

ALLENDOERFER, CARL B., and CLETUS O. OAKLEY, *Principles of Mathematics*. New York: McGraw-Hill Book Co., Inc., 1963.

ANDRÉE, RICHARD V., *Selections from Modern Abstract Algebra*. New York: Holt, Rinehart and Winston, Inc., 1958.

BECKENBACH, EDWIN F., and RICHARD E. BELLMAN, *An Introduction to Inequalities*. New York: Random House, 1961.

CARROLL, LEWIS, *Symbolic Logic and the Game of Logic*. New York: Dover, 1951.

CHRISTIAN, R. R., *An Introduction to Logic and Sets*. Boston: Ginn and Co., 1958.

FLETCHER, T. J., "The Solution of Inferential Problems by Boolean Algebra," *The Mathematical Gazette*, vol. 35 (1952), pp. 183–88.

FUJII, JOHN N., *An Introduction to the Elements of Mathematics*. New York: John Wiley, 1961.

HOHN, FRANZ E., "Some Mathematical Aspects of Switching," *The American Mathematical Monthly*, vol. 62 (1955), pp. 75–90.

JONES, BURTON W., *Elementary Concepts of Mathematics* (Second Edition). New York: The Macmillan Co., 1963.

KELLEY, JOHN L., *Introduction to Modern Algebra*. Princeton: D. Van Nostrand, 1960.

MAY, KENNETH O., *Elements of Modern Mathematics*. Reading, Mass.: Addison-Wesley Publishing Co., 1959.

SAWYER, W. W., *A Concrete Approach to Abstract Algebra*. San Francisco: W. H. Freeman and Co., 1961.

STABLER, E. R., *An Introduction to Mathematical Thought*. Reading, Mass.: Addison-Wesley Publishing Co., 1953.

SUPPES, PATRICK, *Introduction to Logic*. Princeton: D. Van Nostrand Company, Inc., 1957.

John von Neumann

Is it possible for a certain economy with a constant rate of expansion to be in equilibrium? What will be the chances for fair weather tomorrow if it rained every day last week? Today, the answers to these questions would quite likely be reached through a mathematical analysis of the situation involved. This, however, has not always been the case, for until mathematicians such as John von Neumann developed techniques for handling problems of this nature, mathematics was not commonly used in their solution.

Von Neumann (1903–1957) was born in Budapest, studied and taught in Germany and Hungary, became a professor at Princeton University in 1930, and, following that, was a professor at the Institute for Advanced Study and a member of the Atomic Energy Commission. His early work in set theory and theoretical physics provided the foundation for his later work in the logical design of electronic high-speed computers. Von Neumann first became involved with computers while he was a consultant on the Atomic Bomb Project at Los Alamos. Here he was confronted with having to perform an immense number of calculations in a short time and, as a result, became extremely interested when he heard that an all-electronic computer was being built at the University of Pennsylvania. He joined forces with the men developing this machine and contributed many ideas for its design and construction. In the years that followed he was responsible for a large number of advances and improvements in the theory and construction of computers, and eventually he expanded his work in this field into a general theory of automata.

Von Neumann is generally considered to be the founder of the theory of games, that is, the mathematics of situations in which two or more opponents (competitors) are each trying to win (gain) as much as possible. He established basic theorems which give methods for determining the best strategy for each competitor involved, regardless of the actions of his opponents. His research (with Oskar Morgenstern) resulted in the publication in 1944 of *The Theory of Games and Economic Behavior*. The theories and methods presented in this work have been applied to many diverse situations in modern life.

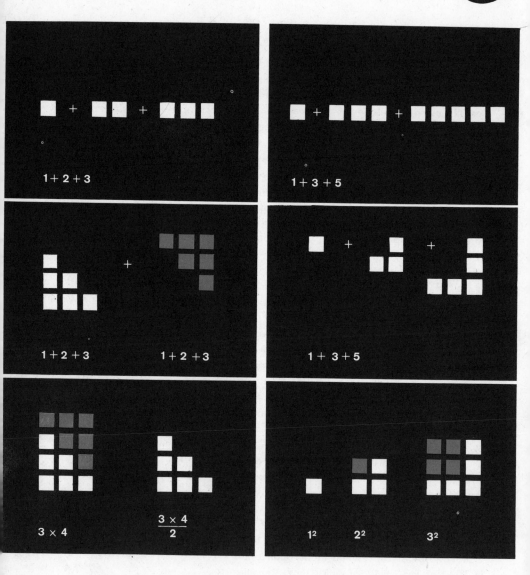

1 + 2 + 3

1 + 3 + 5

1 + 2 + 3   1 + 2 + 3

1 + 3 + 5

3×4 $\dfrac{3 \times 4}{2}$

1^2 2^2 3^2

Many of the theorems you will prove by mathematical induction were proved by Greek mathematicians using geometrical arguments. The first column of diagrams demonstrates the theorem $1 + 2 + 3 + \cdots + n = \dfrac{n(n+1)}{2}$ for $n = 3$. The second column of diagrams illustrates $1 + 3 + 5 + \cdots + 2n - 1 = n^2$ for $n = 3$.

Mathematical Induction —
Sequences and Series

We begin this chapter by noticing that the set of positive integers has a first element and that each positive integer has an immediate successor. By considering infinite sets of rational numbers having these properties, we are led to the concept of limit and to the final axiom characterizing the real number system.

FINITE SEQUENCES AND SERIES

3–1 Mathematical Induction

Do you know how to identify the set N of natural numbers? In Section 2–6 we observed that the set N could be viewed as a subset of J, the set of integers. In turn, $J \subset R \subset \mathcal{R}$. If you think about it, you will see that the set N, or $\{1, 2, 3, \ldots\}$, consists of those and only those positive real numbers which equal either 1 or $x + 1$ for some $x \in N$. More formally,

---

Principle of Mathematical Induction

Any set of positive integers that

1. contains 1, and

2. contains $x + 1$ whenever it contains x

is the set of all natural numbers.

To use this principle to determine whether a set S of positive integers is actually N, you must ascertain two facts about S:

(1) $1 \in S$, and

(2) from the assumption that $x \in S$ (this is called the **induction hypothesis**) it follows that $x + 1 \in S$.

If you establish both of these facts, then $S = N$.

EXAMPLE. Let S be the set of natural numbers n for which

$$2 + 4 + 6 + \cdots + 2n = n(n + 1)$$

is a true statement. Prove that $S = N$.

Proof: (1) $1 \in S$, because, for $n = 1$, the statement becomes $2 = 1(1 + 1)$, or $2 = 2$, which is true.

(2) To show that if $x \in S$ then $(x + 1) \in S$, you assume that the statement is true for the sum of the first x positive integers, and attempt to prove that it is also true for the sum of the first $x + 1$ integers. Thus, you assume that

$$2 + 4 + 6 + \cdots + 2x = x(x + 1).$$

Then, to obtain the sum of the first $x + 1$ even integers, you add the next even integer, namely $2x + 2$, or $2(x + 1)$, to each member of the above equation:

$$2 + 4 + 6 + \cdots + 2x + 2(x + 1) = x(x + 1) + 2(x + 1)$$
$$= (x + 2)(x + 1)$$
$$= [(x + 1) + 1](x + 1)$$

$$\therefore 2 + 4 + 6 + \cdots + 2x + 2(x + 1) = (x + 1)[(x + 1) + 1]$$

Thus, if the statement is true when n is replaced by x, it is also true with $(x + 1)$ in place of n; that is, if $x \in S$, then $(x + 1) \in S$. Since S satisfies both requirements (1) and (2) of the Principle of Mathematical Induction, $S = N$. This means you have proved that for every positive integer n:

$$2 + 4 + 6 + \cdots + 2n = n(n + 1).$$

You can use the principle of mathematical induction to give precise meaning to the concept of a positive integral power of a number.

For any real number r, let:

(1) $r^1 = r$,

and, in general, for each positive integer $n \geq 1$, let

(2) $r^{n+1} = r^n r.$

We call r^n the **nth power** of r, and refer to r as the **base** and to n as the **exponent** of the base. Given r and definitions (1) and (2), you have r^1 and can compute r^2, r^3, r^4, and, in turn, each succeeding integral power of r.

Using the principle of mathematical induction, you can prove the familiar **Laws of Positive Integral Exponents** stated in the following theorem.

| THEOREM | Let r and s denote real numbers, and let m and n denote positive integers. In assertions 4–6, assume also that $r \neq 0$. Then: |

1. $r^m r^n = r^{m+n}$ 4. $\dfrac{r^m}{r^n} = r^{m-n}$, if $m > n$

2. $(rs)^m = r^m s^m$ 5. $\dfrac{r^m}{r^n} = \dfrac{1}{r^{n-m}}$, if $m < n$

3. $(r^m)^n = r^{mn}$ 6. $\left(\dfrac{s}{r}\right)^m = \dfrac{s^m}{r^m}$

7. If $r \notin \{-1, 0, 1\}$, $r^m = r^n$ if and only if $m = n$.

Proof of Law 1: To prove Law 1, assume that r is any given real number, and m is any positive integer. Let S be the set of positive integers n for which the law is valid.

(1) You must first prove that $1 \in S$, that is, that $r^m \cdot r^1 = r^{m+1}$.

$\qquad\qquad r^m r^1 = r^m r$.   Definition of first power.

But $\qquad\quad r^{m+1} = r^m r$.   Definition of $(m + 1)$st power.

$\qquad \therefore\ r^m r^1 = r^{m+1}$.   Transitive property of equality.

(2) Now, suppose that $x \in S$, that is, that x is a positive integer for which the following statement is true:

$$r^m r^x = r^{m+x}. \qquad \text{(Induction hypothesis)}$$

You must show that $(x + 1) \in S$, that is, that

$$r^m r^{x+1} = r^{m+(x+1)}.$$

You have

$\qquad\quad r^m r^{x+1} = r^m(r^x r)$ Def. of $(x + 1)$st power.

$\qquad\qquad\quad = (r^m r^x)r$ Associative axiom.

$\qquad\qquad\quad = r^{m+x}r$ Induction hypothesis.

$\qquad\qquad\quad = r^{(m+x)+1}$ Def. of $[(m + x) + 1]$st power.

$\qquad\qquad\quad = r^{m+(x+1)}$ Associative axiom.

$\qquad \therefore\ r^m r^{x+1} = r^{m+(x+1)}$ Transitive property of equality.

Thus, $1 \in S$, and if $x \in S$, $(x + 1) \in S$. Consequently, by the principle of induction, $S = N$, and Law 1 is proved.

Proof of Law 5: To prove Law 5, notice that if $m < n$, $0 < n - m$; that is, $n - m$ is a positive integer. Note also that $(n - m) + m = n$. Hence, by Law 1, $r^n = r^{(n-m)+m} = r^{n-m}r^m$. Therefore,

$$\frac{r^m}{r^n} = \frac{r^m}{r^{n-m}r^m} = \frac{1}{r^{n-m}} \cdot \frac{r^m}{r^m} = \frac{1}{r^{n-m}} \cdot 1 = \frac{1}{r^{n-m}}.$$

The proofs of the other laws will be required in the exercises.

As a third example of proof by mathematical induction, consider the proof of the following important inequality.

THEOREM If $n \in N$, $a \in \mathcal{R}$, and $a \geq -1$, then $(1 + a)^n \geq 1 + na.$

Proof: Let a be any given real number greater than or equal to -1 and let T be the set of positive integers n for which the theorem is true.

(1) $1 \in T$; for

$$\begin{aligned}(1 + a)^1 &= 1 + a \\ &= 1 + 1 \cdot a \\ &\geq 1 + 1 \cdot a. \\ \therefore (1 + a)^1 &\geq 1 + 1 \cdot a.\end{aligned}$$

(2) For any positive integer x, you know by definition that

$$(1 + a)^{x+1} = (1 + a)^x(1 + a).$$

Because

$$a \geq -1,$$
$$1 + a \geq 0.$$

Now, suppose $x \in T$; that is, $(1 + a)^x \geq 1 + xa$. It follows that

$$(1 + a)^x(1 + a) \geq (1 + xa)(1 + a).$$
$$\therefore (1 + a)^{x+1} \geq (1 + xa)(1 + a) = 1 + (x + 1)a + a^2x.$$

Also,

$$a^2 \geq 0.$$
$$x > 0.$$
$$\therefore a^2x \geq 0.$$

Hence, $1 + (x + 1)a + a^2x \geq 1 + (x + 1)a.$
$$\therefore (1 + a)^{x+1} \geq 1 + (x + 1)a.$$
Thus, if $x \in T$, $(x + 1) \in T$.

After you supply the reasons for the arguments in parts (1) and (2), you can conclude that $T = N$. This proves the theorem.

Notice that a proof based on the principle of mathematical induction actually is a form of *deductive* reasoning in which both parts (1) and (2) of the argument are essential. Omitting one or the other of these parts can produce false statements.

For example, you can show that

$$2 + 4 + 6 + \cdots + 2n = n(n + 1) + (n - 1)$$

is true for $n = 1$; but you cannot show that if it is true for x then it must be true for $x + 1$. On the other hand, you can show that if

$$2 + 4 + 6 + \cdots + 2n = n(n + 1) + 6$$

is true for any natural number x then it is true for the natural number $x + 1$. But you cannot show that the statement is true for any natural number; in particular, it is not true for $n = 1$. In any proof by mathematical induction, you must be sure that *both* requirements are satisfied.

Exercises

Use mathematical induction or an indirect argument to prove the following laws of exponents. In each case, $r, s \in \Re$ and $m, n \in N$. Assume $r \neq 0$ when it appears in a denominator.

(A)

1. $(rs)^m = r^m s^m$

2. $(r^m)^n = r^{mn}$

3. $\dfrac{r^m}{r^n} = r^{m-n}$, if $m > n$

4. $\left(\dfrac{s}{r}\right)^m = \dfrac{s^m}{r^m}$

5. If $r > 1$ and $n > 1$, $r^n > r$.

6. If $r > 1$ and $n \geq 1$, $r^n > 1$.

7. If $0 < r < 1$ and $n > 1$, $r^n < r$.

8. If $0 < r < 1$, $r^n < 1$.

9. If $0 < r < s$, $r^n < s^n$.

10. If $0 \leq s < r$, $r^n > s^n$.

11. If a, b, c are nonnegative, $n \geq 1$, and $a^n < b^n < c^n$, then $a < b < c$.

12. If $r > 1$ and $n > 1$, then $r^n > r^{n-1}$.

By the method of mathematical induction, prove that the following statements are true for all positive integral values of n.

13. $1 + 3 + 5 + \cdots + (2n - 1) = n^2$

14. $1 + 2 + 3 + \cdots + n = \dfrac{n(n + 1)}{2}$

15. $(a_1 - a_2) + (a_2 - a_3) + \cdots + (a_n - a_{n+1}) = a_1 - a_{n+1}$

16. $\dfrac{1}{1 \cdot 2} + \dfrac{1}{2 \cdot 3} + \cdots + \dfrac{1}{n(n + 1)} = \dfrac{n}{n + 1}$

(B)

17. $\dfrac{1}{2} + \dfrac{1}{2^2} + \dfrac{1}{2^3} + \cdots + \dfrac{1}{2^n} = 1 - \dfrac{1}{2^n}$

18. $\dfrac{1}{2} - \dfrac{1}{4} - \dfrac{1}{8} - \cdots - \dfrac{1}{2^n} = \dfrac{1}{2^n}$

19. $1 - \left[\left(1 - \frac{1}{2}\right) + \left(\frac{1}{2} - \frac{1}{3}\right) + \cdots + \left(\frac{1}{n} - \frac{1}{n+1}\right)\right] = \frac{1}{n+1}$

20. $\dfrac{1}{3} + \dfrac{1}{15} + \dfrac{1}{35} + \cdots + \dfrac{1}{4n^2 - 1} = \dfrac{n}{2n+1}$

21. $3^n \geq 2n + 1$

22. $2n \leq 2^n$

23. $n^3 + 2n$ is an integral multiple of 3.

24. $3^{2n} - 1$ is an integral multiple of 8.

Prove that if $h \in \mathcal{R}$, $0 < h < 1$, there is a positive integer k for which each statement is true.

C 25. $\dfrac{1}{3^k} < h$ $\qquad\qquad$ 26. $\dfrac{1}{2^k} < h$

(*Hint:* Let M be the even positive integer such that $M - 2 \leq \dfrac{1}{h} < M$. Choose $k = \dfrac{M}{2}$, and use Exercise 21 or 22.)

By using mathematical induction or an indirect argument, prove each of the following statements for all positive integral values of n and m, as indicated.

27. For all distinct real numbers x and y, $x - y$ is a factor of $x^n - y^n$. (*Hint:* $x^{n+1} - y^{n+1} = x^{n+1} - x^n y + x^n y - y^{n+1}$.)

28. $1 + 2a + 3a^2 + \cdots + na^{n-1} = \dfrac{1 - (n+1)a^n + na^{n+1}}{(1-a)^2}$, $a \neq 1$.

29. Let $S_1 = \frac{1}{2}$, $S_2 = \frac{1}{2} + \frac{2}{3}$, and $S_n = \dfrac{1}{2} + \dfrac{2}{3} + \cdots + \dfrac{n}{n+1}$. Prove that $S_n \geq \dfrac{n}{2}$.

30. Let $S_2 = 1 + \frac{1}{2}$, $S_4 = 1 + \frac{1}{2} + \frac{1}{3} + \frac{1}{4}$ and, for every positive integer n,

$S_{2^n} = 1 + \dfrac{1}{2} + \dfrac{1}{3} + \cdots + \dfrac{1}{2^n}$. Prove that $S_{2^n} \geq 1 + \dfrac{n}{2}$. $\left(\textit{Hint:}\right.$

$S_{2^{n+1}} = S_{2^n} + \dfrac{1}{2^n + 1} + \dfrac{1}{2^n + 2} + \cdots + \dfrac{1}{2^n + 2^n} > S_{2^n} + \dfrac{2^n}{2^n + 2^n}\Big)$

31. Prove that if $r \notin \{-1, 0, 1\}$, then $r^m = r^n$, if and only if $m = n$.

32. If $x > 0$, $y > 0$, and $x^n = y^n$, then $x = y$. (*Hint:* Use Exercise 27.)

33. If $x \in \mathcal{R}$, then $x^n - 1 = (x - 1)(x^{n-1} + x^{n-2} + \cdots + x + 1)$. (*Hint:* $x^{n+1} - 1 = x^{n+1} - x^n + x^n - 1$.)

34. If x denotes a real number and n denotes a positive odd integer, then

$$x^n + 1 = (x + 1)(x^{n-1} - x^{n-2} + x^{n-3} - \cdots + 1).$$

3-2 Sequences and Series

Can you list the numbers specified by the following definitions?

$$a_1 = -1$$
$$a_{n+1} = a_n + 2, n \in \{1, 2, 3, 4, 5\}.$$

Starting with -1 as the first number in your list, you obtain four other numbers one after another by successively adding 2 (row 1 below):

Number:	-1	1	3	5	7
	$\updownarrow$	$\updownarrow$	$\updownarrow$	$\updownarrow$	$\updownarrow$
Position in List:	1	2	3	4	5

The numbers $-1, 1, 3, 5, 7$ in the order stated are in one-to-one correspondence with the subset $\{1, 2, 3, 4, 5\}$ of the set of positive integers and constitute a *finite sequence*. The formula $a_{n+1} = a_n + 2$ with the set of *all* positive integers as the domain of n specifies an *infinite sequence*, namely $-1, 1, 3, 5, 7, 9, 11, \ldots$.

In general, a **sequence** is a set of elements in one-to-one correspondence with the set of positive integers N (an **infinite sequence**) or with a subset $\{1, 2, 3, \ldots, m\}$ of N for some positive integer m (a **finite sequence**). The members of the sequence are called **terms**. The term corresponding to n is called the **nth term** of the sequence and is designated by a symbol such as a_n.

A sequence is said to be specified **recursively** or by means of a **recursion formula** when rules are given that

(1) identify the first term in the sequence, and

(2) state the relationship between each term and its successor.

Thus, the rules $a_1 = 1$, $a_{n+1} = a_n + 2$ constitute a recursive definition of a sequence. Sometimes, instead of specifying a sequence recursively, you identify it by giving a rule expressing a_n directly in terms of n.

EXAMPLE 1. Write the first five terms of the sequence whose nth term is $2n^2 - 1$.

Solution: Replace n successively by 1, 2, 3, 4, and 5.

$$2(1)^2 - 1, 2(2)^2 - 1, 2(3)^2 - 1, 2(4)^2 - 1, 2(5)^2 - 1$$

$$1 \quad , \quad 7 \quad , \quad 17 \quad , \quad 31 \quad , \quad 49, \textbf{ Answer.}$$

EXAMPLE 2. Write the fourth, fifth, and sixth terms of the sequence $4, 8, 16, \ldots, 2^{t+1}, \ldots$, where t is the number of the term.

Solution: Replace t by 4, 5, and 6 in turn.

$$2^5, 2^6, 2^7, \quad \text{or} \quad 32, 64, 128, \textbf{ Answer.}$$

Closely related to the topic of sequences is that of series. A **series** is an expression consisting of the terms of a sequence alternating with the symbol $+$.

Sequence	Corresponding Series
finite $\begin{cases} \text{3, 7, 11, 15.} \\ a_1, a_2, a_3, \ldots, a_k. \end{cases}$	$3 + 7 + 11 + 15.$ $a_1 + a_2 + a_3 + \ldots + a_k.$
infinite $\begin{cases} \text{1, 3, 5,} \ldots, 2n - 1, \ldots \\ a_1, a_2, a_3, \ldots, a_n, \ldots \end{cases}$	$1 + 3 + 5 + \ldots + 2n - 1 + \ldots$ $a_1 + a_2 + a_3 + \ldots + a_n + \ldots$

Keep in mind that a series is an expression rather than a number. It is incorrect to say that the finite series $3 + 7 + 11 + 15$ is 36. The sum of the terms in the series is 36, but the series itself is the expression $3 + 7 + 11 + 15$.

The Greek letter Σ **(sigma)**, called the summation sign, is used to abbreviate the writing of a series. For instance, if you write the series

$$2 + 4 + 6 + 8 + 10$$

in the form

$$2(1) + 2(2) + 2(3) + 2(4) + 2(5),$$

you can see that the general form of each term is $2t$. Therefore, you can designate the series by the symbol:

$$\sum_{t=1}^{5} 2t \quad \text{(read "the sum of } 2t \text{ from } t = 1 \text{ to } t = 5\text{")}.$$

This symbol means that you successively replace t with the integers 1, 2, 3, 4, and 5 and write an expression denoting the sum of the resulting numbers. The letter t is the **index**. Any other letter may be used in place of t.

EXAMPLE 3. Express the series $\sum_{k=1}^{4} (3k - 1)$ in expanded form.

Solution: $\sum_{k=1}^{4} (3k - 1) = [3(1) - 1] + [3(2) - 1]$
$$+ [3(3) - 1] + [3(4) - 1]$$
$$= 2 + 5 + 8 + 11, \textbf{ Answer.}$$

EXAMPLE 4. If n is a positive integer and $a_1, a_2, \ldots, a_n$ are numbers, express $\sum_{i=1}^{n} a_i$ in expanded form.

Solution: $\sum_{i=1}^{n} a_i = a_1 + a_2 + \cdots + a_n.$

The summation symbol is sometimes used to designate the "sum" as well as the expression, which is sometimes called the "indicated sum." In this book, words or phrases such as "evaluate," "compute," "find the sum" will be used with the symbol when you are to compute the sum.

EXAMPLE 5. Compute: $\sum\limits_{j=3}^{7} 2^j$.

Solution: $\sum\limits_{j=3}^{7} 2^j = 2^3 + 2^4 + 2^5 + 2^6 + 2^7$

$$= 8 + 16 + 32 + 64 + 128 = 248, \textbf{ Answer.}$$

Exercises

In each case the first term of a sequence and a recursion formula for succeeding terms are given. If $n \in \{1, 2, 3, 4, 5, 6\}$, write the sequence.

A

1. $a_1 = 2, a_{n+1} = a_n - 1$

2. $a_1 = 5, a_{n+1} = a_n - 3$

3. $a_1 = -1, a_{n+1} = 3a_n$

4. $a_1 = 1, a_{n+1} = -2a_n$

5. $a_1 = \frac{1}{2}, a_{n+1} = (-1)^{n+1} a_n$

6. $a_1 = \frac{1}{3}, a_{n+1} = (-1)^n a_n$

7. $a_1 = 3, a_{n+1} = (a_n - 2)^2$

8. $a_1 = 1, a_{n+1} = \dfrac{n}{n+1} a_n$

Write the first four terms of the sequence specified by the indicated rule. In each case, the initial value of the index is 1.

9. $a_k = 2k + 3$

10. $a_k = \dfrac{2}{k}$

11. $a_n = 4n^2$

12. $a_n = \dfrac{n(n-1)}{2}$

13. $a_t = |1 - 2^t|$

14. $a_t = 3^{t+1}$

Specify each sequence **(a)** recursively; **(b)** by expressing a_n in terms of n.

15. $2, 3, 4, 5$

16. $2, 4, 8, 16$

17. $5, 10, 15, 20$

18. $\dfrac{5}{2}, \dfrac{5}{4}, \dfrac{5}{8}, \dfrac{5}{16}$

19. $1, \dfrac{1}{1 \cdot 2}, \dfrac{1}{1 \cdot 2 \cdot 3}, \dfrac{1}{1 \cdot 2 \cdot 3 \cdot 4}$

20. $1, -1, -3, -5$

Write each series in expanded form.

21. $\sum\limits_{i=2}^{5} i$

22. $\sum\limits_{n=3}^{6} |3 - n|$

23. $\sum\limits_{j=3}^{7} j$

24. $\sum\limits_{k=2}^{5} (2k + 1)$

25. $\displaystyle\sum_{t=1}^{5} (-1)^t t^2$

27. $\displaystyle\sum_{i=1}^{n} P(i)$

26. $\displaystyle\sum_{i=1}^{3} (-1)^i (i^2 - i)$

28. $\displaystyle\sum_{j=0}^{n-1} P(j)$

Use the summation sign to write each series.

29. $6 + 10 + 14 + 18$

31. $a_1 b_1 + a_2 b_2 + a_3 b_3$

30. $6 - 2 + \frac{2}{3} - \frac{2}{9}$

32. $x_1^2 + x_2^2 + x_3^2 + x_4^2 + x_5^2$

Find the sum of the series.

33. $\displaystyle\sum_{n=1}^{4} n^2$

34. $\displaystyle\sum_{k=1}^{5} \frac{k(k+1)}{2}$

35. $\displaystyle\sum_{i=2}^{6} (8 - i)$

36. $\displaystyle\sum_{t=-6}^{-4} \frac{t}{|t|}$

Show that the following expressions name the same series.

37. $\displaystyle\sum_{k=3}^{6} \left(\frac{k}{k+2}\right)$ and $\displaystyle\sum_{k=0}^{3} \left(\frac{k+3}{k+5}\right)$

38. $\displaystyle\sum_{t=5}^{8} \left(\frac{t}{t+4}\right)$ and $\displaystyle\sum_{t=1}^{4} \left(\frac{t+4}{t+8}\right)$

39. $\displaystyle\sum_{k=6}^{9} \left(\frac{k}{k-1}\right)$ and $\displaystyle\sum_{k=8}^{11} \left(\frac{k-2}{k-3}\right)$

40. $\displaystyle\sum_{k=0}^{x} a_{k+1},\ \sum_{k=1}^{x+1} a_k,\ \text{and}\ \sum_{k=t}^{x+t} a_{k-t+1}$

41. What is the sum of the series $\displaystyle\sum_{k=1}^{n} (-1)^k$ if n is odd? if n is even?

42. If a, b, c are successive terms of a sequence, can you conclude that either $a < b < c$ or $a > b > c$? Justify your answer.

43. Write the nth term of the series $\displaystyle\sum_{k=3}^{100} (k^2 - 6k)$.

44. If $\displaystyle\sum_{b=2}^{4} (a^2 b - ab) = \sum_{c=3}^{5} (ac + 6)$, determine a.

By mathematical induction, prove that each assertion is true for every positive integer n. (Exercises 45–50.)

45. $\displaystyle\sum_{k=1}^{n} k^2 = \frac{n(n+1)(2n+1)}{6}$

46. $\displaystyle\sum_{k=1}^{n} k^3 = \left[\frac{n(n+1)}{2}\right]^2$

47. $\displaystyle\sum_{i=1}^{n} (a_i + b_i) = \sum_{i=1}^{n} a_i + \sum_{i=1}^{n} b_i$

48. $\displaystyle\sum_{i=1}^{n} ca_i = c \sum_{i=1}^{n} a_i$

49. $\displaystyle\sum_{k=1}^{n} a = an$

50. $\displaystyle\sum_{j=1}^{n} (a_j + b_j)^2 = \sum_{j=1}^{n} a_j^2 + 2 \sum_{j=1}^{n} a_j b_j + \sum_{j=1}^{n} b_j^2$

3-3 Arithmetic Progressions

The sequence $5, 2, -1, -4, -7$ is called an *arithmetic progression* because each term can be computed by adding a constant, -3, to the preceding term. An **arithmetic progression** (A. P.) is any sequence in which each term after the first is the sum of a given constant and the preceding term. Thus, if a denotes the first term, and d the given constant (called the **common difference**), you can specify the A. P. recursively as follows.

$$t_1 = a,$$

$$t_{n+1} = t_n + d, \quad n \geq 1.$$

The following table suggests an expression for t_n in terms of n, d, and a.

1st term	2nd term	3rd term	4th term	$\cdots$	nth term
t_1	t_2	t_3	t_4	$\cdots$	t_n
a	$a + d$	$a + 2d$	$a + 3d$	$\cdots$	$a + (n-1)d$

Noting that the coefficient of d in each term is 1 less than the number of the term, you can make the following assertion.

> **THEOREM**   In an arithmetic progression in which the first term is a and the common difference is d, the nth term is
>
> $$t_n = a + (n-1)d.$$

Proof: Let T be the set of positive integers n for which the theorem is true.

(1) $1 \in T$, because for $n = 1$ the statement becomes
$t_1 = a + (1-1)d = a + 0 \cdot d$ or $t_1 = a$, which is true.

(*continued on page 80*)

(2) Suppose $x \in T$. Then $t_x = a + (x - 1)d$.

Since $t_{x+1} = t_x + d$, you have:

$$t_{x+1} = [a + (x - 1)d] + d$$
$$= a + [(x - 1)d + d] = a + xd.$$

$$\therefore t_{x+1} = a + [(x + 1) - 1]d.$$

Therefore, if $x \in T$, $(x + 1) \in T$.

By virtue of the principle of mathematical induction, the arguments in (1) and (2) together imply that the theorem is true for all positive integers n.

EXAMPLE 1. Find the twelfth term of the A. P. $2, 9, 16, \ldots$.

Solution: $a = 2, d = 7, n = 12$

$$t_n = a + (n - 1)d$$

$$t_{12} = 2 + (12 - 1)7 = 79, \textbf{Answer.}$$

EXAMPLE 2. What term of the A. P. $-2, 1, 4, \ldots$ is 40?

Solution: $a = -2, d = 3, t_n = 40$

$$\therefore 40 = -2 + (n - 1)(3)$$

$$45 = 3n, \text{ or } n = 15$$

$\therefore$ 40 is the 15th term, **Answer.**

The terms in an A. P. are said to be **in arithmetic progression** and the terms between any two given terms are called **arithmetic means**. For example, in the A. P. 2, 5, 8, 11, 14, the terms 5, 8, and 11 are the arithmetic means between 2 and 14, while 5 and 8 are the arithmetic means between 2 and 11. To insert arithmetic means between numbers in an A. P., you need only find the common difference by using the statement $t_n = a + (n - 1)d$.

EXAMPLE 3. Insert three arithmetic means between 18 and -10.

Solution: $a = 18, n = 5, t_5 = -10.$

$$-10 = 18 + (5 - 1)d$$

$$-28 = 4d$$

$$d = -7$$

$18, 11, 4, -3, -10, \textbf{Answer.}$

A single arithmetic mean between two numbers is the **average** or *the* **arithmetic mean** of the numbers. To show that the average of a and b is $\dfrac{a + b}{2}$, you simply verify that $\dfrac{a + b}{2} - a = b - \dfrac{a + b}{2}$.   (Why?)

A series whose terms are in arithmetic progression is called an **arithmetic series**. To find an expression for the sum S_n of the first n terms of an A. P., write the indicated sum in the usual order in terms of d and a, and then add to this the indicated sum written in reverse order in terms of d and t_n.

$$S_n = a \qquad + (a + d) + (a + 2d) + \cdots + [a + (n - 1)d]$$
$$S_n = t_n \qquad + (t_n - d) + (t_n - 2d) + \cdots + [t_n - (n - 1)d]$$
$$\overline{2S_n = (a + t_n) + (a + t_n) + (a + t_n) + \cdots + (a + t_n)}$$

where $a + t_n$ occurs n times.

$$\therefore 2S_n = n(a + t_n), \qquad \text{or} \qquad S_n = \frac{n}{2}(a + t_n).$$

Since $t_n = a + (n - 1)d$, you can substitute in the expression for S_n to find:

$$S_n = \frac{n}{2}[a + a + (n - 1)d].$$

$$\therefore S_n = \frac{n}{2}[2a + (n - 1)d].$$

This argument suggests the following theorem, which you can also prove by mathematical induction. (Exercise 23, page 82.)

THEOREM   The sum of the first n terms of an arithmetic progression whose first term is a and whose common difference is d is

$$S_n = \frac{n}{2}[2a + (n - 1)d].$$

EXAMPLE 4.   Find the sum of the first 12 terms of the A. P. -5, -1, 3, 7, ….

Solution: $a = -5, d = 4, n = 12$.
$S_{12} = \frac{12}{2}[2(-5) + (12 - 1)4] = 204$, **Answer.**

EXAMPLE 5.   Find the sum of the odd integers from 1 to 49 inclusive.

Solution: $a = 1, t_n = 49, d = 2; \therefore n = 25$.
Hence, $S_{25} = \frac{25}{2}(1 + 49) = 625$, **Answer.**

Exercises

1. If each term of an A. P. is multiplied by k, will the resulting terms form an A.P. **(a)** if $k \neq 0$; **(b)** if $k = 0$?

2. If given the arithmetic mean of two numbers, can you find the numbers?

3. Can the sum of the terms of an A. P. be zero? Explain.

4. If each term of an A. P. is squared, will the resulting terms form an A. P. **(a)** if $d = 0$; **(b)** if $d \neq 0$?

Find the indicated term in the given A. P.

5. Eleventh term in $5, 8, 11, \ldots$

6. Seventh term in $3\sqrt{2}, \sqrt{2}, -\sqrt{2}, \ldots$

7. Sixth term in $a - b, a, a + b, \ldots$

8. Tenth term in $\frac{3}{4}, \frac{13}{12}, \frac{17}{12}, \ldots$

Find the missing terms in the indicated A. P.

9. $3, \underline{\ ?\ }, 7, \underline{\ ?\ }, \underline{\ ?\ }$.

10. $2, \underline{\ ?\ }, \underline{\ ?\ }, 13, \underline{\ ?\ }$.

11. $\underline{\ ?\ }, 8, \underline{\ ?\ }, \underline{\ ?\ }, -7$.

12. $3, \underline{\ ?\ }, \underline{\ ?\ }, \underline{\ ?\ }, 22$.

13. $\underline{\ ?\ }, \underline{\ ?\ }, x, \underline{\ ?\ }, -x$.

14. $a, \underline{\ ?\ }, b, \underline{\ ?\ }, \underline{\ ?\ }$.

15. Which term of the A. P. $2, 9, 16, \ldots$ is 142?

16. Which term of the A. P. $8, 5, 2, \ldots$ is -28?

17. Find the sum of the first eighteen terms of the A. P. $4, 7, 10, \ldots$

18. Find the sum of the first thirty positive integers.

19. The first term of an A. P. is 5. The seventeenth term is 53. Find the third term.

20. The common difference in an A. P. is 3. The tenth term is 23. Find the first term.

Find the sum of each series.

21. $\sum\limits_{k=1}^{20} (3k - 1)$.

22. $\sum\limits_{i=1}^{10} (8 - 2i)$.

23. By mathematical induction, prove the theorem on page 81.

24. How many terms of the A. P. $-5, -1, 3, \ldots$ must be added to give a sum of 400?

25. Find the sum of all positive integers less that 200 that are multiples of 7.

26. Find the first two terms of an A. P. in which the third term is 14 and the ninth term is -1.

27. For what value(s) of t will $t - 2$, $2t - 6$, and $4t - 8$, in this order, form an A. P.?

28. For what real value(s) of k (if any) will -1 be the arithmetic mean of k and k^2?

29. Find three numbers in A. P. whose sum is 27 and whose product is 288.

30. The first four terms of an A. P. are r, s, t, u. Show that $r + u - s = t$.

31. The average of the n terms $a_1, a_2, a_3, \ldots, a_n$ is $\dfrac{1}{n}(a_1 + a_2 + a_3 + \cdots + a_n)$.

Show that if these terms are in arithmetic progression the average of the first and last terms is the same as the average of all n terms.

32. Show that $S_n = \displaystyle\sum_{k=1}^{n} [a + (k - 1)d]$ and then use the theorems stated in Exercises 47, 48, and 49, page 79, and in Exercise 14, page 73, to prove that

$S_n = \dfrac{n}{2}[2a + (n - 1)d]$.

33. A woodsman stacks $8k + 15$ logs in such a way that there are k layers with 8 logs in the top layer. Each layer below contains one more log than the layer immediately above. Find the number of logs.

34. There are k animal feeding stations arranged in a line with a supply hut. The stations are s yards apart and the nearest is t yards from the hut. An attendant carries n bags of feed, one at a time, to each feeding station. How far will he have traveled when he arrives back at the hut after servicing all stations?

3–4 Geometric Progressions

Another important type of sequence is one in which each term after the first can be computed by multiplying the preceding term by a given constant. One such sequence is 3, 6, 12, 24, in which the constant multiplier is 2. A sequence in which each term after the first is the product of a given constant and the preceding term is called a **geometric progression** (G. P.), and its terms are said to be **in geometric progression**. Can you explain why the constant multiplier is called the **common ratio**?

If a denotes the first term and r the common ratio in a G. P., you can specify the sequence recursively as follows:

$$t_1 = a$$
$$t_{n+1} = t_n r, \quad n \geq 1.$$

The following table suggests an expression for t_n in terms of n, r, and a.

1st term	2nd term	3rd term	4th term	$\cdots$	nth term
t_1	t_2	t_3	t_4	$\cdots$	t_n
a	ar	ar^2	ar^3	$\cdots$	ar^{n-1}

Observing that the exponent of r in each term is 1 less than the number of the term, you can make the following conjecture, which can be proved by mathematical induction. (Exercise 17, page 87.)

THEOREM In a geometric progression in which the first term is a and the common ratio is r, the nth term is

$$t_n = ar^{n-1}, \quad n \geq 2.$$

EXAMPLE 1. Find the sixth term of the G. P. 2, 6, 18, 54, ...

Solution: $a = 2, r = 3, n = 6$

$t_n = ar^{n-1}$

$t_6 = 2(3)^{6-1} = 2(243) = 486,$ **Answer.**

EXAMPLE 2. What term of the G. P. $\frac{3}{2}$, -3, 6, . . . is 96?

Solution: $a = \frac{3}{2}, r = -2, t_n = 96$

$96 = \frac{3}{2}(-2)^{n-1}$

$64 = (-2)^{n-1}$,   or $(-2)^6 = (-2)^{n-1}$

$\therefore n - 1 = 6, n = 7;$

and 96 is the 7th term, **Answer.**

In the preceding theorem, the restriction $n \geq 2$ is needed because the statement $t_1 = ar^{1-1}$ is meaningless since the symbol r^{1-1} or r^0 has not been defined. In case $r \neq 0$, we define r^0 to be **1**. No meaning is attached to the symbol 0^0. Thus, if $r \neq 0$, $t_1 = ar^{1-1} = a$ is a true statement, and the theorem holds for $n = 1$. Do the laws of exponents (page 71) remain valid with 0 as an exponent? (Exercise 35, page 88.)

In a geometric progression the terms between any two given terms are **geometric means**. Thus, in the G. P. 3, 6, 12, 24, 48, . . . , the terms 6, 12, and 24 are the geometric means between 3 and 48; 6 and 12 are the geometric means between 3 and 24. To insert geometric means between numbers, you can use the statement $t_n = ar^{n-1}$ to find the common ratio.

EXAMPLE 3. Insert three real geometric means between 1 and 16.

Solution: $a = 1, n = 5, t_5 = 16$

$t_n = ar^{n-1}$

$16 = 1 \cdot r^{5-1}$

$r^4 = 16$

$r^4 - 16 = 0$

$(r^2 - 4)(r^2 + 4) = 0$

and since $r^2 + 4 \neq 0$ for any $r \in \mathcal{R}$,

you have to consider only $r^2 - 4 = 0$,

which is equivalent to $r = 2$ *or* $r = -2$.

$\therefore 1, 2, 4, 8, 16$ or $1, -2, 4, -8, 16,$ **Answer.**

A single geometric mean between two numbers is *the* **geometric mean,** or **mean proportional,** of the numbers.

EXAMPLE 4. If x and y denote nonzero real numbers, find the geometric mean of x^2 and y^2.

Solution: $\quad a = x^2, n = 3, t_3 = y^2$

$$y^2 = x^2 r^{(3-1)}$$

$$r^2 = \frac{y^2}{x^2} ; r^2 = \left(\frac{y}{x}\right)^2 \quad \text{or} \quad r^2 = \left(-\frac{y}{x}\right)^2$$

$$\therefore r = \frac{y}{x} \quad \text{or} \quad r = -\frac{y}{x}$$

$$x^2, xy, y^2 \quad \text{or} \quad x^2, -xy, y^2,$$

and the geometric mean is xy or $-xy$, **Answer.**

A series whose terms are in geometric progression is a **geometric series.** You can find an expression for the sum, S_n, of the first n terms of a G. P. by writing the series and subtracting from it, term by term, the product of r and that series.

$$S_n = a + ar + ar^2 + \cdots + ar^{n-2} + ar^{n-1}$$
$$rS_n = \quad\quad ar + ar^2 + \cdots + ar^{n-2} + ar^{n-1} + ar^n$$

$$S_n - rS_n = a + 0 + 0 + \cdots + 0 + 0 - ar^n$$
$$S_n - rS_n = a - ar^n, \quad \text{or} \quad S_n(1 - r) = a - ar^n$$

$$\therefore S_n = \frac{a - ar^n}{1 - r} \quad (r \neq 1)$$

This suggests the following theorem, which you can also prove by induction. (Exercise 18, p. 87.)

THEOREM The sum of the first n terms of a geometric progression whose first term is a and whose common ratio is r $(r \neq 1)$ is

$$S_n = \frac{a - ar^n}{1 - r}.$$

COROLLARY. $S_n = \dfrac{a - t_n r}{1 - r}, \quad r \neq 1.$

The corollary can be deduced by noting that $ar^{n-1} = t_n$, so that $ar^n = t_n r$.

EXAMPLE 5. Find the sum of the first six terms of the G. P. 5, -10, 20, ...

Solution: Applying the preceding theorem with $a = 5$, $r = -2$, $n = 6$, you have

$$S_6 = \frac{5 - 5(-2)^6}{1 - (-2)} = \frac{-315}{3} = -105, \textbf{Answer.}$$

EXAMPLE 6. Find the sum of the G. P. in which the first term is 4, the last term is $\frac{1}{8}$, and the common ratio is $\frac{1}{2}$.

Solution: $a = 4$, $r = \frac{1}{2}$, $t_n = \frac{1}{8}$. Therefore, the corollary above implies

$$S_n = \frac{4 - \frac{1}{8}(\frac{1}{2})}{1 - \frac{1}{2}} = \frac{\frac{63}{16}}{\frac{1}{2}} = \frac{63}{8}, \textbf{Answer.}$$

Exercises

A 1. Can a term of a G. P. be zero? Explain your answer.

2. By how much does the arithmetic mean of 4 and 9 exceed the absolute value of their geometric mean?

3. Find t_n in the G. P. in which $a = 12$, $n = 5$, and $r = \frac{1}{3}$.

4. Insert three real geometric means between $\frac{27}{8}$ and $\frac{2}{3}$.

5. Find the seventh term in the G. P. $\frac{3}{64}$, $-\frac{3}{16}$, $\frac{3}{4}$, -3, ...

6. Find the sum of 100 terms of the geometric series $1 - 1 + 1 - 1 + \cdots$.

7. In a G. P. containing only real terms, the first term is 3 and the fourth term 24. Find the common ratio.

8. The first term of a G. P. is 4 and the last term is 324. Find the sum if the ratio of two successive terms is 3.

In Exercises 9 through 12, find the sum of the indicated geometric series.

9. $\displaystyle\sum_{k=1}^{5} 2^{k-1}$

11. $\displaystyle\sum_{i=1}^{5} 3(-\tfrac{1}{3})^{i-1}$

10. $\displaystyle\sum_{j=1}^{3} 5(4)^{j-1}$

12. $\displaystyle\sum_{r=1}^{6} 24(\tfrac{1}{2})^{r-1}$

13. Find the seventh term of a G. P. whose third and fifth terms are respectively $\frac{9}{4}$ and $\frac{81}{64}$.

#7: odd 1-29

14. Under conditions favorable to the growth of a certain bacteria, one organism can divide into two every half-hour. How many times the original number of organisms will there be at the end of a six-hour period?

15. For what value(s) of k will $k - 4$, $k - 1$, and $2k - 2$, in this order, form a G. P.?

16. Solve $\displaystyle\sum_{k=1}^{n} 2^k = 62$ for n by testing successive values of n.

The statements in Exercises 17 and 18 refer to a G. P. whose first term is a, whose common ratio is r, and whose nth term is t_n. Prove each statement by mathematical induction.

17. $t_n = ar^{n-1}$, $n \geq 1$

18. $\displaystyle\sum_{k=1}^{n} t_k = \frac{a(1 - r^n)}{1 - r}$, $r \neq 1$

In Exercises 19 through 24, three of the five real numbers, a, t_n, r, n, and S_n for a G. P. are given. Find the two numbers not given.

B

19. $a = 1$, $r = 2$, $n = 7$

20. $a = -1$, $n = 3$, $S_n = -7$

21. $a = -2$, $r = 2$, $t_n = -64$

22. $r = \frac{1}{2}$, $n = 5$, $S_n = \frac{31}{2}$

23. $a = \frac{1}{3}$, $r = 3$, $S_n = \frac{40}{3}$

24. $a = \frac{4}{3}$, $r = \frac{3}{2}$, $t_n = \frac{27}{4}$

25. Insert two real numbers between 2 and 9 so that the first three terms form an A. P. and the last three terms form a G. P.

26. A car purchased for $2500 depreciates 15% in value every year. Find the value of the car at the end of a four-year period.

27. Find the second term of an A. P. whose first term is 2 and whose first, third, and seventh terms form a G. P.

28. The sum of the first and last terms of a G. P. of fourteen real terms is 7. The fifth term is the mean proportional between the second and last terms. Find the third term.

29. One-third of the air in a tank is removed with each stroke of a vacuum pump. What part of the original amount of air remains in the tank after five strokes?

30. Show that the reciprocals of the terms of a G. P. ($a \neq 0$, $r \neq 0$) form a G. P.

C

31. Prove: If $a \in \mathcal{R}$ and $b \in \mathcal{R}$, the arithmetic mean of a^2 and b^2 is not less than the absolute value of their geometric mean.
[*Hint:* $(a - b)^2 \geq 0$.]

32. For every sequence which is both an A. P. and a G. P., determine the common (a) difference; (b) ratio.

33. Given a circle of radius t. Show that the area of the inscribed regular hexagon is a mean proportional between the areas of the inscribed and circumscribed equilateral triangles.

34. Let a, b, and c denote real numbers that are not successive terms of an A. P. or a G. P. If $a < b < c$, find a number which when added to a, b, and c yields consecutive terms of a G. P.

35. Discuss the validity of the theorem on page 71 in case m is any nonnegative integer, $n = 0$, $r \neq 0$, and $s \neq 0$.

36. Discuss the validity of the theorem on page 85 in case $n = 0$.

3–5 The Binomial Theorem

The following statements suggest the pattern used to find the successive terms in the expansion of the nth power of the sum of two numbers a and b:

$$(a + b)^1 = a + b$$
$$(a + b)^2 = a^2 + 2ab + b^2$$
$$(a + b)^3 = a^3 + 3a^2b + 3ab^2 + b^3$$
$$(a + b)^4 = a^4 + 4a^3b + 6a^2b^2 + 4ab^3 + b^4$$
$$(a + b)^5 = a^5 + 5a^4b + 10a^3b^2 + 10a^2b^3 + 5ab^4 + b^5.$$

In general, the expansion of $(a + b)^n$ has $(n + 1)$ terms. In each term the exponents of a and b and the numerical factor or **coefficient** follow the pattern outlined below.

Expansion of $(a + b)^n$

The first term is a^n and the last is b^n.

In any other term, the sum of the exponents of a and b is n, and:

1. The coefficient is the product of the coefficient of the preceding term and the exponent of a in the preceding term, divided by the number of the preceding term;

2. The exponent of a is 1 less than the exponent of a in the preceding term;

3. The exponent of b is 1 more than the exponent of b in the preceding term.

EXAMPLE 1. Expand $(2x - y)^6$.

Solution: $(2x)^6 + 6(2x)^5(-y) + 15(2x)^4(-y)^2 + 20(2x)^3(-y)^3$
$$+ 15(2x)^2(-y)^4 + 6(2x)(-y)^5 + (-y)^6,$$
or

$$64x^6 - 192x^5y + 240x^4y^2 - 160x^3y^3$$
$$+ 60x^2y^4 - 12xy^5 + y^6, \textbf{ Answer.}$$

To expand $(a + b)^n$ for any $n \in N$, we introduce some convenient symbols. First, if n is any nonnegative integer, $n!$ (read "n factorial") is defined recursively as follows:

$$0! = 1$$

$$1! = 1$$

$$(n + 1)! = n!(n + 1), \quad n \geq 1.$$

Thus, $2! = 1 \cdot 2 = 2$, $3! = (1 \cdot 2) \cdot 3 = 6$, $4! = (1 \cdot 2 \cdot 3) \cdot 4 = 24$, and in general, $n! = 1 \cdot 2 \cdot 3 \cdots n$.

Next, if $n \in N$ and $k \in N$, and $k \leq n$, then $\binom{n}{k}$ is defined by

$$\binom{n}{k} = \frac{\overbrace{n(n - 1) \cdots (n - k + 1)}^{k \text{ factors}}}{k!}.$$

Also, we define

$$\binom{n}{0} = 1.$$

For example,

$$\binom{4}{0} = 1, \quad \binom{4}{1} = \frac{4}{1!} = 4, \quad \binom{4}{2} = \frac{4 \cdot 3}{2!} = 6,$$

$$\binom{4}{3} = \frac{4 \cdot 3 \cdot 2}{3!} = 4 \quad \text{and} \quad \binom{4}{4} = \frac{4 \cdot 3 \cdot 2 \cdot 1}{4!} = 1.$$

Comparing these values with the coefficients in the expansion of $(a + b)^4$, you can see that

$$(a + b)^4 = \binom{4}{0} a^4 + \binom{4}{1} a^3 b + \binom{4}{2} a^2 b^2 + \binom{4}{3} ab^3 + \binom{4}{4} b^4.$$

This suggests the general result stated in the following theorem, which will be proved on pages 91 and 92.

BINOMIAL THEOREM If $n \in N$, and $a, b \in \mathfrak{R}$, then

$$(a + b)^n = \sum_{k=0}^{n} \binom{n}{k} a^{n-k} b^k.$$

Note that the rth term in the expansion is

$$\binom{n}{r - 1} a^{n-(r-1)} b^{r-1}.$$

EXAMPLE 2. Find the fifth term in the expansion of $(t^2 + s)^{12}$.

Solution: $r = 5$;

$$\therefore \text{ the term is } \binom{12}{4} (t^2)^{12-4} s^4 = 495 t^{16} s^4, \textbf{ Answer.}$$

EXAMPLE 3. In the expansion of $(x^3 - y)^7$, give the term in which the exponent of x is 15.

Solution: The term occurs when the exponent of x^3 is 5, or $7 - 2$.

$$\therefore \text{ the term is } \binom{7}{2} (x^3)^{7-2} (-y)^2 = 21 x^{15} y^2, \textbf{ Answer.}$$

A useful alternative symbolism for $\binom{n}{k}$ can be obtained from

$$\binom{n}{k} = \frac{n(n-1) \cdots (n-k+1)}{k!}$$

by multiplying the numerator and denominator of the expression in the right-hand member by $(n-k)!$. You have

$$\binom{n}{k} = \frac{n(n-1) \cdots (n-k+1)[(n-k)(n-k-1) \cdots 3 \cdot 2 \cdot 1]}{k!(n-k)!}$$

or

$$\binom{n}{k} = \frac{n!}{k!(n-k)!}, \quad 0 \le k \le n.$$

The seventeenth-century French mathematician Blaise Pascal proposed arranging the coefficients in the expansions of $(a + b)^n$ for successive integers n in the triangular array whose first few rows are shown below.

$$
\begin{array}{ccccccccccc}
 & & & & & 1 & & & & & \\
 & & & & 1 & & 1 & & & & \\
 & & & 1 & & 2 & & 1 & & & \\
 & & 1 & & 3 & & 3 & & 1 & & \\
 & 1 & & 4 & & 6 & & 4 & & 1 & \\
1 & & 5 & & 10 & & 10 & & 5 & & 1 \\
\end{array}
$$

$$\cdots \cdots$$

Several interesting facts are evident in this **Pascal triangle.** You can see that each term other than the 1's is the sum of the two terms to the right and to the left of it in the row directly above. This suggests the following theorem, whose proof is left as Exercise 62, page 94.

| THEOREM | $\binom{n+1}{k} = \binom{n}{k-1} + \binom{n}{k}, k \in \{1, 2, \ldots, n\}.$ |

The symmetry of the coefficients in each row suggests the following.

| THEOREM | $\binom{n}{k} = \binom{n}{n-k}, k \in \{1, 2, \ldots, n\}.$ |

The proof of this theorem follows quite directly if k is replaced by $n - k$ in the alternative formula for $\binom{n}{k}$, and is left as an exercise (Exercise 61, page 94).

Still other properties of the symbol $\binom{n}{k}$ can be guessed by studying the sequences of numbers along the various diagonals of the array.

The following proof of the binomial theorem* requires an understanding of the principle of mathematical induction and the properties of summation notation (Exercises 37–40, 47 and 48, pages 78 and 79).

C *Proof of Binomial Theorem:*

Let S be the set of positive integers n for which the statement

$$(a + b)^n = \sum_{k=0}^{n} \binom{n}{k} a^{n-k} b^k$$

is true, where a and b denote nonzero real numbers.

(1) $1 \in S$; for, if $n = 1$, the statement becomes

$$(a + b)^1 = \binom{1}{0} a^1 b^0 + \binom{1}{1} a^0 b^1 = a + b.$$

(2) For *any* positive integer x, you know:

$$(a + b)^{x+1} = (a + b)^x (a + b) = a(a + b)^x + b(a + b)^x.$$

Now, suppose $x \in S$; In this case, you have

$$(a + b)^x = \sum_{k=0}^{x} \binom{x}{k} a^{x-k} b^k.$$

Therefore, using Exercises 40 and 48, pages 78, 79 you find:

---

* Another proof of this theorem is described in Chapter 15.

$$a(a + b)^x = a \sum_{k=0}^{x} \binom{x}{k} a^{x-k}b^k = \sum_{k=0}^{x} \binom{x}{k} a^{x+1-k}b^k; \text{ and}$$

$$b(a + b)^x = b \sum_{k=0}^{x} \binom{x}{k} a^{x-k}b^k = \sum_{k=0}^{x} \binom{x}{k} a^{x-k}b^{k+1} = \sum_{k=1}^{x+1} \binom{x}{k-1} a^{x+1-k}b^k.$$

$$\therefore a(a + b)^x + b(a + b)^x = \sum_{k=0}^{x} \binom{x}{k} a^{x+1-k}b^k + \sum_{k=1}^{x+1} \binom{x}{k-1} a^{x+1-k}b^k.$$

Combining the terms on the right for $k = 1, k = 2, \ldots, k = x$, you have:

$$a(a + b)^x + b(a + b)^x$$

$$= \binom{x}{0} a^{x+1} + \sum_{k=1}^{x} \left[\binom{x}{k} + \binom{x}{k-1}\right] a^{x+1-k}b^k + \binom{x}{x} b^{x+1}.$$

Since $\qquad \binom{x}{k} + \binom{x}{k-1} = \binom{x+1}{k},$ (theorem, top of p. 91)

$$\binom{x}{0} = \binom{x+1}{0} = 1, \text{ and } \binom{x}{x} = \binom{x+1}{x+1} = 1,$$

$$a(a + b)^x + b(a + b)^x$$

$$= \binom{x+1}{0} a^{x+1} + \sum_{k=1}^{x} \binom{x+1}{k} a^{x+1-k}b^k + \binom{x+1}{x+1} b^{x+1}.$$

Hence, writing the preceding statement in compact form, you find:

$$(a + b)^{x+1} = \sum_{k=0}^{x+1} \binom{x+1}{k} a^{x+1-k}b^k.$$

Thus, if $x \in S$, $(x + 1) \in S$. By the principle of mathematical induction S is the set of positive integers and the theorem is proved.

Exercises

In Exercises 1–8 compute the indicated number.

1. $7!$

2. $\dfrac{10!}{8!}$

3. $\dfrac{6!}{3!2!}$

4. $\dfrac{10!}{5!5!}$

5. $\binom{5}{3}$

6. $\binom{8}{5}$

7. $\binom{6}{3} + \binom{6}{4}$

8. $\binom{7}{4} + \binom{7}{5}$

9. By trial determine if there is a positive integer n such that $n! = 50$.

10. Is there an integer $n > 1$ such that $n!$ is an odd number? Why or why not?

In Exercises 11–16 express the given product or quotient by means of a single factorial expression. Assume $n > r > 0$.

11. $(n + 1)n!$

12. $\dfrac{(n + 6)!}{n + 6}$

13. $(n - r)(n - r - 1)!$

14. $9 \cdot 8 \cdot 7 \cdot 6!$

15. $n(n - 1)(n - 2)!$

16. $\dfrac{(n - r + 1)!}{n - r + 1}$

17. If the binomial expansion of $(a + b)^n$ has a middle term, what must be true of n?

18. What is the sum of the exponents of x and y in the kth term of the expansion of $(x + y)^n$? Assume $1 < k < n$.

19. State the term in the expansion of $(a + b)^6$ having the coefficient $\dbinom{6}{2}$.

20. State the term in the expansion of $(a + b)^7$ having the coefficient $\dbinom{7}{6}$.

In Exercises 21–26 simplify as far as possible, given x and y positive integers with $x > y$ and all denominators meaningful.

21. $\dfrac{x!}{(x - 1)!}$

22. $\dfrac{(x + 6)!}{(x + 5)!}$

23. $\dfrac{(x - y)!}{(x - y - 1)!}$

24. $\dfrac{x!}{(x - 2)!}$

25. $\dfrac{(x + 2)!}{x!}$

26. $\dfrac{(x - y + 2)!}{(x - y + 1)!}$

In Exercises 27–32 write the first three terms of each expansion and simplify.

27. $(a + b)^9$

28. $(x - y)^7$

29. $(2a - 3b)^5$

30. $\left(x^2 - \dfrac{2}{x}\right)^4$

31. $(x + 3h)^4$

32. $\left(\dfrac{2}{a} + \dfrac{b}{2}\right)^5$

In Exercises 33–38 find all integral values of n for which the given statement is meaningful and true.

B 33. $n! = 6$

34. $\dfrac{(n + 1)!}{n!} = 6$

35. $\dbinom{n}{2} = 10$

36. $6 < n! < 121$

37. $(n - 1)! < 24$

38. $\dfrac{(n + 1)!}{(n - 1)!} = 12$

In Exercises 39–44 expand using the binomial theorem and express the result in simplest form.

39. $(x + 2)^4$

40. $(2a - b)^5$

41. $\left(x + \dfrac{2}{x}\right)^4$

42. $(x^2 - 1)^6$

43. $\left(\dfrac{2}{x} + \dfrac{3}{y}\right)^3$

44. $(2x - 3h)^3$

In Exercises 45–50 write the indicated term in the expansion of the binomial.

45. $(a + b)^{10}$; 5th

46. $(x - y)^7$; 4th

47. $\left(\dfrac{2}{x} + \dfrac{x}{2}\right)^8$; middle

48. $(3x^2 - 2y)^6$; middle

49. $(a + b)^n$; $(n - 2)$nd

50. $(x + y)^n$; $(n - r)$th

51. Write the term in the expansion of $(3x - 2y)^7$ in which the exponent of y is 4.

52. Write the term in the expansion of $(a^2 + 2b)^{14}$ in which the exponent of a is 8.

53. If the coefficients of the 4th and 16th terms in the expansion of $(r + s)^n$ are equal, find the middle term.

54. If the coefficients of the 6th and 16th terms in the expansion of $(a - b)^n$ are equal, find the third term.

In Exercises 55 and 56 verify the given statement by direct computation.

55. $\displaystyle\sum_{k=0}^{3} \binom{3}{k} = 2^3$
  56. $\displaystyle\sum_{k=0}^{4} \binom{4}{k} = 2^4$

In Exercises 57–60 find the value to the nearest thousandth.

57. $(1 + .02)^5$ **58.** $(1 - .01)^4$ **59.** $(1.03)^5$ **60.** $(.98)^6$

Prove each statement. Assume $n \in N$, $k \in N$, and $k \le n$.

61. $\dbinom{n}{k} = \dbinom{n}{n - k}$

62. $\dbinom{n + 1}{k} = \dbinom{n}{k - 1} + \dbinom{n}{k}$

63. If $(a + b)^n + (a - b)^n$ yields, when expanded and simplified, an expression containing 4 terms, what conclusion can you reach about n? about a and b?

64. Expand $(a + b - z)^4$ through repeated use of the binomial theorem.

65. By the method of mathematical induction prove that in the expansion of $(a + b)^n$, $a > 0$ and $b > 0$, the sum of the coefficients is 2^n.

66. Using the method of mathematical induction, prove that in the expansion of $(a - b)^n$, $a > 0$ and $b > 0$, the sum of the coefficients is zero.

INFINITE SEQUENCES AND SERIES

3–6 Limit of a Sequence

A sequence may be represented graphically by plotting its terms as points on a number line. Figure 3–1 shows the first few terms of the infinite sequence

$$\frac{1}{2}, \frac{2}{3}, \frac{3}{4}, \frac{4}{5}, \ldots, \frac{n}{n+1}, \ldots$$

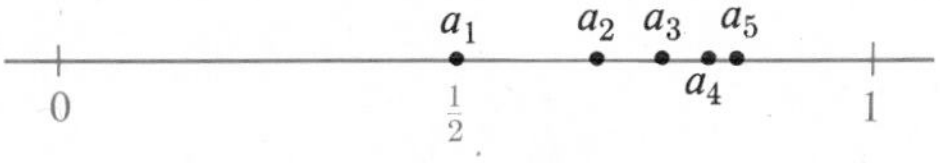

Figure 3–1

and suggests that the points a_1, a_2, etc., representing the terms in the sequence crowd in upon the point 1. This means that for n large enough, the terms approximate 1 as closely as you may demand. For example, suppose you specify that the terms are to approximate 1 with an error of less than $\frac{1}{1000}$. To determine "how far out in the sequence" the terms fulfilling this requirement are to be found, note that the closeness of approximation is measured by the difference between a_n and 1. But

$$|a_n - 1| = \left| \frac{n}{n+1} - 1 \right|$$

$$= \left| \frac{n - (n+1)}{n+1} \right|$$

$$= \left| \frac{-1}{n+1} \right|$$

$$\therefore |a_n - 1| = \frac{1}{n+1}$$

Now, over the set of positive integers, the inequality $\frac{1}{n+1} < \frac{1}{1000}$ is equivalent to $n + 1 > 1000$, or $n > 999$. Thus, for $n \geq 1000$, $|a_n - 1| < \frac{1}{1000}$.

In general, no matter how small a positive number h you may select for the error of approximation, you can choose a positive integer M large enough to ensure that $|a_n - 1| < h$ whenever $n \geq M$. Can you show why you may choose M to be any positive integer greater than $\frac{1}{h} - 1$? Because for any

$h > 0$ we can find an appropriate value for M, we say that the *limit of* $\dfrac{n}{n+1}$ *as n increases without bound is 1* and we write*

$$\lim_{n \to \infty} \frac{n}{n+1} = 1.$$

In general, any infinite sequence $a_1, a_2, \ldots, a_n, \ldots$ has a **limit** A (in symbols, $\lim_{n \to \infty} a_n = A$) provided each positive number h can be paired with a positive integer M such that $|a_n - A| < h$ *if* $n \geq M$.

Figure 3–2

Figure 3–2 illustrates this definition by showing the terms a_M, a_{M+1}, $a_{M+2}, \ldots$ as points within the interval of length $2h$ centered at A. An infinite sequence which has a limit is said to **converge**, or to be **convergent**. We shall speak of *the* limit of a sequence, because it can be proved that a sequence can have no more than one limit (Exercise 48, page 101).

EXAMPLE 1. **a.** Find the limit of the sequence $\dfrac{1}{2}, \dfrac{1}{4}, \dfrac{1}{8}, \ldots, \dfrac{1}{2^n}, \ldots$.

   C **b.** Justify the answer to part (a).

Solution: **a.** The figure suggests that no matter how small a positive margin of error is allowed, the terms $\dfrac{1}{2^n}, \dfrac{1}{2^{n+1}}, \cdots$ all approximate 0 within that margin provided n is chosen sufficiently large. This means that $\lim_{n \to \infty} \dfrac{1}{2^n} = 0$.

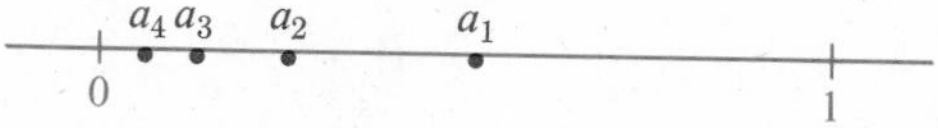

<!-- number line figure: a_4 a_3 a_2 a_1 marked near 0, with 1 at right -->

   C **b.** To support this observation, you must show that for each positive number h, you can choose a positive integer M such that

$$\left| \frac{1}{2^n} - 0 \right| < h \quad \text{for} \quad n \geq M.$$

---

* The symbol $n \to \infty$ is sometimes read "as n approaches infinity." This phrasing is an alternative to "as n increases without bound" and does *not* refer to a number denoted by ∞.

If $h \geq 1$: Choose $M = 1$, because $\dfrac{1}{2^1} < h$ for all such h.

If $h \leq 1$: There is a $k \in N$ such that $\dfrac{1}{2^k} < h$. (Exercise 26, page 74.) Choose $M = k + 1$, because if $n \geq k + 1$,

$$\frac{1}{2^n} \leq \frac{1}{2^{k+1}} < \frac{1}{2^k} < h.$$

EXAMPLE 2. Prove that the sequence of constant terms, defined by $a_n = c$ for all n, converges.

Solution: $\lim\limits_{n \to \infty} a_n = c$ because for any positive number h

$$|a_n - c| = |c - c| = 0 < h$$

for *every* positive integer n.

Given the convergent sequences $a_1, a_2, \ldots, a_n, \ldots$ and $b_1, b_2, \ldots, b_n, \ldots$ you can obtain new sequences by combining their corresponding terms under

(1) addition: $a_1 + b_1, a_2 + b_2, \ldots, a_n + b_n, \ldots$

(2) subtraction: $a_1 - b_1, a_2 - b_2, \ldots, a_n - b_n, \ldots$

(3) multiplication: $a_1 b_1, a_2 b_2, \ldots, a_n b_n, \ldots$

(4) division: $\dfrac{a_1}{b_1}, \dfrac{a_2}{b_2}, \ldots, \dfrac{a_n}{b_n}, \ldots$

The following theorem, which we shall accept without proof, states how the limits of these new sequences depend on the limits of the original sequences.

THEOREM If $\lim\limits_{n \to \infty} a_n = A$ and $\lim\limits_{n \to \infty} b_n = B$, then

(1) $\lim\limits_{n \to \infty} (a_n + b_n) = A + B$.

(2) $\lim\limits_{n \to \infty} (a_n - b_n) = A - B$.

(3) $\lim\limits_{n \to \infty} (a_n b_n) = A \cdot B$.

(4) if $B \neq 0$ and for each positive integer n, $b_n \neq 0$,

$$\lim\limits_{n \to \infty} \frac{a_n}{b_n} = \frac{A}{B}.$$

COROLLARY. If c denotes a constant, $\lim\limits_{n \to \infty} c a_n = cA$.

You will find this theorem and corollary very helpful in finding the limit of a sequence.

EXAMPLE 3. Find the limit of the sequence whose nth term is

$$a_n = \frac{3n^2 + 2n + 4}{n^2 + 1}.$$

Solution: [Plan: To express a_n as a fraction in which the numerator and denominator involve the nth terms of convergent sequences, you can divide the numerator and denominator of the given fraction by n^2.]

$$a_n = \frac{3n^2 + 2n + 4}{n^2 + 1} = \frac{\dfrac{3n^2 + 2n + 4}{n^2}}{\dfrac{n^2 + 1}{n^2}}$$

$$\therefore a_n = \frac{3 + \dfrac{2}{n} + \dfrac{4}{n^2}}{1 + \dfrac{1}{n^2}}$$

But the sequence $\dfrac{1}{1}, \dfrac{1}{2}, \dfrac{1}{3}, \ldots, \dfrac{1}{n}, \ldots$ has 0 as its limit.

(Why?) Hence, $\lim\limits_{n\to\infty} \dfrac{2}{n} = 0$, $\lim\limits_{n\to\infty} \dfrac{1}{n^2} = 0$, and

$\lim\limits_{n\to\infty} \dfrac{4}{n^2} = 0.$

$$\therefore \lim_{n\to\infty} a_n = \frac{3 + 0 + 0}{1 + 0}$$

$$\therefore \lim_{n\to\infty} a_n = 3, \textbf{ Answer.}$$

Not all infinite sequences converge. An infinite sequence that does not have a limit is said to **diverge** or to be **divergent**. For example, the sequence $3, 9, 27, \ldots, 3^n, \ldots$ diverges because it contains terms that are arbitrarily large in absolute value. The sequence $1, -1, 1, \ldots, (-1)^{n+1}, \ldots$ is divergent because its terms are alternately 1 and -1.

Exercises

In Exercises 1–6, a_n represents the general term of a sequence. For each sequence tell whether, as n increases, the absolute value of the difference between successive terms increases, decreases, or remains constant.

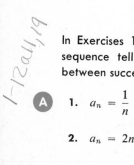

A

1. $a_n = \dfrac{1}{n}$

2. $a_n = 2n - 3$

3. $a_n = (-1)^n \cdot (2n)$

4. $a_n = \dfrac{2n + 3}{4n + 1}$

5. $a_n = \dfrac{n^2 + 3}{n + 2}$

6. $a_n = \dfrac{(n + 1)!}{n!}$

Classify each of the following statements as true or false.

7. A term of a convergent sequence can be equal to the limit of the sequence.

8. If the limit of a convergent sequence is a positive number, all terms of the sequence are positive numbers.

9. If the terms of a sequence are alternately positive and negative numbers, the sequence cannot be convergent.

10. If a_n is the nth term of a convergent sequence with limit L, then for every two successive terms a_k and a_{k+1}, $|a_k - L| \geq |a_{k+1} - L|$.

11. If $\lim\limits_{n \to \infty} a_n = T$ and $\lim\limits_{n \to \infty} b_n = T$, then a_n and b_n designate the same sequence.

12. If $\lim\limits_{n \to \infty} \dfrac{1}{n} = 0$, then $\lim\limits_{n \to \infty} \left(3 + \dfrac{1}{n} \right) = 3$.

In Exercises 13–18 find the indicated limit, given $\lim\limits_{n \to \infty} a_n = K^2 - 1$, $\lim\limits_{n \to \infty} b_n = K + 1$, and $|K| \neq 1$.

13. $\lim\limits_{n \to \infty} 3a_n$

14. $\lim\limits_{n \to \infty} (a_n + b_n)$

15. $\lim\limits_{n \to \infty} (a_n - b_n)$

16. $\lim\limits_{n \to \infty} \left(\dfrac{a_n}{b_n} \right)$

17. $\lim\limits_{n \to \infty} \left(\dfrac{a_n + b_n}{b_n} \right)$

18. $\lim\limits_{n \to \infty} \left(\dfrac{1}{a_n} - \dfrac{1}{b_n} \right)$ $\dfrac{(2-K)}{K^2} \cdot -1$

In Exercises 19–24 determine whether the given sequence is convergent or divergent by means of a number-line representation. For each convergent sequence find the limit and compute the differences between the limit and the ninth and tenth terms.

19. $\dfrac{1}{2}, \dfrac{1}{4}, \dfrac{1}{6}, \ldots, \dfrac{1}{2n}, \ldots$

20. $-1, 2, -3, 4, \ldots, (-1)^n n, \ldots$

21. $\dfrac{1}{5}, \dfrac{2}{7}, \dfrac{3}{9}, \ldots, \dfrac{n}{2n+3}, \ldots$

22. $1, -\dfrac{1}{2}, \dfrac{1}{3}, -\dfrac{1}{4}, \ldots, (-1)^{n+1} \cdot \dfrac{1}{n}, \ldots$

23. $(2 + \tfrac{1}{2}), (2 - \tfrac{1}{2}), (2 + \tfrac{1}{3}), (2 - \tfrac{1}{3}), \ldots$

24. $-\tfrac{1}{2}, -\tfrac{2}{3}, \tfrac{3}{4}, -\tfrac{4}{5}, \ldots$

B   **25.** Given that the limit (A) of the sequence with nth term $a_n = \dfrac{n}{n + 2}$ is 1, find the smallest integral value of n for which $|A - a_n| < \tfrac{1}{7}$.

26. Given that the limit (A) of the sequence with nth term $a_n = \dfrac{n^2}{2n^2 + 1}$ is $\frac{1}{2}$, find the smallest integral value of n for which $|A - a_n| < \frac{1}{66}$.

27. Assuming that the limit (A) of the sequence with nth term $a_n = \dfrac{3n}{2n^2 + 7}$ is 0, find the smallest value of n for which $|A - a_n| < \frac{1}{5}$.

28. Prove that the sequence with nth term $a_n = \dfrac{n^2 + 1}{n + 6}$ diverges.

$$\left(\textit{Hint: } \frac{n^2 + 1}{n + 6} = \frac{(n^2 - 36) + 37}{n + 6} = n - 6 + \frac{37}{n + 6}. \right)$$

In Exercises 29–36 find $\lim\limits_{n \to \infty} a_n$ for each sequence that is convergent. (*Hint:*

Express a_n in a form which permits you to make use of the fact that $\lim\limits_{n \to \infty} \dfrac{1}{n} = 0$.)

29. $a_n = \dfrac{n}{n + 3}$

30. $a_n = \dfrac{n^2}{n + 1}$

31. $a_n = \dfrac{3n - 2}{n + 4}$

32. $a_n = \dfrac{n!}{n}$

33. $a_n = \dfrac{n^2 + 1}{3n^2 - n}$

34. $a_n = \dfrac{2n^2 + 3n - 1}{5n^2 + 4n + 2}$

35. $a_n = \left(1 + \dfrac{2}{n} \right)\left(2 - \dfrac{1}{n} \right)$

36. $a_n = \left(\dfrac{4n + 1}{n} \right)^{10}$

In Exercises 37–44 (**a**) state at least one appropriate nth term of the suggested sequence; (**b**) if the resulting sequence is convergent, find the limit by using the method suggested for Exercises 29–36.

37. $1, \frac{1}{3}, \frac{1}{5}, \frac{1}{7}, \ldots$

38. $1, 3!, 5!, 7!, \ldots$

39. $2, \frac{3}{2}, \frac{4}{3}, \frac{5}{4}, \ldots$

40. $1, \frac{2}{3}, \frac{3}{5}, \frac{4}{7}, \ldots$

41. $\frac{1}{2}, \frac{4}{3}, \frac{9}{4}, \frac{16}{5}, \ldots$

42. $-\frac{1}{2}, \frac{2}{3}, -\frac{3}{4}, \frac{4}{5}, \ldots$

43. $\frac{3}{1}, \frac{4}{3}, \frac{5}{5}, \frac{6}{7}, \ldots$

44. $-\frac{1}{2}, -\frac{2}{5}, -\frac{3}{10}, -\frac{4}{17}, \ldots$

C 45. Given the sequence whose xth term is

$$a_x = \frac{s_0 x^m + s_1 x^{m-1} + s_2 x^{m-2} + \cdots + s_{m-1}x + s_m}{t_0 x^n + t_1 x^{n-1} + t_2 x^{n-2} + \cdots + t_{n-1}x + t_n} \cdot \quad (t_0 \neq 0.)$$

Show that (a) if $m < n$, $\lim\limits_{x \to \infty} a_x = 0$; (b) if $m = n$, $\lim\limits_{x \to \infty} a_x = \dfrac{s_0}{t_0}$.

46. Prove that if $0 < r < 1$ then $\lim\limits_{n \to \infty} r^n = 0$. (*Hint:* Substitute $\dfrac{1}{1 + k}$ $(k > 0)$ for r and apply the theorem stated on page 72 to $(1 + k)^n$.)

47. Given $a_n = \dfrac{1 - n}{1 + n}$. Prove $\lim\limits_{n \to \infty} a_n = -1$ by showing that for any positive integer n greater than $\dfrac{2}{h} - 1$, $|a_n - (-1)| < h$ for any $h > 0$.

48. Prove that a convergent sequence a_n cannot have two distinct limits A and B. (*Hint:* $|A - B| = |(A - a_n) + (a_n - B)| \le |A - a_n| + |a_n - B|$.)

3–7 Infinite Geometric Series

Figure 3–3 pictures the numbers $\frac{1}{2}$, $\frac{1}{2} + \frac{1}{4}$, $\frac{1}{2} + \frac{1}{4} + \frac{1}{8}$, $\frac{1}{2} + \frac{1}{4} + \frac{1}{8} + \frac{1}{16}$, and suggests that no matter how many terms you add in the infinite series $\frac{1}{2} + \frac{1}{4} + \frac{1}{8} + \frac{1}{16} + \cdots + (\frac{1}{2})^n + \cdots$ the sum never exceeds 1. It also suggests, however, that if enough terms are added the sum will approximate 1 as closely as you may demand.

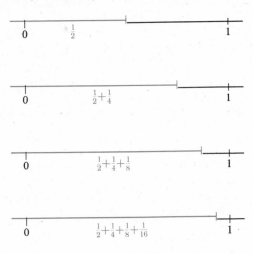

Figure 3–3

This example also gives us an indication of how we could define a sum of such a series. Consider the sequence of *partial sums* beginning with $S_1 = \frac{1}{2}$, $S_2 = \frac{1}{2} + \frac{1}{4}$, and in general,

$$S_n = \sum_{k=1}^{n} \frac{1}{2^k}, \, n \ge 1.$$

Since S_n is the sum of a geometric progression whose first term and common ratio each equal $\frac{1}{2}$, you have

$$S_n = \frac{\frac{1}{2}[1 - (\frac{1}{2})^n]}{1 - \frac{1}{2}} = 1 - \frac{1}{2^n}.$$

Hence,

$$\lim_{n\to\infty} S_n = 1 - \lim_{n\to\infty} \frac{1}{2^n}$$

$$= 1 - 0.$$

$$\therefore \lim_{n\to\infty} \mathbf{S_n} = \mathbf{1}.$$

Accordingly, we *define* the sum of the infinite series $\frac{1}{2} + \frac{1}{4} + \frac{1}{8} + \cdots + \frac{1}{2^n} + \cdots$ to be 1 and write

$$\sum_{k=1}^{\infty} \frac{1}{2^k} = 1.$$

In general, for any infinite series $a_1 + a_2 + \cdots + a_n + \cdots$, $S_n = \sum_{k=1}^{n} a_k$ is called a **partial sum**. If the sequence of partial sums S_1, $S_2, \ldots, S_n, \ldots$ converges, and if $\lim_{n\to\infty} S_n = S$, then the sum of the series $a_1 + a_2 + \cdots + a_n + \cdots$ is defined to be S. We write $\sum_{k=1}^{\infty} a_k = S$, and we say that the series is **convergent**. On the other hand, if the sequence of partial sums diverges, then the series is **divergent** and its sum is not defined.

Can you decide when the infinite geometric series $a + ar + ar^2 + \cdots + ar^n + \cdots$ converges? If $a = 0$, you have $\sum_{i=1}^{\infty} 0$, and the series has the sum 0. Suppose $a \neq 0$ and $r \neq 1$. The nth partial sum is

$$S_n = \frac{a}{1-r}(1 - r^n) = \frac{a}{1-r} - \frac{a}{1-r}r^n.$$

If $|r| < 1$, you can prove that $\lim_{n\to\infty} r^n = 0$ (Exercise 46, page 100).

It follows that

$$\lim_{n\to\infty} S_n = \frac{a}{1-r} - \frac{a}{1-r}\lim_{n\to\infty} r^n$$

$$= \frac{a}{1-r} - 0.$$

Therefore, if $|r| < 1$,

$$\lim_{n\to\infty} S_n = \frac{a}{1-r}.$$

If, however, $|r| > 1$, $|r|^n$ increases steadily with n. (Exercise 12, page 73.) Therefore, r^n does not have a limit as n increases without bound and neither does S_n. If $a \neq 0$ and $r = 1$ or $r = -1$, you have the divergent series $a + a + \cdots + a + \cdots$ or $a - a + a - a + \cdots$. The following theorem summarizes these facts:

| THEOREM | The infinite geometric series $a + ar + ar^2 + \cdots + ar^{n-1} + \cdots$ converges and has the sum $\dfrac{a}{1-r}$ if $|r| < 1$. If $a = 0$, the series converges and has the sum 0. If $|r| \geq 1$ and $a \neq 0$, the series diverges. |

EXAMPLE 1. Determine the sum S of the series $\displaystyle\sum_{k=1}^{\infty} 5(-\tfrac{1}{6})^{k-1}$.

Solution: $a = 5, r = -\tfrac{1}{6}; |r| < 1.$

$$\therefore S = \frac{5}{1 - (-\tfrac{1}{6})} = \frac{5}{\tfrac{7}{6}} = \frac{30}{7}, \text{ Answer.}$$

The decimal system of notation employs infinite series. For example, the number denoted by 4572.36277 . . . , where the digit 7 is understood to repeat indefinitely, can be represented as a sum:

$$4(10)^3 + 5(10)^2 + 7(10) + 2 + \frac{3}{10^1} + \frac{6}{10^2} + \frac{2}{10^3}$$

$$+ \frac{7}{10^4} + \frac{7}{10^5} + \cdots + \frac{7}{10^n} + \cdots.$$

In general, the notation

$$a_k a_{k-1} \ldots a_1 a_0 \cdot b_1 b_2 b_3 \ldots b_n \ldots$$

is called a **nonnegative decimal numeral**, or **decimal** for short. The number denoted by this numeral (if such a number exists) is also representable as the sum of a finite and an infinite series:

Finite series: $a_k 10^k + a_{k-1} 10^{k-1} + \cdots + a_1 10^1 + a_0$

Infinite series: $\dfrac{b_1}{10^1} + \dfrac{b_2}{10^2} + \dfrac{b_3}{10^3} + \cdots + \dfrac{b_n}{10^n} + \cdots,$

in which all the digits a_j and b_j belong to $\{0, 1, 2, 3, 4, 5, 6, 7, 8, 9\}$. The convergence of such series will be discussed in Section 3–8. An expression such as $-a_k a_{k-1} \ldots a_0 \cdot b_1 b_2 \ldots b_n \ldots$ is a **negative decimal**.

Examples of decimals are

$$7134.00000 \ldots, \quad \text{or} \quad 7134.\overline{0}, \quad \text{or} \quad 7134$$
$$0.25000 \ldots, \quad \text{or} \quad 0.25\overline{0}, \quad \text{or} \quad 0.25$$
$$-58.72222 \ldots, \quad \text{or} \quad -58.7\overline{2},$$
$$4.13636 \ldots, \quad \text{or} \quad 4.1\overline{36},$$

where the bar means that the indicated *block* of digits is repeated without end.

The following example suggests how to show that a given *repeating decimal**
represents a rational number.

EXAMPLE 2. Find the value of the repeating decimal $4.1\overline{36}$, or
4.1363636 . . .

Solution: $4.13\overline{6} = 4 + \dfrac{1}{10} + \left[\dfrac{36}{10^3} + \dfrac{36}{10^5} + \dfrac{36}{10^7} + \cdots\right]$

Since the expression within braces is an infinite geometric

series with $a = \dfrac{36}{10^3}$ and $r = \dfrac{1}{10^2}$, you have

$$4.1\overline{36} = \dfrac{41}{10} + \dfrac{\dfrac{36}{10^3}}{1 - \dfrac{1}{10^2}}$$

$$= \tfrac{41}{10} + \dfrac{\frac{36}{1000}}{\frac{99}{100}}$$

$$= \tfrac{41}{10} + \tfrac{2}{55} = \tfrac{91}{22}, \textbf{ Answer.}$$

Do you see that the statement, "Every repeating decimal represents a
rational number," is a corollary of the following theorem whose proof is
left as an exercise? (Exercise 47, page 106.)

THEOREM The sum of any convergent infinite geometric series
whose first term and common ratio are rational
numbers is a rational number.

Exercises

Write the decimal equivalent of each fraction, using the bar symbol to indicate
a repeating digit or block of digits.

1. $\frac{16}{45}$ 2. $\frac{3}{7}$ 3. $\frac{5}{7}$ 4. $\frac{157}{300}$

Find the sum of the infinite geometric series for which

5. $a = 3, r = \frac{1}{2}$ 7. $a = 2, r = \dfrac{\sqrt{2}}{2}$

6. $a = -4, r = -\frac{1}{3}$ 8. $a = \sqrt{3}, r = \sqrt{\frac{1}{3}}$

---

* Note that a repeating decimal, such as $0.25\overline{0}$, in which the recurring block consists
of the single digit 0 can be rewritten as a *terminating decimal*: 0.25.

Write the first three terms of the infinite geometric progression for which

9. $a = \frac{2}{3}, S = \frac{4}{3}$

11. $r = -\frac{1}{3}, S = \frac{3}{8}$

10. $a = 1.5, S = 1$

12. $r = .01, S = \frac{3}{11}$

Find the sum of the given infinite geometric series.

13. $18 + 12 + 8 + \cdots$

15. $.2 - .02 + .002 - \cdots$

14. $\sqrt{3} + \sqrt{\frac{3}{2}} + \frac{1}{2}\sqrt{3} + \cdots$

16. $3 + 3(10)^{-1} + 3(10)^{-2} + \cdots$

Find the indicated sum.

17. $\displaystyle\sum_{k=0}^{\infty} 3(\tfrac{1}{2})^k$

18. $\displaystyle\sum_{k=0}^{\infty} 2(-\tfrac{1}{3})^k$

Write the given repeating decimal as an equivalent common fraction.

19. $.\overline{4}$ **20.** $.\overline{324}$ **21.** $1.\overline{24}$ **22.** $2.1\overline{3}$

In Exercises 23–28 support your answer with an explanation.

23. If two infinite geometric series have the same finite sum, are they the same series?

24. Can the sum of a convergent infinite geometric series be less than the first term?

25. Can the series $\displaystyle\sum_{i=1}^{\infty} a$ be convergent for any $a \in \mathcal{R}$?

26. Given an infinite geometric series in which $a > 0$ and $|r| < 1$. Can the sum of this series be negative?

27. Is there an infinite geometric series for which $a = 6$ and $S = \frac{2}{3}$?

28. Given the statement: Every repeating decimal represents a rational number. Is the converse of this statement true?

B **29.** An infinite geometric series has the sum 8. If the sum of the first two terms is 2, find a and r.

30. An infinite geometric series has 2 as its sum. If the second term is $\frac{3}{8}$, find a and r.

Express the exact error involved in each of the indicated approximations.

31. $\frac{8}{3} \doteq 2.67$

32. $3\frac{7}{11} \doteq 3.65$

In Exercises 33–36, find the range of values of x for which the sum of each geometric progression can be obtained.

33. $\frac{3}{5}, \frac{3}{5}(x-1), \frac{3}{5}(x-1)^2, \frac{3}{5}(x-1)^3, \ldots$

34. $1, 2(x-2), 4(x-2)^2, 8(x-2)^3, \ldots$

35. $1, 3(4 - x), 9(4 - x)^2, 27(4 - x)^3, \ldots$

36. $\frac{1}{2}, \frac{1}{4}(2 - x), \frac{1}{8}(2 - x)^2, \frac{1}{16}(2 - x)^3, \ldots$

37. Find r for the infinite geometric series in which $S = \dfrac{4 + 3\sqrt{2}}{2}$ and $a = \sqrt{2} + 1$.

38. The sum of the first two terms of an infinite geometric series is 2, the sum of the first three terms is 3, and $r \neq 1$. Show that this series is convergent.

Solve for x, given that each infinite geometric series converges to the indicated limit.

39. $\frac{3}{4} = 1 + 2x + 4x^2 + \cdots$

41. $\dfrac{8x}{4x - 1} = x + x^2 + x^3 + \cdots$

40. $\frac{6}{7} = 1 + 3x + 9x^2 + \cdots$

42. $\dfrac{2x}{x + 1} = x + x^2 + x^3 + \cdots$

43. A ball is dropped from a height of 32 ft. Each time it strikes the ground it rebounds $\frac{3}{8}$ths of the distance from which it had fallen. Theoretically, how far will the ball travel before coming to rest?

44. Given a square of side 20 in. The midpoints of its sides are joined to form an inscribed square. The midpoints of this second square are joined to form a third square. If the process is continued endlessly, find the sum of the perimeters and the sum of the areas of all the squares, including the initial one.

C **45.** Given the infinite geometric series $a + ar + ar^2 + ar^3 + \cdots + ar^{n-1} \cdots$ $(a > 0)$. If $0 < r < 1$, what fractional part of the sum is the sum of the odd-numbered terms? the even-numbered terms?

46. Given the series $a + \displaystyle\sum_{n=1}^{\infty} ar^n$, in which $|r| < 1$. If each term in the series is k times the sum of all the terms that follow it ($k > 0$), express the series in terms of a and k.

47. Prove the theorem on page 104.

48. Prove that every repeating decimal represents a rational number.

3–8 Axiom of Completeness

Deciding whether a geometric series converges or not is easy because you know how to express S_n in terms of n. Several of the statements concerning finite series that you have proved by induction (pages 73–74) suggest other infinite series you can either sum or show to be divergent.

EXAMPLE 1. Find the sum of the series $\dfrac{1}{1 \cdot 2} + \dfrac{1}{2 \cdot 3} + \dfrac{1}{3 \cdot 4} + \cdots + \dfrac{1}{n(n + 1)} + \cdots.$

Solution: $S_1 = \frac{1}{2}$, $S_2 = \frac{1}{2} + \frac{1}{6} = \frac{2}{3}$, $S_3 = \frac{1}{2} + \frac{1}{6} + \frac{1}{12} = \frac{3}{4}$; in general, $S_n = \dfrac{n}{n+1}$ (Exercise 16, page 73).

$$\lim_{n \to \infty} S_n = \lim_{n \to \infty} \frac{n}{n+1} = 1. \quad \text{(See page 96.)}$$

$$\therefore \sum_{n=1}^{\infty} \frac{1}{n(n+1)} = 1, \text{ Answer.}$$

You can sometimes decide whether or not a series is convergent even if you are unable to express S_n in terms of n.

EXAMPLE 2. Show that the series $1 + \frac{1}{2} + \frac{1}{3} + \frac{1}{4} + \cdots$ is divergent.

Solution: If you write out several terms in the series,

$$1 + \tfrac{1}{2} + \tfrac{1}{3} + \tfrac{1}{4} + \tfrac{1}{5} + \tfrac{1}{6} + \tfrac{1}{7} + \tfrac{1}{8} + \tfrac{1}{9} + \tfrac{1}{10} + \tfrac{1}{11}$$
$$+ \tfrac{1}{12} + \tfrac{1}{13} + \tfrac{1}{14} + \tfrac{1}{15} + \tfrac{1}{16} + \cdots,$$

and then group the terms after the first so that the denominator of the last term in each group is a power of 2, you have

$$1 + (\tfrac{1}{2}) + (\tfrac{1}{3} + \tfrac{1}{4}) + (\tfrac{1}{5} + \tfrac{1}{6} + \tfrac{1}{7} + \tfrac{1}{8})$$
$$+ (\tfrac{1}{9} + \cdots + \tfrac{1}{16}) + (\tfrac{1}{17} + \cdots + \tfrac{1}{32}) + \cdots.$$

Since, in each group, each term is greater than its successor, i.e., $\frac{1}{3} > \frac{1}{4}$, $\frac{1}{5} > \frac{1}{6} > \frac{1}{7} > \frac{1}{8}$, etc., you can see that any partial sum of the given series is greater than the corresponding partial sum of the series

$$1 + (\tfrac{1}{2}) + (\tfrac{1}{4} + \tfrac{1}{4}) + (\tfrac{1}{8} + \tfrac{1}{8} + \tfrac{1}{8} + \tfrac{1}{8})$$
$$+ (\tfrac{1}{16} + \cdots + \tfrac{1}{16}) + (\tfrac{1}{32} + \cdots + \tfrac{1}{32}) + \cdots.$$

But this latter series can be written

$$1 + \tfrac{1}{2} + \tfrac{1}{2} + \tfrac{1}{2} + \tfrac{1}{2} + \tfrac{1}{2} + \cdots.$$

Hence, for the original series, you have

$$S_2 = 1 + \tfrac{1}{2}$$
$$S_4 > 1 + \tfrac{1}{2} + \tfrac{1}{2} = 1 + \tfrac{2}{2}$$
$$S_8 > 1 + \tfrac{1}{2} + \tfrac{1}{2} + \tfrac{1}{2} = 1 + \tfrac{3}{2}$$
$$\vdots$$
$$S_{2^k} > 1 + \tfrac{1}{2} + \tfrac{1}{2} + \cdots + \tfrac{1}{2} = 1 + \frac{k}{2},$$

so that S_{2^k} increases steadily and without bound as k increases; therefore the series diverges.

To decide whether the series of positive numbers

$$\frac{1}{10} + \frac{1}{10^3} + \frac{1}{10^6} + \cdots + \frac{1}{10^{\frac{n(n+1)}{2}}} + \cdots$$

converges, consider its partial sums.

$$S_1 = \frac{1}{10}$$

$$S_n = S_{n-1} + \frac{1}{10^{\frac{n(n+1)}{2}}}, \, n \geq 2.$$

Do you see that $S_1 \leq S_2 \leq \cdots \leq S_{n-1} \leq S_n \leq \cdots$? Because each term in the sequence of partial sums is less than or equal to the succeeding term, this sequence is said to be **nondecreasing**.

You can also see that the partial sums do not become arbitrarily large, because the terms of this series are all less than or equal to the corresponding terms of the convergent geometric series shown below:

$$\frac{1}{10} + \frac{1}{10^3} + \frac{1}{10^5} + \cdots + \frac{1}{10^{2n-1}} + \cdots = \frac{10}{99}$$

$$\updownarrow \quad \updownarrow \quad \updownarrow \qquad \qquad \updownarrow$$

$$\frac{1}{10} + \frac{1}{10^3} + \frac{1}{10^6} + \cdots + \frac{1}{10^{\frac{n(n+1)}{2}}} + \cdots.$$

Therefore $\frac{10}{99}$, the sum of the geometric series, must certainly exceed each partial sum of the given series. Whenever there exists a number which equals or exceeds the absolute value of every term of a sequence, we say the sequence is **bounded** by the number. Thus, the sequence of partial sums of the given series is bounded by $\frac{10}{99}$. The **axiom of completeness**, mentioned on page 60, is the last assumption needed to characterize the real number system. It guarantees that any sequence that is both nondecreasing and bounded has a limit. Can you explain why a sequence that is not bounded must diverge?

Axiom of Completeness

Every bounded, nondecreasing sequence of real numbers converges and its limit is a real number.

Thus, the series $\frac{1}{10} + \frac{1}{10^3} + \cdots + \frac{1}{10^{\frac{n(n+1)}{2}}} + \cdots$ has a sum. Al-

though you cannot compute the sum, you can approximate it as closely as you wish by adding enough of its terms. For example, to 10 decimal places the sum is 0.1010010001.

C **EXAMPLE 3.** Prove that every decimal represents a real number.

Proof: Each nonnegative decimal can be written in the form (page 103):

$$a_r \cdot 10^r + a_{r-1}10^{r-1} + \cdots + a_1 \cdot 10 + a_0$$

$$+ \frac{b_1}{10} + \frac{b_2}{10^2} + \cdots + \frac{b_n}{10^n} + \cdots .$$

The expression printed in red denotes the sum of a finite number of real numbers, and therefore represents a real number.

Now, consider the infinite series $\frac{b_1}{10} + \frac{b_2}{10^2} + \cdots + \frac{b_n}{10^n} + \cdots .$

Because for each positive integer n, $b_n \geq 0$, the sequence of partial sums is nondecreasing. Also, since each term of this infinite series is less than or equal to the corresponding term of the geometric series

$$\frac{9}{10} + \frac{9}{10^2} + \frac{9}{10^3} + \cdots + \frac{9}{10^n} + \cdots ,$$

whose sum is 1, the partial sums form a bounded sequence. By the axiom of completeness the sequence of partial sums converges to a real limit, so that the sum of the infinite series is a real number. Because the decimal represents the sum of two real numbers, it also designates a real number.

For a negative decimal, you first consider its negative. This is positive and therefore represents a positive real number. Accordingly, the original negative decimal represents a negative real number.

It can also be proved that every real number can be represented by a decimal. This assertion together with the statement proved in Example 3 constitutes the following important theorem.

THEOREM Every real number can be represented by a decimal, and every decimal represents a real number.

You know that the repeating decimals represent rational numbers (Exercise 48, page 106). The familiar division process yields a decimal for any rational number, and suggests a fact that can be proved:* *Every decimal for a rational number must repeat.* The nonrepeating decimals, therefore, represent real numbers that are *not* rational. Such numbers are called **irrational numbers**.

A subset consisting of real numbers is called **complete** if it contains the limit of every convergent sequence of its elements. Can you explain why the set of rational numbers is not complete?

Exercises

1. Does the axiom of completeness permit you to conclude that a sequence which does not have a limit cannot be a nondecreasing sequence? Explain.

2. Explain why a sequence that is not bounded cannot converge.

3. If $\displaystyle\sum_{k=1}^{\infty} t_k$ is a convergent series, is $\displaystyle\sum_{k=1}^{\infty} (t_k + 1)$ also a convergent series?

4. Can the product of two repeating decimals be a nonrepeating, nonterminating decimal? Give a reason in support of your answer.

In Exercises 5–10 classify the given statements as true or false. For each you classify as false, provide a counterexample.

5. The sum of an infinite series is the limit of a sequence of partial sums.

6. The partial sums of a series must increase without bound as n increases.

7. A sequence of partial sums $S_1, S_2, \ldots S_n \ldots$ is nondecreasing if S_n never decreases as n increases.

8. If each odd-numbered term of a series is greater than zero and each even-numbered term is less than zero, the series cannot be convergent.

9. In the series $\displaystyle\sum_{n=1}^{\infty} a_n$, $\quad S_n - S_{n-1} = a_n$ for $n > 1$.

10. Every nondecreasing sequence of partial sums is bounded.

In Exercises 11–14 write the first four terms of the sequence of partial sums for the given series and tell whether the sequence is nondecreasing.

11. $\frac{1}{2} + \frac{1}{4} + \frac{1}{8} + \cdots + \left(\frac{1}{2}\right)^n + \cdots$

12. $1 - 2 + 3 - 4 + \cdots (-1)^{n-1} n + \cdots$

13. $\left(\frac{1}{2} - 1\right) + \left(\frac{1}{3} - \frac{1}{2}\right) + \cdots + \left(\frac{1}{n+1} - \frac{1}{n}\right) + \cdots$

---

* See, for example, *Modern Algebra and Trigonometry, Structure and Method, Book 2,* Dolciani, Berman, and Wooton, Houghton Mifflin Company, 1963, pp. 184–185.

14. $\dfrac{3}{2} + \dfrac{5}{4} + \dfrac{9}{8} + \cdots + \dfrac{2^n + 1}{2^n} + \cdots$

15. Given the infinite geometric series $\displaystyle\sum_{n=0}^{\infty} ar^n$ with $a > 0$. For the indicated value of r tell whether the series is convergent or divergent.

    a. $r = 1$ **b.** $r = \frac{1}{2}$ **c.** $r = -\frac{1}{3}$ **d.** $r = -\frac{3}{2}$

16. Given the series $\displaystyle\sum_{n=1}^{\infty} t_n$, in which all terms are positive. What conclusions, if any, can you make about its convergence or divergence if for all n

    a. $t_n < \frac{1}{2}$?   **b.** $t_n > \frac{1}{2}$?   **c.** $\displaystyle\lim_{n\to\infty} t_n = 1$?   **d.** $\displaystyle\lim_{n\to\infty} t_n < 0$?

In Exercises 17–20 prove the given series convergent by citing a convergent geometric series whose sum bounds the given series.

17. $\dfrac{1}{5} + \dfrac{1}{5^3} + \dfrac{1}{5^6} + \cdots + \dfrac{1}{5^{\frac{n(n+1)}{2}}} \cdots$ $\frac{1}{5} + \frac{1}{5}2 + \frac{1}{5}3 \ldots r\frac{1}{5}n$

18. $\dfrac{1}{3 + 1} + \dfrac{1}{3^2 + 1} + \dfrac{1}{3^3 + 1} + \cdots + \dfrac{1}{3^n + 1} \cdots$ $\frac{1}{3} + \frac{1}{32} + \frac{1}{33}$

19. $1 + \dfrac{1}{2^2} + \dfrac{1}{3^3} + \cdots + \dfrac{1}{n^n} + \cdots$ $1 + \frac{1}{2} + \frac{1}{2^2} + \frac{1}{2^3} + \ldots + \frac{1}{2^{n-1}}$

20. $\dfrac{1}{2} \cdot \dfrac{1}{2} + \dfrac{2}{3} \cdot \dfrac{1}{4} + \cdots + \dfrac{n}{n+1} \cdot \dfrac{1}{2^n} \cdots$ $\frac{1}{2} + \frac{1}{4} + \frac{1}{8} \ldots + \frac{1}{2^n}$

In Exercises 21–26 the nth partial sum S_n of a series is given. By investigating $\displaystyle\lim_{n\to\infty} S_n$ determine whether the series is convergent or divergent. When convergent, give the sum.

B   **21.** $S_n = \frac{1}{2}n(n + 1)$ **23.** $S_n = \dfrac{n}{2n + 1}$ **25.** $S_n = \dfrac{2n + 3}{3n + 2}$

     22. $S_n = 1 - \dfrac{1}{2^n}$ **24.** $S_n = \dfrac{n(2n - 1)}{n + 3}$ **26.** $S_n = \dfrac{n + 1}{n^2 + n + 1}$

In Exercises 27–30 the numbers given are the first four partial sums of a series. Form an appropriate series and tell whether it is convergent or divergent.

27. $18, 24, 26, 26\frac{2}{3}$ **29.** $\frac{1}{2}, \frac{1}{4}, \frac{3}{8}, \frac{5}{16}$

28. $1, 3, 6, 10$ **30.** $1, 0, 1, 0$

31. Prove: If $\displaystyle\sum_{n=1}^{\infty} u_n$ converges with a sum S and k is any constant, then $\displaystyle\sum_{n=1}^{\infty} ku_n$ converges with a sum kS.

32. Prove: If $\sum_{k=1}^{\infty} t_k$ and $\sum_{k=1}^{\infty} p_k$ are convergent series with sums T and P respectively, then $\sum_{k=1}^{\infty} (t_k + p_k)$ and $\sum_{k=1}^{\infty} (t_k - p_k)$ are convergent and $T + P$ and $T - P$ are their respective sums.

C   33. Using the method of Example 2, page 107, show that $1 + \dfrac{1}{2^p} + \dfrac{1}{4^p} + \cdots + \dfrac{1}{2^{np}} + \cdots$ is convergent for $p \in N, p > 1$.

34. Show that the series $\dfrac{1}{1 \cdot 2} + \dfrac{1}{2 \cdot 3} + \dfrac{1}{3 \cdot 4} + \cdots + \dfrac{1}{n(n+1)}$ is convergent.

    Hint: Write S_n in the form $\left(1 - \dfrac{1}{2}\right) + \left(\dfrac{1}{2} - \dfrac{1}{3}\right) + \left(\dfrac{1}{3} - \dfrac{1}{4}\right) + \cdots + \left(\dfrac{1}{n} - \dfrac{1}{n+1}\right)$.

35. Show that the following series converges and find its sum.

$$\left(\frac{1}{2} + \frac{1}{3}\right) + \left(\frac{1}{4} + \frac{1}{9}\right) + \cdots + \left(\frac{1}{2^n} + \frac{1}{3^n}\right) + \cdots.$$

    (*Hint:* Express S_n as the sum of two separate geometric series.)

36. Given $\sum_{k=1}^{\infty} a_k$ and $\sum_{k=1}^{\infty} b_k$, in which all terms are positive and $a_k \geq b_k$ for all k.

    Prove that if $\sum_{k=1}^{\infty} b_k$ is divergent, then $\sum_{k=1}^{\infty} a_k$ is divergent.

37. Find the range of values of x for which the series $\sum_{n=1}^{\infty} \left(\dfrac{2x+1}{2}\right)^n$ is convergent.

38. If $\dfrac{p}{q}$ and $\dfrac{r}{s}$ are any two positive rational numbers such that $\dfrac{p}{q} < \dfrac{r}{s}$, show that $\dfrac{ps + qr}{2sq}$ is a rational number which lies between the given numbers.

3–9 Positive Roots of Positive Numbers

Does the equation $x^3 = 2$ have a positive root? You can use the axiom of completeness to prove that such a root exists, and at the same time obtain as many places as you wish in the decimal for this root. Since $1^3 = 1$ and $2^3 = 8$, any positive number satisfying the equation $x^3 = 2$ would have to be between 1 and 2. (Exercise 11, page 73.) Hence, its decimal would be of the form $1.b_1 b_2 \ldots b_m \ldots$.

Choose b_1 to be the largest digit such that $(1.b_1)^3 \leq 2$. Computing cubes, you find that $(1.2)^3 = 1.728$ and $(1.3)^3 = 2.197$. Therefore, $b_1 = 2$.

Next choose b_2 to be the largest digit such that $(1.2b_2)^3 \leq 2$. Successive trials show that $(1.25)^3 = 1.953125$ and $(1.26)^3 = 2.000376$, so that $b_2 = 5$.

Continuing, you find that $(1.259)^3 = 1.995616979$ and $(1.260)^3 = 2.000376000$; therefore $b_3 = 9$.

Repeating the procedure, you obtain two sequences:

$$1, 1.2, 1.25, 1.259, \ldots, S_m, \ldots$$

and

$$2, 1.3, 1.26, 1.260, \ldots, T_m, \ldots,$$

where $S_m = 1.b_1b_2 \ldots b_m \ (m \geq 1)$ is the largest decimal with $m + 1$ digits such that $S_m^3 \leq 2$, and where $T_m = S_m + \dfrac{1}{10^m}$ so that $T_m^3 > 2$.

The axiom of completeness ensures that $\lim_{m \to \infty} S_m$ is a real number; call it S. The theorem stated on page 97 implies that

$$\lim_{m \to \infty} T_m = \lim_{m \to \infty} S_n + \lim_{m \to \infty} \frac{1}{10^m} = S + 0 = S.$$

The same theorem also shows that $\lim_{m \to \infty} S_m^3 = S^3$ and $\lim_{m \to \infty} T_m^3 = S^3$. Moreover, since $S_m^3 \leq 2 < T_m^3$, $\lim_{m \to \infty} S_m^3 \leq 2 \leq \lim_{m \to \infty} T_m^3$, or $S^3 \leq 2 \leq S^3$. This means that $S^3 = 2$ and that S satisfies the given equation.

Thus, we have proved that there is a positive real number whose cube is 2 and whose decimal representation begins $1.259 \ldots$. Can you explain why the cube of no other positive number can be 2? (See Exercise 32, page 74.)

We have proved a special case of the following important theorem. A similar argument would establish the general result.

THEOREM   If $a \in \Re$, $a > 0$, and $n \in N$, then there exists a unique positive real number x satisfying the equation $x^n = a$.

We call the positive root of $x^n = a$, the positive **nth root of a** and denote it by the symbol $\sqrt[n]{a}$, called a **radical**. Usually n, the **root index**, which signifies the root denoted, is omitted from square-root radicals. For example, $\sqrt[4]{81} = 3$, $\sqrt{16} = 4$, $\sqrt[3]{\frac{1}{27}} = \frac{1}{3}$. For any positive integer n, we define $\sqrt[n]{0}$ to be 0. Thus, for $a \geq 0$, $\sqrt[n]{a}$ is the unique nonnegative number whose nth power is a.

From the laws of positive integral exponents (page 71) and the uniqueness of nonnegative nth roots, you can prove the properties of radicals stated in the following theorem.

THEOREM	If $n, m \in N$, $a, b \in \mathcal{R}$, and $a \geq 0$, $b \geq 0$, then

$$1. \quad \sqrt[n]{ab} = \sqrt[n]{a}\sqrt[n]{b} \qquad 3. \quad \sqrt[n]{\frac{a}{b}} = \frac{\sqrt[n]{a}}{\sqrt[n]{b}}, \text{ if } b \neq 0$$

$$2. \quad \sqrt[n]{a^m} = (\sqrt[n]{a})^m \qquad 4. \quad \sqrt[m]{\sqrt[n]{a}} = \sqrt[mn]{a}$$

Proof of (1). To prove the first property, you must show that $\sqrt[n]{a}\sqrt[n]{b}$ is the nonnegative number whose nth power is ab. First, $\sqrt[n]{a} \geq 0$ and $\sqrt[n]{b} \geq 0$; therefore, $\sqrt[n]{a}\sqrt[n]{b} \geq 0$. Next,

$$(\sqrt[n]{a} \cdot \sqrt[n]{b})^n = (\sqrt[n]{a})^n(\sqrt[n]{b})^n \quad \text{(Why?)}$$
$$= a \cdot b. \qquad \text{(Why?)}$$

This completes the proof. The proofs of the other properties are left as exercises. (Exercises 39–41, page 116.)

EXAMPLES.

$$\sqrt[3]{72} = \sqrt[3]{8}\sqrt[3]{9} = 2\sqrt[3]{9}$$

$$\sqrt{\frac{x^2}{50}} = \frac{\sqrt{x^2}}{\sqrt{50}} = \frac{|x|}{5\sqrt{2}} \cdot \frac{\sqrt{2}}{\sqrt{2}} = \frac{|x|\sqrt{2}}{10}$$

$$2\sqrt[4]{64t^8} - \sqrt[4]{4t^8} - \sqrt[4]{324} = 2\sqrt[4]{16t^8 \cdot 4} - t^2\sqrt[4]{4} - \sqrt[4]{81 \cdot 4}$$
$$= 4t^2\sqrt[4]{4} - t^2\sqrt[4]{4} - 3\sqrt[4]{4}$$
$$= 3t^2\sqrt[4]{4} - 3\sqrt[4]{4}, \quad \text{or} \quad (3t^2 - 3)\sqrt[4]{4}$$
$$= 3t^2\sqrt{2} - 3\sqrt{2} \quad \text{or} \quad (3t^2 - 3)\sqrt{2}$$

$$\frac{2}{\sqrt{3}+\sqrt{5}} = \frac{2}{\sqrt{3}+\sqrt{5}} \cdot \frac{\sqrt{3}-\sqrt{5}}{\sqrt{3}-\sqrt{5}} = \frac{2(\sqrt{3}-\sqrt{5})}{3-5}$$
$$= \sqrt{5} - \sqrt{3}$$

Exercises

A

1. Is $\sqrt{a^2} = a$ for all real values of a? Explain.

2. For what values of x is $\sqrt{(x-3)^2} = x - 3$ a true statement?

3. Express .0000284 in the form $p\left(\dfrac{1}{10}\right)^k$, where $1 \leq p < 10$ and k is an integer.

4. Is 1 an element of the solution set of $\sqrt{2x-1} = x - 2$?

Given $a = 2 + \sqrt{3}$ and $b = 2 - \sqrt{3}$. Find each number and state whether it is rational or irrational.

5. $a + b$ **7.** ab **9.** $a^2 - b^2$

6. $a - b$ **8.** $\sqrt{a} \cdot \sqrt{b}$ **10.** $\sqrt{a^2 + b^2}$

Using the approximations $\sqrt{2} \doteq 1.414$ and $\sqrt{3} \doteq 1.732$, find an approximation for the given number correct to three significant figures. (*Hint:* Where possible, first express the number in a simpler radical form.)

11. $2\sqrt{12}$ **14.** $(\sqrt{3} + \sqrt{2})^2$ **17.** $\dfrac{4}{\sqrt{3} + 2}$

12. $(3\sqrt{2})^3$ **15.** $5\sqrt{\frac{1}{3}}$ **18.** $\dfrac{\sqrt{3}}{\sqrt{2} - 1}$

13. $\dfrac{6}{\sqrt{2}}$ **16.** $\sqrt{18} + \sqrt{12}$

Name a rational number r and an irrational number s lying between the given numbers.

19. $1\frac{7}{10}$ and $\sqrt{3}$ **21.** $\sqrt{2}$ and $\sqrt{3}$

20. $\frac{3}{4}$ and $\frac{7}{8}$ **22.** $\frac{1}{2}$ and $\sqrt{.27}$

Using the approximation method described in this section, find the first three digits in the decimal representation for each number.

23. $\sqrt{5}$ **24.** $\sqrt[3]{7}$ **25.** $8 + \sqrt{10}$ **26.** $4 - \sqrt[3]{3}$

Perform the indicated operation and express the result in simple radical form.

27. $(2\sqrt{3})(4\sqrt{6})$ **30.** $6\sqrt{\frac{1}{3}} - \dfrac{9}{\sqrt{3}}$

28. $(3\sqrt{2} + 1)^2$ **31.** $\dfrac{5}{2 - \sqrt{3}}$

29. $(3\sqrt{2} + 1)(5\sqrt{3} - 1)$ **32.** $\dfrac{7 + \sqrt{5}}{3 - \sqrt{5}}$

Find the positive root(s) of each equation correct to tenths.

33. $2x^2 = 5$ **35.** $(x - 2)^2 = \sqrt{2}$

34. $(2x - 1)^2 = 8$ **36.** $(x - 1)^3 = 10$

B   **37.** Prove: If r is an irrational number > 0, then $\sqrt[n]{r}$ is an irrational number.

38. Prove: The reciprocal of an irrational number is an irrational number.

Prove the following properties of radicals (see theorem on page 114) for $m, n \in N$, $a \in \mathcal{R}$, $b \in \mathcal{R}$, and $a \geq 0, b > 0$.

39. $\sqrt[n]{a^m} = (\sqrt[n]{a})^m$

41. $\sqrt[m]{\sqrt[n]{a}} = \sqrt[mn]{a}$

40. $\sqrt[n]{\dfrac{a}{b}} = \dfrac{\sqrt[n]{a}}{\sqrt[n]{b}}$

42. $\sqrt[km]{a^{kn}} = \sqrt[m]{a^n}$

43. Given the irrational number $\sqrt{a}$, prove that $1 + \sqrt{a}$ cannot be rational.

44. Given the irrational numbers $(a + b\sqrt{x})$ and $(c + d\sqrt{x})$ where a, b, c, and d are nonzero rational numbers, determine under what conditions the product of the two numbers is rational.

45. Given $a > 0, b > 0$, prove $\dfrac{2ab}{a + b} \leq \sqrt{ab}$.

46. Express $\sqrt[3]{2}$ and $\sqrt{3}$ as radicals having the same root index.

47. Given a line segment of unit length, describe a method by which you can construct a segment of length $\sqrt{5}$.

48. If $b > 0$ and $\dfrac{1}{\sqrt{3}} + \dfrac{1}{\sqrt{b}} > \sqrt{3} + \sqrt{b}$, find the range of values of b.

C **49.** Form an equation with integral coefficients which has $2 + \sqrt[3]{3}$ as one of its roots.

50. Find the sum of the infinite geometric series $(\sqrt{3} + \sqrt{2}) + 1 + (\sqrt{3} - \sqrt{2}) + \cdots$ and express your result in a form containing no radicals in the denominator.

Chapter Summary

1. To prove a statement by **mathematical induction**, you must show two facts: (1) the statement is true for 1, and (2) whenever the statement is true for x, it is true for $x + 1$.

2. A **sequence** is a set of numbers listed in a particular order. You can define a sequence **recursively** by (1) stating the first term, and (2) providing a **recursion formula** that relates each term with its successor. A **series** is an expression for the sum of the terms in a sequence, and the Greek letter Σ is used to denote both a series and its sum.

3. Any sequence in which each term after the first is the sum of a given constant and the preceding term is an **arithmetic progression** (A. P.). The **nth term** in an A. P. is given by $t_n = a + (n - 1)d$, where a is the first term, n is the number of terms, and d is the common difference. The terms between any two given terms in an A. P. are called the **arithmetic means** of the given terms. An **arithmetic series** is a series whose terms are in A. P., and the sum of the first n terms in such a series is given by $S_n = \dfrac{n}{2}[2a + (n - 1)d]$, or $S_n = \dfrac{n}{2}[a + t_n]$.

4. A **geometric progression** (G. P.) is a sequence in which each term after the first is the product of a given constant and the preceding term. The nth term in a G. P. is given by $t_n = ar^{n-1}$, and the sum of n terms of a **geometric series** is given, for $r \neq 1$, by $S_n = \dfrac{a - ar^n}{1 - r}$ or $S_n = \dfrac{a - t_n r}{1 - r}$, where a is the first term, n is the number of terms, and r is the common ratio. Terms between two given terms in a G. P. are called **geometric means** of the given terms.

5. The symbol $n!$ denotes the product $n(n - 1)(n - 2)\ldots 3 \cdot 2 \cdot 1$, and the symbol $\dbinom{n}{k}$ is defined by $\dbinom{n}{k} = \dfrac{n(n - 1)\ldots(n - k + 1)}{k!}$, or $\dbinom{n}{k} = \dfrac{n!}{k!(n - k)!}$. The **Binomial Theorem** asserts that

$$(a + b)^n = \sum_{k=0}^{n} \binom{n}{k} a^{n-k} b^k.$$

6. A sequence $a_1, a_2, a_3, \ldots, a_n$ is said to **converge**, or to **approach a limit** A, if, for each $h > 0$, there exists a positive number M such that

$$|a_n - A| < h, \text{ for all } n > M.$$

A sequence that does not converge is said to **diverge**.

7. The **infinite geometric series** $\sum_{i=1}^{\infty} ar^{i-1}$ converges for all $|r| < 1$; otherwise it diverges unless $a = 0$. The sum of a convergent infinite geometric series is given by $S = \lim_{n \to \infty} S_n = \dfrac{a}{1 - r}$. Any **decimal numeral** is expressible as a geometric series. Any *rational* number is expressible by a **repeating** decimal numeral.

8. When there exists a number equal to or greater than the absolute value of every term in a sequence, the sequence is **bounded**. If each term in a sequence is less than or equal to its successor, the sequence is said to be **nondecreasing**. The **axiom of completeness** asserts that every bounded, nondecreasing sequence of real numbers converges to a real number.

9. Every positive real number has a unique **positive nth root**.

Chapter Test

3–1   **1.** Prove by the method of mathematical induction:

$$1 + 4 + 7 + \cdots + (3n - 2) = \frac{n(3n - 1)}{2}.$$

3–2   **2.** Write the series $\displaystyle\sum_{k=1}^{4} (k^2 - k)$ in expanded form. $0+2+6+12$

3–3   **3.** Insert three arithmetic means between 18 and -6. $18, 12, 6, 0, -6$

     4. Find the sum of the first twenty positive odd integers. 400

3–4   **5.** The fifth term of a G. P. is -2 and the seventh term is -8. Find the first term. $-\frac{1}{8}$

     6. Find the sum of the geometric series $\displaystyle\sum_{k=1}^{5} 3(-\tfrac{1}{3})^{k-1}$. $\frac{61}{27}$

3–5   **7.** Write the first three terms in the expansion of $(2x - 3y)^5$. $32x^5 - 240x^4y$ $720x^3y^2 -$

3–6   **8.** Given $a_n = \dfrac{n(n - 2)}{3n^2 + 2n}$, find $\displaystyle\lim_{n \to \infty} a_n$. $\frac{1}{3}$

3–7   **9.** Write the decimal equivalent of $\frac{2}{7}$. $.285714$

    10. Find the sum of the infinite geometric progression: $4, -2, 1, \ldots$. $\frac{8}{3}$

3–8   **11.** Find the first three terms of the sequence of partial sums of the series $\frac{1}{3} + \frac{1}{9} + \cdots + (\frac{1}{3})^n$.

    12. Write a convergent geometric series whose sum bounds the series

$$\sum_{n=1}^{\infty} \left(\frac{1}{5^n + 1} \right).$$

3–9   **13.** Name an irrational number lying between $\sqrt{3}$ and $\sqrt{5}$.

    14. Find the positive root of $x^3 = 11$ correct to hundredths without using tables.

Reading List

DeNoya, Louis E. *The Geometric Progression Presented Geometrically*, The Mathematics Teacher, vol. 56, pp. 146–147, 1963.

Freitag, Herta Taussig, and Arthur H. Freitag. *The Number Story*. Washington, D.C.: National Council of Teachers of Mathematics, 1960.

Henken, Leon. *On Mathematical Induction*. American Mathematical Monthly, vol. 67, pp. 323–338, 1960.

Niven, Ivan. *Numbers: Rational and Irrational*. New York: Random House, Inc., 1961.

Ringenberg, Lawrence A. *A Portrait of 2*. Washington, D.C.: National Council of Teachers of Mathematics, 1956.

Richard Dedekind

How would you define an irrational number? Perhaps, recalling the discussion in this chapter, you would say that it is a real number with an infinite, non-repeating decimal representation or, alternatively, a real number which cannot be expressed in the form $\frac{a}{b}$, where a, b are integers. You may have encountered both definitions. Probably, though, you are not familiar with the definition which led to our present understanding of irrational numbers, the one given by the German mathematician Richard Dedekind (1831–1916) in his book *Continuity and Irrational Numbers*.

Although the existence of irrational numbers had been established by Greek philosophers in the 5th century B.C., Dedekind was the first to publish (in 1872) a mathematically rigorous definition of irrational numbers and an explanation of their place in the real-number system. Dedekind's definition is essentially this: Suppose that the set of all rational numbers is divided into two non-empty subsets, A and B, with every number in A less than every number in B. This division is called a *cut*. Then there is some number *t*, such that every number less than *t* is in A and every number greater than *t* is in B. The number *t* itself may belong to A or to B. If it does, it is a rational number. But it may also happen that *t* does not belong to either A or B. In this case *t* is an irrational number defined by the specified cut.

Now consider an application. Let A be the set of all negative numbers and of all nonnegative numbers whose squares are less than 7, and B, the set of all positive numbers whose squares are greater than 7. What is *t*?

By applying his interpretation of irrational numbers, Dedekind was able to demonstrate the completeness of the real number line. He filled in the "holes" in the system of rational numbers with irrational numbers.

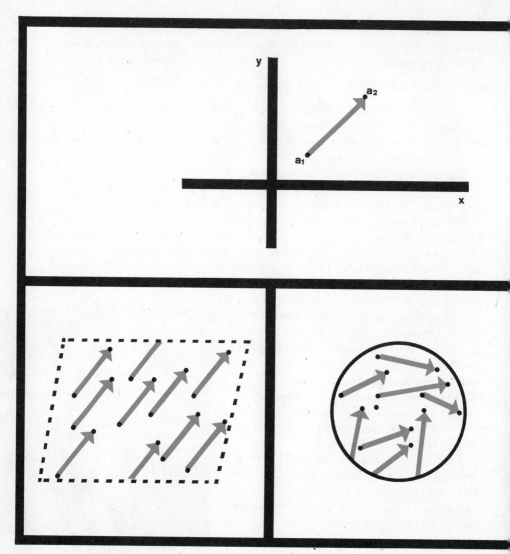

A vector can be used to represent the mapping of a point a_1 into a point a_2. In a mapping of a plane onto itself, every point can be mapped into a point other than itself. In a continuous mapping of a circle and its interior, a subset of a plane, onto itself, some point will always be mapped into itself.

The Algebra of Vectors

Physical quantities such as temperature, length, time, and mass can be represented in terms of a single real number on a linear scale; they are called scalar quantities. Concepts like velocity, acceleration, force, and displacement, on the other hand, require two or more numbers for their expression; they are called vector quantities. The mathematics needed to study these latter quantities is the algebra of vectors. In this chapter, you will study a few of the basic concepts of this algebra, and will begin by considering some properties of ordered pairs of real numbers.

NUMBER PAIRS AND GEOMETRY

4–1 Ordered Pairs and Points

The city index of an automobile tour map usually lists a letter and a numeral enabling you to locate a horizontal strip (identified by letter) and a vertical strip (identified by numeral) within which a given city lies. The map shown is partitioned into 5 horizontal and 4 vertical strips, and contains twenty sectors, each identified by ordered pairs of characters such as $(B, 3)$ or $(E, 2)$. In each ordered pair the *first entry*, or *first coordinate*, is a letter chosen from the set $K = \{A, B, C, D, E\}$, and the *second entry*, or *second coordinate*, is a numeral belonging to $M = \{1, 2, 3, 4\}$. The set of all such ordered pairs is called the Cartesian product of the sets K and M, and is denoted by $K \times M$ (read "K cross M"). Thus $K \times M$

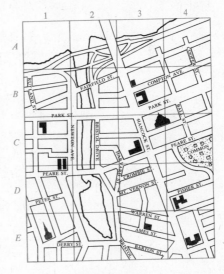

$$= \{(A, 1), (A, 2), (A, 3), (A, 4),$$
$$(B, 1), (B, 2), (B, 3), (B, 4),$$
$$(C, 1), (C, 2), (C, 3), (C, 4),$$
$$(D, 1), (D, 2), (D, 3), (D, 4),$$
$$(E, 1), (E, 2), (E, 3), (E, 4)\}.$$

Figure 4–1

121

In general, the Cartesian product of the sets K and M is defined by:

$$K \times M = \{(x, y): x \in K \text{ and } y \in M\}.$$

The Cartesian product in which we shall be most interested in this book is the set $\Re \times \Re$, where, of course, $\Re$ is the set of real numbers.

We define equality in $\Re \times \Re$ as follows:

Two ordered pairs in $\Re \times \Re$, (x, y) and (a, b), are **equal** if and only if $x = a$ and $y = b$.

Thus, $(7 + 1, 2 \cdot 0) = (8, 0)$, but $(0, 8) \neq (8, 0)$.

EXAMPLE 1. Determine the set of all real numbers x for which

$$(x^2 - 2x, x + 3) = (0, 5).$$

Solution: $(x^2 - 2x, x + 3) = (0, 5)$ if and only if:

$$x^2 - 2x = 0 \qquad \text{and} \quad x + 3 = 5$$

that is, $$x(x - 2) = 0 \qquad \text{and} \qquad x = 2$$

that is, $$x = 0 \quad \text{or} \quad x = 2 \quad \text{and} \qquad x = 2.$$

Thus the only possible value of x is 2. To verify that 2 satisfies the equation, note that $[2^2 - 2(2), 2 + 3] = (0, 5)$.

$\therefore \{x: (x^2 - 2x, x + 3) = (0, 5)\} = \{2\}$, **Answer.**

EXAMPLE 2. Give a roster of $S = \{(x, y): (x - 2y, x - y) = (3, 4)\}$.

Solution: $(x - 2y, x - y) = (3, 4)$ is true if and only if

$$x - 2y = 3 \quad \text{and} \quad x - y = 4.$$

Solving this system, you find that it is equivalent to $x = 5$ *and* $y = 1$.

Since $$[5 - 2(1), 5 - (1)] = (3, 4),$$

$$S = \{(5, 1)\}, \textbf{ Answer.}$$

You can easily verify that the equality of ordered pairs obeys the reflexive, symmetric, and transitive laws just as the equality of real numbers does. (Exercises 20, 21, and 22, page 124.)

Just as real numbers can be associated with the points on a geometric line, ordered pairs of real numbers can be pictured as points in a geometric plane. To represent the members of $\mathcal{R} \times \mathcal{R}$, think of a plane determined by two lines, or **axes**, intersecting at right angles at a point O, the **origin**. One axis is taken to be horizontal (the x-axis) and the other to be vertical (the y-axis). Next, using convenient units of length (not necessarily the same), make each axis a number line with O as its zero point and with positive and negative numbers assigned as shown in Figure 4–2. The four regions, or **quadrants**, into which the plane is separated by the axes are also indicated in the figure.

To associate an ordered pair of real numbers (a, b) with a particular point in the plane, you can draw a vertical line through the graph of a on the horizontal axis and a horizontal line through b on the vertical axis. Figure 4–3 illustrates the case $a = -1$ and $b = 3$. P, the point of intersection of these lines, is the **graph** of (a, b).

By reversing this procedure, and starting with a point P in a plane containing two perpendicular number lines, you can determine its **rectangular** or **Cartesian coordinates**. Thus, the *first coordinate* or **abscissa** of P is the number associated with the point in which the vertical line through P intersects the horizontal axis; the *second coordinate* or **ordinate** of P is the number associated with the point in which the horizontal line through P intersects the vertical axis.

As you are aware from your earlier study of algebra, this pairing of the elements of the set of points in a plane with the elements of $\mathcal{R} \times \mathcal{R}$ is called a *rectangular* or *Cartesian coordinate system*.

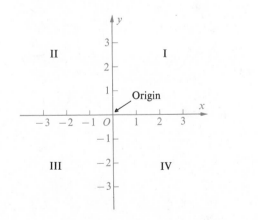

Figure 4–2

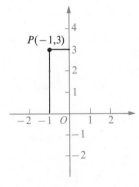

Figure 4–3

Exercises

Unless otherwise stated, assume that lowercase letters a, b, c, ... represent real numbers and capital letters A, B, C, ... represent sets of real numbers.

1. If $K = \{a\}$ and $M = \{b\}$, specify $K \times M$ and $M \times K$ by roster.
2. If $K \times M = \{(a, b), (a, c)\}$, specify K and M by roster.
3. If K is not the empty set, is K a subset of $K \times M$? Explain.
4. If K is the empty set and M a nonempty set, is $K \times M$ a set of ordered pairs? Why or why not?
5. Find x and y if $(x + 3, y - 2)$ and $(6, 4)$ have the same point as graph.
6. Name the quadrant in which the graph of (a, b) lies if $b > 0$ and $ab < 0$.
7. Is $(-3, 2) \in \{(x, y): 2x - 3y = 12\}$?
8. If $(2, -1) \in \{(x, y): 2x + ky = 16\}$, determine k.
9. Is the solution set of $\{(x, y): 2x + 3y = 18\}$ a finite set? Why or why not?
10. If $K = \{0\}$ and $S = \{0\}$, name the point that is the graph of $K \times S$.
11. If the graph of (a, b) is a point on the y-axis, which coordinate of (a, b) is zero?
12. Given: $I = \{$positive integers$\}$; $K = \{$negative integers$\}$. In which quadrant will the graph of each element of $I \times K$ lie? of $K \times I$?
13. Given: $X = \{$real numbers$\}$; $Y = \{$irrational numbers$\}$. Will there be a one-to-one correspondence between the elements of $X \times Y$ and all the points in a coordinate plane? Explain.

In Exercises 14–19, specify by roster (**a**) the set $X \times Y$; (**b**) the set $Y \times X$. (**c**) Represent the elements of $X \times Y$ as points in a coordinate plane.

14. $X = \{3, 2\}$, $Y = \{-1\}$
15. $X = \{2, -1\}$, $Y = \{2, 3\}$
16. $X = \{0, 1\}$, $Y = \{0, -2\}$

17. $X = \{-2, 0, 1\}$, $Y = \{3\}$
18. $X = \{1, 2, 3\}$, $Y = \{-2\}$
19. $X = \{-1, 0, 1\}$, $Y = \{2, 3\}$

On the basis of the definition of equality of ordered pairs, show that the following equality properties hold for ordered pairs of real numbers.

20. $(a, b) = (a, b)$. (*Reflexive*)
21. If $(a, b) = (c, d)$, then $(c, d) = (a, b)$. (*Symmetric*)
22. If $(a, b) = (c, d)$ and $(c, d) = (r, s)$, then $(a, b) = (r, s)$. (*Transitive*)

Find the values of x and y for which each of the following is true.

23. $(3x - 2, y + 1) = (7, 4)$
24. $(x^2, 2y - 1) = (9, 3)$
25. $(x - 1, \sqrt{y}) = (-4, 3)$
26. $(|x|, |y|) = (3, 5)$

27. $(2x - 1, x + 2) = (3, 4)$
28. $(x^2 + 3x, 2x + 1) = (0, 7)$
29. $(x^2 + 2x - 3, 2x + 7) = (0, 1)$
30. $(x^2 + x - 4, 3x - 2) = (2, 4)$

31. Under what circumstances is $A \times B = B \times A$ a true statement?

32. A is a finite set containing n elements and B a finite set containing s elements. How many elements are contained in $A \times B$? in $B \times A$?

33. $M \times N$ is a finite set containing $(n + 1)!$ ordered pairs. If M contains $n!$ elements, how many elements are contained in N?

34. The ordered pairs $(3, 2)$, $(4, 1)$, and $(5, 3)$ are among the elements in the set $X \times Y$. Name six other ordered pairs belonging to $X \times Y$.

Specify K by roster, given that

35. $K = \{(x, y): (x + y, 2x - y) = (6, 3)\}$

36. $K = \{(x, y): (2x + y, x + y) = (4, 6)\}$

37. $K = \{(x, y): (y - 2, 2x - 1) = (x, y)\}$

38. $K = \{(x, y): (y - x^2, y - x) = (0, 0)\}$

39. $K = \{(x, y): (|x + 1|, |y + 1|) = (2, 3)\}$

40. If $R = \{1, 2, 4\}$ and $S = \{2, 4, 5\}$, specify the set $(R \cap S) \times (R \cup S)$ by roster.

4–2 Ordered Pairs, Displacements, and Arrows

In addition to associating each real number with a point on a geometric line, you can also associate each real number with a **displacement** or change of position along a geometric line. Thus, while the numbers 2 and -2 are associated with specific points on a number line, you can also associate them with a movement of two units from any point on the line, 2 being associated with a movement in the positive direction and -2 with a movement in the negative direction. Figure 4–4 depicts several such displacements, or

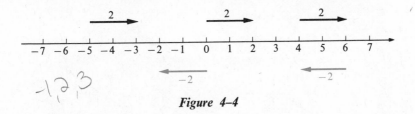

Figure 4–4

translations as they are sometimes called. More generally, the real number $c - a$ can be associated with the displacement from the point located at a on the number line to the point c on the number line, and the real number $a - c$ with a displacement from c to a (Figure 4–5). Clearly, each real number can be associated with infinitely many specific displacements. For

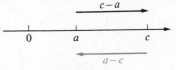

Figure 4–5

example, 2 can be associated with the displacement from -5 to -3, from 0 to 2, from 4 to 6, or, in general, from a to c whenever $c - a = 2$. Such displacements are generally represented in graphical form by arrows, with the arrowhead showing the direction of movement.

Representing real numbers by displacements on the number line suggests interpreting ordered pairs of real numbers as displacements in the coordinate plane. Given the ordered pair $(3, 2)$, you can represent its first entry, 3, by a displacement on the horizontal axis, say from $(5, 0)$ to $(8, 0)$; and you can picture its second entry, 2, by a displacement on the vertical axis from, say,

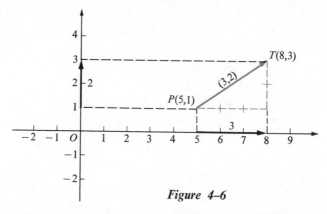

Figure 4–6

$(0, 1)$ to $(0, 3)$ (Figure 4–6). Now, if you draw an arrow $\overrightarrow{PT}$ directed from the point P with coordinates $(5, 1)$ to the point T with coordinates $(8, 3)$, then this arrow can be associated with the ordered pair $(3, 2)$. Do you see that, starting at the *initial point P* of the arrow, you can locate the *terminal point T* by moving horizontally 3 units to the *right* and then vertically 2 units *upward*? As indicated in Figure 4–7, you can, of course, associate $(3, 2)$ with

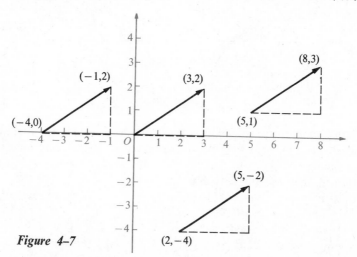

Figure 4–7

a displacement from any point (a, b) along a straight line to the point $(a + 3, b + 2)$, and you can represent this displacement by drawing an arrow from any point (a, b) to $(a + 3, b + 2)$.

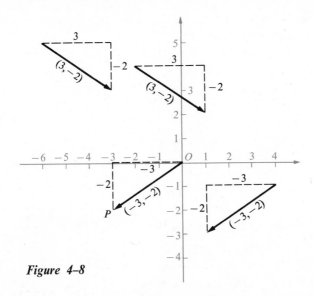

Figure 4–8

Figure 4–8 shows two different arrows representing $(-3, -2)$, as well as two corresponding to $(3, -2)$. In general, you can represent the ordered pair (x, y) by an arrow from an arbitrarily selected point (a, b) to the point $(a + x, b + y)$. To represent $(0, 0)$, you think of any "arrow" whose initial and terminal points coincide; or, in other words, you think of any single point.

Notice that when the initial point of an arrow is the origin, the coordinates of its terminal point are also the coordinates of the ordered pair which it represents. We call this arrow the **standard representation** of the ordered pair, and the arrow is said to be in **standard position**. For example, in Figure 4–8, $\overrightarrow{OP}$ is the standard representation of $(-3, -2)$.

EXAMPLE 1. If $\overrightarrow{OP}$ and $\overrightarrow{OT}$ are the standard representations of $(2, 3)$ and $(-1, 5)$, respectively, what displacement does $\overrightarrow{TP}$ represent? Sketch $\overrightarrow{OP}$, $\overrightarrow{OT}$, and $\overrightarrow{TP}$.

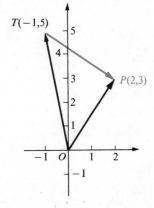

Solution: P and T have coordinates $(2, 3)$ and $(-1, 5)$.

$\therefore \overrightarrow{TP}$ represents

$[2 - (-1), 3 - 5] = (3, -2)$.

EXAMPLE 2. If $\overrightarrow{OR}$ represents $(-2, -4)$ and $\overrightarrow{RS}$ represents $(-1, 7)$, what displacement does $\overrightarrow{OS}$ represent? Sketch $\overrightarrow{OR}$, $\overrightarrow{RS}$, and $\overrightarrow{OS}$.

Solution: R has coordinates $(-2, -4)$. If S has coordinates (c, d), $\overrightarrow{RS}$ represents $[c - (-2),\ d - (-4)]$. But $\overrightarrow{RS}$ represents $(-1, 7)$.
$\therefore (c + 2, d + 4) = (-1, 7)$.

$$c + 2 = -1 \qquad d + 4 = 7$$
$$c = -3 \qquad d = 3$$

$\therefore \overrightarrow{OS}$ represents $(-3, 3)$.

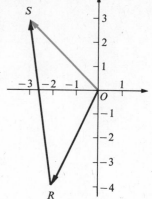

Exercises

Exercises 1–6 refer to the given diagram.

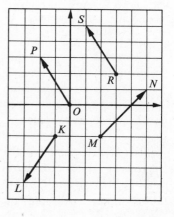

(A)

1. Name the ordered pair whose representation is shown in standard position.

2. Name two arrows which represent the same ordered pair.

3. Name the ordered pair represented by $\overrightarrow{KL}$.

4. If the ordered pair represented by $\overrightarrow{MN}$ were shown in standard position, what would be the coordinates of its terminal point?

5. If the ordered pair which $\overrightarrow{RS}$ represents were to be represented by an arrow with terminal point at L, what would be the coordinates of the arrow's initial point?

6. For which of the ordered pairs represented is the first coordinate less than 0?

Let $\overrightarrow{PT}$ be a representation of the ordered pair $(-2, 3)$. Find the coordinates of T when the coordinates of P are

7. $(0, 0)$	**9.** $(2, -1)$	**11.** $(-2, -3)$
8. $(5, 2)$	**10.** $(-3, 4)$	**12.** (a, b)

Name the ordered pair which $\overrightarrow{RS}$ represents when the respective coordinates of R and S are

13. $(3, 2); (4, 6)$	**15.** $(0, 0); (3, -2)$
14. $(-2, 1); (3, -5)$	**16.** $(0, 3); (5, -2)$

1-6all
7-230

17. $(2, 3); (2, 3)$

18. $(a, b); (2a, 3b)$

19. $(a, b); (c, d)$

20. $(a + k, b + t); (2a - k, 2b + 3t)$

Let $\overrightarrow{OR}$ and $\overrightarrow{OS}$ be the respective standard representations of the ordered pairs named. In each exercise **(a)** sketch $\overrightarrow{OR}$, $\overrightarrow{OS}$, and $\overrightarrow{RS}$; and **(b)** name the ordered pair represented by $\overrightarrow{SR}$.

B

21. $(2, 3); (-2, 1)$ **23.** $(-3, 2); (5, -3)$ **25.** $(3, 4); (-3, -4)$

22. $(3, -5); (4, 2)$ **24.** $(-1, -2); (-1, -2)$ **26.** $(-2, 3); (2, -3)$

Let $\overrightarrow{OT}$ be the standard representation of the first ordered pair named. Let $\overrightarrow{TS}$ be a representation of the second ordered pair. In each exercise **(a)** name the ordered pair represented by $\overrightarrow{OS}$, **(b)** sketch $\overrightarrow{OT}$, $\overrightarrow{TS}$, and $\overrightarrow{OS}$.

27. $(5, 1); (-2, 1)$ **29.** $(3, -1); (2, 3)$ **31.** $(1, 0); (0, 1)$

28. $(-2, 3); (3, 2)$ **30.** $(-2, 3); (3, -2)$ **32.** $(5, 3); (-5, -3)$

C

33. Given three points R, S, and T with respective coordinates (a_1, b_1), (a_2, b_2), and (a_3, b_3). Find the coordinates of a point X such that:

  a. $\overrightarrow{RS}$ and $\overrightarrow{TX}$ represent the same ordered pair.

  b. $\overrightarrow{RS}$ and $\overrightarrow{XT}$ represent the same ordered pair.

  c. $\overrightarrow{RX}$ and $\overrightarrow{TS}$ represent the same ordered pair.

34. Given three points A, B, C in a coordinate plane. Prove that there is one and only one point D such that $\overrightarrow{AB}$ and $\overrightarrow{CD}$ represent the same ordered pair.

THE ALGEBRA OF NUMBER PAIRS

$-2, 3 - 2, -1 = -4, 2$

4–3 Vector Addition

Interpreting real numbers as displacements on a line provides a way of visualizing addition. To add 2 to 4, for example, you can start at 0 and move *4* units to the *right*, and then move *2* more units to the *right*. Following one displacement by the other has the total effect, shown in Figure 4–9, of a shift to the *right* of 6 units; thus, $4 + 2 = 6$. To picture the fact that $-4 + (-2) = -6$, you can first move *4* units *left* from 0, to -4, and then from -4 move 2 units to the *left*. The effect is the same as a displacement of 6 units to the *left* (Figure 4–10).

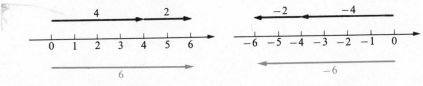

Figure 4–9   Figure 4–10

Although it is convenient to represent the first term in the sum by an arrow from the origin, it is not necessary. In Figures 4–11 and 4–12, showing the sums $4 + (-2) = 2$ and $-4 + 2 = -2$, respectively, the first displacement is measured from the point 1.

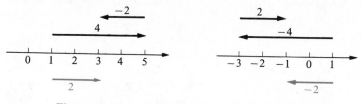

Figure 4–11   *Figure 4–12*

To picture the sum $a + c$ on the number line, you take the following steps (Figure 4–13):

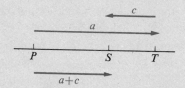

Figure 4–13

1. Draw an arrow $\overrightarrow{PT}$ representing a.

2. From T draw an arrow $\overrightarrow{TS}$ representing c.

3. The arrow $\overrightarrow{PS}$ represents $a + c$.

Now suppose that, in a plane, $\overrightarrow{PT}$ is an arrow representing the ordered pair (a, b) and $\overrightarrow{TS}$ represents (c, d). Figure 4–14 shows that $\overrightarrow{PS}$ represents the ordered pair $(a + c,\ b + d)$ and motivates the definition of **addition of ordered pairs** which follows.

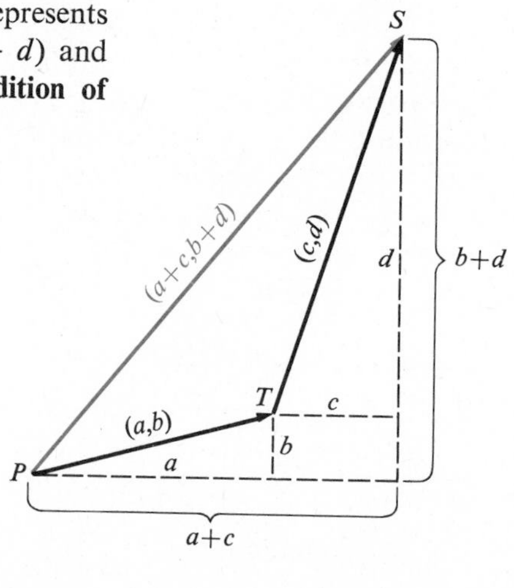

Figure 4–14

If $(a, b) \in \mathcal{R} \times \mathcal{R}$, $(c, d) \in \mathcal{R} \times \mathcal{R}$, then $(a, b) + (c, d) = (a + c, b + d)$.

For example:
$$(3, 5) + (-2, 1) = [3 + (-2), 5 + 1] = (1, 6)$$
$$(4, -8) + (0, 0) = (4 + 0, -8 + 0) = (4, -8)$$
$$(-2, -3) + (2, 3) = (-2 + 2, -3 + 3) = (0, 0)$$

Having defined an operation, addition, over $\mathcal{R} \times \mathcal{R}$, let us now introduce a new name for an element of $\mathcal{R} \times \mathcal{R}$. We will call any ordered pair of real numbers (x, y) a **vector**. Thus the sum of two ordered pairs in $\mathcal{R} \times \mathcal{R}$ will be called a **vector sum**, and the operation associated with the sum, **vector addition**.

A variable whose domain is a set of vectors will be denoted by boldface symbols* such as $\mathbf{v}$ or $\mathbf{F}$, while lightface symbols will stand for real numbers, which we shall call **scalars**. For example, if $\mathbf{v}$ denotes a vector whose entries are equal integers, then $\mathbf{v} \in \{(0, 0), (1, 1), (-1, -1), (2, 2), \ldots\}$; that is, $\mathbf{v} \in \{(x, y): x \text{ and } y \text{ are integers and } x = y\}$.

Is $\mathcal{R} \times \mathcal{R}$ closed under vector addition? Since sums of real numbers are real numbers, the definition of vector addition implies that the sum of vectors in $\mathcal{R} \times \mathcal{R}$ is a vector in $\mathcal{R} \times \mathcal{R}$. It is also easy to see that equal vectors may be substituted for each other in a sum. Below is an argument proving the substitution property of vector addition.

THEOREM   If $\mathbf{s}$, $\mathbf{t}$, $\mathbf{u}$, and $\mathbf{v}$ are vectors, and $\mathbf{s} = \mathbf{u}$ and $\mathbf{t} = \mathbf{v}$, then $\mathbf{s} + \mathbf{t} = \mathbf{u} + \mathbf{v}$.

Proof:

There exist real numbers, $s_1, s_2, t_1, t_2,$ $u_1, u_2, v_1,$ and $v_2,$ such that $\mathbf{s} = (s_1, s_2),$ $\mathbf{t} = (t_1, t_2),$ $\mathbf{u} = (u_1, u_2),$ $\mathbf{v} = (v_1, v_2).$	Definition of a vector.
$(s_1, s_2) = (u_1, u_2)$ and $(t_1, t_2) = (v_1, v_2).$	Hypothesis.
$\therefore s_1 = u_1, s_2 = u_2;$ $t_1 = v_1, t_2 = v_2.$	Def. of equality of vectors.
$s_1 + t_1 = u_1 + v_1,$ $s_2 + t_2 = u_2 + v_2.$	Substitution Axiom.
$\therefore (s_1 + t_1, s_2 + t_2)$ $= (u_1 + v_1, u_2 + v_2)$	Def. of equality of vectors.
$\mathbf{s} + \mathbf{t} = (s_1 + t_1, s_2 + t_2)$ and $(u_1 + v_1, u_2 + v_2) = \mathbf{u} + \mathbf{v}$	Def. of vector addition.
$\mathbf{s} + \mathbf{t} = \mathbf{u} + \mathbf{v}$	Transitive property of $=$.

---

* Symbols such as $\vec{F}, \vec{v},$ or $\overrightarrow{F}$ are also used as vector variables.

You can similarly deduce the commutative and associative properties of vector addition from the corresponding properties of addition of real numbers. Figures 4–15 and 4–16 illustrate these properties in terms of

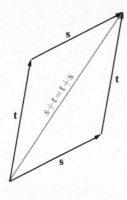

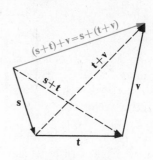

Figure 4–15   *Figure 4–16*

arrows. Figure 4–15 also suggests why vector addition is sometimes called "addition according to the parallelogram law."

Since addition of vectors is associative, the sum of three or more vectors can be defined simply as the vector whose first entry is the sum of the first entries of the given vectors and whose second entry is the sum of the second entries.

EXAMPLE 1. Given $\mathbf{u} = (4, 4)$, $\mathbf{v} = (2, -2)$, $\mathbf{t} = (-3, 0)$, determine $\mathbf{s} = \mathbf{u} + \mathbf{v} + \mathbf{t}$, and represent $\mathbf{u}$, $\mathbf{v}$, $\mathbf{t}$, and $\mathbf{s}$ by arrows in the coordinate plane.

Solution: $\mathbf{u} + \mathbf{v} + \mathbf{t} = (4 + 2 - 3, 4 - 2 + 0)$

$\therefore \mathbf{s} = \mathbf{u} + \mathbf{v} + \mathbf{t} = (3, 2)$, **Answer.**

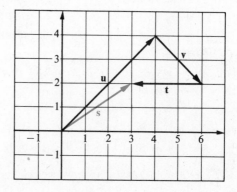

EXAMPLE 2. A psychologist studying communications in a small group lists as the respective entries of a vector the number of times a certain man speaks and the number of times the man is addressed. If the following vectors comprise the data collected for this man during four observation periods, give the vector representing the total in each communication category: $(5, 4)$, $(2, 2)$, $(6, 3)$, $(0, 0)$.

Solution: $(5, 4) + (2, 2) + (6, 3) + (0, 0)$
$$= (5 + 2 + 6 + 0, 4 + 2 + 3 + 0)$$
$$= (13, 9), \textbf{Answer.}$$

Do you see that $(0, 0)$, also denoted by **0**, serves as the identity element for vector addition? For all real numbers v_1 and v_2, you have

$$(v_1, v_2) + (0, 0) = (v_1 + 0, v_2 + 0) = (v_1, v_2)$$

and

$$(0, 0) + (v_1, v_2) = (0 + v_1, 0 + v_2) = (v_1, v_2).$$

Thus, $(0, 0)$ is the identity element for vector addition.

Does each vector **v** in $\Re \times \Re$ have an additive inverse $-\textbf{v}$? A vector (v_1, v_2) has an additive inverse if and only if there exist real numbers x and y such that

$$(v_1, v_2) + (x, y) = (0, 0).$$

This means $v_1 + x = 0$ and $v_2 + y = 0$. Since every real number has a unique negative, these equations have unique solutions, namely $-v_1$ and $-v_2$, respectively. Thus, $(-v_1, -v_2)$ is the **additive inverse**, or **negative**, of (v_1, v_2); that is, $(-v_1, -v_2) = -(v_1, v_2)$.

Can you explain why the arrows $\overrightarrow{PS}$ and $\overrightarrow{SP}$ in Figure 4–17 represent vectors that are additive inverses of each other?

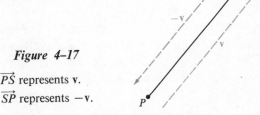

Figure 4–17

$\overrightarrow{PS}$ represents **v**.
$\overrightarrow{SP}$ represents $-\textbf{v}$.

The list on the following page summarizes the basic properties of vector addition. (See Exercises 43, 44, 46, pages 136, 137.)

Properties of Vector Addition

Let **s**, **t**, **u**, and **v** denote any elements of $\Re \times \Re$.

CLOSURE PROPERTY   **s** + **t** belongs to $\Re \times \Re$.

SUBSTITUTION PROPERTY   If **s** = **u** and **t** = **v**, **s** + **t** = **u** + **v**.

COMMUTATIVE PROPERTY   **s** + **t** = **t** + **s**.

ASSOCIATIVE PROPERTY   (**s** + **t**) + **u** = **s** + (**t** + **u**).

IDENTITY PROPERTY   There is a unique vector **0** such that **v** + **0** = **v** and **0** + **v** = **v**.

INVERSE PROPERTY   **v** has a unique additive inverse −**v** such that **v** + (−**v**) = **0** and −**v** + **v** = **0**.

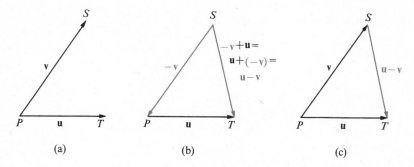

(a)   (b)   (c)

Figure 4–18

You can also define the operation of **vector subtraction**. For example, $(7, -2) - (4, 6) = (7, -2) + (-4, -6) = (3, -8)$. Figure 4–18 gives a visualization of vector subtraction: $\overrightarrow{PT}$ and $\overrightarrow{PS}$ represent **u** and **v**, respectively; therefore, $\overrightarrow{SP}$ pictures −**v**, and $\overrightarrow{ST}$ represents −**v** + **u** or **u** + (−**v**). The same figure also illustrates the equality **v** + (**u** − **v**) = **u** (Exercise 45, page 137) and indicates why **u** − **v** is sometimes called "the vector from **v** to **u**."

If $\mathbf{u} \in \Re \times \Re$ and $\mathbf{v} \in \Re \times \Re$, then $\mathbf{u} - \mathbf{v} = \mathbf{u} + (-\mathbf{v})$.

EXAMPLE 3. If $\overrightarrow{OA}, \overrightarrow{OB}$, and $\overrightarrow{OC}$ represent the vectors **s**, **t**, and **u**, respectively, verify that the sum of the vectors represented by $\overrightarrow{AB}, \overrightarrow{BC}$, and $\overrightarrow{CA}$ is **0**.

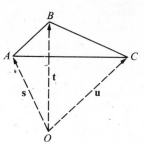

Solution: $\overrightarrow{AB}$ represents **t** − **s**;

$\overrightarrow{BC}$ represents **u** − **t**;

$\overrightarrow{CA}$ represents **s** − **u**.

$$(\mathbf{t} - \mathbf{s}) + (\mathbf{u} - \mathbf{t}) + (\mathbf{s} - \mathbf{u}) = [\mathbf{t} + (-\mathbf{s})] + [\mathbf{u} + (-\mathbf{t})] + [\mathbf{s} + (-\mathbf{u})]$$
(Definition of vector subtraction.)

$$= [\mathbf{t} + (-\mathbf{t})] + [\mathbf{u} + (-\mathbf{u})] + [\mathbf{s} + (-\mathbf{s})]$$

(Commutative and associative properties.)

$$= \mathbf{0} + \mathbf{0} + \mathbf{0} \quad \text{(Inverse property.)}$$

$$= \mathbf{0}. \qquad \text{(Identity property.)}$$

p28: 1−41 odd, 36

Exercises

Tell whether the given expression can be used to represent a vector, a scalar, or neither.

 1. $(3 + \sqrt{5})$ **2.** $(2, -3)$ **3.** $(\sqrt{-7})$ **4.** $(2, 3 + \sqrt{2})$

Give the additive inverse of each of the following vectors.

5. $(3, 2)$ **6.** $(-1, 3)$ **7.** $(4, 3 - \sqrt{2})$ **8.** $(-3, -1 + \sqrt{5})$

Given $\mathbf{v} = (-3, 4)$, represent by an arrow in standard position:

9. $\mathbf{v}$ **10.** $-\mathbf{v}$ **11.** $\mathbf{v} + \mathbf{v}$ **12.** $\mathbf{v} + \mathbf{v} + \mathbf{v}$

Which of these are correct vector sum (or difference) representations?

13.   **14.**   **15.**   **16.**

Find r and s so that each statement is true.

17. $(r, s) + (3, 2) = (5, 7)$ **20.** $(5, r) + (s, 3) = (8, -1)$

18. $(5, -2) + (r, s) = (7, 3)$ **21.** $(-3, r) + (s, -2) = (0, 0)$

19. $(2, 3) + (r, s) = (2, 3)$ **22.** $(4, -1) + (3, 1) = (r, s)$

From the coordinate plane vector representation shown, determine the vector represented by the arrow named.

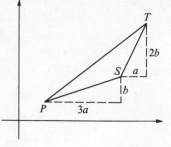

23. $\overrightarrow{PT}$ **26.** $\overrightarrow{TS}$

24. $\overrightarrow{PS}$ **27.** $\overrightarrow{SP}$

25. $\overrightarrow{ST}$ **28.** $\overrightarrow{TP}$

If **s** = $(3, 2)$, **t** = $(-4, 3)$, and **u** = $(2, -4)$, find **v** satisfying each equation.

29. $\mathbf{v} = \mathbf{s} + \mathbf{t}$ **32.** $\mathbf{v} - \mathbf{s} = \mathbf{u} + \mathbf{t}$

30. $\mathbf{v} = \mathbf{t} - \mathbf{u}$ **33.** $\mathbf{v} = \mathbf{s} - \mathbf{t} + \mathbf{u}$

31. $\mathbf{t} = \mathbf{s} + \mathbf{v}$ **34.** $\mathbf{t} = \mathbf{s} + \mathbf{u} + \mathbf{v}$

35. From the given figure, determine the vectors **r, s, t, u, v, w**.

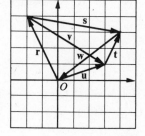

B **36.** Express the vector $(3, -2)$ as a sum using only the vectors $(1, 0)$, $(0, 1)$, and their additive inverses.

Given the parallelogram *RSTU*. Sketch the arrows connecting the given vertices and express $\overrightarrow{US}$ in terms of the designated vectors.

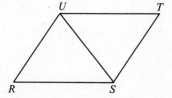

37. $\overrightarrow{UT}$ and $\overrightarrow{TS}$.   **39.** $\overrightarrow{RS}$ and $\overrightarrow{ST}$.

38. $\overrightarrow{UT}$ and $\overrightarrow{UR}$.   **40.** $\overrightarrow{SR}$ and $\overrightarrow{ST}$.

41. Given: $\overrightarrow{AB}$ having (a, b) as initial-point coordinates and (c, d) as terminal-point coordinates. Prove that $\overrightarrow{AB} + \overrightarrow{BA} = \overrightarrow{O}$.

42. Given $\mathbf{v}_1 = (a, b)$ and $\mathbf{v}_2 = (b, a)$. If $\mathbf{v}_3 = \mathbf{v}_1 + \mathbf{v}_2$, prove that $\mathbf{v}_3 \in \{(x, y): x = y\}$.

Let **s, t, u,** and **v** be respectively the vectors (a, b), (c, d), (e, f), and (g, h). Using the definition of vector addition, prove each statement.

43. $\mathbf{s} + \mathbf{t} = \mathbf{t} + \mathbf{s}$ (commutative prop. of vector addition).

44. $(\mathbf{s} + \mathbf{t}) + \mathbf{u} = \mathbf{s} + (\mathbf{t} + \mathbf{u})$ (assoc. prop. of vector addition).

45. $v + (u - v) = u$.

46. If $u + v = 0$, then $u = -v$.

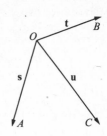

In the adjacent figure, $\overrightarrow{OA}$, $\overrightarrow{OB}$, and $\overrightarrow{OC}$ represent respectively the vectors **s, t,** and **u.** Using the method of Example 3, page 135, verify each statement.

47. $\overrightarrow{OB} + \overrightarrow{BC} + \overrightarrow{CA} + \overrightarrow{AO} = \vec{O}$.

48. $\overrightarrow{CB} + \overrightarrow{BO} + \overrightarrow{OA} = \overrightarrow{CA}$.

4–4 The Norm of a Vector

In science and engineering, vectors are described as "quantities having magnitude and direction." To represent a *physical vector* such as a velocity, a force, or a displacement, you draw an arrow whose length and direction indicate the magnitude and direction of the vector. In Figure 4–19 arrows represent:

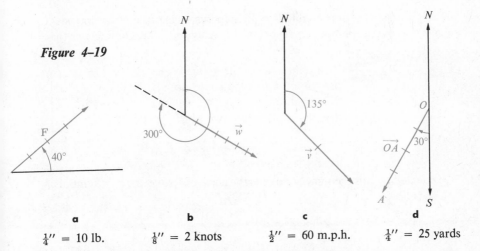

Figure 4–19

a	b	c	d
$\frac{1}{4}'' = 10$ lb.	$\frac{1}{8}'' = 2$ knots	$\frac{1}{2}'' = 60$ m.p.h.	$\frac{1}{4}'' = 25$ yards

a. A force **F** of 40 pounds at 40° (the angle is measured counterclockwise from the positive side of the horizontal axis).

b. Wind velocity $\vec{w}$ of 12 knots* from 300° (the angle is measured clockwise from north to the direction *from* which the wind blows, but the arrow is drawn in the direction of movement of the air).

c. A velocity $\vec{v}$ of 120 m.p.h. at 135° (the angle, called the *heading, bearing,* or *course,* is measured clockwise from north).

d. A displacement from O to A of 100 yards in the direction S30°W (the angle is described by a ray turned from south 30° west).

---

* 1 knot = 1 nautical mile per hour $\doteq$ 6076 feet per hour.

The **resultant** of two physical vectors corresponds to what we have called the sum of two vectors.

EXAMPLE 1. A jet heads 15° at 600 m.p.h. If a 100 m.p.h. wind is blowing from 120°, determine graphically the plane's ground speed.

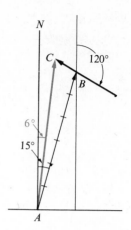

Solution: Use the scale $\frac{1}{4}'' = 100$ m.p.h.

1. At A draw $\overrightarrow{AB}$ to represent the jet's velocity.

2. At B draw $\overrightarrow{BC}$ to represent wind velocity.

3. The resultant velocity, represented by $\overrightarrow{AC}$, is approximately 630 m.p.h. at approximately 6°.

The famous assertion credited to Pythagoras suggests how to introduce an algebraic concept that corresponds to magnitude for physical vectors.

THEOREM In a right triangle the square of the length of the hypotenuse equals the sum of the squares of the lengths of the other two sides.

Figure 4–20

Motivated by this theorem, we define the **norm** of any vector **v**, in symbols,* $\|\mathbf{v}\|$, as follows:

$$\text{If } \mathbf{v} = (a, b) \in \Re \times \Re, \ \|\mathbf{v}\| = \sqrt{a^2 + b^2}.$$

Note that the *norm of a vector is a real number*, that is, a scalar. For example,

$$\|(3, 4)\| = \sqrt{(3)^2 + 4^2} = \sqrt{9 + 16} = 5$$
$$\|(0, 0)\| = \sqrt{0^2 + 0^2} = \sqrt{0 + 0} = 0$$
$$\|(0, -6)\| = \sqrt{0^2 + (-6)^2} = \sqrt{0 + 36} = 6$$

---

* The symbol $|\mathbf{v}|$ is also used for the norm of **v** and is sometimes spoken of as the "absolute value of the vector **v**." When you see this symbolism, you must be careful to distinguish between the absolute value of a vector $|\mathbf{v}|$ and the absolute value of a scalar $|v|$.

The preceding examples suggest the following theorem that you can easily prove. (Exercises 30 and 31, page 141.)

THEOREM   If **v** denotes a vector, then

1. $\|\mathbf{v}\| \geq 0$;   2. $\|\mathbf{v}\| = 0$ if and only if $\mathbf{v} = \mathbf{0}$.

In geometry you learned that the length of one side of a triangle is less than or (in the limiting case) equal to the sum of the lengths of the other two sides. Picturing the norm of a vector as the length of any arrow representing the vector suggests an important property called the **triangle inequality**, illustrated in Figure 4–21 and proved on page 140.

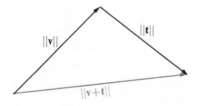

Figure 4–21

THEOREM   If **v** and **t** denote vectors, then $\|\mathbf{v} + \mathbf{t}\| \leq \|\mathbf{v}\| + \|\mathbf{t}\|$.

Since the norm of a vector is never a negative number, the triangle inequality is equivalent to the assertion

$$\|\mathbf{v} + \mathbf{t}\|^2 \leq (\|\mathbf{v}\| + \|\mathbf{t}\|)^2.$$

EXAMPLE 2.   Verify the triangle inequality for the vectors $\mathbf{v} = (-3, 4)$ and $\mathbf{t} = (-15, -8)$.

Solution: $\mathbf{v} + \mathbf{t} = (-3 - 15, 4 - 8) = (-18, -4)$

$\|\mathbf{v} + \mathbf{t}\|^2 = (-18)^2 + (-4)^2 = 324 + 16 = 340$

$\|\mathbf{v}\| = \sqrt{(-3)^2 + 4^2} = \sqrt{9 + 16} = 5$

$\|\mathbf{t}\| = \sqrt{(-15)^2 + (-8)^2} = \sqrt{225 + 64} = 17$

$(\|\mathbf{v}\| + \|\mathbf{t}\|)^2 = (5 + 17)^2 = 484$

$\therefore$ In this case, $\|\mathbf{v} + \mathbf{t}\|^2 \leq (\|\mathbf{v}\| + \|\mathbf{t}\|)^2$, since
$$340 < 484.$$

C *Proof of the Triangle Inequality.* Let $\mathbf{v} = (v_1, v_2)$ and $\mathbf{t} = (t_1, t_2)$. Then

$$\mathbf{v} + \mathbf{t} = (v_1 + t_1, v_2 + t_2).$$

$$\|\mathbf{v} + \mathbf{t}\|^2 = (v_1 + t_1)^2 + (v_2 + t_2)^2.$$

∴ (1) $\|\mathbf{v} + \mathbf{t}\|^2 = (v_1^2 + v_2^2 + t_1^2 + t_2^2) + 2(v_1 t_1 + v_2 t_2).$

Also, $\|\mathbf{v}\| = \sqrt{v_1^2 + v_2^2}$, and $\|\mathbf{t}\| = \sqrt{t_1^2 + t_2^2}.$

∴ (2) $(\|\mathbf{v}\| + \|\mathbf{t}\|)^2 = (v_1^2 + v_2^2 + t_1^2 + t_2^2) + 2\sqrt{(v_1^2 + v_2^2)(t_1^2 + t_2^2)}.$

Comparing statements (1) and (2), you see that $\|\mathbf{v} + \mathbf{t}\|^2 \le (\|\mathbf{v}\| + \|\mathbf{t}\|)^2$ if and only if

$$v_1 t_1 + v_2 t_2 \le \sqrt{(v_1^2 + v_2^2)(t_1^2 + t_2^2)}.$$

If the left-hand member of the preceding inequality denotes a negative number or 0, the inequality is certainly true because its right-hand member is either a positive number or 0. If the left-hand member is a positive number, the inequality is equivalent to

$$(v_1 t_1 + v_2 t_2)^2 \le (v_1^2 + v_2^2)(t_1^2 + t_2^2), \qquad \text{which is valid}$$

if and only if

$$0 \le v_1^2 t_2^2 - 2v_1 t_2 v_2 t_1 + v_2^2 t_1^2, \quad \text{which in turn}$$

is equivalent to

$$0 \le (v_1 t_2 - v_2 t_1)^2.$$

But the square of every real number either equals or exceeds 0, so that the last inequality is true. This means that in every case the triangle inequality is also true.

Exercises

Make an accurate drawing to represent the given physical vector(s).

A 1. A force $\mathbf{F}$ of 40 lb. acting on an object at 60°.

2. A car traveling at a velocity $\mathbf{v}$ of 60 m.p.h. at 120°.

3. A plane traveling at a velocity $\mathbf{v}$ of 200 m.p.h. at 300°.

4. A horizontal force $\mathbf{F}_1$ of 30 lb. to the right and a vertical force $\mathbf{F}_2$ of 40 lb. upward acting on the same object.

Making use of the relationships existing between the sides in special right triangles, find the magnitude and direction angle with the horizontal of the resultant in each vector diagram.

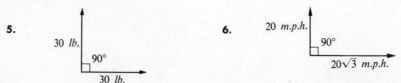

5.

30 *lb.*

90°

30 *lb.*

6.

20 *m.p.h.*

90°

$20\sqrt{3}$ *m.p.h.*

7.

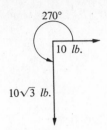

8.

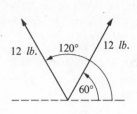

In Exercises 9–14 find the norm of the given vector.

9. $(3, -4)$ **11.** $(-2, -3)$ **13.** $(\sqrt{3}, \sqrt{5})$

10. $(-5, 12)$ **12.** $(\sqrt{3}, 1)$ **14.** $(3k, 4k)$

Find the length of the arrow representation of the vector **v**, that is, find $\|\mathbf{v}\|$.

15. $\mathbf{v} = (3\sqrt{2}, 3\sqrt{2})$ **17.** $\mathbf{v} = (1, 1) + (2, 3)$

16. $\mathbf{v} = (\sqrt{3} + 1, \sqrt{3} - 1)$ **18.** $\mathbf{v} = (5, 2) - (2, 1)$

Given $\mathbf{r} = (2, 3)$, $\mathbf{s} = (-3, 1)$, and $\mathbf{t} = (4, -2)$. Find each of the following scalars.

B

19. $\|\mathbf{r} + \mathbf{s}\|$ **21.** $\|\mathbf{t} - \mathbf{s}\|$ **23.** $\|\mathbf{r} + \mathbf{s} - \mathbf{t}\|$

20. $\|\mathbf{r} - \mathbf{s}\|$ **22.** $\|\mathbf{r} + \mathbf{s} + \mathbf{t}\|$ **24.** $\|\mathbf{r} - \mathbf{s} - \mathbf{t}\|$

Verify the triangle inequality for the vectors **r** and **s**.

25. $\mathbf{r} = (5, 2); \mathbf{s} = (2, 1)$ **27.** $\mathbf{r} = (0, -2); \mathbf{s} = (3, 4)$

26. $\mathbf{r} = (3, 1); \mathbf{s} = (2, -1)$ **28.** $\mathbf{r} = (-1, -1); \mathbf{s} = (3, 2)$

29. Prove: $\|-\mathbf{v}\| = \|\mathbf{v}\|$ for every vector **v**.

30. Prove: $\|\mathbf{v}\| \geq 0$ for every vector **v**.

31. Prove: $\|\mathbf{v}\| = 0$ if and only if $\mathbf{v} = \mathbf{0}$.

32. Prove: If $\mathbf{v}_1 = (a, b)$ and $\mathbf{v}_2 = (b, a)$, then $\|\mathbf{v}_1\| = \|\mathbf{v}_2\|$.

In Exercises 33–36 make an accurate scale vector drawing. Where possible, make use of special right-triangle relationships. In other cases give an approximate answer on the basis of your drawing.

33. A boat sets out to travel north at 20 m.p.h. A wind from the west moves the boat eastward at 4 m.p.h. Determine the boat's velocity along the path it travels.

34. Suppose a force of 50 lb. is exerted on an object in a direction of 60° from the horizontal. What two forces, one in a horizontal direction and one in a vertical direction, would have the same effect on the object?

35. A trunk is dragged along a horizontal plane by a rope which makes an angle of 30° with the horizontal. What force must be exerted on the rope to give the same result as a horizontal force of 20 lb.?

$d30: p.141-142!, 33-37 all$

36. A plane flies a course of 315° at 324 m.p.h. If a 54 m.p.h. wind is blowing from 90°, determine the plane's ground speed and course.

37. Prove: For any two vectors **r** and **t**, $\|\mathbf{r}\| - \|\mathbf{t}\| \leq \|\mathbf{r} - \mathbf{t}\|$. (*Hint:* Apply the triangle inequality with $\mathbf{v} = \mathbf{r} - \mathbf{t}$.)

38. Prove: For any three vectors **r**, **s**, and **t**,

$$\|\mathbf{r} - \mathbf{s}\| + \|\mathbf{s} - \mathbf{t}\| \geq \|\mathbf{r} - \mathbf{t}\|.$$

PARALLEL AND PERPENDICULAR VECTORS

4–5 Multiplication of a Vector by a Scalar

Figure 4–22 pictures the sum $\mathbf{v} + \mathbf{v}$,

where $\mathbf{v} = (-4, 2)$.

You have

$$\mathbf{v} + \mathbf{v} = [-4 + (-4), 2 + 2].$$
$$\therefore \mathbf{v} + \mathbf{v} = [2(-4), 2(2)]$$

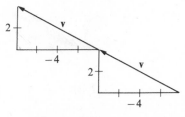

Figure 4–22

Analogy with real numbers suggests that $\mathbf{v} + \mathbf{v}$ should equal $2\mathbf{v}$, and therefore that $2\mathbf{v}$ should mean $[2(-4), 2(2)]$. This example prompts us to define **multiplication of a vector by a scalar** as follows:

If $\mathbf{v} \in \mathfrak{R} \times \mathfrak{R}$, $r \in \mathfrak{R}$, *and* $\mathbf{v} = (a, b)$, then $r\mathbf{v} = \mathbf{v}r = (ra, rb)$.

We call $r\mathbf{v}$ a **scalar multiple** of **v** or a **real number multiple** of **v**. For example, if $\mathbf{v} = (-4, 2)$, then

$$1\mathbf{v} = (1 \cdot -4, 1 \cdot 2) = (-4, 2) = \mathbf{v}$$
$$2\mathbf{v} = (2 \cdot -4, 2 \cdot 2) = (-8, 4)$$
$$\tfrac{1}{2}\mathbf{v} = (\tfrac{1}{2} \cdot -4, \tfrac{1}{2} \cdot 2) = (-2, 1)$$
$$0\mathbf{v} \doteq (0 \cdot -4, 0 \cdot 2) = (0, 0) = \mathbf{0}$$
$$(-1)\mathbf{v} = (-1 \cdot -4, -1 \cdot 2) = (4, -2) = -\mathbf{v}$$
$$(-2)\mathbf{v} = (-2 \cdot -4, -2 \cdot 2) = (8, -4) = -(2\mathbf{v})$$

You can verify that in each of the preceding examples $\|r\mathbf{v}\| = |r| \cdot \|\mathbf{v}\|$. Indeed, it is easy to prove this fact in general. For, if $\mathbf{v} = (a, b)$, then $r\mathbf{v} = (ra, rb)$, and:

$$\|\mathbf{v}\| = \sqrt{a^2 + b^2}$$

$$\|r\mathbf{v}\| = \sqrt{(ra)^2 + (rb)^2} = \sqrt{r^2(a^2 + b^2)} = |r| \cdot \sqrt{a^2 + b^2} = |r| \cdot \|\mathbf{v}\|.$$

As a corollary of this result, you can deduce that if $r\mathbf{v} = \mathbf{0}$, then $r = 0$ or $\mathbf{v} = \mathbf{0}$ (Exercise 52, page 148). These and the other basic properties of the multiplication of a vector by a real number are summarized in the following list. Proofs of most of the properties are left as exercises (page 148).

Properties of Multiplication of a Vector by a Scalar

Let $\mathbf{v}$ and $\mathbf{t}$ denote any elements of $\mathcal{R} \times \mathcal{R}$ and let r and s denote any real numbers.

CLOSURE PROPERTY	$r\mathbf{v}$ belongs to $\mathcal{R} \times \mathcal{R}$.
SUBSTITUTION PROPERTY	If $r = s$ and $\mathbf{v} = \mathbf{t}$, $r\mathbf{v} = s\mathbf{t}$.
COMMUTATIVE PROPERTY	$r\mathbf{v} = \mathbf{v}r$
ASSOCIATIVE PROPERTY	$(rs)\mathbf{v} = r(s\mathbf{v})$
EXISTENCE OF IDENTITY	$1\mathbf{v} = \mathbf{v}$
ZERO PRODUCT PROPERTY	$r\mathbf{v} = \mathbf{0}$ if and only if $r = 0$ or $\mathbf{v} = \mathbf{0}$.
PROPERTY OF -1	$(-1)\mathbf{v} = -\mathbf{v}$
DISTRIBUTIVE PROPERTIES	1. $r(\mathbf{v} + \mathbf{t}) = r\mathbf{v} + r\mathbf{t}$ and $(\mathbf{v} + \mathbf{t})r = \mathbf{v}r + \mathbf{t}r$;
	2. $(r + s)\mathbf{v} = r\mathbf{v} + s\mathbf{v}$ and $\mathbf{v}(r + s) = \mathbf{v}r + \mathbf{v}s$.
NORM PROPERTY	$\|r\mathbf{v}\| = |r| \cdot \|\mathbf{v}\|$

From these properties you can deduce other assertions about products of vectors and numbers.

EXAMPLE 1. Prove that if $\mathbf{v} = r\mathbf{t}$ and $r \neq 0$, then $\mathbf{t} = \dfrac{1}{r}\mathbf{v}$.

Solution: If $\mathbf{v} = r\mathbf{t}$, then $\dfrac{1}{r}\mathbf{v} = \dfrac{1}{r}(r\mathbf{t})$. (Why?) Therefore,

$$\frac{1}{r}\mathbf{v} = \left(\frac{1}{r} \cdot r\right)\mathbf{t} = 1 \cdot \mathbf{t} = \mathbf{t} \text{ (Why?)}. \text{ Thus, } \mathbf{t} = \frac{1}{r}\mathbf{v}. \text{ (Why?)}$$

Recall that $\dfrac{1}{r} > 0$ or $\dfrac{1}{r} < 0$ according as $r > 0$ or $r < 0$ (Exercises 27, 28, page 56). This means that you can state, as a corollary of the result of Example 1, the following fact.

> If **v** is a positive (negative) scalar multiple of **t**, then **t** is a positive (negative) scalar multiple of **v**.

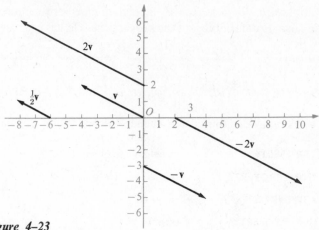

Figure 4–23

To visualize $r\mathbf{v}$, look at Figure 4–23, which pictures the products of $(-4, 2)$ by $1, 2, \frac{1}{2}, -1$ and -2. Since $\|r\mathbf{v}\| = |r| \cdot \|\mathbf{v}\|$, any arrow representing $r\mathbf{v}$ is $|r|$ times as long as an arrow for **v**. The figure further suggests that arrows for **v** and $r\mathbf{v}$ are in the same direction or in opposite directions according as $r > 0$ or $r < 0$. This observation leads us to the following agreement:

> Nonzero vectors have the **same direction**, or are in the same direction, if and only if one is the product of the other by a positive scalar; nonzero vectors have **opposite directions**, or are in opposite directions, if and only if one is the product of the other by a negative scalar.

EXAMPLE 2. Show that $(10, -4)$ and $(-5, 2)$ are in opposite directions.

Solution: $(10, -4) = -2(-5, 2)$. Since $-2 < 0$, the vectors are in opposite directions.

EXAMPLE 3. On a scale drawing, estimate the magnitude and direction of the resultant of three forces $\mathbf{F}_1$, $\mathbf{F}_2$, and $\mathbf{F}_3$, where $\mathbf{F}_1 = 40$ lb. in a direction of $45°$, $\mathbf{F}_2 = 2\mathbf{F}_1$, and $\mathbf{F}_3 = 60$ lb. in a direction of $0°$.

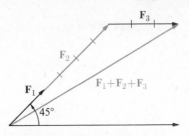

Solution: Scale $\frac{1}{4}'' = 20$ lb.

$F_1 + F_2 + F_3 \doteq 170$ lb. in
a direction of 30°.

> Nonzero vectors in the same direction or in opposite directions are
> called **parallel**. It is convenient also to agree that **0** *is parallel to*
> *every vector.*

Do you see that these definitions mean that two vectors are parallel if and
only if one is the product of the other by a scalar? In fact, if **t** and **v** are
parallel vectors such that $\mathbf{v} \neq \mathbf{0}$, **t** must be a scalar multiple of **v**. (Exercise
58, page 148.)

EXAMPLE 4.   Determine whether or not $(-3, -6)$ and $(-6, 10)$ are parallel
vectors.

Solution: Since neither vector is **0**, the vectors are parallel if and only
if there is a nonzero scalar r such that $(-3, -6) = r(-6, 10)$;
that is, $-3 = -6r$ *and* $-6 = 10r$, or $r = \frac{1}{2}$ *and* $r = -\frac{3}{5}$.
No number satisfies both of these equations.

∴ the vectors are not parallel, **Answer.**

It is reasonable to expect that vectors parallel to the same nonzero vector
are parallel to each other.

> **THEOREM**   If **v** and **t** are both parallel to a nonzero vector **u**,
> then **v** and **t** are parallel vectors.

Proof: 1. If either $\mathbf{v} = \mathbf{0}$ or $\mathbf{t} = \mathbf{0}$, then **v** and **t** are parallel vectors by
definition.

2. If neither **v** nor **t** is the zero vector, then because $\mathbf{u} \neq \mathbf{0}$ by
hypothesis, the definition of parallel vectors requires that there
exist nonzero scalars r and s such that

$$\mathbf{v} = r\mathbf{u} \quad \text{and} \quad \mathbf{u} = s\mathbf{t}.$$

Hence, $\mathbf{v} = r(s\mathbf{t}) = (rs)\mathbf{t}$. Because rs denotes a real number, it
follows that **v** and **t** are parallel vectors.

COROLLARY. For each nonzero scalar s, the set of vectors parallel to $\mathbf{v}$ equals the set of vectors parallel to $s\mathbf{v}$.

For example, since $(1, 1) = \sqrt{2}\left(\dfrac{\sqrt{2}}{2}, \dfrac{\sqrt{2}}{2}\right)$, you can specify the set of all vectors parallel to $(1, 1)$ as

$$\{(x, y): (x, y) = t(1, 1), t \in \mathcal{R}\}$$

or as

$$\left\{(x, y): (x, y) = q\left(\frac{\sqrt{2}}{2}, \frac{\sqrt{2}}{2}\right), q \in \mathcal{R}\right\}.$$

The vector $\left(\dfrac{\sqrt{2}}{2}, \dfrac{\sqrt{2}}{2}\right)$ is called a **unit vector** because its norm is 1; that is,

$$\sqrt{\left(\frac{\sqrt{2}}{2}\right)^2 + \left(\frac{\sqrt{2}}{2}\right)^2} = \sqrt{\frac{1}{2} + \frac{1}{2}} = 1.$$ It is the unit vector in the same direction as $(1, 1)$. In general, if $\mathbf{w}$ is any nonzero vector, $\dfrac{\mathbf{w}}{\|\mathbf{w}\|}$ is the unit vector in the same direction as $\mathbf{w}$, whereas $-\dfrac{\mathbf{w}}{\|\mathbf{w}\|}$ is the unit vector opposite in direction to $\mathbf{w}$.

Exercises

Given $\mathbf{v} = (3, -2)$. Find the following scalar multiples of $\mathbf{v}$.

A   **1.** $2\mathbf{v}$ **2.** $-3\mathbf{v}$ **3.** $\frac{2}{3}\mathbf{v}$ **4.** $-\sqrt{2}\,\mathbf{v}$

Given $\mathbf{s} = (-3, 4)$. Find the following vector norms.

5. $\|2\mathbf{s}\|$ **6.** $\|4\mathbf{s}\|$ **7.** $\|-3\mathbf{s}\|$ **8.** $\|\frac{1}{3}\mathbf{s}\|$

Where possible, find k such that $\mathbf{v} = k\mathbf{t}$.

9. $\mathbf{v} = (6, 3)$ and $\mathbf{t} = (2, 1)$ **11.** $\mathbf{v} = (4, -6)$ and $\mathbf{t} = (-6, 10)$

10. $\mathbf{v} = (2, \sqrt{3})$ and $\mathbf{t} = (\sqrt{2}, \sqrt{6})$ **12.** $\mathbf{v} = (-\sqrt{3}, 4\sqrt{3})$ and $\mathbf{t} = (-1, 4)$

Exercises 13 and 14 refer to the adjacent co-ordinate-plane vector representation.

13. Find k_1, k_2, k_3, and k_4.

14. Find the norm of each vector represented.

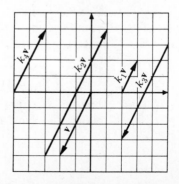

Tell whether the given vectors **s** and **t** have the same direction, opposite directions, or neither.

15. $s = (2, 4), t = (1, 2)$ **18.** $s = (-1, 6), t = (\frac{2}{3}, -4)$

16. $s = (1, -3), t = (-2, 6)$ **19.** $s = (2, 1), t = (-1, -2)$

17. $s = (3, 1), t = (1, 3)$ **20.** $s = (2, \sqrt{6}), t = (\sqrt{2}, 3\sqrt{2})$

Describe in words the coordinate-plane representation of the set of vectors specified by the following. (Assume $k \in \mathcal{R}$, and all arrows involved are in standard position.)

21. $\{(x, y): (x, y) = k(2, 3)\}$ **22.** $\{(x, y): (x, y) = k\sqrt{3}(\sqrt{2}, 2\sqrt{3})\}$

For what $k \in \mathcal{R}$ will **v** and **u** be parallel vectors?

23. $v = (2, 5), u = (6, k)$ **25.** $v = (a, b), u = \left(k, -\dfrac{b}{a}\right), a \neq 0$

24. $v = (4, -6), u = (k, 3)$ **26.** $v = (2, \sqrt{3}), u = (k, -6)$

Find: (a) the unit vector in the same direction as **t**; (b) the unit vector in the opposite direction from **t**.

27. $t = (3, 4)$ **29.** $t = (-\sqrt{3}, 1)$

28. $t = (-2, 3)$ **30.** $t = (\sqrt{2}, -\sqrt{7})$

Given that **v** and **t** are elements of $\mathcal{R} \times \mathcal{R}$, and r and s are real numbers. Prove the following properties of the multiplication of a vector by a scalar.

31. Closure: $rv \in \mathcal{R} \times \mathcal{R}$ **33.** Associative: $(rs)v = r(sv)$

32. Property of -1: $(-1)v = -v$ **34.** Identity Element: $1v = v$

If $s = (5, 2)$ and $t = (-4, 3)$, determine the indicated vector.

35. $2(s + t)$ **37.** $-2s + 3t$

36. $3s - 2t$ **38.** $\frac{1}{3}s + \frac{2}{3}t$

Simplify each vector sum and represent the result as an arrow in standard position in the coordinate plane.

39. $5(0, 1) + 3(1, 0)$ **41.** $2(1, 3) + (-3)(2, 1)$

40. $2(-3, 4) + 1(3, -2)$ **42.** $0(1, 0) + 1(0, 1)$

For what values of x and y is the given statement true?

43. $x(2, 3) + y(3, -1) = (14, 10)$ **45.** $x(1, 2) + y(2, 4) = (6, 12)$

44. $x(3, 1) + y(2, 3) = (0, 7)$ **46.** $x(3, 6) + y(1, 2) = (7, 10)$

On a scale drawing, estimate the magnitude and direction of the resultant of the three forces $\mathbf{F}_1$, $\mathbf{F}_2$, and $\mathbf{F}_3$.

47. $\mathbf{F}_1$ is a horizontal force of 30 lbs. to the right, $\mathbf{F}_2$ is a force of 40 lbs. acting in a counterclockwise direction 40° from the direction of $\mathbf{F}_1$, and $\mathbf{F}_3 = 2\mathbf{F}_1$.

48. $\mathbf{F}_1$ is a vertical force upward of 59 tons, $\mathbf{F}_2$ is a force of 60 tons acting in a clockwise direction 40° from the direction of $\mathbf{F}_1$, and $\mathbf{F}_3 = -\frac{1}{2}\mathbf{F}_2$.

Let **v** and **u** be the given vectors and $L = \{\mathbf{v} + k\mathbf{u}: k \in \{0, 1, 2, 3\}\}$. Draw standard representations of the elements of L.

49. $\mathbf{v} = (-4, 1); \mathbf{u} = (-1, -2)$ **50.** $\mathbf{v} = (3, 7); \mathbf{u} = (2, -1)$

Given **v** and **t** are elements of $\mathcal{R} \times \mathcal{R}$ and r and s are elements of $\mathcal{R}$. Prove the following properties of the multiplication of a vector by a scalar.

51. Substitution: If $r = s$ and $\mathbf{v} = \mathbf{t}$, then $r\mathbf{v} = s\mathbf{t}$.

52. Zero Product: $r\mathbf{v} = \mathbf{0}$ if and only if $r = 0$ or $\mathbf{v} = \mathbf{0}$.

53. Distributive: $r(\mathbf{v} + \mathbf{t}) = r\mathbf{v} + r\mathbf{t} = \mathbf{v}r + \mathbf{t}r$.

54. Distributive: $(r + s)\mathbf{v} = r\mathbf{v} + s\mathbf{v} = \mathbf{v}r + \mathbf{v}s$.

55. $r(\mathbf{v} - \mathbf{t}) = r\mathbf{v} - r\mathbf{t} = \mathbf{v}r - \mathbf{t}r$.

56. $(r - s)\mathbf{v} = r\mathbf{v} - s\mathbf{v} = \mathbf{v}r - \mathbf{v}s$.

57. Prove: $\|\mathbf{v} + \mathbf{t}\| = \|\mathbf{t} + \mathbf{v}\|$.

58. Let **t** and **v** be parallel vectors. Prove: If $\mathbf{v} = \mathbf{0}$, then **v** is a scalar multiple of **t**; if $\mathbf{v} \neq \mathbf{0}$, then **t** is a scalar multiple of **v**.

59. Prove: **v** and **t** have the same direction if and only if $\|\mathbf{v} + \mathbf{t}\| = \|\mathbf{v}\| + \|\mathbf{t}\|$.

60. Prove: If **v** and **t** have opposite directions, then $\|\mathbf{v} + \mathbf{t}\| < \|\mathbf{v}\| + \|\mathbf{t}\|$.

61. Given: $L = \{(x, y): (x, y) = (0, 1) + k(1, 1), \quad k \in \mathcal{R}\}$. Show that $(x, y) \in L$ if and only if $y - x = 1$.

62. Prove: If **v** and **t** are a pair of nonzero, nonparallel vectors, and a and b are scalars such that $a\mathbf{v} + b\mathbf{t} = \mathbf{0}$, then $a = b = 0$.

4–6 Inner Product

In geometry you learned to identify a right triangle by verifying that it satisfied the Pythagorean Theorem. Figure 4.24, therefore, suggests that the vectors **v** and **t** be considered *perpendicular* if and only if

$$\|\mathbf{v} - \mathbf{t}\|^2 = \|\mathbf{v}\|^2 + \|\mathbf{t}\|^2.$$

Let us write the left-hand member of this equation in terms of the entries (v_1, v_2) and (t_1, t_2) of **v** and **t**.

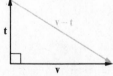

Figure 4–24

$$\|\mathbf{v} - \mathbf{t}\|^2 = \|(v_1 - t_1, v_2 - t_2)\|^2$$
$$= (v_1^2 + v_2^2) + (t_1^2 + t_2^2) - 2(v_1 t_1 + v_2 t_2).$$
$$\therefore \|\mathbf{v} - \mathbf{t}\|^2 = \|\mathbf{v}\|^2 + \|\mathbf{t}\|^2 - 2(v_1 t_1 + v_2 t_2).$$

Thus, $\|\mathbf{v} - \mathbf{t}\|^2 = \|\mathbf{v}\|^2 + \|\mathbf{t}\|^2$ if and only if $v_1 t_1 + v_2 t_2 = 0$.

The expression $v_1 t_1 + v_2 t_2$ appears so often in studying vectors that it is designated by a special symbol, $\mathbf{v} \cdot \mathbf{t}$, and is given a name, the **inner product***
of $\mathbf{v}$ and $\mathbf{t}$.

If $\mathbf{v} = (v_1, v_2)$ and $\mathbf{t} = (t_1, t_2)$ are elements of $\mathcal{R} \times \mathcal{R}$, then $\mathbf{v} \cdot \mathbf{t} = v_1 t_1 + v_2 t_2$.

Notice that *the inner product of two vectors is a real number;* it is *not* a vector. For example,

$$(3, 2) \cdot (-5, \tfrac{1}{2}) = 3(-5) + 2(\tfrac{1}{2}) = -15 + 1 = -14$$
$$(0, 0) \cdot (-14, \sqrt{2}) = 0(-14) + 0\sqrt{2} = 0$$
$$(-2, 7) \cdot (-2, 7) = (-2)^2 + 7^2 = 53$$

EXAMPLE 1. Suppose the entries in the vector (200, 150) are the numbers of shares of stock an investor holds in companies A and B, and the respective entries in (2.25, 3.50) are the dollar dividends per share from these stocks. Find the total income from the stocks.

Solution: Total income $= (200, 150) \cdot (2.25, 3.50)$
$$= 450 + 525 = \$975, \textbf{ Answer.}$$

The argument in the first paragraph of this section provides motivation for the following definition:

> Two vectors are said to be **perpendicular** to each other if and only if their inner product is zero.

Perpendicular vectors are also called **orthogonal** vectors.

---

* Other names for $\mathbf{v} \cdot \mathbf{t}$ are the **dot product** and the **scalar product** of $\mathbf{v}$ and $\mathbf{t}$.

EXAMPLE 2.   Is $(6, -9)$ perpendicular to $(3, 2)$? to $(1, \frac{1}{3})$?

Solution: $(6, -9) \cdot (3, 2) = 6 \cdot 3 + (-9) \cdot 2 = 18 - 18 = 0;$

$(6, -9) \cdot (1, \frac{1}{3}) = 6 \cdot 1 + (-9) \cdot \frac{1}{3} = 6 - 3 = 3 \neq 0.$

$\therefore (6, -9)$ is perpendicular to $(3, 2)$ but not to $(1, \frac{1}{3})$, **Answer.**

EXAMPLE 3.   Let $M = \{(x, y): (x, y) \text{ and } (5, -2) \text{ are perpendicular}\}$ and
$N = \{(x, y): 5x = 2y\}$ be subsets of $\Re \times \Re$.
Prove that $M = N$.

Solution: $(x, y) \cdot (5, -2) = 5x - 2y$

$\therefore (x, y) \cdot (5, -2) = 0$ if and only if $5x = 2y.$

$\therefore M = N.$

The following example indicates several important properties of inner products.

EXAMPLE 4.   Verify that each statement is true:

a. $(4, -1) \cdot (7, 1) = (7, 1) \cdot (4, -1)$

b. $-5[(4, -1) \cdot (7, 1)] = [-5(4, -1)] \cdot (7, 1)$

c. $(4, -1) \cdot [(7, 1) + (-3, 0)]$
$= (4, -1) \cdot (7, 1) + (4, -1) \cdot (-3, 0)$

d. $(4, -1) \cdot (4, -1) = \|(4, -1)\|^2$

Solution: **a.** $(4, -1) \cdot (7, 1) = 4 \cdot 7 + (-1)1 = 27$
$(7, 1) \cdot (4, -1) = 7 \cdot 4 + 1(-1) = 27$

b. $-5[(4, -1) \cdot (7, 1)] = -5(27) = -135$
$[-5(4, -1)] \cdot (7, 1) = (-20, 5) \cdot (7, 1) = -135$

c. $(4, -1) \cdot [(7, 1) + (-3, 0)] = (4, -1) \cdot (4, 1) = 15$
$(4, -1) \cdot (7, 1) + (4, -1) \cdot (-3, 0) = 27 - 12 = 15$

d. $(4, -1) \cdot (4, -1) = 4^2 + (-1)^2 = \|(4, -1)\|^2.$

The proofs of the following properties are left as exercises (page 153).

Properties of the Inner Product of Vectors

Let **v**, **t**, **u**, and **s** denote any elements of $\mathcal{R} \times \mathcal{R}$, and let r denote any real number.

SUBSTITUTION PROPERTY   If $\mathbf{v} = \mathbf{u}$ and $\mathbf{t} = \mathbf{s}$, $\mathbf{v} \cdot \mathbf{t} = \mathbf{u} \cdot \mathbf{s}$.

COMMUTATIVE PROPERTY $\mathbf{v} \cdot \mathbf{t} = \mathbf{t} \cdot \mathbf{v}$.

ASSOCIATIVE PROPERTY $r(\mathbf{v} \cdot \mathbf{t}) = (r\mathbf{v}) \cdot \mathbf{t}$.

DISTRIBUTIVE PROPERTY $\mathbf{v} \cdot (\mathbf{t} + \mathbf{s}) = \mathbf{v} \cdot \mathbf{t} + \mathbf{v} \cdot \mathbf{s}$ and
$(\mathbf{t} + \mathbf{s}) \cdot \mathbf{v} = \mathbf{t} \cdot \mathbf{v} + \mathbf{s} \cdot \mathbf{v}$.

NORM PROPERTY $\mathbf{v} \cdot \mathbf{v} = \|\mathbf{v}\|^2$.

Using inner products, we can deduce other facts concerning vectors.

EXAMPLE 5.   Prove that for any vectors **v** and **t**

   a. $\|\mathbf{v} + \mathbf{t}\|^2 = \|\mathbf{v}\|^2 + 2\mathbf{v} \cdot \mathbf{t} + \|\mathbf{t}\|^2$ and

   b. $\|\mathbf{v} - \mathbf{t}\|^2 = \|\mathbf{v}\|^2 - 2\mathbf{v} \cdot \mathbf{t} + \|\mathbf{t}\|^2$.

Solution: **a.** By the properties of inner products:

$$\|\mathbf{v} + \mathbf{t}\|^2 = (\mathbf{v} + \mathbf{t}) \cdot (\mathbf{v} + \mathbf{t})$$
$$= (\mathbf{v} + \mathbf{t}) \cdot \mathbf{v} + (\mathbf{v} + \mathbf{t}) \cdot \mathbf{t}$$
$$= \mathbf{v} \cdot \mathbf{v} + \mathbf{t} \cdot \mathbf{v} + \mathbf{v} \cdot \mathbf{t} + \mathbf{t} \cdot \mathbf{t}$$
$$= \|\mathbf{v}\|^2 + \mathbf{v} \cdot \mathbf{t} + \mathbf{v} \cdot \mathbf{t} + \|\mathbf{t}\|^2.$$
$$\therefore \|\mathbf{v} + \mathbf{t}\|^2 = \|\mathbf{v}\|^2 + 2\mathbf{v} \cdot \mathbf{t} + \|\mathbf{t}\|^2.$$

Since $\mathbf{v} - \mathbf{t} = \mathbf{v} + (-\mathbf{t})$ and $\|-\mathbf{t}\| = \|\mathbf{t}\|$, and also $\mathbf{v} \cdot (-\mathbf{t}) = (-1)\mathbf{v} \cdot \mathbf{t}$, (b) follows as a corollary of (a).

EXAMPLE 6.   An aircraft carrier is traveling due north at 25 knots.   A crew member runs across the deck in an easterly direction at 5 knots. How fast is he traveling with respect to the earth?

Solution: **s** represents the ship's velocity, and **w** the velocity of the crew member. $\therefore$ **s** + **w** represents the resultant velocity of the man relative to the earth.   North and East are perpendicular directions.   Hence:

$$\|\mathbf{s} + \mathbf{w}\|^2 = \|\mathbf{s}\|^2 + \|\mathbf{w}\|^2 + 2\mathbf{s} \cdot \mathbf{w} \text{ (Ex. 5)}$$
$$= 625 + 25 + 2 \cdot 0 = 650$$
$$\therefore \|\mathbf{s} + \mathbf{w}\| \doteq 25.5$$

From the second equality proved in Example 5 you can obtain an interesting expression for $\mathbf{v} \cdot \mathbf{t}$. You find:

$$2\mathbf{v} \cdot \mathbf{t} = \|\mathbf{v}\|^2 + \|\mathbf{t}\|^2 - \|\mathbf{v} - \mathbf{t}\|^2,$$
$$\text{or } \mathbf{v} \cdot \mathbf{t} = \tfrac{1}{2}[\|\mathbf{v}\|^2 + \|\mathbf{t}\|^2 - \|\mathbf{v} - \mathbf{t}\|^2].$$

EXAMPLE 7. Determine the inner product of two vectors $\mathbf{v}$ and $\mathbf{t}$ whose norms are 5 and 3, if the norm of the vector $\mathbf{v} - \mathbf{t}$ is 6.

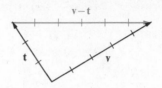

Solution: Using the expression obtained above, you obtain

$$\mathbf{v} \cdot \mathbf{t} = \tfrac{1}{2}[5^2 + 3^2 - 6^2] = \tfrac{1}{2}(-2) = -1, \textbf{ Answer.}$$

Exercises

Given: **v** and **u** are vectors and r and s are scalars. State which of the following are vectors and which are scalars.

1. $-\mathbf{v}$
2. $\|\mathbf{u}\|$ S
3. $\mathbf{u} + \mathbf{v}$

4. $\mathbf{u} \cdot \mathbf{v}$ S
5. $r\mathbf{u}$
6. rs S

7. $\|\mathbf{u} + \mathbf{v}\|$
8. $s(\mathbf{u} + \mathbf{v})$ ✓
9. $\mathbf{v}(r + s)$

10. $\|\mathbf{v}\| + \|\mathbf{u}\|$ S
11. $\mathbf{v} \cdot (\mathbf{v} + \mathbf{u})$
12. $|r + s|$ S

Find each inner product.

13. $(3, 2) \cdot (5, -1)$
14. $(2, -1) \cdot (3, 4)$ 2
15. $(0, 3) \cdot (3, 0)$

16. $(\sqrt{2}, 5) \cdot (\sqrt{2}, -3)$ -13
17. $(2\sqrt{3}, \sqrt{3}) \cdot (\sqrt{2}, 4\sqrt{3})$
18. $(a, b) \cdot (c, d)$ $(ac + bd)$

State whether the given vectors are perpendicular or nonperpendicular.

19. $(3, -1); (2, -6)$
20. $(-2, 8); (-3, -\tfrac{3}{4})$
21. $(\tfrac{2}{3}, -\tfrac{1}{4}); (-\tfrac{3}{2}, 4)$

22. $(6, 2\sqrt{3}); (\sqrt{3}, -3)$
23. $\mathbf{r}; -\mathbf{r}$ $(\mathbf{r} \neq 0)$
24. $(a, 0); (0, -a)$ $(a \neq 0)$

Find k if the given vectors are **(a)** perpendicular, **(b)** parallel.

25. $(3, 4); (6, k)$
26. $(-2, 5); (10, k)$

27. $(k, 2); (\sqrt{3}, 6)$
28. $(2, 4); (k, \sqrt{3})$

29. $(\sqrt{3}, k); (2, 6)$
30. $(4, 3); (-3, k)$

Show that the specified subsets of $\Re \times \Re$ are equal.

31. $\{(x, y): (x, y) \text{ and } (4, -5) \text{ are perpendicular}\}$; $\{(x, y): y = \frac{4}{5}x\}$

32. $\{(x, y): (x, y) \text{ and } (5, -2) \text{ are parallel}\}$; $\{(x, y): x = 5k, y = -2k; k \in \Re\}$

Let $\mathbf{r} = (-2, 3)$, $\mathbf{s} = (3, -2)$, and $\mathbf{t} = (4, -1)$. Verify each statement.

33. $\mathbf{r} \cdot \mathbf{s} = \mathbf{s} \cdot \mathbf{r}$ 35. $\mathbf{t} \cdot (\mathbf{r} + \mathbf{s}) = \mathbf{t} \cdot \mathbf{r} + \mathbf{t} \cdot \mathbf{s}$

34. $3(\mathbf{s} \cdot \mathbf{t}) = (3\mathbf{s}) \cdot \mathbf{t}$ 36. $\mathbf{s} \cdot (\mathbf{t} - \mathbf{r}) = \mathbf{s} \cdot \mathbf{t} - \mathbf{s} \cdot \mathbf{r}$

In each exercise find a vector $\mathbf{v} \neq \mathbf{0}$ such that $\mathbf{r} \cdot \mathbf{v} = 0$.

37. $\mathbf{r} = (0, 2)$ 38. $\mathbf{r} = (-1, 3)$ 39. $\mathbf{r} = (\sqrt{2}, 2)$ 40. $\mathbf{r} = (0, \sqrt{3})$

Given: $\mathbf{v}$, $\mathbf{t}$, elements of $\Re \times \Re$; $r \in \Re$. Prove the given property of inner products.

B

41. Commutative: $\mathbf{v} \cdot \mathbf{t} = \mathbf{t} \cdot \mathbf{v}$ 43. Norm: $\mathbf{v} \cdot \mathbf{v} = \|\mathbf{v}\|^2$

42. Associative: $r(\mathbf{v} \cdot \mathbf{t}) = (r\mathbf{v}) \cdot \mathbf{t}$ 44. $\mathbf{v} \cdot \mathbf{0} = 0$

45. Show that $[(2, 3) \cdot (5, 1)] (-2, 4) \neq (2, 3) [(5, 1) \cdot (-2, 4)]$.

46. In the given vector representation the ordered pairs are coordinates of points. Find $\mathbf{v}$ and $\mathbf{t}$ and show that:

$$2\mathbf{v} \cdot \mathbf{t} = \|\mathbf{v}\|^2 + \|\mathbf{t}\|^2 - \|\mathbf{v} - \mathbf{t}\|^2.$$

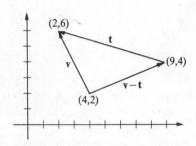

In Exercises 47–48 prove the given property of inner products assuming $\mathbf{v}$, $\mathbf{u}$, $\mathbf{t}$, and $\mathbf{s}$ are elements of $\Re \times \Re$.

47. Substitution: If $\mathbf{v} = \mathbf{u}$ and $\mathbf{t} = \mathbf{s}$, $\mathbf{v} \cdot \mathbf{t} = \mathbf{u} \cdot \mathbf{s}$.

48. Distributive: $\mathbf{v} \cdot (\mathbf{t} + \mathbf{s}) = \mathbf{v} \cdot \mathbf{t} + \mathbf{v} \cdot \mathbf{s}$ and $(\mathbf{t} + \mathbf{s}) \cdot \mathbf{v} = \mathbf{t} \cdot \mathbf{v} + \mathbf{s} \cdot \mathbf{v}$.

49. A ship sails east at 18 m.p.h. A man walks across the deck directly south at 3 m.p.h. What is his velocity relative to the water?

50. A man wishes to go by motor boat directly across a river of width 2 miles. The water is moving south at 5 m.p.h. and the boat can travel 20 m.p.h. On the basis of a vector diagram, approximate the angle at which he should head the boat upstream if he wishes to reach a point directly opposite his starting point.

Given: **v** and **t** elements of $\mathcal{R} \times \mathcal{R}$. Prove each assertion.

51. **v** is perpendicular to **t** if and only if $\|\mathbf{v} + \mathbf{t}\| = \|\mathbf{v} - \mathbf{t}\|$.

52. $(\mathbf{v} - \mathbf{t}) \cdot (\mathbf{v} + \mathbf{t}) = \|\mathbf{v}\|^2 - \|\mathbf{t}\|^2$.

53. For any vectors **v** and **t**, $\mathbf{v} \cdot \mathbf{t} \leq \|\mathbf{v}\| \cdot \|\mathbf{t}\|$.

54. Show that the specified subsets of $\mathcal{R} \times \mathcal{R}$ are equal.

$$\{(x, y): (x, y) = (2, 3) + k(-1, 1)\} \,;\, \{(x, y): y = 5 - x\}$$

4–7 Relationships among Parallel and Perpendicular Vectors

To discover an easy way of deciding whether two vectors are parallel, examine the representations of the parallel vectors (2, 3) and (4, 6) in Figure 4–25. The diagram suggests that asserting $(2, 3)$ and (4, 6) to be parallel is equivalent to claiming that $(-3, 2)$ and (4, 6) are perpendicular. The latter vectors are indeed perpendicular since $(-3, 2) \cdot (4, 6) = 0$.   Noting that $(-3, 2)$ is formed by interchanging the coordinates of (2, 3) and replacing one coordinate by its negative leads to the following assertion.

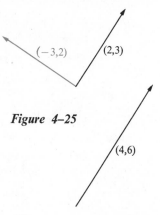

Figure 4–25

| THEOREM | Let $\mathbf{t} = (t_1, t_2)$ and $\mathbf{v} = (v_1, v_2)$ denote vectors in $\mathcal{R} \times \mathcal{R}$. Then **t** is parallel to **v** if and only if **t** and $\mathbf{v_p}$, where $\mathbf{v_p} = (-v_2, v_1)$, are perpendicular vectors.

Proof: 1. We begin with the "only if" part. Suppose **t** is parallel to **v**. If $\mathbf{v} = \mathbf{0}$, then $\mathbf{v_p} = \mathbf{0}$ and $\mathbf{t} \cdot \mathbf{v_p} = 0$. If $\mathbf{v} \neq \mathbf{0}$, there is a real number r such that $\mathbf{t} = r(v_1, v_2)$. Hence we may write $\mathbf{t} \cdot \mathbf{v_p} = r(v_1, v_2) \cdot (-v_2, v_1) = r(-v_1 v_2 + v_2 v_1) = r(0) = 0$. In each case, $\mathbf{t} \cdot \mathbf{v_p} = 0$, so that **t** and $\mathbf{v_p}$ are perpendicular vectors.

2. Next, for the "if" part, suppose **t** and $\mathbf{v_p}$ are perpendicular vectors. Then, $\mathbf{t} \cdot \mathbf{v_p} = 0$. Hence $-t_1 v_2 + t_2 v_1 = 0$, or $t_2 v_1 = t_1 v_2$. If $\mathbf{v_p} = \mathbf{0}$, then $\mathbf{v} = \mathbf{0}$; and **t** and **v** are parallel. (Why?) If $\mathbf{v_p} \neq \mathbf{0}$, either $v_1 \neq 0$ or $v_2 \neq 0$. If $v_1 \neq 0$, $t_2 = \dfrac{t_1}{v_1} v_2$ and

$(t_1, t_2) = \dfrac{t_1}{v_1} (v_1, v_2)$; if $v_2 \neq 0$, $t_1 = \dfrac{t_2}{v_2} v_1$ and

$(t_1, t_2) = \dfrac{t_2}{v_2} (v_1, v_2)$.

Thus, in each case **t** and **v** are parallel.

The following corollary provides another way to test whether vectors are parallel.

COROLLARY. $t = (t_1, t_2)$ and $v = (v_1, v_2)$ are parallel vectors if and only if

$$t \cdot v_P = -t_1 v_2 + t_2 v_1 = 0.$$

EXAMPLE. State whether the vectors in each pair are parallel:

      a. $(\frac{15}{2}, -6)$, $(-5, 4)$; **b.** $(-3, -6)$, $(6, 10)$.

Solution: **a.** $(\frac{15}{2}, -6) \cdot (-4, -5)$
            $= -\frac{15}{2}(4) + (-6)(-5)$
            $= -30 + 30 = 0.$
     $\therefore (\frac{15}{2}, -6)$ and $(-5, 4)$ are parallel, **Answer.**

      b. $(-3, -6) \cdot (-10, 6)$
            $= -3(-10) + (-6)6$
            $= 30 - 36 \neq 0.$
     $\therefore (-3, -6)$ and $(6, 10)$ are not parallel, **Answer.**

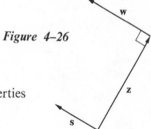

Figure 4–26

Figure 4–26 suggests two important properties of vectors.

THEOREM	In $\Re \times \Re$ a vector perpendicular to one of two non-zero parallel vectors is perpendicular to the other.

THEOREM	In $\Re \times \Re$ two vectors perpendicular to the same nonzero vector are parallel.

To deduce the first property, suppose that **w** and **s** are nonzero parallel vectors, and that **z** is a vector perpendicular to **w**. Then, for some real number a, $s = aw$, and $w \cdot z = 0$. Therefore, $s \cdot z = (aw) \cdot z = a(w \cdot z) = a(0) = 0$. Hence, **z** is perpendicular to **s**.

To prove the second property, let **s** and **w** be vectors, each perpendicular to $z = (z_1, z_2) \neq 0$. Write $v = (z_2, -z_1)$, so that $v_P = z$. Therefore, **s** and **w** are both perpendicular to v_P, and by the theorem stated on page 154, must both be parallel to **v**. Consequently, since $v \neq 0$, the theorem stated on page 145 implies that **s** and **w** are parallel vectors.

Exercises

In the given vector representation
determine **r, s, t, u,** and **v.** Then
verify each statement.

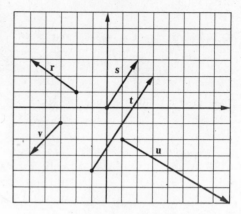

A   1.   **r** is perpendicular to **s.**

     2.   **s** is parallel to **t.**

     3.   **v** is not parallel to **t.**

     4.   **v** is not perpendicular to **u.**

     5.   **u** is not parallel to **r.**

     6.   **s** is not perpendicular to **u.**

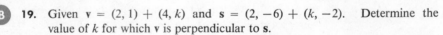

Determine whether the vectors in each pair are parallel, perpendicular, or
neither.

   7. $(3, -5); (4, -\frac{20}{3})$ **10.** $(\sqrt{2}, \sqrt{3}); (\sqrt{6}, -2)$

   8. $(3, 7); (7, -3)$ **11.** $(\frac{2}{3}, \frac{2}{3}); (1, -1)$

   9. $(4, 6); (-2, 3)$ **12.** $(\sqrt{3}, -2); (6, -4\sqrt{3})$

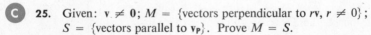

Find the value of k for which each pair of vectors is **(a)** perpendicular; **(b)** parallel.
In Exercises 17–18 assume no vector entry is zero.

   13. $(3, -5); (5, k)$ **16.** $(3, \sqrt{2}); (-\sqrt{2}, k)$

   14. $(k, 5); (\sqrt{3}, 3)$ **17.** $(r, s); (-s, k)$

   15. $(k, -1); (5, -10)$ **18.** $(a, k); (c, d)$

B   **19.**   Given $\mathbf{v} = (2, 1) + (4, k)$ and $\mathbf{s} = (2, -6) + (k, -2)$. Determine the
value of k for which **v** is perpendicular to **s.**

     20.   Given $\mathbf{r} = (6, 4\sqrt{2})$ and $\mathbf{s} = (-2, 8)$. Show that $\mathbf{r} + \mathbf{s}$ is perpendicular to
$\mathbf{r} - \mathbf{s}$.

     21.   Prove: No vector other than $(0, 0)$ can be perpendicular to itself.

     22.   Prove: **0** is perpendicular to every vector.

     23.   Prove: If a nonzero vector **s** is perpendicular to **t,** $-\mathbf{s}$ is perpendicular to **t.**

     24.   Prove: If **v** is perpendicular to **s,** then, for any scalars k and r, $k\mathbf{v}$ is per-
pendicular to $r\mathbf{s}$.

C   **25.**   Given: $\mathbf{v} \neq \mathbf{0}$; $M = \{$vectors perpendicular to $r\mathbf{v}, r \neq 0\}$;
$S = \{$vectors parallel to $\mathbf{v_P}\}$. Prove $M = S$.

     26.   Prove: $(\mathbf{v_P})_P = -\mathbf{v}$.

4-8 Perpendicular Components of Vectors

In $\Re \times \Re$ two perpendicular vectors **w** and **t** whose sum is **v** are called **perpendicular components** of **v** (Figure 4–27). Expressing a vector as a sum of perpendicular components, one of which has a prescribed direction, is called **resolving the vector**.

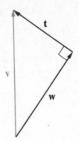

Figure 4–27

EXAMPLE 1. Setting a course of 145° at 20 knots, a freighter sails from a port on a straight coastline whose direction is 165°. How far from shore is the ship 30 minutes after departure?

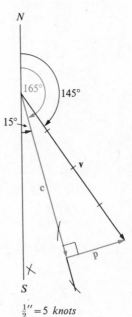

Solution: In the scale drawing, **v**, the velocity of the freighter, is shown as the sum of two velocities: **c** parallel to the coastline, and **p** perpendicular to the coast. Measurement on the diagram shows $\|\mathbf{p}\|$ to be approximately 7 knots. Therefore, 30 minutes after departure the ship is about $7 \times 6076 \times \frac{1}{2}$, or 21,300, feet from shore, **Answer.**

$\frac{1}{2}'' = 5$ *knots*

Let $\mathbf{u} = (u_1, u_2)$ be a unit vector in a prescribed direction. Every vector parallel to **u** is a real-number multiple of **u**, while every vector perpendicular to **u** is a real-number multiple of $\mathbf{u_p} = (-u_2, u_1)$. Consequently, a graphical argument as in the solution of Example 1 would suggest that for any vector **v** you can find unique real numbers a and b such that $\mathbf{v} = a\mathbf{u} + b\mathbf{u_p}$ (Figure 4–28).

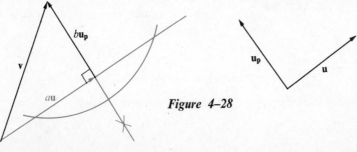

Figure 4–28

You can prove that **v** can be resolved in this fashion by proving that:
(1) There is *at most one pair* of real numbers a and b such that
   $\mathbf{v} = a\mathbf{u} + b\mathbf{u_P}$; and
(2) There *is a pair* of real numbers a and b such that $\mathbf{v} = a\mathbf{u} + b\mathbf{u_P}$.

Proof: (1) Let a and b be real numbers such that

$$\mathbf{v} = a\mathbf{u} + b\mathbf{u_P}.$$

Then
$$\mathbf{u} \cdot \mathbf{v} = \mathbf{u} \cdot (a\mathbf{u} + b\mathbf{u_P})$$
$$= a(\mathbf{u} \cdot \mathbf{u}) + b(\mathbf{u} \cdot \mathbf{u_P}).$$

Since **u** is a unit vector, $\mathbf{u} \cdot \mathbf{u} = \|\mathbf{u}\|^2 = 1^2 = 1$. Also, $\mathbf{u} \cdot \mathbf{u_P} = 0$.

$$\mathbf{u} \cdot \mathbf{v} = a(1) + b(0) = a.$$

Similarly,
$$\mathbf{u_P} \cdot \mathbf{v} = \mathbf{u_P} \cdot (a\mathbf{u} + b\mathbf{u_P})$$
$$= a(\mathbf{u_P} \cdot \mathbf{u}) + b(\mathbf{u_P} \cdot \mathbf{u_P})$$
$$= a(0) + b(1)$$
$$= b.$$

Thus, the only real numbers that can possibly play the roles of a and b are $\mathbf{u} \cdot \mathbf{v}$ and $\mathbf{u_P} \cdot \mathbf{v}$.

(2) To complete the argument, you must verify that $\mathbf{u} \cdot \mathbf{v}$ and $\mathbf{u_P} \cdot \mathbf{v}$ really do play the roles required of a and b, that is, that

$$\mathbf{v} = (\mathbf{u} \cdot \mathbf{v})\mathbf{u} + (\mathbf{u_P} \cdot \mathbf{v})\mathbf{u_P}.$$

You have

$$(\mathbf{u} \cdot \mathbf{v})\mathbf{u} = (u_1 v_1 + u_2 v_2)(u_1, u_2) \quad = (u_1^2 v_1 + u_1 u_2 v_2, \, u_1 u_2 v_1 + u_2^2 v_2)$$
$$(\mathbf{u_P} \cdot \mathbf{v})\mathbf{u_P} = (-u_2 v_1 + u_1 v_2)(-u_2, u_1) = (u_2^2 v_1 - u_1 u_2 v_2, \, -u_1 u_2 v_1 + u_1^2 v_2)$$
$$\therefore \ (\mathbf{u} \cdot \mathbf{v})\mathbf{u} + (\mathbf{u_P} \cdot \mathbf{v})\mathbf{u_P} = [(u_1^2 + u_2^2)v_1, \, (u_1^2 + u_2^2)v_2].$$

But **u** is a unit vector; therefore, $u_1^2 + u_2^2 = 1$. Hence,

$$(\mathbf{u} \cdot \mathbf{v})\mathbf{u} + (\mathbf{u_P} \cdot \mathbf{v})\mathbf{u_P} = (v_1, v_2) = \mathbf{v}.$$

Thus, the following theorem is true.

THEOREM   Let **u** be a unit vector and **v** be any vector in $\mathcal{R} \times \mathcal{R}$. Then there are unique real numbers $a = \mathbf{u} \cdot \mathbf{v}$ and $b = \mathbf{u_P} \cdot \mathbf{v}$ such that

$$\mathbf{v} = a\mathbf{u} + b\mathbf{u_P},$$

where $\mathbf{u} = (u_1, u_2)$ and $\mathbf{u_P} = (-u_2, u_1)$.

We call the expression $a\mathbf{u} + b\mathbf{u_P}$ a *linear combination* of **u** and $\mathbf{u_P}$.

EXAMPLE 2. Express $\mathbf{v} = (7, 3)$ as a linear combination of $\mathbf{u} = (1, 0)$ and $\mathbf{u_P} = (0, 1)$.

Solution: $\mathbf{u} \cdot \mathbf{v} = (1, 0) \cdot (7, 3) = 7$
$\mathbf{u_P} \cdot \mathbf{v} = (0, 1) \cdot (7, 3) = 3$
$\therefore \mathbf{v} = 7(1, 0) + 3(0, 1)$, **Answer.**

Frequently, it is convenient to express a vector as a linear combination of nonzero perpendicular vectors which are not unit vectors. The theorem stated on page 158 provides the method. For, if $\mathbf{w} \neq \mathbf{0}$, $\dfrac{\mathbf{w}}{\|\mathbf{w}\|}$ is the unit vector in the same direction as $\mathbf{w}$. Applying the theorem with $\mathbf{u} = \dfrac{\mathbf{w}}{\|\mathbf{w}\|}$ and $\mathbf{u_P} = \dfrac{\mathbf{w_P}}{\|\mathbf{w}\|}$, you find

$$\mathbf{v} = \left(\frac{\mathbf{w}}{\|\mathbf{w}\|} \cdot \mathbf{v}\right) \frac{\mathbf{w}}{\|\mathbf{w}\|} + \left(\frac{\mathbf{w_P}}{\|\mathbf{w}\|} \cdot \mathbf{v}\right) \frac{\mathbf{w_P}}{\|\mathbf{w}\|}.$$

$$\therefore \mathbf{v} = \left(\frac{\mathbf{w} \cdot \mathbf{v}}{\|\mathbf{w}\|^2}\right) \mathbf{w} + \left(\frac{\mathbf{w_P} \cdot \mathbf{v}}{\|\mathbf{w}\|^2}\right) \mathbf{w_P}.$$

We call $\left(\dfrac{\mathbf{w} \cdot \mathbf{v}}{\|\mathbf{w}\|^2}\right) \mathbf{w}$ the **component** of $\mathbf{v}$ **parallel** to $\mathbf{w}$, and denote it by $\mathbf{Comp_w\, v}$. The vector $\dfrac{\mathbf{w_P} \cdot \mathbf{v}}{\|\mathbf{w}\|^2} \mathbf{w_P}$ is the **component** of $\mathbf{v}$ **perpendicular** to $\mathbf{w}$; its designation is $\mathbf{Comp_{w_P}\, v}$.

EXAMPLE 3. Determine the components of $\mathbf{v} = (-7, 4)$ parallel and perpendicular to $\mathbf{w} = (1, -2)$.

Solution: $\mathbf{Comp_w\, v} = \dfrac{\mathbf{w} \cdot \mathbf{v}}{\|\mathbf{w}\|^2} \mathbf{w}$

$$= \frac{(1, -2) \cdot (-7, 4)}{(1, -2) \cdot (1, -2)} (1, -2) = -3(1, -2)$$

$\mathbf{Comp_{w_P}\, v} = \dfrac{\mathbf{w_P} \cdot \mathbf{v}}{\|\mathbf{w}\|^2} \mathbf{w_P}$

$$= \frac{(2, 1) \cdot (-7, 4)}{(1, -2) \cdot (1, -2)} (2, 1) = -2(2, 1)$$

$[-3(1, -2), -2(2, 1)]$, **Answer.**

As a check, verify that

$\mathbf{v} = \mathbf{Comp_w\, v} + \mathbf{Comp_{w_P}\, v}$.
$(-7, 4) \overset{?}{=} -3(1, -2) - 2(2, 1)$
$\overset{?}{=} (-3, 6) + (-4, -2)$
$(-7, 4) = (-7, 4)$

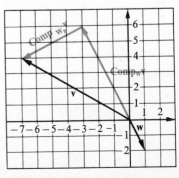

The scalars $\dfrac{\mathbf{w} \cdot \mathbf{v}}{\|\mathbf{w}\|}$ and $\dfrac{\mathbf{w_p} \cdot \mathbf{v}}{\|\mathbf{w}\|}$ are called the **scalar components of v parallel** and

perpendicular to w. We write $\mathrm{Comp_w}\ \mathbf{v} = \dfrac{\mathbf{w} \cdot \mathbf{v}}{\|\mathbf{w}\|}$ and $\mathrm{Comp_{w_p}}\ \mathbf{v} = \dfrac{\mathbf{w_p} \cdot \mathbf{v}}{\|\mathbf{w}\|}$.

Do you see that $\mathrm{Comp_w}\ \mathbf{v} = \|\mathbf{Comp_w}\ \mathbf{v}\|$ or $-\|\mathbf{Comp_w}\ \mathbf{v}\|$ according as w and $\mathbf{Comp_w}\ \mathbf{v}$ have the same direction or opposite directions?

(handwritten: $\|v\| = \sqrt{3^2 + 2^2} = \sqrt{9+4} = \sqrt{13}$ $\frac{3}{\sqrt{13}}, \frac{-2}{\sqrt{13}}$)

Exercises

For each given vector **v** determine a unit vector in the same direction.

A

1. $\mathbf{v} = (3, -2)$ *(handwritten: $\frac{3\sqrt{13}}{13}, \frac{-2\sqrt{13}}{13}$)*

2. $\mathbf{v} = (-2, 5)$

3. $\mathbf{v} = (a, -b)$, $\mathbf{v} \neq \mathbf{0}$

4. $\mathbf{v} = (3 + \sqrt{2}, 3 - \sqrt{2})$

Which of the following are unit vectors?

5. $(4, \frac{1}{2})$

6. $\left(-\frac{1}{2}, \frac{\sqrt{3}}{2}\right)$ *(handwritten: $\sqrt{3+4}\quad ?\cdot 5$)*

7. $\left(\dfrac{1}{\sqrt{2}}, -\dfrac{1}{\sqrt{2}}\right)$

8. $\left(\dfrac{1 - \sqrt{2}}{2}, \dfrac{1 + \sqrt{2}}{2}\right)$

For what value(s) of k is each of the following a unit vector?

9. $\left(\dfrac{3}{k}, \dfrac{4}{k}\right)$ 10. $\left(\dfrac{1}{3}, \dfrac{k}{3}\right)$ 11. $\left(\dfrac{\sqrt{2}}{k}, \dfrac{\sqrt{7}}{k}\right)$ 12. $\left(\dfrac{2}{5}, \dfrac{k}{10}\right)$

Represent the vector **v** as an arrow in a coordinate plane with initial point at $(2, 3)$. Draw and give a formula for the resolution of **v** into two perpendicular components **w** and **t** such that **t** is parallel to the x-axis. Represent **w** and **t** as arrows with the same initial point as **v** and indicate the norm of each.

13. $\mathbf{v} = (4, 6)$ 14. $\mathbf{v} = (-3, 4)$ 15. $\mathbf{v} = (2, -5)$ 16. $\mathbf{v} = (-4, -5)$

Given $\mathbf{w} + \mathbf{t} = \mathbf{v}$. In each exercise find **t** and tell whether **w** and **t** are perpendicular components of **v**.

17. $\mathbf{w} = (-3, 5)$; $\mathbf{v} = (8, -2)$

18. $\mathbf{w} = (5, 3)$; $\mathbf{v} = (8, 8)$

19. $\mathbf{w} = (-5, 10)$; $\mathbf{v} = (-1, 12)$

20. $\mathbf{w} = (2, -4)$; $\mathbf{v} = (10, 8)$

In Exercises 21–22 make a scale drawing of the given figure. Then graphically resolve **v** into two perpendicular component vectors, one of which lies along l. Approximate the norm of each component vector.

21.

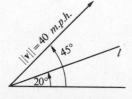

22.

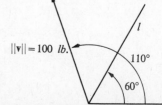

Express **v** as a linear combination of **u** $= (1, 0)$ and $\mathbf{u_P} = (0, 1)$.

23. $\mathbf{v} = (5, -2)$ **25.** $\mathbf{v} = (-4, -2)$ **27.** $\mathbf{v} = (-2, \sqrt{5})$

24. $\mathbf{v} = (3, -1)$ **26.** $\mathbf{v} = (0, 5)$ **28.** $\mathbf{v} = (\sqrt{3}, -2)$

For what value(s) of k will the given vector be a unit vector?

B

29. $\left(\dfrac{1}{k}, 0\right)$ **31.** $\left(\dfrac{k}{5}, \dfrac{k+1}{5}\right)$

30. $(k - 1, k)$ **32.** $\left(\dfrac{k-2}{13}, \dfrac{k+5}{13}\right)$

In Exercises 33–38 determine the components of **v** parallel to and perpendicular to **w**. In each exercise show that the sum of the components is **v**.

33. $\mathbf{v} = (5, 3); \mathbf{w} = (1, -3)$ **36.** $\mathbf{v} = (3, 2); \mathbf{w} = (-1, -4)$

34. $\mathbf{v} = (3, -1); \mathbf{w} = (4, 2)$ **37.** $\mathbf{v} = (2\sqrt{3}, \sqrt{3}); \mathbf{w} = (2, -1)$

35. $\mathbf{v} = (6, -2); \mathbf{w} = (0, 3)$ **38.** $\mathbf{v} = (4, \sqrt{3}); \mathbf{w} = (\sqrt{3}, -1)$

Find the unit vector **u** such that

39. $(2, 11) = 10\mathbf{u} + 5\mathbf{u_P}$ **40.** $(8, 2) = 3\sqrt{2}\mathbf{u} + 5\sqrt{2}\mathbf{u_P}$

In Exercises 41–42 state approximations on the basis of a scale drawing.

41. A force of 50 pounds is applied in a direction 40° north of east. Find the scalar components of this force in the directions east and north.

42. A ship heads in the direction 80° at 25 knots. The tide is running at 5 knots in the direction 45°. Find the resultant speed and direction of the ship.

C

43. Find a scalar r and a vector **v** such that **v** is perpendicular to $(-2, 4)$ and $r(-2, 4) + \mathbf{v} = (2, 16)$.

44. Prove: For any two vectors **v** and **w**,

$$\|\mathbf{v}\|^2 \cdot \|\mathbf{w}\|^2 = (\mathbf{v} \cdot \mathbf{w})^2 + (\mathbf{v} \cdot \mathbf{w_P})^2$$

(*Hint:* Case 1: $\mathbf{w} = \mathbf{0}$. Case 2: $\mathbf{w} \neq \mathbf{0}$; then $\mathbf{v} = \dfrac{(\mathbf{v} \cdot \mathbf{w})\mathbf{w} + (\mathbf{v} \cdot \mathbf{w_P})\mathbf{w_P}}{\|\mathbf{w}\|^2}$.)

45. Show that $\|\mathbf{v}\|^2 \cdot \|\mathbf{w}\|^2 \geq (\mathbf{v} \cdot \mathbf{w})^2$ follows from the assertion in Exercise 44.

46. Show that if **v** and **w** are parallel vectors, then $\|\mathbf{v}\|^2 \cdot \|\mathbf{w}\|^2 = (\mathbf{v} \cdot \mathbf{w})^2$ follows from the assertion in Exercise 44.

47. Given $\mathbf{v} \neq \mathbf{0}$ and $\mathbf{w} \neq \mathbf{0}$. Prove: (**a**) If $\|\mathbf{v}\| \cdot \|\mathbf{w}\| = \mathbf{v} \cdot \mathbf{w}$, then **v** and **w** have the same direction. (**b**) If $-\|\mathbf{v}\| \cdot \|\mathbf{w}\| = \mathbf{v} \cdot \mathbf{w}$, then **v** and **w** have opposite directions.

48. On the basis of the assertion in Exercise 47 prove that for $\mathbf{v} \neq \mathbf{0}$ and $\mathbf{w} \neq \mathbf{0}$, $\|\mathbf{v}\| + \|\mathbf{w}\| = \|\mathbf{v} + \mathbf{w}\|$ if and only if **v** and **w** have the same direction.

Chapter Summary

1. An ordered pair belonging to the set $\mathcal{R} \times \mathcal{R}$ is called a **vector**.

2. A **scalar** is a number belonging to $\mathcal{R}$.

3. Equality of vectors $\qquad$ $(a, b) = (c, d)$, if and only if $a = c$ and $b = d$.

4. Vector arrow representation $\qquad$ The arrow from point (a, b) to point (c, d) represents the unique vector $(c - a, d - b)$.

5. Vector addition $\qquad$ If $\mathbf{v} = (a, b)$ and $\mathbf{t} = (c, d)$, then $\mathbf{v} + \mathbf{t} = (a + c, b + d)$.

6. The zero vector $\qquad$ $(0, 0)$, the identity element for vector addition, is designated by $\mathbf{0}$.

7. The additive inverse vector $\qquad$ If $\mathbf{v} = (a, b)$, its additive inverse is $-\mathbf{v} = (-a, -b)$.

8. Norm of a vector $\qquad$ The norm of $\mathbf{v}$ is designated by $\|\mathbf{v}\|$. If $\mathbf{v} = (a, b)$, $\|\mathbf{v}\| = \sqrt{a^2 + b^2}$.

9. Triangle inequality $\qquad$ $\|\mathbf{v} + \mathbf{t}\| \leq \|\mathbf{v}\| + \|\mathbf{t}\|$.

10. Scalar vector product $\qquad$ If $\mathbf{v} = (a, b)$, $r\mathbf{v} = (ra, rb)$ and $\|r \cdot \mathbf{v}\| = |r| \cdot \|\mathbf{v}\|$.

11. Vector inner product $\qquad$ If $\mathbf{v} = (a, b)$ and $\mathbf{t} = (c, d)$, $\mathbf{v} \cdot \mathbf{t} = (ac + bd)$ and $\mathbf{v} \cdot \mathbf{v} = \|\mathbf{v}\|^2$.

12. Parallel vectors $\qquad$ If $\mathbf{v} = (a, b) \neq (0, 0)$ and $\mathbf{t} = (c, d)$, $\mathbf{v}$ and $\mathbf{t}$ are parallel vectors if, for a scalar r, $c = ra$ and $d = rb$. If $r > 0$, the parallel vectors have same direction. If $r < 0$, the parallel vectors have opposite directions.

13. Perpendicular vectors $\qquad$ If $\mathbf{v} = (a, b)$ and $\mathbf{t} = (c, d)$, $\mathbf{v}$ and $\mathbf{t}$ are perpendicular if and only if $ac + bd = 0$.

14. Unit vector $\qquad$ $\mathbf{v} = (a, b)$ is a unit vector if and only if $a^2 + b^2 = 1$; that is, $\|\mathbf{v}\| = 1$.

15. Perpendicular to a vector $\qquad$ If $\mathbf{v} = (a, b)$, then $\mathbf{v_p}$ designates $(-b, a)$.

16. Expressing a vector in terms of a unit vector $\mathbf{u}$ $\qquad$ $\mathbf{v} = (\mathbf{u} \cdot \mathbf{v})\mathbf{u} + (\mathbf{u_p} \cdot \mathbf{v})\mathbf{u_p}$

17. Expressing a vector in terms of a nonzero vector $\mathbf{w}$ $\qquad$ $\mathbf{v} = \left(\dfrac{\mathbf{w} \cdot \mathbf{v}}{\|\mathbf{w}\|^2}\right)\mathbf{w} + \left(\dfrac{\mathbf{w_p} \cdot \mathbf{v}}{\|\mathbf{w}\|^2}\right)\mathbf{w_p}$

18. The component of $\mathbf{v}$ parallel to $\mathbf{w}$ $\qquad$ $\mathbf{Comp_w}\, \mathbf{v} = \left(\dfrac{\mathbf{w} \cdot \mathbf{v}}{\|\mathbf{w}\|^2}\right)\mathbf{w} \quad (\mathbf{w} \neq \mathbf{0})$

19. The component of $\mathbf{v}$ perpendicular to $\mathbf{w}$ $\qquad$ $\mathbf{Comp_{w_p}}\, \mathbf{v} = \left(\dfrac{\mathbf{w_p} \cdot \mathbf{v}}{\|\mathbf{w}\|^2}\right)\mathbf{w_p} \quad (\mathbf{w} \neq \mathbf{0})$

Chapter Test

4-1   **1.** Find x and y if $(3x - 2, y + 3) = (7, -2)$.

2. If $A = \{3, 2\}$ and $B = \{-1, 4\}$, specify by roster $A \times B$. (3,-1),(2,-1)(2,4)(3

4-2   **3.** Name the vector represented by $\overrightarrow{MN}$ when the respective coordinates of M and N are $(3, -2)$ and $(5, 6)$. (2,8)

4. Sketch the vectors $(3, 5)$ and $(-2, 7)$ in standard position and label the terminal points S and T respectively. Name the vector represented by $\overrightarrow{ST}$. (-5,2)

4-3   **5.** Find r and s in the vector sum: $(r, s) + (-3, 2) = (4, -1)$. r=7 s=-3

6. If $\mathbf{v} = (3, -2)$ and $\mathbf{t} = (5, -4)$, determine the vector $\mathbf{v} - \mathbf{t}$. (-2,2)

4-4   **7.** Find the norm of the vector $(3, -2)$. √13

8. If $\mathbf{r} = (3, 5)$ and $\mathbf{s} = (-2, 1)$, find the scalar $\|\mathbf{r} + \mathbf{s}\|$. √37

4-5   **9.** Are $(5, -3)$ and $(-10, 6)$ vectors having the same direction, opposite directions, or neither? (3/5 -4/5) opposite

10. Find the unit vector with the same direction as $(3, -4)$. $(\frac{3}{5}, -\frac{4}{5})$

4-6   **11.** Find the inner product of $(3, -2)$ and $(5, 3)$. 9

12. For what value of k will $(3, -4)$ and $(k, 6)$ be parallel vectors? k=-9/2

4-7   **13.** If $\mathbf{v} = (2, -3)$, what is $\mathbf{v_p}$? (3,2)

14. What must be true if (a, b) and (c, d) are nonzero perpendicular vectors? ac+bd=0

4-8   **15.** Given $\mathbf{v} = (6, -2)$. Express $\mathbf{v}$ as a linear combination of $\mathbf{u} = (1, 0)$ and $\mathbf{u_p} = (0, 1)$. V=6(1,0) - 2(0,1)

16. Given $\mathbf{s} = (4, 5)$. Determine the vector components of $\mathbf{s}$ parallel to and perpendicular to $\mathbf{w}$ if $\mathbf{w} = (-2, 3)$. componets s||w= $(-\frac{14}{13}, \frac{21}{13})$ s⊥w = $(\frac{66}{13}, \frac{44}{13})$

Reading List

BARNETT, RAYMOND A., and JOHN N. FUJII. *Vectors.* New York: John Wiley and Sons, 1963.

COPELAND, ARTHUR H., SR. *Geometry, Algebra, and Trigonometry by Vector Methods.* New York: The Macmillan Company, 1962.

KELLEY, JOHN L. *Introduction to Modern Algebra.* Princeton, N.J.: D. Van Nostrand Co., Inc., 1960.

NORTON, M. *Basic Concepts of Vectors.* St. Louis: Webster Publishing Company, 1963.

SAWYER, W. W. *A Concrete Approach to Abstract Algebra.* San Francisco: W. H. Freeman and Co., 1959.

SCHOOL MATHEMATICS STUDY GROUP. Mathematics for High School: *Introduction to Matrix Algebra.* New Haven, Conn.: Yale University Press, 1961.

SCHUSTER, S. *Elementary Vector Geometry.* New York: John Wiley and Sons, 1962.

TAYLOR, HOWARD E., and THOMAS L. WADE. *University Freshman Mathematics.* New York: John Wiley and Sons, Inc., 1963.

WESTERN, DONALD W., and VINCENT H. HAAG. *An Introduction to Mathematics.* New York: Holt, Rinehart, & Winston, Inc., 1959.

David Hilbert

Suppose you were asked the following question: Do the medians from adjacent vertices of a triangle to the opposite sides intersect inside or outside the triangle? Most likely you would think that this was a rather simple question whose answer was intuitively obvious. It turns out, however, that the answer cannot be deduced by logical reasoning from Euclid's postulates.

It was difficulties such as this that led the German mathematician David Hilbert (1862–1943) to conclude that Euclid's geometry contained inconsistencies and omissions. He attempted to correct this situation by providing a rigorous logical basis for Euclid's geometry which took into account the omissions he had noted. The results of his study appeared in the classic volume, *Foundations of Geometry* (1899). In this work Hilbert proposed a new set of postulates for Euclidean geometry. Many of them were very similar to those given by Euclid, but there were some important differences. For example, Hilbert included postulates concerning the order of points on a line, an aspect which Euclid had neglected. This work, however, represented a great deal more than a few added or changed postulates; it proposed a whole philosophy of geometry and stirred up a philosophical controversy which has not yet completely subsided.

Euclid had attempted to define concepts such as "point," "line," and "plane." In addition, his postulates were considered to be self-evident truths. Hilbert, on the other hand, made no attempt to define "point," "line," "plane," or relations such as "on" or "between." In fact, he insisted that these terms remain undefined and that they have no intuitive physical interpretation attached to them. Similarly, he did not regard his postulates as obvious truths, but rather as a set of rules stating the way in which the undefined elements and operations could be characterized.

His attitude summarized that of the "Formalists." Their theories were opposed by the "Intuitionists," who believed that mathematics merely records existing physical realities. Both viewpoints have persisted, but the emphasis today seems to be on the formal axiomatic approach. You might be interested in comparing modern high school textbooks with those used ten years ago and noting the degree to which Hilbert's ideas have influenced the teaching of mathematics.

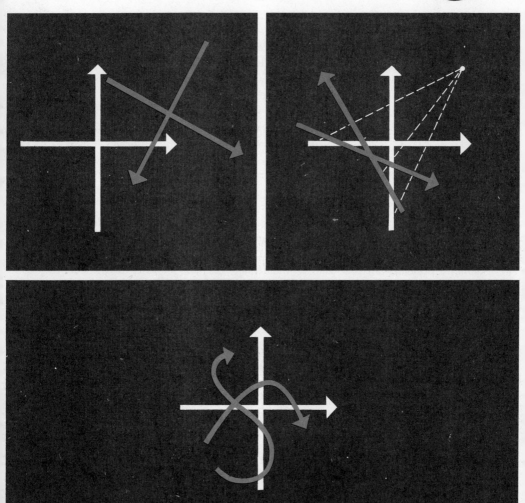

Geometries differ in the kind of transformations (mappings) that may be performed on figures and in the result of these transformations. In Euclidean geometry a transformation of 2 perpendicular lines (white lines) results in 2 perpendicular lines (red lines). In projective geometry a transformation of 2 perpendicular lines results in 2 intersecting lines, not necessarily perpendicular. In topology a transformation of 2 perpendicular lines results in 2 intersecting curves.

Plane Analytic Geometry

of Points and Lines

In Chapter 4, you learned that an ordered pair of real numbers is a vector, and you saw how a vector can be viewed as a displacement and represented by arrows in the plane. In this chapter, you will see how vectors can be used to help you study relationships between points and lines in the plane.

VECTORS, POINTS, AND LINES

5-1 Points in the Plane

In your course in plane geometry, such words as "point," "line," and "distance" were undefined terms about which certain assumptions were made. On the basis of these axioms, other terms were defined and theorems proved. In your course in algebra, you learned that by establishing a co-ordinate system in a plane, you can analyze properties of sets of points and lines by representing these properties in terms of equations and inequalities.

The algebra of vectors also provides an algebraic or *analytic* way of studying plane geometry. In this approach, the notions of geometry are *defined* in terms of vector concepts. The fact that a vector is defined to be any member of $\mathcal{R} \times \mathcal{R}$, and that the members of $\mathcal{R} \times \mathcal{R}$ can be placed in one-to-one correspondence with the points in the geometric plane, makes it possible for us to associate a vector with every point in the plane. Indeed, there is nothing inconsistent *in defining a point to be a vector*, and the plane to be the set of all points (vectors).

You are accustomed to picturing a point such as the one with coordinates $(2, 3)$ by a dot in a rectangular coordinate system and referring to the point by a letter, say P or $P(2, 3)$ (Figure 5–1 on the following page).* You can

---

* Having identified points with vectors, we shall hereafter use boldface letters to designate points.

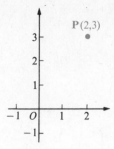

Figure 5–1

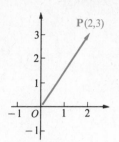

Figure 5–2

also picture (2, 3) as an arrow in standard position (Figure 5–2), which is the way you visualized vectors in Chapter 4. In either case, the diagram has no mathematical significance, but serves simply to guide you in thinking about the abstract concept "point" or "ordered pair of numbers." Therefore, to illustrate or motivate concepts, we shall picture points (ordered pairs of real numbers) by dots or by arrows, depending on which representation provides the greater understanding.

To illustrate the usefulness of this dual interpretation of a vector, look at Figure 5–3. Figure 5–3a shows an *arrow* depiction of two vectors $\mathbf{P} = (x_1, y_1)$

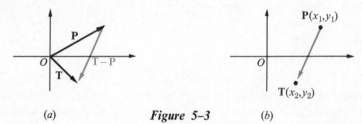

(a)   *Figure 5–3*   (b)

and $\mathbf{T} = (x_2, y_2)$ in standard position, together with the arrow depiction $\mathbf{T} - \mathbf{P}$. Figure 5–3b shows the *point* depiction of the vectors $\mathbf{P}$ and $\mathbf{T}$, together with the arrow representing $\mathbf{T} - \mathbf{P}$. Do you see that these diagrams suggest that the distance between $\mathbf{P}$ and $\mathbf{T}$ should be the norm of the vector $\mathbf{T} - \mathbf{P}$? Hence, let us define the distance between the points $\mathbf{P}(x_1, y_1)$ and $\mathbf{T}(x_2, y_2)$ as follows:

$$d(\mathbf{P}, \mathbf{T}) = \|\mathbf{T} - \mathbf{P}\|.$$

Since (Exercise 29, page 141)

$$\|\mathbf{T} - \mathbf{P}\| = \|\mathbf{P} - \mathbf{T}\|,$$

it follows that $d(\mathbf{P}, \mathbf{T}) = d(\mathbf{T}, \mathbf{P})$. Since $\mathbf{P} = (x_1, y_1)$ and $\mathbf{T} = (x_2, y_2)$, $\mathbf{T} - \mathbf{P} = (x_2 - x_1, y_2 - y_1)$. Therefore, the definition of the norm of a vector implies that

$$d(\mathbf{P}, \mathbf{T}) = \sqrt{(x_2 - x_1)^2 + (y_2 - y_1)^2}.$$

This is, of course, the distance formula with which you are familiar from your earlier study of algebra. When you consider that we motivated our definition of the norm of a vector by using the Pythagorean theorem, which is also used in deriving the distance formula in algebra, this consistency is to be expected.

EXAMPLE. Compute the distance between the points $P(1, 2)$ and $T(-3, 8)$.

Solution: $d(P, T) = \sqrt{(-3 - 1)^2 + (8 - 2)^2} = \sqrt{(-4)^2 + 6^2}$

$\therefore d(P, T) = \sqrt{52} = 2\sqrt{13}$, **Answer.**

Since $d(P, T) = \|T - P\|$, the properties of the norm of a vector that are stated in the theorems on page 139 imply the following properties of the distance between two points.

THEOREM If P, T, and R denote points of the plane, then:

1. $d(P, T) \geq 0$;
2. $d(P, T) = 0$ if and only if $P = T$;
3. $d(P, T) \leq d(P, R) + d(R, T)$.

Exercises

For the given points **P** and **T**, compute $d(P, T)$.

A

1. $P(0, 0); T(1, 3)$
2. $P(0, -3); T(2, 0)$
3. $P(2, 3); T(-2, 1)$
4. $P(-3, 5); T(4, 3)$

5. $P(3\sqrt{2}, \sqrt{3}); T(\sqrt{2}, -3\sqrt{3})$
6. $P(a, b); T(c, d)$
7. $P(a, b); T(2a, 3b)$
8. $P(a - b, c + d); T(a + b, c - d)$

For the given points **A**, **B**, and **C** determine whether $<$ or $=$ is the appropriate symbol in the assertion $d(A, B) \leq d(A, C) + d(C, B)$.

9. $A(0, 0); B(-6, 8); C(0, 8)$
10. $A(0, 0); B(6, 2); C(2, 6)$
11. $A(8, 6); B(8, -4); C(10, -4)$

12. $A(2, 0); B(5, 0); C(-1, 4)$
13. $A(-4, 3); B(2, -5); C(3, 2)$
14. $A(5, 3); B(-1, -5); C(2, -1)$

15. Show that the distance between $P(a, b)$ and $T(a, c)$ is not dependent upon a.
16. Represent the ordered pairs $P(4, 3)$ and $T(-2, 7)$ as arrows in standard position. Find the length of the arrow between P and T.

B

17. Write an equation which expresses the fact that $P(x, y)$ is equidistant from $R(-2, 6)$ and $S(4, 8)$.
18. Write an equation which expresses the fact that the distance from $P(x, y)$ to $R(2, 3)$ is twice the distance from $P(x, y)$ to $S(-6, 4)$.

In each exercise, find the values of k for which $d(\mathbf{M}, \mathbf{N})$ is the given number.

19. $\mathbf{M}(6, k)$; $\mathbf{N}(2, 0)$; $d(\mathbf{M}, \mathbf{N}) = 5$

20. $\mathbf{M}(2, k)$; $\mathbf{N}(4, 2k)$; $d(\mathbf{M}, \mathbf{N}) = \sqrt{13}$

21. $\mathbf{M}(3, 2)$; $\mathbf{N}(4, k)$; $d(\mathbf{M}, \mathbf{N}) = \sqrt{17}$

22. $\mathbf{M}(-2, 1)$; $\mathbf{N}(4, k)$; $d(\mathbf{M}, \mathbf{N}) = 3\sqrt{5}$

23. $\mathbf{M}(5, k)$; $\mathbf{N}(2, 5)$; $d(\mathbf{M}, \mathbf{N}) = \sqrt{34}$

24. $\mathbf{M}(2a, k)$; $\mathbf{N}(a, 3b)$; $d(\mathbf{M}, \mathbf{N}) = \sqrt{a^2 + b^2}$

25. Given $\mathbf{R}(2, 2)$ and $\mathbf{S}(6, 6)$. Find the coordinates of a point $\mathbf{K}$ whose representation in the coordinate plane lies on the x-axis and is such that $d(\mathbf{R}, \mathbf{K}) = d(\mathbf{K}, \mathbf{S})$.

26. Given $\mathbf{A}(-2, 8)$ and $\mathbf{B}(4, 2)$. Find the coordinates of a point $\mathbf{P}$ whose representation in the coordinate plane lies on the y-axis and such that $d(\mathbf{A}, \mathbf{P}) = d(\mathbf{P}, \mathbf{B})$.

C **27.** Show that $\mathbf{P}\left(\dfrac{x_1 + x_2}{2}, \dfrac{y_1 + y_2}{2}\right)$ is equidistant from $\mathbf{M}(x_1, y_1)$ and $\mathbf{N}(x_2, y_2)$.

28. Prove that, if $\mathbf{P}$, $\mathbf{S}$, and $\mathbf{T}$ are vectors, then $d(\mathbf{P}, \mathbf{S}) = d(\mathbf{P} + k\mathbf{T}, \mathbf{S} + k\mathbf{T})$ for every $k \in \Re$.

29. Prove that, if $\mathbf{P}$, $\mathbf{S}$, and $\mathbf{T}$ are vectors, then $d(\mathbf{P}, \mathbf{S}) = d(\mathbf{P} + \mathbf{T}, \mathbf{S} + \mathbf{T})$.

30. Prove that, if $\mathbf{P}$, $\mathbf{S}$, and $\mathbf{T}$ are vectors, then $d(\mathbf{P}, \mathbf{S}) = d(\mathbf{P} - \mathbf{T}, \mathbf{S} - \mathbf{T})$.

5–2 Lines in the Plane

How shall we define the concept *line* in terms of vectors? A line should certainly be a set of points. It is also reasonable to expect that given two different points there should be exactly one line containing both of them. In fact, if $\mathbf{P}$ and $\mathbf{S}$ are distinct points, you would expect that the line containing $\mathbf{P}$ and $\mathbf{S}$ should consist of all the points "traversed" by starting at $\mathbf{P}$ and moving in the direction of the vector $\mathbf{S} - \mathbf{P}$ or in the opposite direction (Figure 5–4). Of course, any nonzero vector $\mathbf{v}$ parallel to $\mathbf{S} - \mathbf{P}$ should serve equally well to establish direction on the line. These intuitive notions about lines are made precise in the following definition.

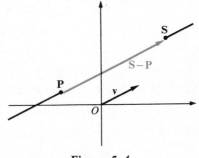

Figure 5–4

A set $\mathcal{L}$ of points $\mathbf{X}(x, y)$ in $\Re \times \Re$ is called a **line** if there exists a point $\mathbf{P}$ and a nonzero vector $\mathbf{v}$ such that $\mathcal{L} = \{\mathbf{X}: \mathbf{X} = \mathbf{P} + t\mathbf{v}, t \in \Re\}$.

$\mathcal{L}$ is called the **line through P with direction vector v**. For brevity of notation, we often write $\mathcal{L} = \{\mathbf{P} + t\mathbf{v}\}$ and call $\mathbf{X} = \mathbf{P} + t\mathbf{v}$ a **vector equation** of the line. The points of £ are said to **belong to** or to **lie on** £, while £ is said to **contain** or to **pass through** its points. Notice that **0** is never a direction vector.

EXAMPLE 1. Determine a vector equation of the line £ through $P(-2, 1)$ with direction vector $\mathbf{v} = (1, 4)$.

Solution: $£ = \{\mathbf{P} + t\mathbf{v}\} = \{(-2, 1) + t(1, 4)\} = \{(-2 + t, 1 + 4t)\}$.

∴ a vector equation of £ is $(x, y) = (-2 + t, 1 + 4t)$,
Answer.

EXAMPLE 2. Identify the line $\mathfrak{N} = \{(4r, 2 - r)\}$.

Solution: $\mathfrak{N} = \{(4r, 2 - r)\} = \{(0 + 4r, 2 + (-1)r)\}$
∴ $\mathfrak{N} = \{(0, 2) + r(4, -1)\}$

$\mathfrak{N}$ is the line through the point $(0, 2)$ parallel to the vector $(4, -1)$, **Answer.**

The vector equation $(x, y) = (-2 + t, 1 + 4t)$ found in Example 1 is equivalent to the compound sentence

$$x = -2 + t \quad and \quad y = 1 + 4t.$$

The equations in this sentence are called *parametric equations* of the line £. To obtain particular points on £ you replace the variable t, called the **parameter**, by specific real numbers. The points corresponding to the values 0, 1, 2, and −1 for t are shown in the table. Figures 5–5a and b show two interpretations of these data. Figure 5–5a uses dots to locate the points $\mathbf{P} + t\mathbf{v}$ of £, while Figure 5–5b employs arrows in standard position to show the location of these points.

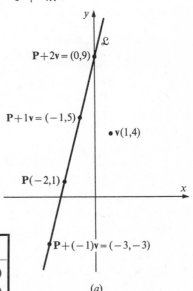

(a)

Figure 5–5

(b) and (c) on page 172

t	X
0	$[-2 + \quad 0, 1 + 4(\quad 0)] = (-2, \quad 1)$
1	$[-2 + \quad 1, 1 + 4(\quad 1)] = (-1, \quad 5)$
2	$[-2 + \quad 2, 1 + 4(\quad 2)] = (\quad 0, \quad 9)$
−1	$[-2 + (-1), 1 + 4(-1)] = (-3, -3)$

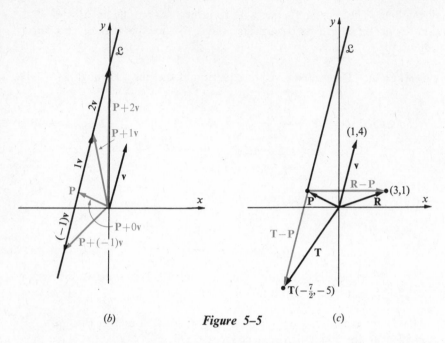

(b)   **Figure 5-5**   (c)

Figure 5–5c suggests that the point $R(3, 1)$ does not lie on line $\mathcal{L}$, but that $T(-\frac{7}{2}, -5)$ does. The figure also indicates that $R - P$, the vector from P to R, is *not* parallel to v but that $T - P$ *is* parallel to v. These observations lead to the following assertion.

> **THEOREM** Let P be a point and v a nonzero vector in the plane. If $\mathcal{L}$ is a line through P with direction vector v, then a point X lies on $\mathcal{L}$ if and only if $X - P$ is parallel to v.

Proof: The proof is in two parts, each using the fact that $\mathcal{L} = \{P + tv\}$.

1. Suppose $X \in \mathcal{L}$. Then for some replacement of t by a real number, the equation $X = P + tv$ is true. Therefore, $X - P = tv$, so that $X - P$ is parallel to v.

2. On the other hand, suppose that $X - P$ is parallel to v. Since $v \neq 0$ (Why?), there is a real number t such that $X - P = tv$. Therefore, $X = P + tv$, so that $X \in \mathcal{L}$.

The corollary stated on page 155 enables you to deduce the following test to decide whether a point lies on a line.

COROLLARY. A point X lies on the line through P with direction vector $v = (v_1, v_2)$ if and only if $(X - P) \cdot v_P = 0$, where $v_P = (-v_2, v_1)$.

EXAMPLE 3. If $\mathcal{L}$ is a line through the point $(-2, 1)$ with direction vector $(1, 4)$, (Figure 5–5c), show that

(a) $(3, 1) \notin \mathcal{L}$;   (b) $(-\frac{7}{2}, -5) \in \mathcal{L}$.

Solution: $\mathbf{v} = (1, 4); \mathbf{v_P} = (-4, 1)$.

(a) $\mathbf{X} - \mathbf{P} = (3, 1) - (-2,1) = (5, 0)$
$(5, 0) \cdot (-4, 1) = -20 \neq 0.$ $(3, 1) \notin \mathcal{L}$, **Answer.**

(b) $\mathbf{X} - \mathbf{P} = (-\frac{7}{2}, -5) - (-2, 1) = (-\frac{3}{2}, -6)$
$(-\frac{3}{2}, -6) \cdot (-4, 1) = 6 - 6 = 0$
$\therefore (-\frac{7}{2}, -5) \in \mathcal{L}$, **Answer.**

The points of $\mathcal{L} = \{X: X = P + t\mathbf{v}\}$ for which $t \geq 0$ is called the **ray** with $\mathbf{P}$ as endpoint and $\mathbf{v}$ as direction vector. Notice that a point $\mathbf{X}$ belongs to this ray if and only if $\mathbf{X} - \mathbf{P}$ is a *nonnegative* real-number multiple of $\mathbf{v}$.

EXAMPLE 4. **a.** Find a vector equation of the ray $\mathcal{S}$ having $\mathbf{P}(1, 3)$ as endpoint and $(-2, 5)$ as direction vector.

b. Is $(3, -2) \in \mathcal{S}$?

Solution: **a.** $\mathbf{P} = (1, 3); \mathbf{v} = (-2, 5)$
$\therefore \mathcal{S} = \{X: X = (1, 3) + t(-2, 5), t \geq 0\}$
$= \{X: X = (1 - 2t, 3 + 5t), t \geq 0\}.$
$\therefore$ a vector equation of $\mathcal{S}$ is $(x, y) = (1 - 2t, 3 + 5t),$
$t \geq 0$, **Answer.**

b. $\mathbf{X} - \mathbf{P} = (3, -2) - (1, 3) = (2, -5) = -1(-2, 5).$
$\therefore (3, -2) \notin \mathcal{S}$, **Answer.**

Note that $(3, -2)$ belongs to the ray $\mathcal{S}'$ with $(1, 3)$ as endpoint and $-(-2, 5)$ as direction vector. Because $\mathcal{S}$ and $\mathcal{S}'$ have a common endpoint but have direction vectors in opposite directions, $\mathcal{S}$ and $\mathcal{S}'$ are called *opposite rays*.

Exercises

1. Is a line a set of points? a set of vectors? a set of ordered pairs?
2. Can two different pairs of parametric equations identify the same line?

Determine a vector equation of the line $\mathcal{L}$ through $\mathbf{P}$ with direction vector $\mathbf{v}$.

3. $P(3, 4); \mathbf{v} = (1, 3)$ 6. $P(-1, -3); \mathbf{v} = (-1, 2)$
4. $P(0, -2); \mathbf{v} = (2, 5)$ 7. $P(-2, 1); \mathbf{v} = (-2, 3)$
5. $P(-5, 4); \mathbf{v} = (-5, 3)$ 8. $P(3, -4); \mathbf{v} = (-3, -1)$

Assume that in the given coordinate plane representation
v is a direction vector of $\mathcal{L}$.

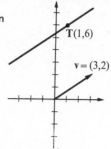

9. Write a vector equation of $\mathcal{L}$.

10. Is $(-2, 4) \in \mathcal{L}$?

11. For what value of y is $(4, y) \in \mathcal{L}$?

12. For what value of x is $(x, 0) \in \mathcal{L}$?

Represent the given line $\mathcal{L}$ in the coordinate plane and name three points
P(a, b) such that **P**$(a, b) \in \mathcal{L}$.

13. $\mathcal{L} = \{(4, 1) + t(1, 3)\}$

14. $\mathcal{L} = \{(-2, 3) + t(2, 4)\}$

15. $(x, y) = (3 + t, 4 - 2t)$

16. $(x, y) = (2 - t, 5 + 3t)$

Determine whether the point **P** lies on the line $\mathcal{L}$.

17. **P**$(4, 5)$; $\mathcal{L} = \{(2, 3) + t(1, 1)\}$

18. **P**$(4, 1)$; $\mathcal{L} = \{(3, 5) + t(1, -2)\}$

19. **P**$(4, 12)$; $\mathcal{L} = \{(-2, 3) + t(2, 3)\}$

20. **P**$(-1, 4)$; $\mathcal{L} = \{(5, 1) + t(2, -1)\}$

21. **P**$(5, 8)$; $(x, y) = (3 + t, 4 + 2t)$

22. **P**$(5, 4)$; $(x, y) = (4 - t, 3 + t)$

In Exercises 23–26, determine whether the point **A** lies on the ray having **P**
as endpoint and **v** as direction vector.

23. **A**$(2, 6)$; **P**$(0, 4)$; **v** $= (1, 1)$

24. **A**$(7, -3)$; **P**$(5, 0)$; **v** $= (-2, 3)$

25. **A**$(2, 8)$; **P**$(-1, 4)$; **v** $= (3, 4)$

26. **A**$(-5, 1)$; **P**$(1, 5)$; **v** $= (-2, -1)$

Without resorting to a coordinate plane representation, determine whether
the pair of equations given in each exercise specify the same line.

B

27. $\mathcal{L} = \{(2, 3) + t(3, -2)\}$ and $\mathcal{L} = \{(2, 3) + t(6, -4)\}$

28. $\mathcal{L} = \{(4, -6) + t(3, 1)\}$ and $\mathcal{L} = \{(7, -5) + t(-3, -1)\}$

29. $(x, y) = (4 + 3r, -6 + r)$ and $(x, y) = (7 - 3r, -5 - r)$

30. $(x, y) = (6 - 2r, 5 + r)$ and $(x, y) = (4 - 2r, 5 + 2r)$

Identify the line specified by each equation.

31. $(x, y) = (-3 - 2r, -5 + 3r)$

32. $(x, y) = (2 - 4r, 3 + 5r)$

33. $(x, y) = (3r, 5 - 2r)$

34. $(x, y) = (-2r, 3r)$

In Exercises 35, 36 let the line $\mathcal{L} = \{(a, b) + t(c, d)\}$ where $\|(c, d)\| = 1$.

C

35. What must be true if the representation of $\mathcal{L}$ in the coordinate plane is the
horizontal axis?

36. What must be true if the representation of $\mathcal{L}$ in the coordinate plane is the
vertical axis?

37. Prove: For all real numbers a and b and those real numbers c and d such that $(c, d) \neq \mathbf{0}$, $\{(x, y): (x, y) = (a + tc, b + td)\}$ and $\{(x, y): dx - cy = ad - bc\}$ identify the same line.

38. Let **P** be a point and **v** a nonzero vector. Prove that through **P** there is one and only one line whose direction vector is **v**.

5–3 Coincident and Parallel Lines

Lines that consist of the same set of points are said to **coincide**, or be **coincident**. Thus, to prove that two lines $\mathcal{L}$ and $\mathfrak{M}$ coincide, you must show that every point of $\mathcal{L}$ belongs to $\mathfrak{M}$, and that every point of $\mathfrak{M}$ belongs to $\mathcal{L}$. Figure 5–6 suggests that if $\mathcal{L}$ is the line through **P** with direction vector **v** and if **T** lies on $\mathcal{L}$, then $\mathcal{L}$ coincides with $\mathfrak{M}$, the line through **T** with direction vector **v**. (The figure pictures $\mathcal{L}$ as a red line and $\mathfrak{M}$ as a dash line.) We state this conjecture as a theorem, whose proof depends largely on the corollary given on page 172.

Figure 5–6

THEOREM   If **P** and **T** denote points in the plane and **v** denotes a nonzero vector, and if $.\mathbf{T} \in \{\mathbf{P} + t\mathbf{v}\}$, then $\{\mathbf{P} + t\mathbf{v}\} = \{\mathbf{T} + s\mathbf{v}\}$.

Proof: Since $\mathbf{T} \in \{\mathbf{P} + t\mathbf{v}\}$, $(\mathbf{T} - \mathbf{P}) \cdot \mathbf{v_P} = 0$. (Why?)

Now, suppose **R** is any point of $\{\mathbf{P} + t\mathbf{v}\}$. Then $(\mathbf{R} - \mathbf{P}) \cdot \mathbf{v_P} = 0$. (Why?) To prove that $\mathbf{R} \in \{\mathbf{T} + s\mathbf{v}\}$, you must show that $(\mathbf{R} - \mathbf{T}) \cdot \mathbf{v_P} = 0$. But

$$\mathbf{R} - \mathbf{T} = (\mathbf{R} - \mathbf{P}) + (\mathbf{P} - \mathbf{T}) = (\mathbf{R} - \mathbf{P}) - (\mathbf{T} - \mathbf{P}).$$

$$\therefore (\mathbf{R} - \mathbf{T}) \cdot \mathbf{v_P} = (\mathbf{R} - \mathbf{P}) \cdot \mathbf{v_P} - (\mathbf{T} - \mathbf{P}) \cdot \mathbf{v_P}$$
$$= 0 - 0.$$

$\therefore (\mathbf{R} - \mathbf{T}) \cdot \mathbf{v_P} = 0$, so that $\mathbf{R} \in \{\mathbf{T} + s\mathbf{v}\}$.

On the other hand, if **W** is any point of $\{\mathbf{T} + s\mathbf{v}\}$, $(\mathbf{T} - \mathbf{W}) \cdot \mathbf{v_P} = 0$. Since

$$\mathbf{W} - \mathbf{P} = (\mathbf{W} - \mathbf{T}) + (\mathbf{T} - \mathbf{P}),$$

you can show as above that $(\mathbf{W} - \mathbf{P}) \cdot \mathbf{v_P} = 0$; therefore,

$$\mathbf{W} \in \{\mathbf{P} + t\mathbf{v}\}.$$

Because any point on either of the lines $\{\mathbf{P} + t\mathbf{v}\}$ and $\{\mathbf{T} + s\mathbf{v}\}$ also lies on the other, the lines must coincide.

Figure 5–7 pictures in red the line $\mathcal{L}$ through a point **P** with **v** as direction vector. Shown as a dash line is the line $\mathfrak{M}$ through **P** with **w** as direction vector. The figure suggests that if **v** is parallel to **w**, then $\mathcal{L} = \mathfrak{M}$. This assertion and its converse form the next theorem.

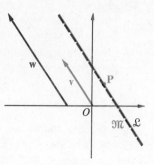

Figure 5–7

THEOREM
If **P** denotes a point in the plane and **v** and **w** denote nonzero vectors, then $\{P + tv\} = \{P + sw\}$ if and only if **v** and **w** are parallel vectors.

Proof: 1. Suppose the nonzero vectors **v** and **w** are parallel. Let X be any point of $\{P + tv\}$. Then $X - P$ is parallel to **v**, and therefore is parallel to **w**. (Why?) Hence, $X \in \{P + sw\}$. (Why?) Similarly, you can show that every point Y of $\{P + sw\}$ also belongs to $\{P + tv\}$. Therefore, $\{P + tv\} = \{P + sw\}$.

2. Suppose $\{P + tv\} = \{P + sw\}$. Now $P + v \in \{P + tv\}$ because $P + v = P + 1v$. But $P + v$ also belongs to $\{P + sw\}$. (Why?) Therefore, there is a real value of s for which the statement

$$(P + v) - P = sw$$

is true. Hence $v = sw$, and **v** and **w** are parallel vectors.

Together, the theorems proved above mean that you can specify a line through a point **P** with direction vector **v** by naming any one of its points and any nonzero vector parallel to **v**. Thus, each nonzero vector parallel to **v** is also a direction vector of the line.

EXAMPLE 1. Show that the line $\mathcal{L}$ through the point $(-4, 7)$ with direction vector $(0, 3)$ coincides with the line $\mathfrak{M}$ through the point $(-4, 1)$ with $(0, 3)$ as direction vector.

Solution: Since $\mathcal{L}$ and $\mathfrak{M}$ have a common direction vector $v = (0, 3)$, $\mathcal{L} = \mathfrak{M}$ provided $(-4, 1) \in \mathcal{L} = \{(-4, 7) + t(0, 3)\}$. But $v = (0, 3)$; therefore, $v_P = (-3, 0)$ and

$$[(-4, 7) - (-4, 1)] \cdot (-3, 0) = (0, 6) \cdot (-3, 0) = 0.$$

$\therefore (-4, 1) \in \mathcal{L}$; and $\mathcal{L} = \mathfrak{M}$.

EXAMPLE 2. Find a vector equation of the line $\mathcal{L}$ through the point $(0, 0)$ with $(\frac{1}{2}, -\frac{1}{6})$ as direction vector.

Solution: $\mathbf{P} = (0, 0)$; $\mathbf{v} = (\frac{1}{2}, -\frac{1}{6})$.
Let $\mathbf{w} = 6\mathbf{v} = (3, -1)$.
$\mathcal{L} = \{\mathbf{P} + t\mathbf{w}\} = \{(0, 0) + t(3, -1)\}$

$\therefore \mathcal{L} = \{(3t, -t)\}$

A vector equation of $\mathcal{L}$ is $(x, y) = (3t, -t)$, **Answer.**

Two lines are said to be **parallel** if and only if a direction vector of one is parallel to a direction vector of the other.

Thus, if $\mathbf{v}$ and $\mathbf{w}$ are direction vectors of lines $\mathcal{L}$ and $\mathfrak{M}$, then $\mathcal{L}$ is parallel to $\mathfrak{M}$ if and only if $\mathbf{w} \cdot \mathbf{v_P} = 0$ (or equivalently, $\mathbf{v} \cdot \mathbf{w_P} = 0$). Notice that every line is parallel to itself.

EXAMPLE 3. Determine whether the lines $\mathcal{L} = \{(6 - 2t, -3 + t)\}$ and $\mathfrak{M} = \{(s, -\frac{1}{2}s)\}$ are parallel.

Solution: $\mathcal{L} = \{(6 - 2t, -3 + t)\} = \{(6, -3) + t(-2, 1)\}$;

$\therefore (-2, 1)$ is a direction vector of $\mathcal{L}$.

$\mathfrak{M} = \{(s, -\frac{1}{2}s)\} = \{(0, 0) + s(1, -\frac{1}{2})\}$;

$\therefore (1, -\frac{1}{2})$ is a direction vector of $\mathfrak{M}$.

$(1, -\frac{1}{2}) \cdot (-2, 1)_P = (1, -\frac{1}{2}) \cdot (-1, -2) = -1 + 1 = 0$.

$\therefore \mathcal{L}$ and $\mathfrak{M}$ are parallel lines, **Answer.**

The following theorem enables you to recognize lines that coincide.

THEOREM In the plane, lines having a point in common coincide if and only if they are parallel.

Proof: Let $\mathcal{L}$ and $\mathfrak{M}$ denote lines having the common point $\mathbf{P}$ and direction vectors $\mathbf{v}$ and $\mathbf{w}$, respectively. Then, $\mathcal{L} = \{\mathbf{P} + t\mathbf{v}\}$ and $\mathfrak{M} = \{\mathbf{P} + s\mathbf{w}\}$.

1. Suppose $\mathcal{L}$ and $\mathfrak{M}$ are parallel lines. Then $\mathbf{v}$ and $\mathbf{w}$ are parallel vectors. Hence, $\mathcal{L} = \mathfrak{M}$. (Why?)

2. Suppose $\mathcal{L} = \mathfrak{M}$. Then $\mathbf{v}$ and $\mathbf{w}$ must be parallel vectors (Why?), so that $\mathcal{L}$ and $\mathfrak{M}$ are parallel lines.

EXAMPLE 4. Determine whether the lines $\mathcal{L}$ and $\mathfrak{M}$ described in Example 3 coincide.

Solution: $\mathcal{L} = \{(6, -3) + t(-2, 1)\}$; $\mathfrak{M} = \{(0, 0) + s(1, -\frac{1}{2})\}$.
In Example 3, you verified that $\mathcal{L}$ and $\mathfrak{M}$ are parallel.

$\therefore \mathcal{L} = \mathfrak{M}$ if and only if a point of $\mathcal{L}$, say $(6, -3)$, belongs to $\mathfrak{M}$. Now,

$$[(6, -3) - (0, 0)] \cdot (\tfrac{1}{2}, 1) = (6, -3) \cdot (\tfrac{1}{2}, 1) = 3 - 3 = 0.$$

$\therefore (6, -3) \in \mathfrak{M}$; hence, $\mathcal{L} = \mathfrak{M}$, **Answer.**

Can you explain why noncoincident parallel lines have no point in common? (Exercise 27, page 179.)

Exercises

For each line $\mathcal{L}$ name a direction vector with integral entries.

1. $\mathcal{L} = \{(2, -1) + t(-\frac{1}{2}, 3)\}$ **4.** $\mathcal{L} = \{(6 - \frac{1}{2}t, 4 + \frac{2}{3}t)\}$

2. $\mathcal{L} = \{(-2, 0) + t(\frac{1}{3}, -\frac{3}{2})\}$ **5.** $\mathcal{L} = \{(-3t, 6 + \frac{1}{2}t)\}$

3. $\mathcal{L} = \{(3 + 2t, 5 + 2t)\}$ **6.** $\mathcal{L} = \{(5 + \frac{1}{3}t, \frac{3}{2}t)\}$

If in the plane $\mathcal{L}$ and $\mathfrak{M}$ are lines having **v** as direction vector and containing points **P** and **T**, respectively, determine whether $\mathcal{L}$ and $\mathfrak{M}$ coincide.

7. $P(0, 4)$; $T(-2, 1)$; $v = (2, 3)$ **10.** $P(-2, 1)$; $T(-5, 6)$; $v = (-3, 5)$

8. $P(5, 0)$; $T(3, 4)$; $v = (-1, 2)$ **11.** $P(3, 1)$; $T(4, -2)$; $v = (-1, -3)$

9. $P(1, 2)$; $T(-1, 4)$; $v = (-2, 3)$ **12.** $P(-1, -3)$; $T(-7, 1)$; $v = (3, -2)$

In each exercise determine whether $\mathcal{L}$ and $\mathfrak{M}$ are parallel lines, and, if parallel, whether they coincide.

13. $\mathcal{L} = \{(5 - 3t, -2 + 2t)\}$ and $\mathfrak{M} = \{(2 - 6s, -1 - 4s)\}$

14. $\mathcal{L} = \{(2 + t, -3 - 3t)\}$ and $\mathfrak{M} = \{(5 - 3s, 2 + 9s)\}$

15. $\mathcal{L} = \{(4 - \frac{1}{2}t, 1 + \frac{2}{3}t)\}$ and $\mathfrak{M} = \{(3 + s, -2 + \frac{4}{3}s)\}$

16. $\mathcal{L} = \{(\frac{2}{3}t, 5 + t)\}$ and $\mathfrak{M} = \{(2 - s, -\frac{3}{2}s)\}$

17. $\mathcal{L} = \{(t, -\frac{2}{5}t)\}$ and $\mathfrak{M} = \{(-3 + \frac{2}{3}s, 6 + \frac{2}{5}s)\}$

18. $\mathcal{L} = \{(5 + \sqrt{3}t, -2 - \sqrt{2}t)\}$ and $\mathfrak{M} = \{(-1 - \sqrt{6}t, 5 + 2t)\}$

Find two nonzero vectors **v** such that $T \in \{P + tv\}$.

19. $T(2, 3)$; $P(6, -4)$ **21.** $T(4, 0)$; $P(3, -5)$

20. $T(-3, 5)$; $P(2, 6)$ **22.** $T(4, 3)$; $P(0, -2)$

23. If $(2, -3) \in \{(a, 2a) + t(1, 3)\}$, find a.

24. If $(2a, -3a) \in \{(4, 3) + t(-1, 3)\}$, find a.

25. Let $\mathcal{L}$ be a line and **w** a nonzero vector which is not a direction vector of $\mathcal{L}$. Prove that for some scalar r, $r\mathbf{w} \in \mathcal{L}$.

26. Show that the line $\mathcal{L} = \{\mathbf{P} + t(\mathbf{S} - \mathbf{P})\}$ can also be denoted by the equation $\mathcal{L} = \{(1 - t)\mathbf{P} + t\mathbf{S}\}$. Use this result to show that $\mathbf{P} \in \mathcal{L}$ and $\mathbf{S} \in \mathcal{L}$.

27. Prove that if $\mathcal{L}$ and $\mathfrak{M}$ are parallel lines, and $\mathcal{L} \neq \mathfrak{M}$, then $\mathcal{L} \cap \mathfrak{M} = \emptyset$.

28. Prove that if $\mathcal{L}$ and $\mathfrak{M}$ are lines, and $\mathcal{L}$ and $\mathfrak{M}$ are not parallel, then $\mathcal{L} \cap \mathfrak{M}$ contains just one point.

5–4 The Line through Two Points

A line containing two different points is called a *line through the points*.

EXAMPLE 1. Determine a vector equation of a line $\mathfrak{M}$ through the points $\mathbf{P}(4, -3)$ and $\mathbf{S}(0, 5)$.

Solution: Consider the line $\mathfrak{M}$ through **P**, with direction vector $\mathbf{S} - \mathbf{P}$. Now $\mathbf{S} - \mathbf{P} = [0 - 4, 5 - (-3)] = (-4, 8) = \mathbf{v}$. Using the letter r for the parameter, you have

$$\mathfrak{M} = \{\mathbf{P} + r\mathbf{v}\} = \{(4, -3) + r(-4, 8)\}$$
$$= \{(4 - 4r, -3 + 8r)\}.$$

$\therefore$ a vector equation of $\mathfrak{M}$ is

$$(x, y) = (4 - 4r, -3 + 8r), \quad \textbf{Answer.}$$

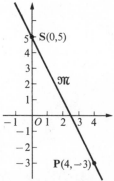

How many lines contain both points $\mathbf{P}(4, -3)$ and $\mathbf{S}(0, 5)$? Figure 5–8 indicates that $\mathfrak{M}$, the solution in Example 1, is the only line containing both **P** and **S**.

Figure 5–8

| THEOREM | If **P** and **S** are different points in the plane, one and only one line in the plane contains both **P** and **S**.

Proof: 1. Since $\mathbf{P} \neq \mathbf{S}$, $\mathbf{S} - \mathbf{P} \neq \mathbf{0}$. Let $\mathfrak{M}$ be the line through **P** having $\mathbf{S} - \mathbf{P}$ as direction vector. Then

$$\mathfrak{M} = \{\mathbf{P} + t(\mathbf{S} - \mathbf{P})\} = \{(1 - t)\mathbf{P} + t\mathbf{S}\}.$$

Now, $\mathbf{P} \in \mathfrak{M}$ because $\mathbf{P} = (1 - 0)\mathbf{P} + 0\mathbf{S}$; $\mathbf{S} \in \mathfrak{M}$ because $\mathbf{S} = (1 - 1)\mathbf{P} + 1\mathbf{S}$. Therefore, $\mathfrak{M}$ contains both **P** and **S**.

2. Suppose that $\mathcal{L}$ is also a line through **P** and **S**. Then, for some nonzero vector **v**,

$$\mathcal{L} = \{\mathbf{P} + s\mathbf{v}\}. \qquad \text{(cont. on p. 180)}$$

Since $S \in \mathcal{L}$ and $P \in \mathcal{L}$, $S - P$ is parallel to **v**. Therefore, $\mathcal{L}$ and $\mathfrak{M}$ have parallel direction vectors and have a common point **P**. Hence, $\mathcal{L} = \mathfrak{M}$. (Why?) Thus, there is exactly one line, namely $\mathfrak{M}$, containing both **P** and **S**.

The symbol **PS** denotes the line containing the distinct points **P** and **S**.

EXAMPLE 2. Determine an equation of the line $\mathcal{L}$ through $(-4, 2)$ parallel to **PS** where $P = (0, 5)$ and $S = (4, -3)$.

Solution: $S - P = (4, -3) - (0, 5) = (4, -8)$;

$\therefore$ a direction vector of $\mathcal{L}$ is $\frac{1}{4}(4, -8) = (1, -2)$.

$\therefore \mathcal{L} = \{(-4, 2) + t(1, -2)\} = \{(-4 + t, 2 - 2t)\}$,

Answer.

Is there more than one line through $(-4, 2)$ parallel to the line containing $(4, -3)$ and $(0, 5)$? Figure 5–9 suggests that the answer is "No." The following theorem confirms this guess.

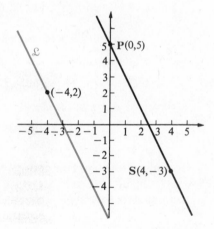

Figure 5–9

| THEOREM | If **P** is any point and $\mathfrak{M}$ any line in the plane, one and only one line in the plane passes through **P** parallel to $\mathfrak{M}$. |

Proof of the theorem is left as Exercise 33, page 182.

Can you propose a test to determine whether three points **P**, **T**, and **S** are **collinear**, that is, lie on the same line? The lines **PT** and **PS** have a common point **P**; they coincide if and only if they are parallel. This suggests the following assertion. (Exercise 34, page 182.)

| THEOREM | The points **P**, **T**, and **S** in the plane are collinear if and only if $T - P$ and $S - P$ are parallel vectors. |

EXAMPLE 3. Determine whether the points $P(7, -6)$, $S(1, -2)$, and $T(4, -4)$ are collinear.

Solution: $S - P = (1, -2) - (7, -6) = (-6, 4)$

$T - P = (4, -4) - (7, -6) = (-3, 2) = \frac{1}{2}(S - P)$

$\therefore$ $T - P$ and $S - P$ are parallel; hence, P, T, and S are collinear, **Answer.**

Exercises

Determine a vector equation for the line $\mathcal{L}$ passing through **S** and **T**.

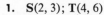

A

1. $S(2, 3); T(4, 6)$

2. $S(0, 5); T(3, 0)$ 3t, 5-5t

3. $S(-3, 1); T(2, -5)$

4. $S(3, -2); T(-4, -2)$ -4+7t, -2

5. $S(5, 1); T(2, -3)$

6. $S(0, 0); T(a, b)$ ta, tb (0,0)+t(a,b)

7. $S(a, 0); T(0, a)$

8. $S(\sqrt{3}, 1); T(2\sqrt{3}, -4)$ √3+√3t, 1-5t (√3, 1)+t(√3, -5)

Show that **PS** is parallel to **RT**.

9. $P(1, 2); S(-2, 4); R(3, -6); T(-3, -2)$

10. $P(0, -1); S(-5, 2); R(7, 0); T(-3, 6)$

Write a vector equation of the line $\mathcal{L}$ through **M** parallel to **PS**.

11. $M(2, 3); P(1, 4); S(3, 5)$ -4t, 3+3t (0,1)+t(-4,3)

12. $M(0, 1); P(-2, 3); S(2, 0)$

13. $M(2, -3); P(3, -1); S(-1, 3)$

14. $M(0, 0); P(3, 5); S(-2, 6)$ (0,0)+t(5,-1)

15. $M(3, 6); P(-1, 2); S(4, -1)$

16. $M(4, 3); P(2, -1); S(1, -2)$ 4+t, 3+t (4,3)+t(1,1)

Determine an equation of ray **PQ** having **P** as endpoint and containing the point **Q**.

17. $P(0, 0); Q(5, -1)$

18. $P(0, 0); Q(-2, -4)$ t, 2t t≥0 (0,0)+t(-1,-2)

19. $P(3, -1); Q(0, 0)$

20. $P(-2, -4); Q(1, 6)$ (-2, -4)+t(3, 10) -2+3t, -4+10t t≥0

Determine whether the given line $\mathcal{R}$ coincides with the line **PQ**.

B

21. $\mathcal{R} = \{(6 + t, 2 - 3t)\}; P(6, 2); Q(4, -4)$

22. $\mathcal{R} = \{(2 - 3t, -3 + 2t)\}; P(5, -5); Q(-4, 3)$ no

23. $\mathcal{R} = \{(3, -1) + t(-1, 2)\}; P(2, 1); Q(5, -5)$

24. $\mathcal{R} = \{(-2, 4) + t(2, -3)\}; P(0, 3); Q(-2, 4)$

If **P**, **S**, and **R** are distinct points in the plane, which of the following permit you to conclude that the points are collinear?

25. $P \in SR$

26. $d(SP) = d(PR)$ no

27. $R - P = t(S - P)$

28. $S + P = R$ no

Find the value of k for which **S**, **T**, and **P** will be collinear.

29. $S(1, -1); T(3, 1); P(k, 4)$ **31.** $S(4, 6); T(-3, 8); P(-k, k)$

30. $S(0, 2); T(1, 1); P(-1, k)$ **32.** $S(2, 4); T(6, k); P(-2, 0)$

$K = 8$

33. Prove: If **P** is any point and $\mathfrak{M}$ any line in the plane, one and only one line in the plane passes through **P** parallel to $\mathfrak{M}$.

34. Prove the second theorem stated on page 180.

35. Prove: If $P(x, y)$ lies on the line through $S(x_1, y_1)$ and $R(x_2, y_2)$, then

$$x = x_1 + t(x_2 - x_1) \text{ and } y = y_1 + t(y_2 - y_1).$$

36. Let **T** and **S** be points other than **P** belonging to the respective rays **PT** and **PS**, each having **P** as endpoint. Prove that the rays coincide if and only if $T - P$ and $S - P$ are vectors having the same direction.

5–5 Line Segments

You can show (Exercise 26, page 179) that the line **PS** consists of the points **X** expressible in the form

$$\mathbf{X} = (1 - t)\mathbf{P} + t\mathbf{S}$$

where t is any real number. If you restrict the domain of t to the subset of numbers between 0 and 1, inclusive, the resulting subset of the line is called the **line segment** with **end points P** and **S** and is denoted by $\overline{\mathbf{PS}}$:

$$\overline{\mathbf{PS}} = \{\mathbf{X}: \mathbf{X} = (1 - t)\mathbf{P} + t\mathbf{S}, 0 \leq t \leq 1\}.$$

$\overline{\mathbf{PS}}$ is also called the *line segment* (or simply the *segment*) *joining* **P** and **S**. The **length** of a line segment is the distance between its end points. Thus:

$$\text{length of } \overline{\mathbf{PS}} = d(\mathbf{P}, \mathbf{S}) = \|\mathbf{S} - \mathbf{P}\|.$$

EXAMPLE 1. Determine the length of the segment joining the points $P(4, -7)$ and $S(12, 8)$.

Solution: $d(\mathbf{P}, \mathbf{S}) = \sqrt{(12 - 4)^2 + [8 - (-7)]^2} = \sqrt{8^2 + 15^2} = 17,$
                                                              Answer.

Line segments are said to be parallel provided the lines containing them are parallel. Thus, $\overline{\mathbf{PS}}$ and $\overline{\mathbf{TR}}$ are parallel segments if and only if $S - P$ and $R - T$ are parallel vectors.

EXAMPLE 2. Show that the segment joining $P(4, -7)$ and $S(12, 8)$ is parallel to and twice as long as the segment joining $T(-\frac{7}{2}, \frac{1}{2})$ and $R(\frac{1}{2}, 8)$.

Solution: $S - P = (12, 8) - (4, -7) = (8, 15)$,

$R - T = (\frac{1}{2}, 8) - (-\frac{7}{2}, \frac{1}{2}) = (4, \frac{15}{2}) = \frac{1}{2}(8, 15) = \frac{1}{2}(S - P)$.

$\therefore S - P$ is parallel to $R - T$.

Since $R - T = \frac{1}{2}(S - P)$,

$\|R - T\| = \|\frac{1}{2}(S - P)\| = \frac{1}{2}\|S - P\|$.

$\therefore S - P$ is twice as long as $R - T$.

On a line segment each point that is not an endpoint is said to be **between** the endpoints. This means that T is between P and S if and only if $T \in \overline{PS}$, and $T \neq P$, $T \neq S$. To decide whether T is between P and S, you compute the lengths of $\overline{PT}$, $\overline{TS}$, and $\overline{PS}$ and apply the following theorem.

·THEOREM If P, S, and T are distinct points in the plane, then T is between P and S if and only if

$$d(P, T) + d(T, S) = d(P, S).$$

Exercise 35, page 185, asks for a proof of this proposition.

EXAMPLE 3. Determine whether $T(4, -4)$ is between $P(7, -6)$ and $S(1, -2)$.

Solution: $d(P, T) = \sqrt{(7 - 4)^2 + (-6 + 4)^2}$

$= \sqrt{3^2 + (-2)^2} = \sqrt{13}$

$d(T, S) = \sqrt{(1 - 4)^2 + (-2 + 4)^2}$

$= \sqrt{(-3)^2 + 2^2} = \sqrt{13}$

$d(P, S) = \sqrt{(1 - 7)^2 + (-2 + 6)^2}$

$= \sqrt{(-6)^2 + 4^2} = \sqrt{52} = 2\sqrt{13}$

$\therefore d(P, T) + d(T, S) = d(P, S)$.

Hence T is between P and S, **Answer.**

To locate the point **T** of a line segment $\overline{PS}$ that partitions $\overline{PS}$ into two segments whose lengths are in a prescribed ratio r, note that, for $\mathbf{T} = (1 - t)\mathbf{P} + t\mathbf{S}$, $0 \le t \le 1$,

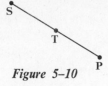

Figure 5–10

$$d(\mathbf{P}, \mathbf{T}) = \|\mathbf{T} - \mathbf{P}\| = \|(1 - t)\mathbf{P} + t\mathbf{S} - \mathbf{P}\| = \|t(\mathbf{S} - \mathbf{P})\| = t\|\mathbf{S} - \mathbf{P}\|;$$

$$d(\mathbf{T}, \mathbf{S}) = \|\mathbf{S} - \mathbf{T}\| = \|\mathbf{S} - (1 - t)\mathbf{P} - t\mathbf{S}\| = (1 - t)\|\mathbf{S} - \mathbf{P}\|,$$

Hence $d(\mathbf{P}, \mathbf{T}) = rd(\mathbf{T}, \mathbf{S})$ if and only if

$$t\|\mathbf{S} - \mathbf{P}\| = r(1 - t)\|\mathbf{S} - \mathbf{P}\|, \text{ or } t = r(1 - t)$$

$$\therefore t = \frac{r}{1 + r} \text{ and } 1 - t = \frac{1}{1 + r} \cdot \text{ Thus, } \mathbf{T} = \frac{1}{1 + r}\mathbf{P} + \frac{r}{1 + r}\mathbf{S}.$$

EXAMPLE 4. Determine the midpoint of the segment joining $(-3, 4)$ and $(1, -6)$.

Solution: $\mathbf{P} = (-3, 4)$, $\mathbf{S} = (1, -6)$. Since $d(\mathbf{P}, \mathbf{T}) = d(\mathbf{T}, \mathbf{S})$, $r = 1$.

$$\therefore \mathbf{T} = \frac{1}{1 + 1}\mathbf{P} + \frac{1}{1 + 1}\mathbf{S} = \frac{1}{2}(\mathbf{P} + \mathbf{S})$$

$$\therefore \mathbf{T} = \frac{1}{2}[(-3, 4) + (1, -6)] = \left(\frac{-3 + 1}{2}, \frac{4 - 6}{2}\right)$$

$$= (-1, -1), \text{ Answer.}$$

EXAMPLE 5. Find the point of segment $\overline{PS}$ that is half as far from $P(0, 8)$ as it is from $S(-6, 5)$.

Solution: $d(\mathbf{P}, \mathbf{T}) = \frac{1}{2}d(\mathbf{T}, \mathbf{S})$; $\therefore r = \frac{1}{2}$.

$$\mathbf{T} = \frac{1}{1 + \frac{1}{2}}\mathbf{P} + \frac{\frac{1}{2}}{1 + \frac{1}{2}}\mathbf{S} = \frac{2}{3}\mathbf{P} + \frac{1}{3}\mathbf{S}.$$

$$\therefore \mathbf{T} = \frac{2}{3}(0, 8) + \frac{1}{3}(-6, 5) = (0 - 2, \frac{16}{3} + \frac{5}{3}) = (-2, 7), \text{ Answer.}$$

Exercises

If **P, S,** and **T** are distinct points in the plane, which of the following permit you to conclude that **P** is between **S** and **T**?

1. $\mathbf{P} \in \mathrm{ST}$
2. $\mathbf{P} \in \overline{\mathrm{ST}}$
3. $d(\mathbf{S}, \mathbf{P}) < d(\mathbf{S}, \mathbf{T})$
4. $d(\mathbf{S}, \mathbf{P}) + d(\mathbf{P}, \mathbf{T}) = d(\mathbf{S}, \mathbf{T})$

Find the length of $\overline{ST}$.

5. $S(2, 3); T(-1, 5)$
6. $S(0, 2); T(3, -1)$
7. $S(1, 4); T(-2, 3)$

8. $S(\sqrt{3}, 1); T(0, 4)$
9. $S(3\sqrt{2}, \sqrt{3}); T(\sqrt{2}, 4\sqrt{3})$
10. $S(2a, b); T(-a, 3b)$

Represent in the coordinate plane the set of points specified by

11. $\{X: X = (1 - t)(2, 3) + t(-1, 4), 0 \le t \le 1\}$
12. $\{X: X = (1 - t)(-2, 1) + t(3, -2), 0 \le t \le 1\}$

In each exercise determine whether **P** lies between **T** and **S**.

13. $P(3, 0); T(0, -2); S(9, 4)$
14. $P(1, 1\frac{1}{2}); T(-2, 0); S(4, 3)$

15. $P(2, \frac{9}{7}); T(5, 0); S(-1, 3)$
16. $P(a, -2); T(a, 3); S(a, 0)$

B 17. To what subset of numbers must the domain of r be restricted if $\{X: X = (1 - 3r)P + 3rS\}$ defines the segment $\overline{PS}$?

18. In what ratio does $P(-2, 3)$ divide the segment joining $S(-5, 1)$ and $T(4, 7)$?

Find k such that **P** lies between **S** and **T**.

19. $P(1, k); S(-2, -3); T(5, 4)$
20. $P(k, \frac{4}{5}); S(-1, 5); T(4, -2)$

21. $P(1, 4); S(-3, 1); T(5, k)$
22. $P(1, -1); S(k, 0); T(5, -3)$

In each exercise find a point **P** on $\overline{TS}$ such that $d(T, P) = r \cdot [d(P, S)]$. $P = \frac{1}{1+r} T + \frac{r}{1+r} S$

23. $T(1, 4); S(5, 8); r = \frac{1}{2}$
24. $T(-3, 6); S(0, 6); r = \frac{2}{3}$
25. $T(-2, -6); S(8, 8); r = \frac{3}{2}$

26. $T(-2, -4); S(-3, 6); r = \frac{3}{5}$
27. $T(1, 4); S(-2, 3); r = 2$
28. $T(5, 2); S(-2, 8); r = \frac{4}{3}$

29. Show that the segment between $P(3, 2)$ and $S(5, 1)$ is parallel to and of the same length as the segment between $R(1, 5)$ and $T(-1, 6)$.

30. Given $T(-1, 4)$. Find two distinct points **R** and **S** such that $\overline{RT}$ and $\overline{TS}$ are both parallel and equal in length to the segment joining $M(-1, -2)$ and $N(2, 2)$.

31. Prove that $P(4, 4)$ is on the line through the points $S(6, 6)$ and $T(2, 2)$ and is equidistant from them.

32. Given $S(8, 4)$ and $T(10, 8)$. Find two points **M** and **N** which divide $\overline{ST}$ into three segments of equal length.

33. Prove: If **P** is the midpoint of $\overline{ST}$, then $P = \frac{1}{2}(S + T)$.

34. Given: $P(2, 3)$, $T(-4, -2)$, and $S(x, y)$. If **P** is the midpoint of $\overline{ST}$, find x and y.

C 35. Prove: If **P**, **S**, and **T** are distinct points in the plane, then **T** is between **P** and **S** if and only if $d(P, T) + d(T, S) = d(P, S)$.

36. Given $R(-7, -3)$, $S(x, y)$ and $P(3, 5)$. Determine x and y so that

$$\frac{d(R, P)}{d(P, S)} = \frac{2}{3}.$$

PLANE ANALYTIC GEOMETRY

*You will now use the concepts and theorems developed in Chapter 4 and in
the preceding sections of this chapter to prove some of the theorems of plane
geometry and to solve a number of the problems you studied in algebra and
geometry. Familiarity with these applications of vector concepts will help
you to understand the power and elegance of vector methods.*

5–6 Proving Geometric Theorems

Many of the theorems that you studied in plane geometry are easy to
prove by vector methods. You recall that a
triangle is a set consisting of three noncollinear
points **A**, **B**, and **C**, called **vertices**, and the three
line segments $\overline{AB}$, $\overline{BC}$, and $\overline{CA}$, called **sides**. You
denote the triangle by **ABC** (or by $\triangle ABC$).
Figure 5–11 illustrates the following theorem.

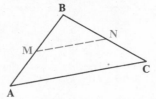

Figure 5–11

| THEOREM | The line segment joining the midpoints of two sides
of a triangle is parallel to and has a length half that
of the third side. |

Proof: Let **A**, **B**, and **C** be the vertices of a triangle, and let **M** and **N** be
the midpoints of $\overline{AB}$ and $\overline{BC}$, respectively. Then, $\mathbf{M} = \frac{1}{2}(\mathbf{A} + \mathbf{B})$
and $\mathbf{N} = \frac{1}{2}(\mathbf{B} + \mathbf{C})$. Hence,

$$\mathbf{M} - \mathbf{N} = \tfrac{1}{2}(\mathbf{A} + \mathbf{B}) - \tfrac{1}{2}(\mathbf{B} + \mathbf{C})$$

$$\therefore \mathbf{M} - \mathbf{N} = \tfrac{1}{2}(\mathbf{A} - \mathbf{C}).$$

Since $\mathbf{M} - \mathbf{N}$ is a scalar multiple of $\mathbf{A} - \mathbf{C}$, $\mathbf{M} - \mathbf{N}$ is parallel
to $\mathbf{A} - \mathbf{C}$. Therefore, $\overline{MN}$ is parallel to $\overline{CA}$. Also $\|\mathbf{M} - \mathbf{N}\| =
\frac{1}{2}\|\mathbf{A} - \mathbf{C}\|$. Therefore, the length of $\overline{MN}$ is half that of $\overline{CA}$.

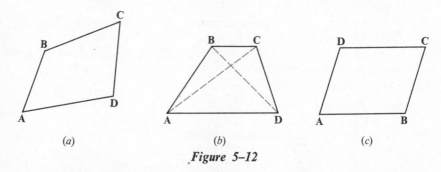

(a)   *(b)*   *(c)*

Figure 5–12

Figure 5–12 pictures several quadrilaterals. A **quadrilateral** is a set consisting of four points **A**, **B**, **C**, and **D**, called **vertices**, no three of which are

collinear, and the four line segments $\overline{AB}$, $\overline{BC}$, $\overline{CD}$, and $\overline{DA}$, called **sides**. The quadrilateral is denoted by **ABCD**. Vertices joined by a side are called **adjacent vertices**. Vertices that are not adjacent are called **opposite vertices**. For example, in quadrilateral **ABCD** vertices **A** and **D** are adjacent, but **A** and **C** are opposite. The line segments joining opposite vertices, such as $\overline{BD}$ and $\overline{AC}$ (Figure 5–12(b)), are called **diagonals**.

In a quadrilateral, sides with a vertex as a common endpoint are called **adjacent sides**, while sides without an endpoint in common are termed **opposite sides**. Thus, $\overline{AB}$ is adjacent to $\overline{BC}$, but opposite to $\overline{CD}$. A quadrilateral whose opposite sides are parallel is called a **parallelogram** (Figure 5–12(c)). A familiar theorem of geometry is the following assertion, illustrated in Figure 5–13.

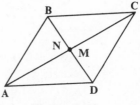

Figure 5–13

THEOREM   The diagonals of a parallelogram bisect each other.

To prove this theorem, you need the fact stated in the following **lemma**. (A **lemma** is a proposition introduced to help prove another theorem.)

LEMMA   If **ABCD** is a parallelogram, then $C - D = B - A$ and $C - B = D - A$.

Proof of lemma: Since $\overline{DC}$ is parallel to $\overline{AB}$, and $\overline{BC}$ is parallel to $\overline{AD}$ (Why?), there exist real numbers r and s such that

$$C - D = r(B - A) \text{ and } C - B = s(D - A).$$

Now, $(C - D) - (C - B) = B - D.$

$\therefore B - D = r(B - A) - s(D - A).$

Hence, $B - D = rB - sD + (s - r)A$, or

(*) $(1 - r)B = (1 - s)D + (s - r)A.$

Unless $1 - r = 0$, the starred equation is equivalent to

$$B = \left(\frac{1 - s}{1 - r}\right) D + \left(\frac{s - r}{1 - r}\right) A.$$

As you can see, $\dfrac{1 - s}{1 - r} + \dfrac{s - r}{1 - r} = 1$, so that $\dfrac{1 - s}{1 - r} = 1 - \dfrac{s - r}{1 - r}.$

Thus, you can rewrite the equation for **B** as follows:

$$\mathbf{B} = \left(1 - \frac{s - r}{1 - r}\right)\mathbf{D} + \left(\frac{s - r}{1 - r}\right)\mathbf{A}.$$

Therefore, unless $1 - r = 0$, $\mathbf{B}$ is a point of the line $\mathbf{DA}$. (Why?) But this is impossible, because no three vertices of a parallelogram are collinear. Therefore, it must be true that $1 - r = 0$, or that $r = 1$. In this case, the starred $(*)$ statement on page 187 becomes

$$0 = (1 - s)\mathbf{D} + (s - 1)\mathbf{A},$$

or

$$(1 - s)\mathbf{A} = (1 - s)\mathbf{D}.$$

Since $\mathbf{A}$ and $\mathbf{D}$ are distinct points (Why?), this means that $1 - s = 0$, and $s = 1$. (Why?) Thus,

$$\mathbf{C} - \mathbf{D} = 1(\mathbf{B} - \mathbf{A}) = \mathbf{B} - \mathbf{A}$$

and

$$\mathbf{C} - \mathbf{B} = 1(\mathbf{D} - \mathbf{A}) = \mathbf{D} - \mathbf{A}.$$

Do you see that the lemma implies that opposite sides of a parallelogram have the same length? Now that the lemma has been proved, we can use it to prove the theorem.

Proof of theorem: Let $\mathbf{M}$ and $\mathbf{N}$ be the respective midpoints of the diagonals $\overline{\mathbf{AC}}$ and $\overline{\mathbf{BD}}$. You know (page 186) that

$$\mathbf{M} = \tfrac{1}{2}(\mathbf{A} + \mathbf{C}) \text{ and } \mathbf{N} = \tfrac{1}{2}(\mathbf{B} + \mathbf{D}).$$

To prove the theorem, we shall show that $\mathbf{N} = \tfrac{1}{2}(\mathbf{A} + \mathbf{C})$. You can easily verify that

$$\mathbf{N} - \mathbf{A} = \tfrac{1}{2}(\mathbf{B} + \mathbf{D}) - \mathbf{A} = \tfrac{1}{2}(\mathbf{B} - \mathbf{A}) + \tfrac{1}{2}(\mathbf{D} - \mathbf{A}).$$

Using the lemma, you therefore find

$$\mathbf{N} - \mathbf{A} = \tfrac{1}{2}(\mathbf{C} - \mathbf{D}) + \tfrac{1}{2}(\mathbf{C} - \mathbf{B});$$
$$\therefore \mathbf{N} - \mathbf{A} = \mathbf{C} - \tfrac{1}{2}(\mathbf{B} + \mathbf{D}).$$

Hence,

$$\mathbf{N} - \mathbf{A} = \mathbf{C} - \mathbf{N},$$
$$\therefore 2\mathbf{N} = \mathbf{A} + \mathbf{C},$$
$$\mathbf{N} = \tfrac{1}{2}(\mathbf{A} + \mathbf{C}).$$

Thus, $\mathbf{N} = \mathbf{M}$, and the theorem is proved.

The exercises on page 189 suggest other theorems to prove by vector methods.

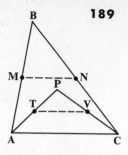

Exercises

A

1. In the figure shown, **M**, **N**, **T**, and **V** are respectively the midpoints of $\overline{AB}$, $\overline{BC}$, $\overline{AP}$, and $\overline{PC}$. Prove that $\overline{MN}$ is equal in length and parallel to $\overline{TV}$.

2. In quadrilateral **ABCD**, **R**, **S**, **T**, and **U** are respectively the midpoints of $\overline{AB}$, $\overline{BC}$, $\overline{CD}$, and $\overline{DA}$. Prove that **RSTU** is a parallelogram.

3. In the given quadrilateral **EFGH**, **M** is the midpoint of $\overline{EG}$ and also the midpoint of $\overline{FH}$. Prove that **EFGH** is a parallelogram.

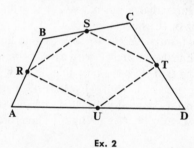

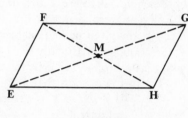

Ex. 2

Ex. 3

4. In the figure for Exercise 3 prove that if $\overline{FG}$ is parallel to $\overline{EH}$ and equal in length to $\overline{EH}$, then **EFGH** is a parallelogram.

B

5. Prove: If a line bisects one side of a triangle and is parallel to a second side, then it bisects the third side.

6. Prove: The segment which joins the midpoints of the two nonparallel sides of a trapezoid (the median) is parallel to both bases and has length equal to half the sum of their lengths.

C

7. In the given triangle, assume that $\overline{AB}$ and $\overline{AC}$ are segments of equal length. Prove that the medians to these sides, $\overline{CM}$ and $\overline{BN}$, are of equal length.

8. Prove that the medians of any triangle meet in a point whose distance from each vertex is two-thirds the length of the median from that vertex.

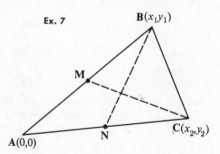

Ex. 7

5–7 Equation of a Line

Suppose $\mathcal{L}$ is the line through $(4, 0)$ with direction vector $(1, -3)$, (Figure 5–14). The vector $(3, 1)$, which is perpendicular to $(1, -3)$, is called a *normal vector* to $\mathcal{L}$. In general, any nonzero vector perpendicular to a direction vector of a line is called a **normal vector** to the line. Of course,

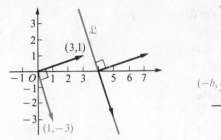

Figure 5-14   Figure 5-15

the first theorem stated on page 155 ensures that a normal vector to a line is perpendicular to every direction vector of the line.

Every nonzero vector $\mathbf{n} = (a, b)$ is a normal vector to at least one line through any given point $\mathbf{T}$, namely, the line $\mathfrak{M}$ through $\mathbf{T}$ with $\mathbf{n_p} = (-b, a)$ as direction vector (Figure 5-15). Proving that $\mathfrak{M}$ is the only line through $\mathbf{T}$ with $\mathbf{n}$ as a normal vector is left as an exercise for you. (Exercise 49, page 194.) Now, you know that a point $\mathbf{X}$ in the plane lies on $\mathfrak{M}$ if and only if $\mathbf{X} - \mathbf{T} = 0$ or $\mathbf{X} - \mathbf{T}$ is a direction vector of $\mathfrak{M}$. (Why?) Therefore, $\mathbf{X} \in \mathfrak{M}$ if and only if

$$(\mathbf{X} - \mathbf{T}) \cdot \mathbf{n} = 0$$

or

(*) $$\mathbf{X} \cdot \mathbf{n} = \mathbf{T} \cdot \mathbf{n}.$$

Thus, $\mathfrak{M}$ is the set of points, each point having its inner product with the nonzero vector $\mathbf{n}$ equal to the constant $\mathbf{T} \cdot \mathbf{n}$.

Writing $\mathbf{X} = (x, y)$ and $\mathbf{T} \cdot \mathbf{n} = c$, you can express the starred (*) equation above in the form

$$(x, y) \cdot (a, b) = c \quad \text{or} \quad ax + by = c.$$

This equation is said to be a **scalar equation** of the line $\mathfrak{M}$, or simply an equation of $\mathfrak{M}$. Any equation of the form $ax + by = c$, where a, b, and c denote real constants and $(a, b) \neq \mathbf{0}$, is called a **linear equation** in the variables x and y. Therefore, every line consists of the points whose coordinates (x, y) satisfy a linear equation in two variables.

EXAMPLE 1. Determine an equation of the line through $(4, 0)$ having $(3, 1)$ as normal vector.

Solution: $\mathbf{T} = (4, 0)$; $\mathbf{n} = (3, 1)$

An equation of the line is $(x, y) \cdot (3, 1) = (4, 0) \cdot (3, 1)$ or

$$3x + y = 12, \textbf{ Answer.}$$

Is every linear equation in two variables an equation of a line? Consider the equation $5x - 2y = -10$. The point $(0, 5)$ belongs to the solution set of this equation because

$$5 \cdot 0 - 2(5) = -10;$$

that is, $(5, -2) \cdot (0, 5) = -10.$

Thus, the equation can be written in the form

$$(5, -2) \cdot (x, y) = (5, -2) \cdot (0, 5)$$

which is an equation of the line through $(0, 5)$ with $(5, -2)$ as normal vector. In general, you can prove the following assertion (Exercise 47, page 194):

THEOREM   If $(a, b) \neq \mathbf{0}$, then $ax + by = c$ is an equation of the line having (a, b) as normal vector and containing $\left(0, \dfrac{c}{b}\right)$ if $b \neq 0$, and $\left(\dfrac{c}{a}, 0\right)$ if $a \neq 0$.

COROLLARY.   If $(a, b) \neq \mathbf{0}$, then $ax + by = c$ is an equation of a line having $(-b, a)$ as direction vector.

Two lines are said to be **perpendicular** to each other if a direction vector of one is perpendicular to a direction vector of the other. Thus, any direction vector of one of two perpendicular lines is a normal vector to the other.

EXAMPLE 2.   Determine an equation of the line $\mathcal{L}$ through $(1, -1)$ perpendicular to the line whose equation is $5x + 7y = 3$.

Solution: Because $(5, 7)$ is a normal vector to $5x + 7y = 3$, it is a direction vector of $\mathcal{L}$. Hence, a normal vector to $\mathcal{L}$ is $(5, 7)_P = (-7, 5)$.

$$\therefore \mathcal{L} = \{(x, y): \ (x, y) \cdot (-7, 5) = (1, -1) \cdot (-7, 5)\}$$
$$= \{(x, y): \ -7x + 5y = -12\}$$
$$= \{(x, y): \ \ 7x - 5y = \ \ 12\}$$
$$7x - 5y = 12, \textbf{ Answer.}$$

Line segments are called **perpendicular** provided the lines containing them are perpendicular lines. Thus, $\overline{BC}$ and $\overline{CA}$ are perpendicular segments if and only if $\mathbf{B} - \mathbf{C}$ and $\mathbf{C} - \mathbf{A}$ are perpendicular vectors; that is, if and only if $(\mathbf{B} - \mathbf{C}) \cdot (\mathbf{C} - \mathbf{A}) = 0$. (Why?) A triangle in which two sides are perpendicular is a **right triangle**.
The Pythagorean theorem and its converse are easily

Figure 5–16

deduced consequences of our vector definitions. You should recall, however, that the definition of the distance $d(\mathbf{X}, \mathbf{Y})$ between points $\mathbf{X}$ and $\mathbf{Y}$ was adopted with this theorem in mind.

THEOREM   In triangle $\mathbf{ABC}$,

$$[d(\mathbf{A}, \mathbf{B})]^2 = [d(\mathbf{A}, \mathbf{C})]^2 + [d(\mathbf{B}, \mathbf{C})]^2$$

if and only if $\overline{\mathbf{AC}}$ and $\overline{\mathbf{BC}}$ are perpendicular segments.

Proof: $[d(\mathbf{A}, \mathbf{B})]^2 = \|\mathbf{B} - \mathbf{A}\|^2 = (\mathbf{B} - \mathbf{A}) \cdot (\mathbf{B} - \mathbf{A})$

$[d(\mathbf{A}, \mathbf{C})]^2 = \|\mathbf{C} - \mathbf{A}\|^2 = (\mathbf{C} - \mathbf{A}) \cdot (\mathbf{C} - \mathbf{A})$

$[d(\mathbf{B}, \mathbf{C})]^2 = \|\mathbf{B} - \mathbf{C}\|^2 = (\mathbf{B} - \mathbf{C}) \cdot (\mathbf{B} - \mathbf{C})$

Now,

$$\mathbf{B} - \mathbf{A} = (\mathbf{C} - \mathbf{A}) + (\mathbf{B} - \mathbf{C})$$

$\therefore (\mathbf{B} - \mathbf{A}) \cdot (\mathbf{B} - \mathbf{A}) = [(\mathbf{C} - \mathbf{A}) + (\mathbf{B} - \mathbf{C})] \cdot [(\mathbf{C} - \mathbf{A}) + (\mathbf{B} - \mathbf{C})]$

$\therefore \|\mathbf{B} - \mathbf{A}\|^2 = \|\mathbf{C} - \mathbf{A}\|^2 + 2(\mathbf{B} - \mathbf{C}) \cdot (\mathbf{C} - \mathbf{A}) + \|\mathbf{B} - \mathbf{C}\|^2$

$\therefore \|\mathbf{B} - \mathbf{A}\|^2 = \|\mathbf{C} - \mathbf{A}\|^2 + \|\mathbf{B} - \mathbf{C}\|^2$

if and only if $2(\mathbf{B} - \mathbf{C}) \cdot (\mathbf{C} - \mathbf{A}) = 0$; that is, if and only if $\mathbf{B} - \mathbf{C}$ and $\mathbf{C} - \mathbf{A}$ are perpendicular vectors.

Exercises

1. Line $\mathcal{L}$ is perpendicular to line $\mathfrak{N}$. The vector (r, s) is a normal vector to $\mathcal{L}$. Name a direction vector of $\mathcal{L}$, a direction vector of $\mathfrak{N}$, and a normal vector to $\mathfrak{N}$.

2. If two segments in the plane are perpendicular, can you assume there is some point $\mathbf{P}$ **(a)** through which both segments pass; **(b)** which lies on both of the lines which contain the segments?

In Exercises 3 and 4 name three ordered pairs (x, y) for which the given statement is true.

3. $(x, y) \cdot (2, 3) = (6, 1) \cdot (2, 3)$ 4. $(x, y) \cdot (1, -2) = (4, 3) \cdot (1, -2)$

In Exercises 5–8 determine which one, or ones, of the given vectors **r, s, u,** and **v** are normal vectors to the given line $\mathcal{L}$.

5. $\mathcal{L} = \{(3, 2) + t(4, 1)\}$; $\mathbf{r} = (-1, 4)$,
   $\mathbf{s} = (-\frac{1}{2}, 2), \mathbf{u} = (-3, 12), \mathbf{v} = (-1, -4)$

6. $\mathcal{L} = \{(-5, 2) + q(-2, 3)\}$; $\mathbf{r} = (2, 5)$,
   $\mathbf{s} \neq (-3, 2), \mathbf{u} = (-3, -2), \mathbf{v} = (-\frac{3}{2}, -1)$

7. $\mathcal{L} = \{(2 + 3t, 1 - t)\}; r = (-1, 3),$
   $s = (1, 3), u = (-2, -6), v = (4, 12)$

8. $\mathcal{L} = \{(5 - 2t, 1 + t)\}; r = (-1, -2),$
   $s = (-3, -6), u = (3, -6), v = (-1, \frac{1}{2})$

In Exercises 9–14 write an equation in the form $ax + by = c$ for the line through **P** having **n** as a normal vector.

9. $P(5, 2); n = (2, 3)$

10. $P(-2, 3); n = (-1, 4)$

11. $P(2, -3); n = (5, -1)$

12. $P(-1, -1); n = (3, 2)$

13. $P(4, 1); n = (0, 2)$

14. $P(5, -1); n = (-3, 0)$

Name a normal vector and a direction vector for each given line $\mathcal{L}$. Then, make a representation of the given line in the coordinate plane.

15. $\mathcal{L} = \{(x, y): 2x + 3y = 6\}$

16. $\mathcal{L} = \{(x, y): 5x - 2y = 12\}$

17. $\mathcal{L} = \{(x, y): x = 2y + 4\}$

18. $\mathcal{L} = \{(x, y): 5x = 10 - 2y\}$

Exercises 19–22 refer to the adjacent figure:

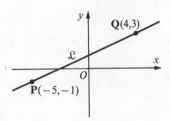

19. Name a direction vector for $\mathcal{L}$.

20. Name a normal vector to $\mathcal{L}$.

21. Write an equation for $\mathcal{L}$ in the form $ax + by = c$.

22. Write an equation in the $ax + by = c$ form for a line through **P** perpendicular to $\mathcal{L}$.

Write the equation of the given line $\mathfrak{N}$ in the form $ax + by = c$.

B

23. $\mathfrak{N} = \{(2, 3) + t(-1, 2)\}$

24. $\mathfrak{N} = \{(3, -2) + t(2, -4)\}$ $2x+y=4$

25. $\mathfrak{N} = \{(-1, 3) + q(0, 2)\}$

26. $\mathfrak{N} = \{(2, 4 + 3q)\}$ $x=2$

27. $\mathfrak{N} = PS$, where $P = (-2, 5)$ and $S = (1, 8)$

28. $\mathfrak{N} = PS$, where $P = (0, 2)$ and $S = (-3, -5)$ $7x-3y=-6$

Which of the lines specified by the given equation are perpendicular to the line whose equation is $3x - 2y = 12$?

29. $2x + 3y = 8$

30. $6x - 4y = 11$ ⊿

31. $4x = 10 - 6y$

32. $\frac{1}{3}x + \frac{1}{2}y = 1$ ⊥

For what value of k will $\mathcal{L}$ and $\mathfrak{N}$ be perpendicular lines?

33. $\mathcal{L} = \{(x, y): 3x - 5y = 10\}$ and $\mathfrak{N} = \{(x, y): 6x + ky = 12\}$

34. $\mathcal{L} = \{(x, y): 2x + 3y = 11\}$ and $\mathfrak{N} = \{(x, y): 5x + ky = 10\}$ $-\frac{10}{3}$

35. $\mathcal{L} = \{(x, y): x - 2y = 4\}$ and $\mathfrak{N} = \{(x, y): kx + 3y = 8\}$

36. $\mathcal{L} = \{(x, y): 2x + y = 5\}$ and $\mathfrak{N} = \{(x, y): kx - 2y = 7\}$ $k=1$

Determine an equation for the line $\mathcal{L}$ through point **P** perpendicular to line $\mathfrak{N}$.

37. $\mathfrak{N} = \{(x,y): 3x + 2y = 6\}$; $P(4, -1)$

38. $\mathfrak{N} = \{(x, y): 2x - 5y = 7\}$; $P(0, -3)$ $5x+2y=-6$

39. $\mathfrak{N} = \{(x, y): 2x = 8\}$; $P(1, 3)$

40. $\mathfrak{N} = \{(x, y): 3y = -6\}$; $P(-2, 1)$ $x=-2$

41. Write a linear equation in the variables x and y for the line perpendicular to the segment joining $P(2, 5)$ and $M(6, -1)$ at its midpoint.

42. Determine k so that the point $P(1, k)$ lies on the line which is the perpendicular bisector of the segment joining $T(4, 0)$ and $S(8, -6)$. $k=\frac{-19}{3}$

Given the line $\mathcal{L} = \{(x, y): ax + by = c\}$ and the point $P(r, s)$ not on $\mathcal{L}$.

43. Write a scalar equation for the line $\mathfrak{N}$ through **P** and parallel to $\mathcal{L}$.

$-ay = br-as$ **44.** Write a scalar equation for the line $\mathfrak{N}$ through **P** and perpendicular to $\mathcal{L}$.

45. Given the four points $A(-1, 0)$, $B(2, 7)$, $C(8, 6)$, and $D(6, 1)$, show that $\overline{AC}$ is perpendicular to $\overline{BD}$.

46. The vertices of triangle **ABC** are $A(-1, 1)$, $B(6, 5)$, and $C(2, -1)$. Show that the triangle is a right triangle.

C **47.** Prove: If $(a, b) \neq 0$, $ax + by = c$ is an equation of the line having (a, b) as a normal vector and containing $\left(0, \dfrac{c}{b}\right)$ if $b \neq 0$, and $\left(\dfrac{c}{a}, 0\right)$ if $a \neq 0$.

48. Prove: If $P(x_1, y_1)$ and $Q(x_2, y_2)$ are both on the line $ax + by = c$, then $(y_1 - y_2, x_2 - x_1)$ is a normal vector to the line.

49. Prove: There is exactly one line through a given point **T** having a given nonzero vector **n** as normal vector.

50. Prove that in the quadrilateral represented:

a. the diagonals are perpendicular;

b. the diagonals are equal in length;

c. all pairs of adjacent sides are perpendicular;

d. the diagonals bisect each other.

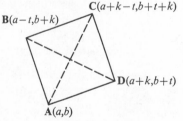

5–8 Distance between a Point and a Line

To discover how to define the distance in the plane between any point **S** and any line $\mathcal{L}$ with direction vector **v**, notice that Figure 5–17 suggests that the scalar component of $S - T$ perpendicular to **v** is constant for all points **T** of the line. But

$$\text{Comp}_{v_p}(S - T) = \frac{(S - T) \cdot v_p}{\|v_p\|}.$$

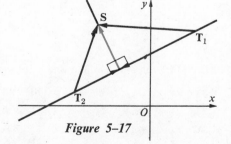

Figure 5–17

Hence, the figure indicates that if T_1 and T_2 are any points of $\mathcal{L}$, then the equation

$$\frac{(S - T_1) \cdot v_P}{\|v_P\|} = \frac{(S - T_2) \cdot v_P}{\|v_P\|}$$

should be a true statement. To verify the truth of this equation, observe that because $T_1 \in \mathcal{L}$ and $T_2 \in \mathcal{L}$, $T_1 - T_2$ is parallel to v (Why?), and, therefore, $(T_1 - T_2) \cdot v_P = 0$ (Why?). But

$$S - T_1 = (S - T_2) + (T_2 - T_1).$$

$$\therefore (S - T_1) \cdot v_P = (S - T_2) \cdot v_P + (T_2 - T_1) \cdot v_P$$

$$= (S - T_2) \cdot v_P + 0.$$

$$\therefore \frac{(S - T_1) \cdot v_P}{\|v_P\|} = \frac{(S - T_2) \cdot v_P}{\|v_P\|}.$$

We are thus led to define the **distance between** $\mathcal{L}$ and S, in symbols, $d(S, \mathcal{L})$, as follows:

$$d(S, \mathcal{L}) = \frac{|(S - T) \cdot v_P|}{\|v_P\|}$$

where T is any point of $\mathcal{L}$.

Using the Pythagorean theorem, you can prove that $d(S, \mathcal{L})$ is the length of the shortest line segment joining S to a point of $\mathcal{L}$ (Exercise 37, page 197). Also because any nonzero vector n normal to $\mathcal{L}$ is parallel to v_P (Why?), you can express $d(S, \mathcal{L})$ in terms of n:

$$d(S, \mathcal{L}) = \frac{|(S - T) \cdot n|}{\|n\|}$$

EXAMPLE 1. Determine the distance between $S(10, 2)$ and the line $\mathcal{L}$ whose parametric equations are

$$x = 3 - q \text{ and } y = 1 + 2q.$$

Solution: $\mathcal{L} = \{(3 - q, 1 + 2q)\}$

$$= \{(3, 1) + q(-1, 2)\}$$

$$S = (10, 2); \ T = (3, 1); \ v = (-1, 2); \ v_P = (-2, -1)$$

Choose $n = -v_P = (2, 1)$.

$$d(S, \mathcal{L}) = \frac{|[(10, 2) - (3, 1)] \cdot (2, 1)|}{\|(2, 1)\|} = \frac{|(7, 1) \cdot (2, 1)|}{\sqrt{4 + 1}}.$$

$$\therefore d(S, \mathcal{L}) = \frac{15}{\sqrt{5}} = 3\sqrt{5}, \text{ **Answer.**}$$

If $\mathcal{L}$ is specified by a linear equation $ax + by = c$, or $(x, y) \cdot (a, b) = c$, then you can choose **n** to be (a, b). Also, for each $\mathbf{T} \in \mathcal{L}$, $\mathbf{T} \cdot \mathbf{n} = c$ (Why?). Therefore, if the coordinates of **S** are (x^*, y^*), you can express $d(\mathbf{S}, \mathcal{L})$ as follows:

$$d(\mathbf{S}, \mathcal{L}) = \frac{|(\mathbf{S} - \mathbf{T}) \cdot \mathbf{n}|}{\|\mathbf{n}\|} = \frac{|\mathbf{S} \cdot \mathbf{n} - \mathbf{T} \cdot \mathbf{n}|}{\|\mathbf{n}\|}$$

$$= \frac{|(x^*, y^*) \cdot (a, b) - c|}{\sqrt{a^2 + b^2}}$$

$$\therefore \ d(\mathbf{S}, \mathcal{L}) = \frac{|ax^* + by^* - c|}{\sqrt{a^2 + b^2}}$$

EXAMPLE 2. Determine the distance between the line $\mathcal{L}$ whose linear equation is $5x - 12y = -6$ and the point $\mathbf{S}(-3, \frac{5}{2})$.

Solution: $a = 5, b = -12, c = -6; x^* = -3, y^* = \frac{5}{2}$

$$d(\mathbf{S}, \mathcal{L}) = \frac{|5(-3) - 12(\frac{5}{2}) + 6|}{\sqrt{5^2 + (-12)^2}}$$

$$= \frac{|-39|}{13} = 3, \ \textbf{Answer.}$$

Do you see that the distance between the line $\{(x, y): \ ax + by = c\}$ and the origin is $\dfrac{|c|}{\sqrt{a^2 + b^2}}$?

Exercises

In the given figure name an ordered pair or a real number for each of the following.

1. A direction vector **v** of $\mathcal{L}$.

2. A normal vector **n** to $\mathcal{L}$. $-4, 3$

3. $\mathbf{S} - \mathbf{T}$

4. $\text{Comp}_{\mathbf{v}} \, (\mathbf{S} - \mathbf{T})$ $10 \ (-10)$

5. $\text{Comp}_{\mathbf{v_p}} \, (\mathbf{S} - \mathbf{T})$

6. $d(\mathbf{S}, \mathcal{L})$ 5

7. $d(\mathbf{S}, \mathbf{K})$

8. $\mathbf{S} - \mathbf{R}$ $7, -1$

9. $\text{Comp}_{\mathbf{v}} \, (\mathbf{S} - \mathbf{R})$

10. $\text{Comp}_{\mathbf{v_p}} \, (\mathbf{S} - \mathbf{R})$ $-5, (5)$

11. $d(\mathbf{R}, \mathbf{K})$

12. $d(\mathbf{S}, \mathbf{R})$ $5\sqrt{2}$

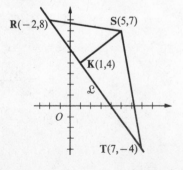

In each exercise determine the distance between **P** and line $\mathcal{L}$ specified by the given equation.

13. $\mathcal{L} = \{(4 + t, 2 - t)\}$; $P(6, 2)$

14. $\mathcal{L} = \{(3 - 2t, 1 + t)\}$; $P(2, -1)$

15. $\mathcal{L} = \{(-1 + q, 2 - 3q)\}$; $P(0, -1)$

16. $\mathcal{L} = \{(2 - q, -3 + q)\}$; $P(2, 0)$

17. $\mathcal{L} = \{(5, 3) + t(1, -2)\}$; $P(0, 0)$

18. $\mathcal{L} = \{(0, 3) + q(-1, 2)\}$; $P(-1, 0)$

19. $3x - 4y = 10$; $P(2, 1)$

20. $3x + 4y = 12$; $P(4, 0)$

21. $5x - 12y = 10$; $P(3, 1)$

22. $3x - y = 7$; $P(-1, 2)$

In each exercise the equations of two parallel lines are given. Find the distance between the two lines by selecting a point on one line and finding the distance between that point and the second line.

23. $3x + 2y = 12$ and $3x + 2y = 16$

24. $4x - 3y = 24$ and $8x - 6y = 36$

25. $\{(2, 1) + t(3, 2)\}$ and $\{(3, 6) + t(3, 2)\}$

26. $\{(4, 1) + t(-3, 4)\}$ and $\{(-2, 1) + t(-6, 8)\}$

Determine k so that **P** is at the given distance from line $\mathcal{L}$.

B

27. $\mathcal{L} = \{(x, y): 3x - 4y = k\}$; $P(2, 3)$; $d(P, \mathcal{L}) = \frac{6}{5}$

28. $\mathcal{L} = \{(x, y): 2x + 3y = k\}$; $P(5, 3)$; $d(P, \mathcal{L}) = \sqrt{13}$

29. $\mathcal{L} = \{(4, 3) + t(2, -1)\}$; $P(3k, k)$; $d(P, \mathcal{L}) = 2\sqrt{5}$

30. $\mathcal{L} = \{(-2k, 3k) + t(3, -4)\}$; $P(3, 2)$; $d(P, \mathcal{L}) = 4$

31. Given the line $\mathcal{L}$ with equation $12x + by + 36 = 0$. Determine b if $\mathcal{L}$ is at a distance of 3 from $P(0, 0)$.

32. Given the line $\mathcal{N}$ with equation $ax + 4y - 14 = 0$. Determine a if $\mathcal{N}$ is a distance of 1 from $P(1, 3)$.

Find the length of the three altitudes of $\triangle ABC$.

33. $A(3, 4)$; $B(-2, 4)$; $C(1, 0)$ 35. $A(2, 5)$; $B(1, -2)$; $C(-1, 4)$

34. $A(2, -1)$; $B(4, 3)$; $C(-1, 2)$ 36. $A(3, -2)$; $B(-1, 3)$; $C(8, 5)$

37. Using the Pythagorean Theorem, prove that $d(S, \mathcal{L})$ is the length of the shortest line segment joining **S** to a point of $\mathcal{L}$.

38. Given line $\mathcal{L}$ with a nonzero direction vector **v**. Prove that if **P** is a point such that $d(P, \mathcal{L}) = 0$, then **P** lies on $\mathcal{L}$.

39. Write an equation of the line on which the point closest to the origin has the coordinates (a, b) where a and b are not both zero.

40. Find all points which lie on the *y*-axis and are at a distance 3 from the line whose equation is $3x + 4y = 12$.

41. Given a triangle with vertices **A, B,** and **C,** show that $\frac{1}{2}|(C - A) \cdot (B - A)_P|$ is an expression for the area of the triangle.

42. Given $\mathcal{L} = \{(x, y) : ax + by + c = 0\}$. Write an equation of a line that is parallel to $\mathcal{L}$ and passes through a point **P** which is at a distance *k* from $\mathcal{L}$.

5–9 Intersection of Lines

A point common to two lines is called an **intersection point** or a **point of intersection** of the lines. Thus, the set of all the intersection points of two lines is the *intersection* (page 8) of the lines.

You know (page 177) that parallel lines either coincide or have no intersection point. Thus, the intersection of parallel lines either is an infinite set of points or is the empty set.

EXAMPLE 1. If $\mathfrak{M} = \{(x, y) : 2x - 3y = 5\}$ and
$\mathfrak{N} = \{(x, y) : -4x + 6y - 7 = 0\}$, determine
$\mathfrak{M} \cap \mathfrak{N}$.

Solution: $\mathfrak{M} = \{(x, y) : (2, -3) \cdot (x, y) = 5\}$;

∴ a normal vector to $\mathfrak{M}$ is $(2, -3)$.

$\mathfrak{N} = \{(x, y) : (-4, 6) \cdot (x, y) = 7\}$;

∴ a normal vector to $\mathfrak{N}$ is $(-4, 6)$.

Since $(-4, 6) = -2(2, -3)$, $(-4, 6)$ is parallel to $(2, -3)$; hence, $\mathfrak{N}$ is parallel to $\mathfrak{M}$. (Why?) But the point $(\frac{5}{2}, 0)$ of $\mathfrak{M}$ does not lie on $\mathfrak{N}$ because

$$-4(\tfrac{5}{2}) + 6(0) = -10 + 0 \neq 7.$$

$$\therefore \mathfrak{M} \cap \mathfrak{N} = \emptyset, \text{ \textbf{Answer.}}$$

Figure 5–18 suggests that the non-parallel lines

$$\mathcal{L} = \{(-2, -2) + q(2, 3)\}$$

and

$$\mathfrak{M} = \{(4, 2) + s(1, -1)\}$$

have exactly one point **I** in common.

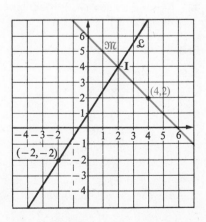

Figure 5–18

To prove that $\mathcal{L} \cap \mathfrak{M}$ consists of a single point, you must show that:
(1) there is only one point that can possibly lie on both $\mathcal{L}$ and $\mathfrak{M}$;
(2) this point actually does lie on both lines.

(1) Suppose $\mathbf{I}$ is a point lying on both $\mathcal{L}$ and $\mathfrak{M}$. Then, you can find real values of q and s for which $\mathbf{I} = (-2, -2) + q(2, 3)$ and $\mathbf{I} = (4, 2) + s(1, -1)$, so that

$$(-2, -2) + q(2, 3) = (4, 2) + s(1, -1).$$

Taking the inner product of each member of this equation with the vector $(2, 3)_\mathbf{P} = (-3, 2)$, you find

$$(-2, -2) \cdot (-3, 2) + q(2, 3) \cdot (-3, 2) = (4, 2) \cdot (-3, 2) + s(1, -1) \cdot (-3, 2),$$
$$2 + q(0) = -8 + s(-5),$$
$$10 = -5s,$$
$$s = -2.$$

Thus, $\mathbf{I} = (4, 2) - 2(1, -1) = (2, 4)$ is the only point that can lie on both lines.
(2) To check that $(2, 4) \in \mathcal{L}$ and $(2, 4) \in \mathfrak{M}$, you verify (Why?) that

$$[(2, 4) - (-2, -2)] \cdot (2, 3)_\mathbf{P} = 0 \quad and \quad [(2, 4) - (4, 2)] \cdot (1, -1)_\mathbf{P} = 0.$$
$$(4, 6) \qquad \cdot (-3, 2) = 0 \qquad\qquad (-2, 2) \qquad \cdot (1, 1) = 0$$

Hence, $\mathcal{L}$ and $\mathfrak{M}$ intersect in the unique point $(2, 4)$.

The reasoning pattern outlined above can be used to prove the following theorem (Exercise 35, page 203).

THEOREM Nonparallel lines in the plane have a unique point of intersection.

Determining the intersection of two lines specified by linear equations is often described as **solving** the linear equations **simultaneously**. The equations are said to form a *system of two simultaneous linear equations in two variables*. In your earlier work in algebra you learned to solve such systems by "elimination" or by "substitution." Now study the solution outlined in the following example.

EXAMPLE 2. Solve:
$$2x - 3y = 4$$
$$5x - 7y = -2$$

Solution: The compound sentence $2x - 3y = 4$ *and* $5x - 7y = -2$ is equivalent to the vector equation

$$(2x - 3y, 5x - 7y) = (4, -2) \text{ which,}$$

in turn, is equivalent to

$$(2, 5)x - (3, 7)y = (4, -2).$$

Taking the inner product of each member of this equation first with $(3, 7)_\mathbf{P} = (-7, 3)$, and then with $(2, 5)_\mathbf{P} = (-5, 2)$, you find

(1) $(-7, 3) \cdot (2, 5)x - (-7, 3) \cdot (3, 7)y = (-7, 3) \cdot (4, -2)$;

∴ $(1)x \qquad\quad - (0)y \qquad\qquad\quad = -34$;

∴ $\qquad\qquad\qquad\qquad\qquad\qquad x = -34.$

(2) $(-5, 2) \cdot (2, 5)x - (-5, 2) \cdot (3, 7)y = (-5, 2) \cdot (4, -2)$;

∴ $\qquad (0)x \quad - (-1)y \qquad\qquad = -24$;

∴ $\qquad\qquad\qquad\qquad\qquad\qquad y = -24.$

Thus, the only possible solution of the given system is $(-34, -24)$. To check, substitute -34 for x and -24 for y in both original equations.

$$2(-34) - 3(-24) \overset{?}{=} 4 \qquad 5(-34) - 7(-24) \overset{?}{=} -2$$
$$4 = 4 \checkmark \qquad -170 + 168 \quad = -2 \checkmark$$

∴ the single solution is $(-34, -24)$, **Answer.**

In general, the system

$$a_1x + b_1y = c_1$$
$$a_2x + b_2y = c_2$$

can be written in vector form

$$(a_1x + b_1y, a_2x + b_2y) = (c_1, c_2),$$

or

$$(a_1, a_2)x + (b_1, b_2)y = (c_1, c_2).$$

Using the method of Example 2, you can therefore prove (Exercise 36, page 203) that if $D = (b_2, -b_1) \cdot (a_1, a_2) = a_1b_2 - a_2b_1 \neq 0$, the given system is equivalent to the system

$$x = \frac{c_1b_2 - c_2b_1}{a_1b_2 - a_2b_1} \quad and \quad y = \frac{a_1c_2 - a_2c_1}{a_1b_2 - a_2b_1}.$$

On the other hand, if $D = 0$, then (Exercise 40, page 203) the lines specified by the equations are either parallel or coincident, and the system of equations has either no solution or infinitely many solutions.

An expression of the form $a_1b_2 - a_2b_1$ is often denoted by the symbol $\begin{vmatrix} a_1 & b_1 \\ a_2 & b_2 \end{vmatrix}$, called a *determinant*. Employing this notation, you can state the above result in the form of a theorem.

THEOREM The system $\begin{matrix} a_1x + b_1y = c_1 \\ a_2x + b_2y = c_2 \end{matrix}$ has a unique solution

if and only if $D = \begin{vmatrix} a_1 & b_1 \\ a_2 & b_2 \end{vmatrix} \neq 0$. If $D \neq 0$, the

solution is $\dfrac{1}{D}\left(\begin{vmatrix} c_1 & b_1 \\ c_2 & b_2 \end{vmatrix}, \begin{vmatrix} a_1 & c_1 \\ a_2 & c_2 \end{vmatrix} \right)$.

EXAMPLE 3. Give a roster of the solution set of the system

$$5x - 3y - 2 = 0$$
$$2y + x \quad\quad = 7.$$

Solution: Writing the system in customary form, you have

$$5x - 3y = 2$$
$$x + 2y = 7$$

$$D = \begin{vmatrix} 5 & -3 \\ 1 & 2 \end{vmatrix} = 10 + 3 = 13 \neq 0$$

$$\therefore x = \tfrac{1}{13}\begin{vmatrix} 2 & -3 \\ 7 & 2 \end{vmatrix} = \tfrac{1}{13}(4 + 21) = \tfrac{25}{13}$$

$$y = \tfrac{1}{13}\begin{vmatrix} 5 & 2 \\ 1 & 7 \end{vmatrix} = \tfrac{1}{13}(35 - 2) = \tfrac{33}{13}$$

Check: $\quad 5(\tfrac{25}{13}) - 3(\tfrac{33}{13}) \overset{?}{=} 2 \quad\quad \tfrac{25}{13} + 2(\tfrac{33}{13}) \overset{?}{=} 7$

$\quad\quad\quad \tfrac{125}{13} - \tfrac{99}{13} = \tfrac{26}{13} = 2\checkmark \quad\quad \tfrac{25}{13} + \tfrac{66}{13} = \tfrac{91}{13} = 7\checkmark$

$\{(\tfrac{25}{13}, \tfrac{33}{13})\}$, **Answer.**

Exercises

If $\mathcal{L}_1 = \mathbf{M} + q\mathbf{v}$ and $\mathcal{L}_2 = \mathbf{N} + t\mathbf{w}$ are two lines with a unique intersection point $\mathbf{T}$, which of the following are correct assertions?

A

1. $(\mathbf{T} - \mathbf{M}) \cdot \mathbf{v_P} = 0$
2. $\mathbf{T} - \mathbf{M} = \mathbf{T} - \mathbf{N}$
3. $(\mathbf{T} - \mathbf{N}) \cdot \mathbf{w_P} = 0$
4. $\mathbf{T} \in (\mathcal{L}_1 \cap \mathcal{L}_2)$
5. $\mathbf{v} \cdot \mathbf{w_P} = 0$
6. $\mathbf{T} - \mathbf{M} = k\mathbf{v} \; (k \neq 0)$

Classify each statement as true or as false. Give a supporting reason.

7. A determinant is an ordered pair.

8. "$x = y$ and $y = 3$" is equivalent to "$(x, y) = (6, 3)$."

9. Given: $\mathcal{L}_1$ and $\mathcal{L}_2$ are two nonparallel lines in the plane, and **P** and **T** two distinct points. If $\mathbf{P} \in \{\mathcal{L}_1 \cap \mathcal{L}_2\}$, then $\mathbf{T} \notin \{\mathcal{L}_1 \cap \mathcal{L}_2\}$.

10. If $ad \neq bc$, $\begin{vmatrix} a & b \\ c & d \end{vmatrix} = \begin{vmatrix} c & d \\ a & b \end{vmatrix}$

Evaluate each of the given determinants.

11. $\begin{vmatrix} -2 & 3 \\ -6 & 9 \end{vmatrix}$
12. $\begin{vmatrix} -2 & 3 \\ 4 & 1 \end{vmatrix}$
13. $\begin{vmatrix} 5 & 3 \\ -2 & 4 \end{vmatrix}$
14. $\begin{vmatrix} 2 & 2 \\ 6 & 6 \end{vmatrix}$ 0

15. $\begin{vmatrix} 8 & 3 \\ 2 & 1 \end{vmatrix} \over \begin{vmatrix} 3 & 4 \\ 2 & 3 \end{vmatrix}$
16. $\begin{vmatrix} 5 & 2 \\ -7 & 2 \end{vmatrix} \over \begin{vmatrix} -1 & 2 \\ -3 & 2 \end{vmatrix}$ 6
17. $\begin{vmatrix} 5 & -3 \\ 6 & 2 \end{vmatrix} \over \begin{vmatrix} 4 & -1 \\ -1 & 2 \end{vmatrix}$
18. $\begin{vmatrix} 4 & 6 \\ 2 & 3 \end{vmatrix} \over \begin{vmatrix} -5 & 3 \\ -1 & 4 \end{vmatrix}$ 0

Determine $\mathcal{L} \cap \mathcal{N}$.

19. $\mathcal{L} = \{(1, 4) + t(-1, 3)\}$; $\mathcal{N} = \{(4, 0) + q(1, 2)\}$

20. $\mathcal{L} = \{(8, -3) + t(-5, 2)\}$; $\mathcal{N} = \{(4, 10) + q(2, 3)\}$ $(-2, 1)$

21. $\mathcal{L} = \{(3 - 2t, 1 - t)\}$; $\mathcal{N} = \{(4 + 5q, 2 + 3q)\}$

22. $\mathcal{L} = \{(3 + 3t, \frac{2}{3} - 2t)\}$; $\mathcal{N} = \{(4 + 2q, 5 + 3q)\}$ $(\frac{24}{13}, \frac{20}{13})$

23. $\mathcal{L} = \{(6 + 3q, 3 - 2q)\}$; $\mathcal{N} = \{(3, 5) + s(-3, 2)\}$

24. $\mathcal{L} = \{(2, -1) + q(1, -4)\}$; $\mathcal{N} = \{s(1, -4)\}$ $\emptyset$

Solve the given system of simultaneous linear equations by (a) the method of Example 2, page 199; (b) using determinants.

25. $x + 4y = 27$
$x + 2y = 21$

26. $2x - 3y = 1$
$3x - 4y = 7$ $(17, 11)$

27. $2x + 5y = 18$
$3x + 4y = 27$

28. $\frac{x}{2} + \frac{y}{3} = 2$ $(2, 3)$
$\frac{x}{3} + \frac{y}{9} = 1$

(B) **29.** $2x + 3y = 19$
$x - y = 12$

30. $3x - 4y = 0$ $(12, 9)$
$2x + y = 33$

31. $8x + 5y = 31$
$16x + 10y = 11$

32. $x + 3y = 26$ $(26, 0)$
$2x - 6y = 52$

33. Find the vertices of a triangle whose sides are segments of the three lines specified by $3x + 2y - 2 = 0$; $x - 3y - 6 = 0$; $x + 3y + 12 = 0$.

34. Find the equation of a line which passes through $(3, 2)$ and the intersection of the lines $2x - y = 3$ and $3x - 2y = 7$.

35. Prove: Nonparallel lines in a plane have a unique point of intersection.

36. Given the system $\begin{cases} a_1x + b_1y = c_1 \\ a_2x + b_2y = c_2 \end{cases}$ where $a_1b_2 - a_2b_1 \neq 0$. Using the method of Example 2 of this section, prove that

$$x = \frac{c_1b_2 - c_2b_1}{a_1b_2 - a_2b_1}, \, y = \frac{a_1c_2 - a_2c_1}{a_1b_2 - a_2b_1}.$$

37. Given: $\mathbf{P}(x_0, y_0)$ as the intersection point of $a_1x + b_1y + c_1 = 0$ and $a_2x + b_2y + c_2 = 0$. Show that $\mathbf{P}$ lies on the line specified by $k(a_1x + b_1y + c_1) + t(a_2x + b_2y + c_2) = 0$ where k and t are any two real numbers, not both 0.

C

38. For what value(s) of k will the three lines specified by $kx + 2y = 5$, $2x - y = 8$, and $x - ky = 9$ have a common point of intersection.

39. Given the triangle $\mathbf{ABC}$ with vertices at $\mathbf{A}(0, 0)$, $\mathbf{B}(r, 0)$, and $\mathbf{C}(t, u)$.

    a. Write the equations of the lines containing the three medians as segments and show that the lines have a common point of intersection.

    b. Do the same for the three altitudes of $\triangle \mathbf{ABC}$.

40. Prove that if $a_1b_2 - a_2b_1 = 0$, then the graphs of the equations

$$a_1x + b_1y = c_1 \quad \text{and} \quad a_2x + b_2y = c_2$$

are either parallel or coincident lines.

5–10 Slope of a Line

The direction of a line $\mathcal{L}$ is specified by a nonzero vector $\mathbf{v} = (v_1, v_2)$ or by any nonzero scalar multiple of $\mathbf{v}$. In particular, if $v_1 \neq 0$, then the direction vector $\dfrac{1}{v_1} \mathbf{v} = \left(1, \dfrac{v_2}{v_1}\right)$ indicates that from any point $\mathbf{T}$ of $\mathcal{L}$ you obtain another point $\mathbf{S}$ of $\mathcal{L}$ by adding 1 to the first coordinate and $\dfrac{v_2}{v_1}$ to the second coordinate of $\mathbf{T}$. Thus, you can think of $\dfrac{v_2}{v_1}$ as the "rise" in the line per unit of horizontal "run." (Figure 5–19) We call $\dfrac{v_2}{v_1}$ the *slope* of $\mathcal{L}$ and designate it by the letter m. Thus, m is the **slope** of a line if and only if $(1, m)$ is a direction vector of the line. Do you see that a line whose slope is a positive number "rises"

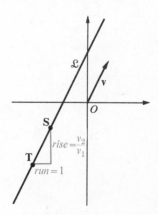

Figure 5–19

from left to right (Figure 5–20), but that a line whose slope is a negative number "falls" from left to right (Figure 5–21)?

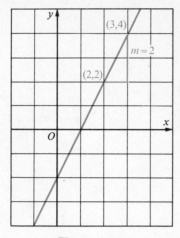

Figure 5–20　　　　　　　　　*Figure 5–21*

EXAMPLE 1. Find the slope of $\{(2 - 2t, -3 + t)\}$.

Solution: $\{(2 - 2t, -3 + t)\} = \{(2, -3) + t(-2, 1)\}$

∴ a direction vector of the line is $(-2, 1) = -2(1, -\frac{1}{2})$.

∴ the slope is $-\frac{1}{2}$, **Answer.**

Lines having $(1, 0)$ as direction vector have slope equal to 0 and are called **horizontal lines**. Thus, as you might expect, the x-axis and the lines parallel to it are horizontal lines.

Lines for which $(0, 1)$ is a direction vector have *no slope;* that is, the slope is not defined for such lines. They are called **vertical lines**. The y-axis, as well as each line parallel to it, is a vertical line, and has no slope. Can you explain why every horizontal line is perpendicular to every vertical line?

You define the slope of a line segment to be the slope of the line containing the segment. It is easy to compute the slope of the line or of the line segment through two points not on a vertical line. For, if $P(x_1, y_1)$ and $S(x_2, y_2)$ are different points, a direction vector of line PS is $(x_2 - x_1, y_2 - y_1)$. Since $x_2 \neq x_1$ (Why?), $x_2 - x_1 \neq 0$ and $\left(1, \dfrac{y_2 - y_1}{x_2 - x_1}\right)$ is also a direction vector of PS. This proves the following theorem.

THEOREM If $x_1 \neq x_2$, the slope of the line through (x_1, y_1) and (x_2, y_2) is $\dfrac{y_2 - y_1}{x_2 - x_1}$.

EXAMPLE 2. Determine the slope m of the line through $(5, -7)$ and $(-3, 9)$.

Solution: $(x_1, y_1) = (5, -7); (x_2, y_2) = (-3, 9)$

$$m = \frac{9 - (-7)}{-3 - 5} = \frac{16}{-8} = -2, \text{ Answer.}$$

Knowing the slope m of a line, you also know a direction vector of the line, namely, $(1, m)$. Therefore, to identify the line and state its equation, you need also know only one point of the line. For, if (x_1, y_1) is any point of line $\mathcal{L}$ with slope m, then a normal vector to $\mathcal{L}$ is $(-m, 1)$. (Why?) Hence, an equation of $\mathcal{L}$ is

$$(x, y) \cdot (-m, 1) = (x_1, y_1) \cdot (-m, 1),$$

or

$$-mx + y = -mx_1 + y_1,$$

or

$$y - y_1 = m(x - x_1).$$

EXAMPLE 3. Give an equation of the line through $(5, -7)$ and $(-3, 9)$.

Solution: **1.** In Example 2 the slope of the line was found to be -2.

2. Choose one of the given points, say $(5, -7)$, and use it with the slope to determine an equation of the line.

$$y - (-7) = -2(x - 5)$$
$$y + 7 = -2x + 10$$
$$y = -2x + 3$$

3. To check, verify that $(-3, 9)$ satisfies

$$y = -2x + 3$$
$$9 \overset{?}{=} -2(-3) + 3$$
$$9 = 6 + 3 \checkmark$$

$\therefore$ An equation of the line is $y = -2x + 3$, **Answer.**

Notice that in the equation given in the answer to Example 3, the coefficient of x, -2, is the slope of the line. The constant term, 3, is the second coordinate of the point $(0, 3)$ in which the line intersects the y-axis; this constant is called the **y-intercept** of the line. See if you can prove that, in general, the line having *slope m* and *y-intercept d* has an equation of the form

$$y = mx + d.$$

EXAMPLE 4. State the slope and y-intercept of $\{(x, y): 3x + 5y = 10\}$.

Solution: $3x + 5y = 10$ is equivalent to $5y = -3x + 10$, *or*

$$y = -\tfrac{3}{5}x + 2.$$

$\therefore$ the slope is $-\tfrac{3}{5}$; the y-intercept is 2, **Answer.**

The **x-intercept** of a line is the x-coordinate of the point in which the line intersects the x-axis. For example, the line described in Example 4 intersects the x-axis at the point $(\tfrac{10}{3}, 0)$ (Why?), so that its x-intercept is $\tfrac{10}{3}$. In Exercise 44, page 208, you are asked to prove that a line having x-intercept a and y-intercept b, where $a \neq 0$ and $b \neq 0$, has an equation of the form

$$\frac{x}{a} + \frac{y}{b} = 1.$$

It is easy to determine whether lines whose slopes are known are parallel or perpendicular to each other. For, if m_1 is the slope of $\mathcal{L}_1$ and m_2 is the slope of $\mathcal{L}_2$, then $(1, m_1)$ and $(1, m_2)$ are direction vectors of the lines. Hence, $\mathcal{L}_1$ and $\mathcal{L}_2$ are:

1. parallel if and only if there exists a real number q such that

$$(1, m_1) = q(1, m_2);$$

that is, $1 = q$ and $m_1 = qm_2$, or $m_1 = m_2$.

2. perpendicular if and only if

$$(1, m_1) \cdot (1, m_2) = 0$$

that is, $1 + m_1 m_2 = 0$,

or $\quad m_1 m_2 = -1$,

or $m_1 = -\dfrac{1}{m_2}, m_2 = -\dfrac{1}{m_1}$

THEOREM In the plane, two lines neither of which is vertical are parallel if and only if their slopes are equal. They are perpendicular if and only if the product of their slopes is -1.

EXAMPLE 5. If $\mathbf{P} = (-3, 4)$ and $\mathbf{S} = (5, 2)$, state an equation of the line $\mathfrak{N}$ through $\mathbf{M}$, the midpoint of $\overline{\mathbf{PS}}$, and perpendicular to line $\mathbf{PS}$.

Solution: $\quad m_{\mathbf{PS}} = \dfrac{4 - 2}{-3 - 5} = \dfrac{2}{-8} = -\dfrac{1}{4}$

$$\therefore m_{\mathfrak{N}} = -\left(\dfrac{1}{-\frac{1}{4}}\right) = 4$$

$$\mathbf{M} = \tfrac{1}{2}(\mathbf{P} + \mathbf{S}) = \tfrac{1}{2}(-3 + 5, 4 + 2) = (1, 3);$$

$\therefore$ an equation of $\mathfrak{N}$ is $y - 3 = 4(x - 1)$.

$$y = 4x - 1, \textbf{Answer.}$$

Exercises

A

1. If the given ordered pair is a direction vector of $\mathcal{L}$, give the slope of $\mathcal{L}$.

   a. $(3, 5)$ **b.** $(1, -\frac{1}{2})$ **c.** $(\frac{1}{2}, \frac{2}{3})$ **d.** $\left(2, -\dfrac{a}{b}\right)$ $(b \neq 0)$

2. If the given number is the slope of line $\mathcal{L}$, name a direction vector of $\mathcal{L}$ in which neither entry is a fraction.

   a. $\frac{2}{3}$ **b.** $-\frac{3}{4}$ **c.** $-\dfrac{a}{b}$ $(b \neq 0)$ **d.** $3\frac{1}{2}k$ $(k \in J)$

Make a coordinate-plane representation of the specified line.

3. Slope 2 and passing through the point $P(-2, 3)$.
4. Slope -3 and passing through the point $M(5, -1)$.
5. Slope $-\frac{4}{3}$ and y-intercept 3.
6. Slope $\frac{3}{5}$ and x-intercept -2.

Classify each statement as *true* or as *false*. Give a supporting reason.

7. The slope of a line is a vector.
8. Segments of the same line have equal slopes.
9. The x-axis has no slope.
10. The sum of the slopes of two perpendicular lines cannot be zero.

Find the slope and the y-intercept of the line whose equation is given.

11. $2x + 3y = 6$
13. $5x - 2y = 7$
12. $y + 2 = 0$
14. $\dfrac{x}{3} = \dfrac{y}{2} + 1$

Write a linear equation in x and y for the line with slope m and y-intercept d. Express your equation in the form $ax + by = c$, where a, b, and c are integers.

15. $m = \frac{3}{5}; d = 3$
17. $m = \frac{1}{2}; d = -\frac{3}{2}$
16. $m = -\frac{4}{3}; d = -1$
18. $m = -\frac{7}{3}; d = 0$

Find: **(a)** the slope of line **PS**, **(b)** the slope of any line perpendicular to line **PS**, **(c)** a scalar equation of line **PS**.

19. $P(3, 2); S(4, 6)$
22. $P(-1, -3); S(4, -3)$
20. $P(-1, 2); S(3, -2)$
23. $P(3, 2); S(\frac{1}{2}, \frac{2}{3})$
21. $P(0, 0); S(-2, 3)$
24. $P(-\frac{1}{2}, \frac{2}{3}); S(\frac{3}{4}, 2)$

By slope comparisons determine whether **P, S,** and **T** are collinear points.

25. $P(-4, 6); S(6, 9); T(2, 3)$
26. $P(1, 6); S(-4, 10); T(3\frac{1}{2}, 4)$

#50: odd 1-41

27. $P(4, -1)$; $S(8, 1)$; $T(0, -4)$

28. $P(a, b)$; $S(b, a)$; $T(a + b, 2b)$, $a \neq 0$, $b \neq 0$, $a \neq b$

In Exercises 29–34 find the value of k which meets the given condition.

B 29. The slope of the line through $(5, k)$ and $(9, 4)$ is $\frac{3}{2}$.

30. The slope of the line $2x - ky = 10$ is $-\frac{3}{2}$.

31. The slope of the line $\{(2 - 3t, 4 + 2kt)\}$ is $-\frac{5}{3}$.

32. The line $\{(3, k) + q(1, -3)\}$ has y-intercept 7.

33. The lines $5x + 3y = 4$ and $2kx - 5y = 10$ are perpendicular.

34. The lines $3x - 2y = 7$ and $kx + 3y = 10$ are parallel.

Write an equation of the specified line in: **(a)** linear form with variables x and y, **(b)** vector form with parameter q.

35. Through the point $(-3, 2)$ with slope $\frac{3}{4}$.

36. Through the points $(-1, 6)$ and $(4, 2)$.

37. Perpendicular to $2x + 3y = 12$ and passing through the point $(-1, 3)$.

38. Parallel to $\{(3 + 2t, 4 - t)\}$ and passing through the point $(2, -1)$.

39. Having slope $-\frac{3}{4}$ and y-intercept 2.

40. Having slope $\frac{5}{3}$ and x-intercept -3.

41. Perpendicular to and bisecting the segment joining $(-2, 3)$ and $(4, 7)$.

42. Having x-intercept 5 and y-intercept -2.

43. By slope comparisons show that the points $P(a, b + c)$, $Q(b, c + a)$, and $C(a + b, c)$ are collinear. (Assume no denominators equal zero.)

44. Prove that an equation of the line with x-intercept a and y-intercept b, where $a \neq 0$ and $b \neq 0$, is $\dfrac{x}{a} + \dfrac{y}{b} = 1$.

45. Given the lines $\mathcal{L}_1 = \{(a + tc, b + td)\}$ and $\mathcal{L}_2 = \{(e + sg, f + sh)\}$ where a, b, c, d, e, f, g, h are real constants, and t and s are parameters. If neither line is perpendicular to an axis and $\begin{vmatrix} d & -c \\ g & h \end{vmatrix} = 0$, prove that the lines are perpendicular.

C 46. If in the given figure $\mathcal{L}_1$ is perpendicular to $\mathcal{L}_2$ and $d(P, M) = \dfrac{d(M, Q)}{2}$, write an equation in x and y for $\mathcal{L}_2$.

47. Two opposite vertices of a square are (a, a) and $(4a, 5a)$. Find the coordinates of the remaining two vertices.

48. Write in parametric form the equation of the line through the point $(-2, 3)$ if the sum of its x- and y-intercepts is 6.

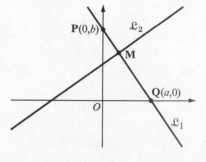

Ex. 46

49. The midpoints of the sides of a triangle have the coordinates $(0, 0)$, $(a, 0)$, and (b, c). Write equations of the lines in which the sides of the triangle lie, and show by finding intersection points that the vertices of the triangle are $(b + a, c)$, $(b - a, c)$ and $(a - b, -c)$.

50. Given triangle **RST** with vertices **R**$(0, 0)$, **S**$(a, 0)$, and **T**(b, c). Find the point in which the lines containing the altitudes intersect, the point in which the perpendicular bisectors of the sides intersect, and the point in which the medians intersect. Then prove that these three intersection points are collinear.

Chapter Summary

1. Vectors can be used to study **points** and **lines** in the plane. The **distance between two points P** and **T** in the plane is given by

$$d(\mathbf{P}, \mathbf{T}) = \|\mathbf{P} - \mathbf{T}\| = \sqrt{(x_2 - x_1)^2 + (y_2 - y_1)^2}.$$

2. A set $\mathcal{L}$ of points in $\mathcal{R} \times \mathcal{R}$ is a **line** if there exists a point **P** and a nonzero vector **v** such that $\mathcal{L} = \{\mathbf{X}: \mathbf{X} = \mathbf{P} + t\mathbf{v}, t \in \mathcal{R}\}$. The variable t in the equation for $\mathcal{L}$ is called a **parameter**. Equations such as $\mathbf{X} = \mathbf{P} + t\mathbf{v}$ or $(x, y) = (a + bt, c + dt)$ are called **vector equations** of lines.

3. If two lines have all their points in common, they are called **coincident** lines. For the line $\mathbf{P} + s\mathbf{v}$, **v** is a **direction vector**. Two lines are **parallel** if their direction vectors are parallel.

4. There is one and only one line in $\mathcal{R} \times \mathcal{R}$ passing through any two distinct points in $\mathcal{R} \times \mathcal{R}$. Points lying on the same line are said to be **collinear**, and the points **P**, **T**, and **S** are collinear if and only if $\mathbf{T} - \mathbf{P}$ and $\mathbf{S} - \mathbf{P}$ are parallel vectors.

5. The set $\overline{\mathbf{PS}} = \{\mathbf{x}: \mathbf{x} = (1 - t)\mathbf{P} + t\mathbf{S}, 0 \le t \le 1\}$ is called a **line segment**. On the segment each point other than an endpoint is said to be **between** the two endpoints **P** and **S** of the segment. Line segments are parallel provided the lines containing the segments are parallel.

6. You can use vector concepts to prove geometric theorems.

7. A **normal vector** to a line $\mathcal{L}$ is a nonzero vector perpendicular to a direction vector for $\mathcal{L}$. An equation of the form $ax + by = c$ is called a **scalar equation** of a line. Two lines are perpendicular if their direction vectors are perpendicular. Line segments are perpendicular provided the lines containing them are perpendicular.

8. The **distance between a point P and a line** $\mathcal{L}$ is given by

$$d(\mathbf{P}, \mathcal{L}) = \frac{|(\mathbf{P} - \mathbf{T}) \cdot \mathbf{v_P}|}{\|\mathbf{v_P}\|},$$

where $\mathbf{T}$ is any point of $\mathcal{L}$ and $\mathbf{v}$ is a direction vector of $\mathcal{L}$.

9. A point common to two lines is called an **intersection point** or **point of intersection** of the lines, and the set of all such points is called the **intersection** of the lines. If two lines are not parallel, then their intersection contains one and only one point. The array

$$\begin{vmatrix} a_1 & b_1 \\ a_2 & b_2 \end{vmatrix}$$

is called a **determinant** and is equal to $a_1 b_2 - a_2 b_1$.

10. If $\mathbf{v} = (v_1, v_2)$ is a direction vector for the line $\mathcal{L}$, and $v_1 \neq 0$, then the ratio $\dfrac{v_2}{v_1}$ is called the **slope** of $\mathcal{L}$. The slope of a line is denoted by m. If $m = 0$, $\mathcal{L}$ is parallel to the x-axis; if $m > 0$, $\mathcal{L}$ rises from left to right; if $m < 0$, $\mathcal{L}$ falls from left to right; and if m is not defined, $\mathcal{L}$ is parallel to the y-axis. The equation $y = mx + d$ is an equation of the line with slope m and **y-intercept** d.

Chapter Test

5-1 **1.** Given points $P(-2, 3)$ and $T(4, 6)$. Compute $d(P, T)$.

2. Determine k if, for the points $M(k, -2)$ and $N(-1, 2)$, $d(M, N) = \sqrt{41}$.

5-2 **3.** Write a vector equation for the line $\mathcal{L}$ passing through the point $P(-2, 3)$ and parallel to the vector $v = (1, -3)$.

5-3 **4.** Name a direction vector of the line $\mathcal{L} = \{(-2t, 4 + 3t)\}$.

5-4 **5.** Write a vector equation of the line $\mathcal{L}$ which passes through the points $P(-2, 3)$ and $S(3, 5)$.

5-5 **6.** Make a coordinate-plane representation of the set of points

$$\{X: \ X = (1 - t)(3, 5) + t(2, -1); 0 \leq t \leq 1\}.$$

7. Given the points $T(-11, 2)$, $S(4, 4)$, and $P(-1, 2)$. Determine whether P lies between T and S.

5-6 **8.** In the given parallelogram ABCD, X and Y are the respective midpoints of $\overline{BC}$ and $\overline{AD}$. Prove that AXCY is a parallelogram.

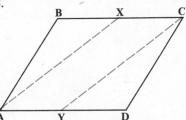

5-7 **9.** Name a normal vector to the line $\mathcal{L} = \{(3, -2) + t(4, -3)\}$.

10. Write an equation in the form $ax + by = c$ for the line $\mathcal{L}$, where $\mathcal{L} = \{(-2 + 4t, 3 - 2t)\}$.

5-8 **11.** Find the distance from the point $(3, -1)$ to the line $3x + 4y = 15$.

5-9 **12.** Evaluate the determinant $\begin{vmatrix} 5 & 4 \\ -3 & 2 \end{vmatrix}$.

13. Find the intersection of the lines $2x + 3y = 8$ and $3x - 4y = 12$.

5-10 **14.** Write an equation of the line which passes through the point $(-2, 3)$ and is perpendicular to the line $3x + 4y = 12$.

Reading List

COPELAND, ARTHUR H. *Geometry, Algebra, and Trigonometry by Vector Methods.* New York: The Macmillan Co., 1962.

JAEGER, ARNO. *Introduction to Analytic Geometry and Linear Algebra.* New York: Holt, Rinehart, and Winston, Inc., 1960.

KELLEY, JOHN L. *Introduction to Modern Algebra.* Princeton, N.J.: D. Van Nostrand Co., Inc., 1960.

PRENOWITZ, WALTER. *"Geometric Vector Analysis and the Concepts of Vector Space,"* Insights into Modern Mathematics, Twenty-third Yearbook. Washington, D.C., National Council of Mathematics, 1957, pp. 145–199.

ROBINSON, GILBERT. *Vector Geometry.* Boston: Allyn and Bacon, Inc., 1962.

SCHOOL MATHEMATICS STUDY GROUP. Mathematics for High School: *Introduction to Matrix Algebra.* New Haven, Conn.: Yale University Press, 1961.

SCHUSTER, S. *Elementary Vector Geometry.* New York: John Wiley and Sons, 1962.

TROYER, ROBERT J. *"An Approach to Vector Geometry."* The Mathematics Teacher, vol. LVI (1963), pp. 290–297.

Hermann Minkowski

Do you think it would be possible to prove complicated theorems in the theory of numbers without numerical calculations? It seems unlikely, but this is exactly what the Russian-German mathematician Hermann Minkowski (1864–1909) did. Minkowski demonstrated his mathematical ability and his remarkable spatial intuition at an early age. He was under 18 when the French Academy awarded him its grand prize for his work in number theory. His principal work in this field was the development of a new area of mathematics known as the geometry of numbers.

Minkowski demonstrated that restating algebraic conjectures in terms of geometry sometimes makes their proofs appear obvious. Consider for a moment what is meant by restating an algebraic problem in geometric terms. One of the problems that 19th-century mathematicians had been working on was the following: How many integral solutions are there to the inequality $x^2 + y^2 \leq c$, where c is a positive constant? In geometric terms the problem would be, How many points with integral coordinates are there inside or on a circle within radius $\sqrt{c}$?

Stating one of Minkowski's most famous theorems may give an idea of the nature of his work. First, though, it is necessary to introduce the concepts "lattice" and "convex region." A lattice is a system of lines which divides the plane into an infinite number of parallelograms. The points at which the lines of the lattice intersect are called "lattice points." Some lattice point is desig-

nated as the origin, and the length from the origin to a collinear vertex of the same parallelogram is defined to be the unit length. A convex region is one with the following property: If two points belong to the region, so does every point on the line segment joining them. Minkowski's theorem, then, is this: Any convex region R symmetrical about the origin and of area greater than 4 includes lattice points other than the origin.

A rectangle with center at the origin and vertices (3, 2), (−3, 2), (−3, −2), (3, −2) satisfies the hypothesis of this theorem. What is a lattice point other than the origin that is in this region? How many such points are there?

213

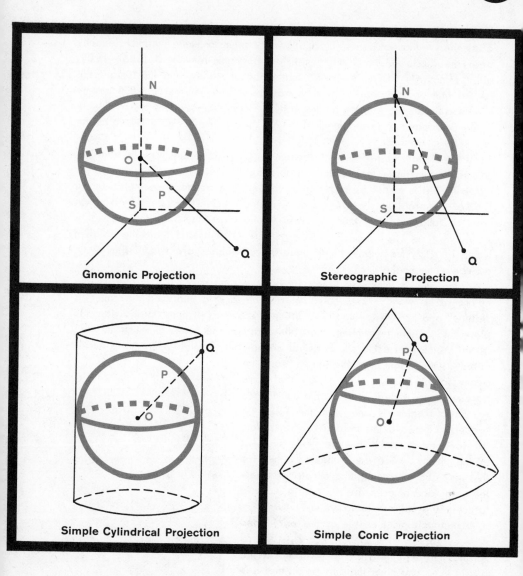

The diagrams above show four methods used in map making for establishing a correspondence between the points of a sphere and those of a plane, cylinder, or cone. The cylinder and cone are then sliced along a generator and unrolled to form a plane map.

unctions

All the sciences using mathematics employ it essentially to study relationships. Physicists, chemists, engineers, biologists, and, increasingly, economists, psychologists, sociologists, and other social scientists, all seek to discern connections among the various elements of their chosen fields and so to arrive at a clearer understanding of why these elements behave the way they do. In this chapter, we shall examine one of the central ideas in the mathematical study of relationships.

RELATIONS AND FUNCTIONS

6–1 Relations

A biology student investigating the way in which the growth of young turkeys is related to their age weighed a turkey every month from the time of hatching until it had reached almost full size. The following table records the weights to the nearest tenth of a kilogram.*

Age in Months	0 (just hatched)	1	2	3	4	5	6	7	8	9
Weight in Kilograms	0.1	0.6	2.1	4.0	6.2	8.4	10.6	12.7	14.6	14.8

Do you see that this table specifies a set of ordered pairs of numbers, the first number in each pair being the age, and the second number the weight of the turkey?

Any set of ordered pairs is called a **relation**. The set of all first coordinates of the ordered pairs is the **domain** of the relation; the set of all second coordinates is its **range**. Thus, the data obtained by the biology student defines a relation $\mathcal{G}$ whose domain is $\{0, 1, 2, 3, 4, 5, 6, 7, 8, 9\}$ and whose range is $\{0.1, 0.6, 2.1, 4.0, 6.2, 8.4, 10.6, 12.7, 14.6, 14.8\}$.

The relation $\mathcal{G}$ consists of ordered pairs of real numbers and is, therefore, a subset of $\mathcal{R} \times \mathcal{R}$. Consequently, in the coordinate plane you can regard

---

* Adapted from page L67, Laboratory Investigations for *Biological Science: Molecules to Man*, Houghton Mifflin Company, 1963.

G as the set of 10 points represented in Figure 6–1. In general, the **graph** of a relation is the set of points whose coordinates are the ordered pairs belonging to the relation.

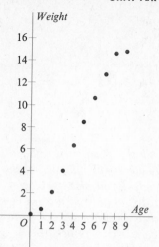

Figure 6–1

EXAMPLE 1. If ℱ is the relation whose graph is shown in the adjoining figure, give a roster of **(a)** ℱ; **(b)** the domain of ℱ; **(c)** the range of ℱ.

Solution: **a.** ℱ = {(−2, 0), (0, 0), (2, 0), (0, 3), (0, −3)};
b. Domain of ℱ = {−2, 0, 2};
c. Range of ℱ = {−3, 0, 3}, **Answer.**

Some-relations can be specified or defined by a rule enabling you to determine the member or members of the range paired with each element of the domain. For example, the solution set over ℜ × ℜ of an open sentence such as $x - y = 4$ is a relation ℒ that you can specify as follows:
ℒ = {(x, y): (x, y) ∈ ℜ × ℜ and $x - y = 4$}.
Another way to denote ℒ is:

$$\mathcal{L} = \{(x, x - 4): x \in \mathcal{R}\}.$$

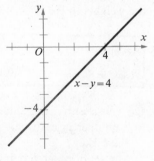

The graph of ℒ is the line partially shown in Figure 6–2. As indicated in the label of the figure, the symbols "$(x, y) \in \mathcal{R} \times \mathcal{R}$" or "$x \in \mathcal{R}$" are often omitted from the rule specifying a relation whose domain and range are sets of real numbers.

Figure 6–2

Whenever an open sentence specifies a relation whose domain and range are not explicitly stated, we agree to include in the domain and range those real numbers and only those real numbers for which the open sentence is true.

EXAMPLE 2. Determine (**a**) the domain and (**b**) the range of

$$\mathcal{H} = \{(x, y): y = \sqrt{1 - x^2}\}.$$

Solution: **a.** Because each value of y is to be a real number, each value of $1 - x^2$ must be a nonnegative number. Since $x^2 = |x|^2$,

$$1 - x^2 \geq 0 \text{ means } 1 - |x|^2 \geq 0,$$

or

$$|x|^2 \leq 1.$$
$$\therefore |x| \leq 1 \quad \text{(Why?)}$$

$\therefore$ The domain of $\mathcal{H}$ is $\{x: -1 \leq x \leq 1\}$, **Answer.**

b. $|x| \leq 1$ implies $0 \leq x^2 \leq 1$ (Why?);

$\therefore 0 \leq 1 - x^2 \leq 1.$

$\therefore$ The range of $\mathcal{H}$ is $\{y: 0 \leq y \leq 1\}$, **Answer.**

EXAMPLE 3. State the domain of $f = \left\{\left(x, \dfrac{3x}{(x - 2)(x + 5)}\right)\right\}.$

Solution: For real values of x, $\dfrac{3x}{(x - 2)(x + 5)}$ denotes a real number

if and only if $(x - 2)(x + 5) \neq 0$.   (Why?)

$\therefore$ the domain of f consists of all the real numbers except 2 and -5, **Answer.**

Although many of the relations to be studied in this book are subsets of $\mathcal{R} \times \mathcal{R}$, the coordinates of the ordered pairs in a relation need not be real numbers. For example, the telephone directory in your town is the roster of a relation pairing names with telephone numbers. Also, the relation

$$\{(\mathbf{v}, \mathbf{w}): \mathbf{v} \text{ and } \mathbf{w} \text{ are vectors and } \mathbf{v} \cdot \mathbf{w} = 0\}$$

pairs each vector with every vector perpendicular to it, and thus has the set of vectors for its domain and range.

Exercises

State the domain and range of each of the following relations.

A

1. $\{(5, 1), (-3, 0), (2, 0)\}$

2. $\{(1, 3), (5, 3), (-8, 3)\}$

3. $\{(2, 4), (3, 9), (\sqrt{7}, 7)\}$

4. $\{(25, -5), (8, -2\sqrt{2})\}$

5. $\{(1, 1), (0, 1), (-\frac{3}{2}, \frac{2}{3})\}$

6. $\left\{\left(\frac{1}{2}, \frac{\pi}{6}\right), \left(\frac{1}{2}, \frac{5\pi}{6}\right), \left(\frac{1}{2}, \frac{7\pi}{6}\right)\right\}$

In Exercises 7 and 8 state which of the ordered pairs named belong to the given relation.

7. $\{(x, y): x^5 > 10y^2 + 20\}$; $(1, 0), (2, 2), (3, -3), (20, 200), (-19, \pi)$

8. $\{(z, w): z^2 < |w|^3 - 5\}$; $(0, 1), (\sqrt{3}, -4), (-\sqrt{3}, 4), (0, 0)$

State the domain of each of the following relations.

9. $\{(x, y): y^2 = x^2\}$

10. $\{(x, y): \sqrt{y} = x\}$

11. $\left\{(m, k): k = \dfrac{2m - 5}{13m}\right\}$

12. $\left\{(z, t): t = \dfrac{z(z - 3)}{(z + 4)(z - 7)}\right\}$

13. $\{(x, u): u = \sqrt{x - 2}\}$

14. $\{(l, y): y = \sqrt{5 - 3l}\}$

15. $\{(x, y): xy = 12\}$

16. $\{(r, s): |r| + |s| = 5\}$

In Exercises 17–22 specify each relation by roster and draw the graph of the relation.

B

17. $\{(x, y): x$ and y are integers and $x^2 + y^2 = 289\}$

18. $\{(x, z): x$ and z are integers and $x^2 + 4z^2 = 13\}$

19. $\{(r + 1, r): r \in \{0, 1, 2, 3\}\}$

20. $\cdot\{(s^2, s^3 - 1): s \in \{-2, -1, 0, 1, 2\}\}$

21. $\{(x, y): y = 2|x + 1|$ and $x \in \{-2, -1, 0, 1, 2\}\}$

22. $\{(x, y): x^2 - 1 \le y \le x^2 + 1$ and $x \in \{-2, -1, 0, 1, 2\}\}$

State which of the following statements are true. In each case give a reason for your answer.

23. $\{(p, q): p = q + 1\} \ne \{(r, s): s = r - 1\}$.

24. The domain of $\{(x, y): y = \sqrt{x - 3}\}$ is $\{t: t \ge 3\}$.

25. $y = x^2$ is not a relation.

26. $\mathcal{R} \times \mathcal{R}$ is a relation and so is $\{(5, 3)\}$.

For the relations S and T stated in Exercises 27–30, specify (**a**) the union and (**b**) the intersection.

27. $S = \{(0, 1), (2, 3)\}$; $T = \{(0, 1), (2, 3), (4, 5)\}$

28. $S = \{(x, y): x = 1$ and $y > x\}$; $T = \{(x, y): x = 1$ and $y > 2x\}$

29. $S = \{(h, k): h = 5$ or 6, and $k < h\}$; $T = \{(x, y): x = 5$ and $y < x\}$

30. $S = \{(u, v): u^2 + v^2 = 4\}$; $T = \{(x, y): x^2 + y^2 > 4\}$

In the relation $\{(\mathbf{v}, \mathbf{w}): \mathbf{v}$ is a vector, $\mathbf{w}$ is a unit vector, and $\mathbf{v} \cdot \mathbf{w} = 0\}$, list the ordered pairs having first element

31. $(1, 0)$ **32.** $(1, 1)$

In the relation $\{(\mathbf{v}, \mathbf{w}): \mathbf{v}$ and $\mathbf{w}$ are vectors with integral coordinates and $\|\mathbf{v} - \mathbf{w}\| = 1\}$, list the ordered pairs whose first element is the given vector.

33. $(0, 0)$ **34.** $(-3, 4)$

6–2 Linear Relations

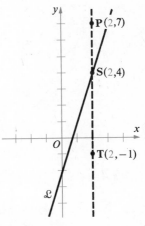

Figure 6–3

Any relation definable by an open sentence in which one member is an expression of the form $ax + by$ (a and b constants and not both zero), and the other member is a constant, is called a **linear relation.** The graph of a linear relation with domain $\Re$ is either a straight line or a region of the plane bounded by a straight line, hence the term "linear."

Figure 6–3 shows a line $\mathcal{L}$ in the plane, together with points $\mathbf{P}(2, 7)$, $\mathbf{S}(2, 4)$, and $\mathbf{T}(2, -1)$. Because the points $\mathbf{P}$, $\mathbf{S}$, and $\mathbf{T}$ have the same abscissa, $\mathbf{P}$, $\mathbf{S}$, and $\mathbf{T}$ lie on the same vertical line. Since the ordinate of $\mathbf{P}$ exceeds that of $\mathbf{S}$ ($7 > 4$), the figure shows $\mathbf{P}$ *above* $\mathbf{S}$. On the other hand, $\mathbf{T}(2, -1)$ is pictured *below* $\mathbf{S}$, because $-1 < 4$.

Now consider the line $\mathcal{L}$ with slope 3 through $\mathbf{S}$. The coordinates of every point *on* $\mathcal{L}$ satisfy the equation $y = 3x - 2$. (Why?) Therefore, the points for which $y > 3x - 2$ are the points which, like $\mathbf{P}$, are *above* the line. On the other hand, $y < 3x - 2$ is true at $\mathbf{T}$ and at all other points below the line. Thus, $\mathcal{L}$ *separates* the plane into two regions, called *half-planes.* The half-plane above $\mathcal{L}$ is the graph of the relation $\{(x, y): y > 3x - 2\}$ and is shown by shading in Figure 6–4(a) on the next page. $\mathcal{L}$ itself appears as a dash line because its points do not belong to the relation. Figure 6–4(b) pictures $\{(x, y): y < 3x - 2\}$ as the half-plane below $\mathcal{L}$. Parts (c) and (d) of Figure 6–4 show the graphs of $\{(x, y): y \geq 3x - 2\}$ and $\{(x, y): y \leq 3x - 2\}$, with $\mathcal{L}$ appearing as a solid line to indicate that it belongs to each graph. If the line is not in the graph, then the half-plane is said to be an *open half-plane;* but if the line is in the graph, then the half-plane is said to be *closed.*

In general, if (a, b) denotes a nonzero vector in $\Re \times \Re$ and c denotes a real number, the line whose equation is $ax + by = c$ separates the plane into two **open half-planes**: $\{(x, y): ax + by > c\}$, and $\{(x, y): ax + by < c\}$.

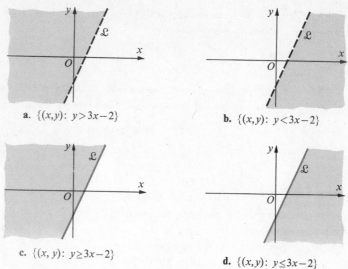

a. $\{(x,y):\ y>3x-2\}$

b. $\{(x,y):\ y<3x-2\}$

c. $\{(x, y):\ y \geq 3x-2\}$

d. $\{(x,y):\ y \leq 3x-2\}$

Figure 6–4

The line is the **boundary** of each half-plane. The union of an open half-plane and its boundary is a **closed half-plane**.

EXAMPLE 1. Draw the graph of $\{(x, y):\ 2x + 3y > 6\}$.

Solution: 1. Transform $2x + 3y > 6$ into an equivalent inequality having y as one member.

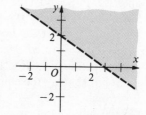

$$2x + 3y > 6$$
$$3y > -2x + 6$$
$$y > -\tfrac{2}{3}x + 2$$

2. Show the solution set of $y = -\tfrac{2}{3}x + 2$ as a dash line.
3. Shade the region above the line.

Figure 6–5 shows in red the graph of the relation $\{(x, y):\ 2x + 3y > 6\}$, and in gray the graph of $\{(x, y):\ x \leq 3\}$. The region where the two colors overlap consists of the points belonging to both relations, and hence indicates the graph of

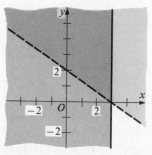

$$\{(x, y):\ 2x + 3y > 6\} \cap \{(x, y):\ x \leq 3\}$$
$$= \{(x, y):\ 2x + 3y > 6 \ \textit{and} \ x \leq 3\}.$$

Figure 6–5

EXAMPLE 2. Graph: $\{(x, y): -2 \leq x - y \leq 1\}$.

Solution: $\{(x, y): -2 \leq x - y \leq 1\}$

$= \underbrace{\{(x, y): -2 \leq x - y\}}_{\text{Shown in red}} \cap \underbrace{\{(x, y): x - y \leq 1\}}_{\text{Shown in gray}}$

$\therefore \{(x, y): -2 \leq x - y \leq 1\}$

$= \underbrace{\{(x, y): y \leq x + 2\}}_{\text{Shown in red}} \cap \underbrace{\{(x, y): y \geq x - 1\}}_{\text{Shown in gray}}$

The region between and including the solid lines pictures the
graph of the given relation.

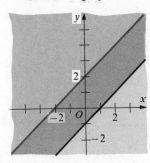

Exercises

Sketch the graph of the relation defined by the given open sentence.

A

1. $y < x$ **3.** $y \leq -2$ **5.** $-x \geq 0$ **7.** $y \leq |x|$

2. $y \leq 2x$ **4.** $x \geq -1$ **6.** $-y < -3$ **8.** $y \leq -|x|$

9. $y - 2x > 1$ **11.** $-y < 3x - 2$ **13.** $2x - 5y \geq 10$

10. $x + y \leq 3$ **12.** $-x > 2x + 1$ **14.** $2x + 3y < 6$

B

15. $0 \leq y \leq 5$ **19.** $-3 \leq y - x \leq 3$ **23.** $y \leq |x| + 2$

16. $-2 \leq x < 3$ **20.** $-2 < x - y \leq 1$ **24.** $y \geq |x + 2|$

17. $x + 2 < y < x + 3$ **21.** $6 > 2x + y > 3$ **25.** $|y| \leq |x|$

18. $4 - x \geq y \geq x + 1$ **22.** $-3 \leq y - 2x \leq 3$ **26.** $|y| \geq -|x|$

Sketch the graphs of **(a)** the intersection, and **(b)** the union, of the given relations.

27. $\{(x, y): 3x - y < 6\}$; $\{(x, y): y \geq 1\}$

28. $\{(x, y): x \geq -2\}$; $\{(x, y): 3x - 2y \leq 12\}$

29. $\{(x, y): x + y \leq 1\}$; $\{(x, y): y - x \leq 1\}$; $\{(x, y): y \geq 0\}$

30. $\{(x, y): 2y - 1 \geq x\}$; $\{(x, y): x + y + 1 \geq 0\}$; $\{(x, y): x \leq 0\}$

C

31. $\{(x, y): |x| + |y| = 1\}$; $\{(x, y): y \geq x\}$

32. $\{(x, y): |x| + |y| \leq 1\}$; $\{(x, y): |x| + |y| \geq \frac{1}{2}\}$

33. $\{(x, y): 2 \leq |x| + |y| \leq 3\}$; $\{(x, y): -1 \leq x + y \leq 1\}$

34. $\{(x, y): |x| + |y - 1| \leq 1\}$; $\{(x, y): |x| + |y| \leq 1\}$

6–3 Functions

When you graph the relation $\{(-2, 0), (1, -1), (1, 3)\}$, you find that two points of the graph lie on the same vertical line (Figure 6–6), because the number 1 in the domain occurs as the first coordinate in two ordered pairs $(1, -1)$ and $(1, 3)$. On the other hand, for the relation $\{(-2, 0), (1, -1), (2, 3), (3, 2)\}$ no two points of the graph lie on the same vertical line (Figure 6–7), since different ordered pairs of the relation have different first elements.

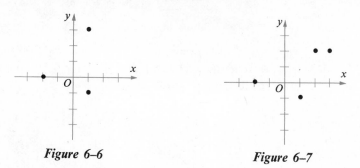

Figure 6–6   Figure 6–7

A relation in which no two different ordered pairs have the same first coordinate is called a **function**. Thus, a function is a relation which assigns to each element in the dómain a *single* element in the range.

You usually denote a function by a letter such as f, h, G, or M. For example, you may write

$$A = \{(x, y):\ y = |x|\}$$

to denote the function which pairs every real number with its absolute value (Figure 6–8). To designate the unique element in the range of A associated with the number -2 in the domain of A, you use the symbol

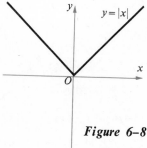

$A(-2)$, read "the *value* of A at -2" or "A at -2."

Figure 6–8

Thus, $A(-2) = |-2| = 2$, $A(0) = |0| = 0$, and $A(3) = |3| = 3$. In general, for any ordered pair (x, y) of a function A, the second element y is the **value of A at x**: $y = A(x)$. Thus, another way to specify A in the example above is

$$A = \{[x, A(x)]:\ A(x) = |x|\}.$$

When the values of a function A are defined by a formula for $A(x)$, such as $A(x) = |x|$, the domain unless otherwise specified consists of those real values of x for which the formula provides a unique real value for $A(x)$;

the range is the set of these values of $A(x)$. With this agreement, if $A(x) = |x|$, the domain of A is the set of real numbers, while the range is the set of nonnegative real numbers. But, to take another example, if $A(x) = \dfrac{1}{\sqrt{x}}$, the domain and range are each the set of positive real numbers.

The values of a function may be specified by different formulas over different subsets of its domain. For example, Figure 6–9 shows the graph of the function s, where

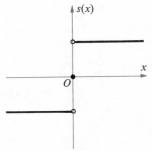

$$s(x) = \begin{cases} 1, & \text{if } x > 0, \\ 0, & \text{if } x = 0, \\ -1, & \text{if } x < 0. \end{cases}$$

Can you suggest why s is called a *step-function?*   **Figure 6–9**

The symbol $[x]$ is frequently used to designate the greatest integer less than or equal to x. For example, $[2] = 2$, $[2\frac{1}{2}] = 2$, $[-2] = -2$, $[-2\frac{1}{2}] = -3$. The step-function $\{(x, y): y = [x]\}$, graphed in Figure 6–10, is called the **greatest integer function** because it pairs each real number x with $[x]$, often read "the greatest integer contained in x." (Note the difference between the brackets [ ] used in specifying the greatest integer function and those used to indicate grouping [ ].)

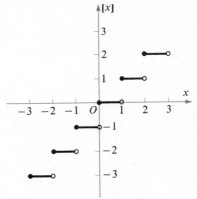

It is often useful to think of a function as a *mapping* from the domain to the range. For example, the definition of the norm of a vector suggests a function n which maps any vector $\mathbf{v} = (a, b)$ onto the real number $r = \sqrt{a^2 + b^2}$:

Figure 6–10

$$n = \{(\mathbf{v}, r): \mathbf{v} \text{ is a vector and } r = \|\mathbf{v}\|\}.$$

This is sometimes stated in symbols,

$$n: \mathbf{v} \to r \quad \text{or} \quad n: (a, b) \to \sqrt{a^2 + b^2},$$

which is read "n maps the vector $\mathbf{v}$ into the real number r" or, perhaps, "n maps (a, b) into $\sqrt{a^2 + b^2}$."

Exercises

State whether the relation indicated by graph, roster, or rule is a function. If it is not a function, explain why. If it is a function, give its domain and range.

A **1.**

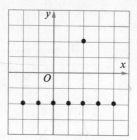

4.

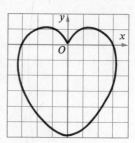

2.

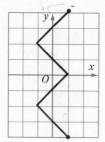

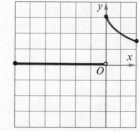

3.

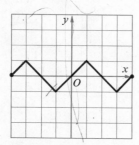

7. $\{(3, -4), (3, 2), (0, 0)\}$

8. $\{(2, 6), (4, 6), (6, 6)\}$

9. $\{(x, y): \ y^2 = 4|x|\}$

10. $\{(m, t): \ t^2 = 16\}$

11. $\{(x, y): \ y = 2[x] - 1\}$

12. $\{(g, h): \ h = [g^2]\}$

13. $\{(x, f(x)): \ x + f(x) = 12\}$

14. $\{(x, f(x)): \ x \cdot f(x) = 12\}$

If $g(x) = 2x^2 - x + 3$, give each of the following.

15. $g(0)$

16. $g(3)$

17. $\frac{1}{2}g(-2)$

18. $3g(\frac{1}{3})$

19. $g(a)$

20. $g(a^2)$

21. $g(2t + 1)$

22. $g(1 - c)$

If $f(x) = |x + 1|$ and $g(x) = 1 - x^2$, find the following.

23. $f(-2) + g(-2)$

24. $f(1) - g(1)$

25. $\dfrac{f(0)}{g(0)}$

27. $f(b^2) + g(b^2)$

26. $f(a) - g(a), a \leq -1$

28. $\dfrac{f(r)}{g(r)}, r > 1$

Graph the function H if its values are given by the indicated formula for $H(x)$ and if its domain is **(a)** {integers}, **(b)** {real numbers}.

B

29. $H(x) = -x$

32. $H(x) = -[x]$

30. $H(x) = -|x|$

33. $H(x) = 2[x]$

31. $H(x) = [2x] - 2[x]$

34. $H(x) = [3x] - 3[x]$

If $t(x) = x^2 + 2$ and $s(x) = x - 1$, find the following.

35. $s(0); t(s(0)); t(0); s(t(0))$

36. $s(-2), t(s(-2)); t(-2); s(t(-2))$

37. a if $s(t(a)) = t(s(a))$.

38. b if $s(t(-b)) = t(s(-b))$.

Graph the function F whose domain is {x: $-3 \leq x \leq 3$} and whose values are indicated.

C

39. $F(x) = \begin{cases} x, & \text{if } x < 0 \\ 0, & \text{if } 0 \leq x < 1 \\ x - 1, & \text{if } x \geq 1 \end{cases}$

42. $F(x) = \begin{cases} 1, & \text{if } |x| > 1 \\ |x|, & \text{if } |x| \leq 1 \end{cases}$

40. $F(x) = x + [x]$

43. $F(x) = 2 - |x + 1|$

41. $F(x) = x - [x]$

44. $F(x) = |x + 2| - 1$

Let f be a function such that for all real numbers a and b, $f(a + b) = f(a) - f(b)$. Prove each of the following statements.

45. $f(0) = 0$. (*Hint:* Let $a = b = 0$.)

46. $f(b) = 0$ for all real numbers b. (*Hint:* Use Exercise 45.)

47. Let g be a function for which $g(a - b) = g(a) \cdot g(b)$ for all real numbers a and b. Prove that the range of g must be a proper subset of {0, 1}.

48. Let s be a function such that $s(x + a) = s(x)$ for every real number x, where a is a given real number. Show that:

a. $s(0) = s(a)$;

b. $s(-a) = s(a)$.

49. Prove: If n denotes an integer and x a real number, then

(a) $[x + n] = [x] + n$; **(b)** $\left[\dfrac{[x]}{n}\right] = \left[\dfrac{x}{n}\right]$ provided $n > 0$.

50. Prove: For all real numbers x and y,

$$[x] + [y] \leq [x + y] \leq [x] + [y] + 1.$$

6–4 The Arithmetic of Functions

Because functions are sets of ordered pairs of elements, you can decide whether two functions are *equal* by determining whether they consist of the same ordered pairs. This means that two functions f and g are **equal** if and only if they have the same domain D and $f(x) = g(x)$ for all x belonging to D.

EXAMPLE 1. If $f = \{(x, y): y = |x|\}$
and $g = \{(x, y): y = \sqrt{x^2}\}$, prove that $f = g$.

Solution: (1) f and g each have the set of real numbers as domain.

(2) If $x \geq 0, f(x) = x$ and $g(x) = x$.

If $x < 0, f(x) = -x$ and $g(x) = -x$.

$\therefore$ for each real number $x, f(x) = g(x)$.

$\therefore f = g$.

When the values of two functions belong to a set in which addition and multiplication are meaningful operations, you can also define the *sum* and *product* of the functions. Let D be the intersection of the domains of functions f and g whose values can be added and multiplied; then, their **sum** $s = f + g$ and **product** $p = fg$ are the functions with domain D and with values defined as follows:

For each $x \in D$,
$$s(x) = [f + g](x) = f(x) + g(x)$$
$$p(x) = [fg](x) = f(x) \cdot g(x).$$

Thus, for any element in D, the value of $f + g$ is the sum of the corresponding values of f and g, while the value of fg is the product of those corresponding values.

EXAMPLE 2. Let f and g be the functions whose values are given by the equations

$$f(x) = \frac{x}{x - 1} \quad \text{and} \quad g(x) = x^2 - 1.$$

Give **(a)** the domain and **(b)** formulas, for the values of $f + g$ and fg.

Solution: **a.** Domain of $f = \{\text{real numbers except } 1\}$.

Domain of $g = \{\text{real numbers}\}$.

Let D = Domain of $f + g$ = Domain of fg;

then D = {real numbers except 1} $\cap$ {real numbers}.

$\therefore D$ = {real numbers except 1}, **Answer.**

b. $[f + g](x) = \dfrac{x}{x - 1} + x^2 - 1$

$[f + g](x) = \dfrac{x^3 - x^2 + 1}{x - 1}$ $(x \neq 1)$, **Answer.**

$[f \cdot g](x) = \dfrac{x}{x - 1} \cdot (x^2 - 1)$

$\therefore [f \cdot g](x) = x(x + 1) = x^2 + x$, $(x \neq 1)$,   **Answer.**

The definition of the product of functions suggests the following recursive definition of a positive integral power of a function. For each positive integer n,

$$f^1 = f,$$

$$f^{n+1} = f \cdot f^n.$$

Thus, if the values of f are defined by the rule $f(x) = x - 1$, then the values of f^2 and f^3 are given by $(x - 1)^2$ and $(x - 1)(x - 1)^2 = (x - 1)^3$, respectively.

You can also define the function $-g$ for any function g whose values have negatives, and $\dfrac{1}{g}$ for any function g whose values have reciprocals. We write

$$[-g](x) = -g(x) \quad \text{and} \quad \left[\dfrac{1}{g}\right](x) = \dfrac{1}{g(x)},$$

where the domain of $-g$ is equal to the domain of g, while the domain of $\dfrac{1}{g}$ consists of those elements of the domain of g for which $g(x) \neq 0$. The functions $f - g$ and $\dfrac{f}{g}$ are defined to be $f + (-g)$ and $f \cdot \dfrac{1}{g}$, respectively.

EXAMPLE 3. If f = {(0, 10), (1, −3), (2, −6)} and g = {(−1, 2), (0, −5), (2, 0)}, specify by roster:

$f + g$; fg; $-g$; $\dfrac{1}{g}$; $f - g$; $\dfrac{f}{g}$.

Solution: $f + g$ = {(0, 5), (2, −6)} $f - g$ = {(0, 15), (2, −6)}

fg = {(0, −50), (2, 0)}

$-g$ = {(−1, −2), (0, 5), (2, 0)} $\dfrac{f}{g}$ = {(0, −2)}

$\dfrac{1}{g}$ = {(−1, $\frac{1}{2}$), (0, −$\frac{1}{5}$)}

We call a function having the same value at each element in its domain and hence having just one element in its range a **constant function**. For example, $\{(x, y): y = \frac{3}{2}\}$ is a constant function over the set of real numbers because for every real number x the value of the function is $\frac{3}{2}$, and its range is simply $\{\frac{3}{2}\}$. Its graph is the horizontal line indicated in Figure 6–11. The **zero function** over a set is the constant function all of whose values equal 0.

Can you assign a meaning to the product $\frac{3}{2}f$, where f is a function whose domain and range consist of real numbers? $\frac{3}{2}f$ is defined to mean the product of the constant function $\{(x, y): y = \frac{3}{2}\}$ and f. It has the same domain as f, while its values are given by $[\frac{3}{2}f](x) = \frac{3}{2}f(x)$. In general, if c is a real number, then $[cf](x) = cf(x)$; similarly, $[c + f](x) = c + f(x)$.

For any domain, the function that pairs each element with itself is called the **identity function**. For example, $I = \{(x, y): y = x\}$ is the identity function over the domain of real numbers; its graph, shown in Figure 6–12, is the straight line of slope 1 through the origin.

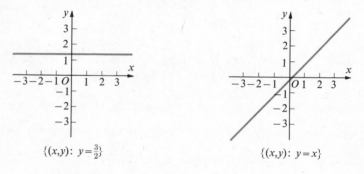

$$\{(x,y): y = \tfrac{3}{2}\}$$

Figure 6–11

$$\{(x,y): y = x\}$$

Figure 6–12

EXAMPLE 4. Determine a formula for the value of the function $2I^2 - 3I + 4$ at x.

Solution:
$$\begin{aligned}
[2I^2 - 3I + 4](x) &= 2(I(x))^2 - 3I(x) + 4 \\
&= 2x^2 - 3x + 4, \textbf{ Answer.}
\end{aligned}$$

Arithmetic operations with functions whose domains and ranges are subsets of a given field have many of the properties of operations in the field. For example, the closure, commutative, associative, and distributive laws are valid for operations with such functions.

EXAMPLE 5. If f, g, and h are functions each with domain and range subsets of the field of real numbers, prove the distributive property: $f(g + h) = fg + fh$.

Solution: (1) Let D_f, D_g, and D_h be the domains of f, g, and h,
respectively. Then:

the domain of $f(g + h) = D_f \cap (D_g \cap D_h)$;

the domain of $fg + fh = (D_f \cap D_g) \cap (D_f \cap D_h)$.

But $(D_f \cap D_g) \cap (D_f \cap D_h) = D_f \cap (D_g \cap D_h)$

∴ the domain of $fg + fh =$ the domain of $f(g + h)$

(2) $[f(g + h)](x) = f(x)[g + h](x)$
$= f(x)[g(x) + h(x)]$

$[fg + fh](x) = [fg](x) + [fh](x)$
$= f(x)g(x) + f(x)h(x)$

By the distributive property for real numbers,

$$f(x)g(x) + f(x)h(x) = f(x)[g(x) + h(x)].$$
$$\therefore fg + fh = f(g + h).$$

Exercises

For the given functions f and g, specify by roster or rule **(a)** $f + g$; **(b)** fg;
(c) f^2; **(d)** $3f - g^3$; **(e)** $\dfrac{f}{g}$.

A

1. $f = \{(-2, 1), (0, 3), (1, -6), (2, -1)\}$; $g = \{(0, 0), (1, 9), (2, 1), (3, -1)\}$
2. $f = \{(4, 1), (6, 2), (8, 3), (10, 4)\}$; $g = \{(4, -1), (6, -2), (10, 0)\}$
3. $f = \{(x, 2x): x \text{ is an integer}\}$; $g = \{(x, -x): x \text{ is a real number}\}$
4. $f = \{(x, x^2): x \text{ is an integer}\}$; $g = \{(x, |x|): x \text{ is a real number}\}$
5. $f = \{(x, y): y = 2x + 1\}$; $g = \{(x, y): y = x - 3\}$
6. $f = \{(x, y): x + y = 2\}$; $g = \{(x, y): x + 2y = 1\}$
7. $f = \left\{(u, v): v = \dfrac{u}{u + 4}\right\}$; $g = \left\{(u, v): v = \dfrac{1}{u}\right\}$
8. $f = \left\{(u, v): v = \dfrac{u - 1}{u}\right\}$; $g = \left\{(u, v): v = \dfrac{2}{u - 2}\right\}$

In Exercises 9–14, find formulas for the values of the given functions at x, and
evaluate each function at 0 and at 2.

9. $I^2 + I + 1$

10. $2I^2 - 1$

11. $I^3 + 2I^2 - I$

12. $I^3 - I^2 + 3I$

13. $2I^4 - 3I^2 + 2I - 6$

14. $3I^4 + I^3 - 2I^2 + I + 7$

Over the domain $\{x: -3 \leq x \leq 3\}$, draw the graphs of (a) $f + g$, and
(b) fg, for the functions f and g whose values are given by the indicated rule.

B　**15.** $f(x) = \begin{cases} 1, & \text{if } x > 0 \\ 0, & \text{if } x = 0 \\ -1, & \text{if } x < 0 \end{cases}$　　**16.** $f(x) = \begin{cases} 1, & \text{if } x > 0 \\ \frac{1}{2}, & \text{if } x = 0 \\ 0, & \text{if } x < 0 \end{cases}$

　　　$g(x) = |x|$　　　　　　　　　　$g(x) = [x]$

17. $f(x) = [x - 1] + 1; g(x) = [x]$　**19.** $f(x) = \dfrac{x + |x|}{2}; g(x) = I$

18. $f(x) = [x - 2] + 3; g(x) = [2x]$　**20.** $f(x) = x - [x]; g(x) = I$

Let $\mathfrak{F}$ be the set of functions whose domains and ranges are subsets of a field.
If f, g, and h belong to $\mathfrak{F}$, prove each of the following statements.

C　**21.** $f + g$ and fg are elements of $\mathfrak{F}$.

　　22. $f + g = g + f$ and $fg = gf$.

　　23. $(f + g) + h = f + (g + h)$ and $(fg)h = f(gh)$.

　　24. If D is the domain of f, then $f + (-f)$ is the zero function over D.

　　25. If D is the domain of f, and $D^* = \{x: x \in D \text{ and } f(x) \neq 0\}$, then $f \cdot \dfrac{1}{f}$
has the value 1 for every element in D^*.

　　26. The zero function is the one and only element in $\mathfrak{F}$ whose sum with *every*
function f in $\mathfrak{F}$ equals f.

POLYNOMIAL FUNCTIONS

6–5 Polynomials

An expression of the form

$$a_0 x^n + a_1 x^{n-1} + \cdots + a_{n-2} x^2 + a_{n-1} x + a_n,$$

where n denotes a nonnegative integer, is called a **polynomial** in the symbol x.
We call $a_0, a_1, \ldots, a_{n-1}, a_n$ the **coefficients** of the polynomial. If the
coefficients are all members of a field F, $a_0 x^n + a_1 x^{n-1} + \cdots + a_{n-2} x^2 +$
$a_{n-1} x + a_n$ is said to be a **polynomial over the field F**. Thus, $2x^3 + 3x - 4$
is a polynomial in x with coefficients 2, 0, 3, -4; $\sqrt{5}y + 7$ is a polynomial
in y with $\sqrt{5}$ and 7 as coefficients. Both $2x^3 + 3x - 4$ and $\sqrt{5}y + 7$ are
polynomials over the field of real numbers. Is either of them a polynomial
over the field of rational numbers?

The exponents n, $n - 1, \ldots, 2, 1$ of x in the terms $a_0 x^n$, $a_1 x^{n-1}, \ldots,$
$a_{n-2} x^2$, $a_{n-1} x$ are the **degrees** of these terms. The term a_n, called the
constant term of the polynomial, has degree 0 if $a_n \neq 0$, but no degree if
$a_n = 0$. If $a_0 \neq 0$, we call $a_0 x^n$ the **leading term** and a_0 the **leading coefficient** of the polynomial; n is then called the **degree** of the polynomial.

EXAMPLES.

$2x^3 + 3x - 4$ has leading coefficient 2 and constant term -4; its degree is 3 and it is called a **cubic polynomial**.

$\sqrt{5}y + 7$ has leading coefficient $\sqrt{5}$ and constant term 7; its degree is 1 and it is called a **linear polynomial**.

9   is a **constant polynomial** because it consists of only a constant term, 9; its degree is 0.

0   is called the **zero polynomial** and has no degree.

Two polynomials in x are equal if their degrees are equal and coefficients of like powers are equal. Thus, $3x - 7 + x^2 = x^2 + 3x - 7$. It is customary to write the terms of a polynomial in a given symbol in order of decreasing degree in that symbol.

If x is a variable whose domain is a set D, any polynomial in x defines a **polynomial function** whose domain is D and whose values are obtained by replacing x by the various elements of D. For example, the polynomial function P whose domain is $\Re$ and whose values are given by

$$P(x) = 2x^3 + 3x - 4$$

assigns to the real number 7 the real number $P(7)$ denoted by the expression

$$2 \cdot 7^3 + 3 \cdot 7 - 4, \quad \text{or} \quad 703.$$

Thus, $(7, 703)$ is an ordered pair in P. Do you see that another way to express P is $2I^3 + 3I - 4$, where I is the identity function? We say that P is a **cubic function**, or a function of degree 3. In general, the degree of a polynomial function is the degree of the corresponding polynomial in the field.

To discover an easy way to compute the values of a polynomial function such as

$$\{[x, P(x)]: P(x) = a_0x^3 + a_1x^2 + a_2x + a_3\},$$

study the following sequence of operations leading to an expression for $P(c)$, where c denotes any real number:

1. Multiply a_0 by c.	a_0c
2. Add a_1.	$a_0c + a_1$
3. Multiply the result of Step 2 by c.	$(a_0c + a_1)c$
4. Add a_2.	$(a_0c + a_1)c + a_2$
5. Multiply the result of Step 4 by c.	$[(a_0c + a_1)c + a_2]c$
6. Add a_3.	$[(a_0c + a_1)c + a_2]c + a_3$

Using the distributive property to restate the expression in Step 6, you find

$$[(a_0c + a_1)c + a_2]c + a_3 = a_0c^3 + a_1c^2 + a_2c + a_3 = P(c).$$

Steps 1–6 are arranged below in three rows. The circled numerals designate each of the steps.

c	a_0	a_1	a_2	a_3
	① a_0c	③ $(a_0c + a_1)c$	⑤ $[(a_0c + a_1)c + a_2]c$	
a_0	② $a_0c + a_1$	④ $(a_0c + a_1)c + a_2$	⑥ $[(a_0c + a_1)c + a_2]c + a_3$	

If $P(x) = 5x^3 - 2x^2 - 3x + 1$, you can find $P(2)$ by following Steps 1–6 with 5, -2, -3, 1, and 2 in place of a_0, a_1, a_2, a_3, and c respectively.

$$\begin{array}{r|rrrr}
2 & 5 & -2 & -3 & 1 \\
  &   & 10 & 16 & 26 \\
\hline
  & 5 & 8 & 13 & 27
\end{array}$$

$$P(2) \qquad \text{Thus } P(2) = 27.$$

This process, called **synthetic substitution**, applies to polynomials of any degree. In essence, it amounts to writing

$$P(x) = a_0x^n + a_1x^{n-1} + \cdots + a_{n-1}x + a_n$$

in the following *nested form:*

$$P(x) = [\therefore \{[(a_0x + a_1)x + a_2]x + a_3\}x + \cdots]x + a_n,$$

and then replacing x by c.

The following example illustrates the fact that in using synthetic substitution you must write the coefficients of the polynomial in order of descending powers of the variable. Also, if a power is missing, 0 must be written in its place.

EXAMPLE. If $A(y) = 2y^4 + 17y - 9y^2 + 3$, find $A(-3)$.

Solution:
$$\begin{array}{r|rrrrr}
-3 & 2 & 0 & -9 & 17 & 3 \\
   &   & -6 & 18 & -27 & 30 \\
\hline
   & 2 & -6 & 9 & -10 & 33
\end{array}$$
$A(-3) = 33$, **Answer.**

Exercises

State the degree, leading coefficient, and constant term of each polynomial.

A

1. $4x^3 - 2x^2 + 3x - 7$

2. $2y^4 - y - 8$

3. $7z^2 - z^6 + 2$

4. $7 - t - t^2$

5. u^4

6. $v^2 + v^3$

In Exercises 7–10 determine a, b, c, and d if the given polynomials are equal.

7. $ax^3 + (b - 3)x^2 - cx + d$; $4x^3 + 7x - 3$

8. $(a + 1)x^2 - bx^3 + cx - (d - 1)$; $2x^3 + 3x^2 - 5x$

9. $(a + b)y^2 + 2y - 3$; $(d - c) + cy + (b - 1)y^2 + 2by^3$

10. $(a - b)y^4 + (c - 1)y^3 + (d + c)y$; $7y^3 - 2y + (2d + b)y^2$

Use synthetic substitution to determine the indicated values.

$$P(x) = 3x^3 - 2x^2 + x + 2$$

11. $P(2)$ **12.** $P(-1)$ **13.** $P(-2)$ **14.** $P(4)$

$$Q(x) = 5x^4 + x^2 - 3x - 1$$

15. $Q(0)$ **16.** $Q(1)$ **17.** $Q(3)$ **18.** $Q(-2)$

$$r(y) = y^2 - \sqrt{2}y^3 + 7y^4$$

19. $r(-5)$ **20.** $r(0)$ **21.** $r(\sqrt{2})$ **22.** $r(-\sqrt{2})$

$$s(y) = y^3 + (a + b + c)y^2 + (ab + ac + bc)y + abc$$

23. $s(-a)$ **24.** $s(-b)$ **25.** $s(-c)$ **26.** $s(0)$

$$t = 16I^3 - 4I^2 - 3I - 7$$

27. $t(\frac{1}{2})$ **28.** $t(-\frac{1}{2})$ **29.** $t(-1)$ **30.** $t(\sqrt{3})$

Ⓑ   **31.** If $P = 2I^3 + 3I^2 - 3I + c$, find c so that $P(2) = 6$.

     32. If $Q = I^3 - 7I + 5c$, find c so that $Q(-1) = 6$.

     33. If $r = 3I^3 - cI^2 + 2I$, find c so that $r(-1) = 1 + c$.

     34. If $s = I^4 + 2I^3 + cI^2 - 4$, find c so that $s(1) = -1 - c$.

     35. If $P = 3I^3 + 2I^2 + cI - k$, determine c and k so that $P(-2) = 37$ and $P(1) = -2$.

     36. If $Q = 2I^4 - 3I^2 - cI + k$, determine c and k so that $Q(-2) = -24$ and $Q(2) = -20$.

Ⓒ   **37.** For any nonzero real number m, the function mI is called a *direct variation*. Prove that for all real numbers x and y, $[mI](x + y) = [mI](x) + [mI](y)$.

     38. Let m and b denote real numbers ($b \neq 0$) and let $g = mI + b$. Prove that for every pair of real numbers x and y, $g(x + y) \neq g(x) + g(y)$.

6–6 The Arithmetic of Polynomials

The definitions of arithmetic operations with functions suggest how to compute sums and products of polynomials.

EXAMPLE 1. Determine **(a)** the sum, **(b)** the difference, and **(c)** the product, of the polynomials: $3x^2 + x + 6$ and $15x^3 - 3x + 1$.

(Solution on page 234)

Solution:

a. $(3x^2 + x + 6) + (15x^3 - 3x + 1)$
$= (0 + 15)x^3 + (3 + 0)x^2 + (1 - 3)x + (6 + 1)$
$= 15x^3 + 3x^2 - 2x + 7$

b. $(3x^2 + x + 6) - (15x^3 - 3x + 1)$
$= (3x^2 + x + 6) + (-15x^3 + 3x - 1)$
$= (0 - 15)x^3 + (3 + 0)x^2 + (1 + 3)x + (6 - 1)$
$= -15x^3 + 3x^2 + 4x + 5$

c. $(3x^2 + x + 6)(15x^3 - 3x + 1)$
$= 3x^2(15x^3 - 3x + 1) + x(15x^3 - 3x + 1) + 6(15x^3 - 3x + 1)$
$= (45x^5 - 9x^3 + 3x^2) + (15x^4 - 3x^2 + x) + (90x^3 - 18x + 6)$
$= 45x^5 + 15x^4 + (-9 + 90)x^3 + (3 - 3)x^2 + (1 - 18)x + 6$
$= 45x^5 + 15x^4 + 81x^3 - 0x^2 - 17x + 6$
$= 45x^5 + 15x^4 + 81x^3 - 17x + 6$

The arithmetic procedures, or *algorithms*, illustrated in Example 1 indicate how one defines the sum, difference, and product of any polynomials over a field.

Example 2 illustrates the process of dividing two polynomials. Notice that the terms of both dividend and divisor are arranged in order of decreasing degree in x, and that the process terminates when the degree of the remainder is less than that of the divisor. The example also shows how to insert missing terms in a dividend by using 0 as a coefficient.

EXAMPLE 2. Divide $15x^3 - 3x + 1$ by $3x^2 + x + 6$.

Solution:

$$
\begin{array}{r}
5x - \frac{5}{3} \\
3x^2 + x + 6 \overline{)15x^3 + 0x^2 - 3x + 1} \\
15x^3 + 5x^2 + 30x \\
\hline
-5x^2 - 33x + 1 \\
-5x^2 - \frac{5}{3}x - 10 \\
\hline
-\frac{94}{3}x + 11
\end{array}
$$

$$\frac{15x^3 - 3x + 1}{3x^2 + x + 6} = 5x - \frac{5}{3} + \frac{-\frac{94}{3}x + 11}{3x^2 + x + 6}, \textbf{ Answer.}$$

Check:

$15x^3 - 3x + 1 \overset{?}{=} (3x^2 + x + 6)(5x - \frac{5}{3}) - \frac{94}{3}x + 11$

$\overset{?}{=} (3x^2 + x + 6)(5x) - (3x^2 + x + 6)(\frac{5}{3}) - \frac{94}{3}x + 11$

$\overset{?}{=} 15x^3 + \frac{85}{3}x - 10 - \frac{94}{3}x + 11$

$= 15x^3 - 3x + 1 \checkmark$

Is it always possible to carry out the *division algorithm* illustrated in Example 2? The following theorem, which we will accept without proof, assures you that not only is division possible but that the quotient and the remainder in each case are unique.

> **THEOREM** If $P(x)$ and $S(x)$ are polynomials over a field F and if $S(x)$ is not the zero polynomial, then there exist unique polynomials $Q(x)$ and $R(x)$ over F such that
>
> $$P(x) = S(x)Q(x) + R(x),$$
>
> where $R(x)$ is either the zero polynomial or else is of degree less than that of $S(x)$.

In case $R(x) = 0$, $P(x) = S(x)Q(x)$, and we say that $P(x)$ is a **multiple** of $S(x)$; $S(x)$ is called a **factor** of $P(x)$.

Applying this theorem to the case in which $S(x)$ is the linear polynomial $x - c$, we find

$$P(x) = (x - c)Q(x) + R(x).$$

Since either $R(x) = 0$ or its degree is less than that of $x - c$, $R(x)$ is a constant. (Why?) Let us call it simply r. Thus,

$$P(x) = (x - c)Q(x) + r.$$

Also, because this equation is a valid statement for every replacement of x by a number in F, it is true, in particular, when x is replaced by c. Therefore:

$$P(c) = (c - c)Q(c) + r$$
$$P(c) = 0 \cdot Q(c) + r$$
$$P(c) = r$$

Thus, the remainder equals $P(c)$, the value of $P(x)$ at c. This fact is the **Remainder Theorem**.

> **THEOREM** For every polynomial $P(x)$ of nonzero degree n over a field, and for every c in the field, there exists a unique polynomial $Q(x)$ such that
>
> $$P(x) = (x - c)Q(x) + P(c).$$

To discover an easy way to determine $Q(x)$ as well as $P(c)$ in applying the Remainder Theorem, consider the special case in which

$$P(x) = a_0x^3 + a_1x^2 + a_2x + a_3 \qquad \text{and}$$
$$P(c) = a_0c^3 + a_1c^2 + a_2c + a_3. \qquad \text{Then}$$

$$P(x) - P(c) = a_0(x^3 - c^3) + a_1(x^2 - c^2) + a_2(x - c) + (a_3 - a_3)$$
$$= a_0(x - c)(x^2 + cx + c^2) + a_1(x - c)(x + c) + a_2(x - c)$$
$$= (x - c)[a_0x^2 + (a_0c + a_1)x + (a_0c^2 + a_1c + a_2)]$$
$$= (x - c)[a_0x^2 + (a_0c + a_1)x + (a_0c + a_1)c + a_2].$$

Therefore, writing $Q(x) = a_0x^2 + (a_0c + a_1)x + (a_0c + a_1)c + a_2$, you have

$$P(x) = (x - c)Q(x) + P(c).$$

Do you recognize the coefficients of $Q(x)$ in the preceding derivation? They are the first three expressions in the last line of the substitution process shown on page 232. Because you can use the synthetic-substitution process to find the quotient $Q(x)$ and the remainder $P(c)$ obtained on dividing a polynomial $P(x)$ by $(x - c)$, synthetic substitution is often called **synthetic division**.

EXAMPLE 3. Use synthetic division to divide
$$P(x) = x^4 + 3x^3 - x^2 + 11x - 4 \text{ by } x + 4.$$

Solution: $x + 4 = x - (-4)$

$$
\begin{array}{r|rrrrr}
-4 & 1 & 3 & -1 & 11 & -4 \\
   &   & -4 & 4 & -12 & 4 \\
\hline
   & 1 & -1 & 3 & -1 & \;|\;0 \\
\end{array}
$$
$Q(x) = x^3 - x^2 + 3x - 1$
$r = 0$

Check: $x^4 + 3x^3 - x^2 + 11x - 4$
$$= (x + 4)(x^3 - x^2 + 3x - 1) + 0 \;\checkmark$$

$$\therefore \frac{x^4 + 3x^3 - x^2 + 11x - 4}{x + 4}$$

$$= x^3 - x^2 + 3x - 1 + \frac{0}{x + 4}$$

$$= x^3 - x^2 + 3x - 1, \textbf{ Answer.}$$

The first theorem stated on page 235 may have reminded you of the proposition stated for integers on page 61. In studying divisibility properties, you will discover numerous analogies between theorems concerning integers and theorems regarding polynomials over a field. For example, Exercises 25–28, page 237 suggest analogues of the familiar properties of integers, stated in Exercises 33–36, page 63, and in the Cancellation Law for Multiplication, page 42.

Exercises

In Exercises 1–4 the first polynomial given is $P(x)$ and the second is $S(x)$. Find
(a) $P(x) + S(x)$; (b) $P(x) - S(x)$; (c) $P(x)S(x)$.

1. $3x^3 + 2x^2 - x + 4$; $5x^3 + x^2 + 3x + 1$
2. $7x^4 - 2x^3 + x^2 + 6$; $x^4 + 2x^3 - x^2 + 6$
3. $3 - x - x^2$; $x + 9 - x^3$
4. $-2x^4 + x^3 - 3 - x$; $3 - x^3 + 2x^4 + x$ a) 0   e) $-4x^3+4x^2-x^6-4x^5-16x^4+6x^3-x^2-6x-9$
   b) $-4x^4+2x^3-2x-6$

5–8. For the polynomials $P(x)$ and $S(x)$ in Exercises 1–4 find the polynomials
$Q(x)$ and $R(x)$ referred to in the theorem at the top of page 235.
   6) $Q(x)$ 7   8 $Q(x) - 1$
   $-16x^3+8x^2-36$ $r(x): 0$

In Exercises 9–14 use synthetic division to determine the polynomial $Q(y)$ or
$Q(z)$ and the constant r obtained on dividing the first polynomial by the second.

9. $5y^3 - y^2 + 2y$; $y - 3$
10. $y^4 + y^2 - 6$; $y + 2$ $y^3-2y^2+5y-10$ $r=14$
11. $y^3 - y^4 + 2y + 1$; $y + 1$
12. $y^2 + 3y^5 - y$; $y - 2$ $3y^4+6y^3+12y^2+25y+49$ $r=98$
13. $z^5 - 1$; $z - 1$
14. $z^6 + 64$; $z + 2$ $z^5-2z^4+4z^3-8z^2+16z-32$ $r=128$

State whether in the field of real numbers the first polynomial in each pair is
a factor of the second. Justify your answer.

15. $2y + 2$; $y + 1$
16. $3x$; $9x^2 + 6x + 12$ no
17. 7; 8
18. 2; -1 yes
19. $5z^2$; $\sqrt{5}\,z^3$
20. $v^3 - 1$; 0 yes

21. Prove that if the product of two polynomials over a field is the zero polynomial, at least one of the factors is the zero polynomial.

22. (a) Prove that the degree of the product of two nonzero polynomials over a field equals the sum of the degrees of the factors. (b) Use this result to explain why no degree is assigned to the zero polynomial.

23. Determine the remainder on dividing $x^{10} + x^4 + x^2 + x + 1$ by
   (a) $x - 1$;
   (b) $x^2 - 1$.

24. Find the remainder on dividing $y^8 - 1$ by $y^2 - 1$.

Let $P(x)$, $S(x)$, and $T(x)$ be polynomials in a field. Prove each assertion.

25. If $P(x) \neq 0$, then $P(x)S(x) = P(x)T(x)$ if and only if $S(x) = T(x)$.

26. If $P(x)$ is a factor of $S(x)$, and $S(x)$ is a factor of $P(x)$, there is a number c in the field such that $P(x) = cS(x)$.

27. If $P(x)$ is a factor of $S(x)$, and $S(x)$ is a factor of $T(x)$, then $P(x)$ is a factor of $T(x)$.

28. If $P(x)$ is a factor of $S(x)$ and $T(x)$, then $P(x)$ is a factor of $S(x) + T(x)$ and of $S(x) - T(x)$.

6–7 The Factor Theorem

The following assertion, called the **Factor Theorem**, shows that determining linear factors of a polynomial $P(x)$ is essentially the same problem as finding the roots of the **polynomial equation** $P(x) = 0$. These roots are also called **zeros** of the function $P = \{(x, y): y = P(x)\}$.

THEOREM For every polynomial $P(x)$ over a field F and for every $c \in F$, $x - c$ is a factor of $P(x)$ if and only if c is a root of $P(x) = 0$.

Proof: If c is a root of $P(x) = 0$, then by the definition of root, $P(c) = 0$. Applying the Remainder Theorem, you know that there exists a polynomial $Q(x)$ over F such that

$$P(x) = (x - c)Q(x) + 0 = (x - c)Q(x).$$

Hence, $x - c$ is a factor of $P(x)$. Conversely, if $x - c$ is a factor of $P(x)$, then over F there exists a polynomial $Q(x)$ such that

$$P(x) = (x - c)Q(x).$$

Therefore,

$$P(c) = (c - c)Q(c) = 0 \cdot Q(c) = 0,$$

so that c is a root of $P(x) = 0$.

EXAMPLE 1. Is $y - 3$ a factor of $P(y) = 2y^3 - 11y^2 + 12y + 9$?

Solution: If $P(3) = 0$, then $y - 3$ is a factor. Use synthetic substitution to substitute 3 for y.

$$\begin{array}{r|rrrr} 3 & 2 & -11 & 12 & 9 \\ & & 6 & -15 & -9 \\ \hline & 2 & -5 & -3 & \;|\; 0 \end{array}$$

$y - 3$ is a factor, **Answer.**

Using the results of Example 1, you find

$$2y^3 - 11y^2 + 12y + 9 = (y - 3)(2y^2 - 5y - 3).$$

It is easy to verify that $y - 3$ is also a factor of $2y^2 - 5y - 3$:

$$\begin{array}{r|rrr} 3 & 2 & -5 & -3 \\ & & 6 & 3 \\ \hline & 2 & 1 & \;|\; 0 \end{array}$$

Thus,

$$2y^3 - 11y^2 + 12y + 9 = (y - 3)^2(2y + 1).$$

Since $y - 3$ is not a factor of $2y + 1$ (Why?), we say that $y - 3$ is a *two-fold* factor of $2y^3 - 11y^2 + 12y + 9$, or a factor of *multiplicity two*. In general, if $P(x) = (x - a)^m Q(x)$, and $x - a$ is not a factor of $Q(x)$, then $x - a$ is called an **m-fold factor** of $P(x)$, or a factor of **multiplicity m**. If $m = 1$, $x - a$ is a **simple factor**; if $m > 1$, $x - a$ is a **multiple factor**. Correspondingly, a is said to be a root of multiplicity m of the equation $P(x) = 0$, or a zero of multiplicity m of the function $\{(x, y): y = P(x)\}$.

EXAMPLE 2. Prove that 1 is a multiple zero of the function f, where $f(x) = x^5 - 3x^4 + 8x^2 - 9x + 3$, and find its multiplicity.

Solution: Use synthetic division to divide repeatedly by $x - 1$. By doing the addition steps in each synthetic division process mentally, you can conveniently arrange the work as shown:

$$
\begin{array}{r|rrrrrr}
1 & 1 & -3 & 0 & 8 & -9 & 3 \\
\hline
 & 1 & -2 & -2 & 6 & -3 & 0 \\
 & 1 & -1 & -3 & 3 & 0 \\
 & 1 & 0 & -3 & 0 \\
 & 1 & 1 & -2 & -2 \\
\end{array}
$$

$(x - 1$ is not a factor of $x^2 - 3)$;

$\therefore f(x) = (x - 1)^3 (x^2 - 3)$.

1 is a zero of f of multiplicity three, **Answer.**

Can a polynomial of degree 5 have 6 or more zeros? The following important by-product of the Factor Theorem gives you the answer.

THEOREM A polynomial $P(x)$ of degree n over F has at most n zeros in F.

Proof: Plan: Use mathematical induction on n.

Let S be the set of nonnegative integers n for which the theorem is true.

(1) $0 \in S$ since every polynomial of degree 0 has no zero in F. (Why?) Also $1 \in S$ because a linear polynomial $a_0 x + a_1$ represents 0 only when x is replaced by $-\dfrac{a_1}{a_0}$.

(2) Suppose $k \in S$; that is, suppose that every polynomial of degree k over F has at most k zeros in F. Let $P(x)$ denote any polynomial of degree $k + 1$ over F. If $P(x)$ has a zero r in F, then

by the Factor Theorem, $P(x) = (x - r)Q(x)$ where $Q(x)$ is of degree k over F. Therefore, the Zero Product Theorem (page 48) implies that a zero of $P(x)$ must be a zero of $x - r$ or a zero of $Q(x)$. But, by the induction hypothesis $Q(x)$ has at most k zeros in F. Hence, $P(x)$ has at most $k + 1$ zeros in F. (Why?) Thus, $0 \in S$, $1 \in S$; and if $k \in S$, $(k + 1) \in S$. Consequently, by the principle of mathematical induction, S is the set of non-negative integers and the theorem is proved.

Does the function f in Example 2 have any real zeros other than 1? Since $f(x) = (x - 1)^3(x^2 - 3)$, the Zero-Product Theorem, page 48, implies that $f(x) = 0$ if and only if either $(x - 1)^3 = 0$ or $x^2 - 3 = 0$. Thus, the other zeros of f are $\sqrt{3}$ and $-\sqrt{3}$, the roots of $x^2 - 3 = 0$. This example suggests the following useful theorem, whose proof is left as Exercise 21, page 241.

THEOREM Let a and b denote different numbers in a field F. If $x - a$ is an m-fold factor of a polynomial $P(x)$ over F and if $P(x) = (x - a)^m Q(x)$, then b is a root of $P(x) = 0$ if and only if b is a root of $Q(x) = 0$.

Exercises

Use the Factor Theorem to determine whether the first polynomial in each pair is a factor of the second.

A

1. $x - 2$; $x^3 + 3x^2 - 2x - 16$
2. $x - 1$; $2x^3 + 5x^2 - x - 6$
3. $y + 1$; $y^4 - 3y^2 + 2y - 4$
4. $y + 3$; $6 - y - y^3 - 2y^2$

5. $z - \sqrt{2}$; $z^3 - 2z + z^2 - 2$
6. $z + \sqrt{5}$; $z^3 + 5z - 3z^2 - 15$
7. $v + 5$; $v^4 + 16v^3 + 80v^2 - 725$
8. $v - 2$; $2v^4 - 3v^3 - 5v^2 + 6v$

Show that the first polynomial in each pair is a multiple factor of the second, and determine its multiplicity.

9. $u + 2$; $u^5 + 4u^4 + 4u^3 - u^2 - 4u - 4$
10. $u - 1$; $2u^4 - 4u^3 + 3u^2 - 2u + 1$

B

11. $2w - 1$; $8w^5 - 4w^4 - 6w^3 + 5w^2 - w$
12. $3w + 1$; $27w^5 - 18w^3 - 8w^2 - w$
13. Determine c so that $y - 2$ shall be a factor of $3y^3 + 2cy^2 + (c - 1)y - 10$.
14. Determine c so that $x + 1$ shall be a factor of $2x^3 - (c + 1)x^2 + 6cx - 11$.
15. Determine a and b so that -1 shall be a double zero of the function $I^4 + aI^3 + (a - b)I^2 + bI + 1$.

16. Determine a and b so that 2 shall be a double zero of the function $I^4 + (a - 2)I^3 + bI^2 + (a + b)I + 4.$ $a = -1 \quad b = 1$

17. Prove that for every positive integer n and every nonzero real number a, $x - a$ is a simple factor of $x^n - a^n$ over the field of real numbers.

18. Prove that for every positive odd integer n and every nonzero real number a, $x + a$ is a simple factor of $x^n + a^n$ over the field of real numbers.

C 19. Prove that for all pairs of real numbers a and b, $y + a + b$ is a factor of $y^3 + a^3 + b^3 + 3ab(a + b)$ over the field of real numbers.

20. Prove that for all pairs of integers a and b and every positive integer n, $(x - b)(x - a)(a - b)$ is a factor of $(a - b)x^n + (b^n - a^n)x + ba^n - ab^n$ over the set of polynomials with integral coefficients.

21. Prove the theorem on page 240.

6-8 Rational Roots

The problem of finding all the roots in a field of a polynomial equation over the field occurs repeatedly in mathematics and its applications. You can completely solve this problem for the field of rational numbers by using the following **Rational Root Theorem**.

THEOREM	If p and q denote integers $(q \neq 0)$ such that $\frac{p}{q}$ is in lowest terms and represents a rational root of a polynomial equation with integral coefficients, then p must be an integral factor of the constant term and q an integral factor of the leading coefficient.

Before proving this assertion, let us apply it.

EXAMPLE 1. Examine $x^3 - x = \frac{1}{5}$ for rational roots.

Solution: Transforming the equation into an equivalent one with integral coefficients and in *simple form* (that is, with 0 as one member), you have $5x^3 - 5x - 1 = 0$. The constant term is -1; the leading coefficient is 5. Therefore, if $\frac{p}{q}$, a fraction in lowest terms, denotes a rational root:

p is a factor of -1;	q is a factor of 5;
that is, $p \in \{1, -1\}$.	that is, $q \in \{1, -1, 5, -5\}$.

Thus, the only rational numbers to test as roots are 1, $-1, \frac{1}{5}, -\frac{1}{5}$. You can use synthetic substitution to test each possibility, as shown on the next page.

$$
\begin{array}{r|rrrr}
 & 5 & 0 & -5 & -1 \\
\hline
1 & 5 & 5 & 0 & -1 \\
-1 & 5 & -5 & 0 & -1 \\
\frac{1}{5} & 5 & 1 & -\frac{24}{5} & -\frac{49}{25} \\
-\frac{1}{5} & 5 & -1 & -\frac{24}{5} & -\frac{1}{25}
\end{array}
$$

$\therefore x^3 - x = \frac{1}{5}$ has no rational root, **Answer.**

The next example illustrates the fact that when you have found a root r of $P(x) = 0$, you determine its multiplicity by testing it in $\dfrac{P(x)}{x - r}, \dfrac{P(x)}{(x - r)^2},$ etc. Notice also the use of the theorem stated on page 241 in testing other numbers as roots.

EXAMPLE 2. Determine the rational roots of
$$2x^5 - 11x^4 + 14x^3 - 2x^2 + 12x + 9 = 0.$$

Solution: Constant term $= 9$; $\therefore p \in \{1, 3, 9, -1, -3, -9\}$.

Leading coefficient $= 2$; $\therefore q \in \{1, 2, -1, -2\}$.

$\therefore$ Test: $1, 3, 9, -1, -3, -9, \frac{1}{2}, \frac{3}{2}, \frac{9}{2}, -\frac{1}{2}, -\frac{3}{2}, -\frac{9}{2}.$

$$
\begin{array}{r|rrrrrr}
 & 2 & -11 & 14 & -2 & 12 & 9 \\
\hline
1 & 2 & -9 & 5 & 3 & 15 & 24 \\
3 & 2 & -5 & -1 & -5 & -3 & 0 \\
\hline
3 & 2 & 1 & 2 & 1 & 0 & \\
-1 & 2 & -1 & 3 & -2 & & \\
\frac{1}{2} & 2 & 2 & 3 & \frac{5}{2} & & \\
-\frac{1}{2} & 2 & 0 & 2 & 0 & & \\
-\frac{1}{2} & 2 & -1 & \frac{5}{2} & & &
\end{array}
$$

3 is a two-fold root. (Why?) The other roots must satisfy $2x^3 + x^2 + 2x + 1 = 0$. (Why?) $\therefore$ the only rational numbers left to test are $-1, \frac{1}{2},$ and $-\frac{1}{2}.$ (Why?)

$-\frac{1}{2}$ is a simple root.

$\therefore 2x^5 - 11x^4 + 14x^3 - 2x^2 + 12x + 9 = (x - 3)^2(x + \frac{1}{2})(2x^2 + 2)$
$$= 2(x - 3)^2(x + \tfrac{1}{2})(x^2 + 1)$$

$\therefore$ the rational roots are 3 (of multiplicity 2) and $-\frac{1}{2},$ **Answer.**

To prove the Rational Root Theorem, we will use not only the field properties valid for all real numbers, but also the following facts about the set J of integers, which you studied earlier in Chapter 2.

(1) J is closed under addition, subtraction, and multiplication.

(2) If p and q are integers having 1 as their greatest common factor in J, and if for some positive integer n there is an integer c such that p is an integral factor of cq^n, then p is an integral factor of c.

Proof of Rational Root Theorem: Let

$$a_0 x^n + a_1 x^{n-1} + \cdots + a_{n-1} x + a_n = 0$$

be an equation with integral coefficients, having $\dfrac{p}{q}$ as a rational root. By hypothesis, p and q have 1 as their greatest common integral factor. (Why?) Substituting $\dfrac{p}{q}$ for x in the equation, you find

$$a_0 \left(\frac{p}{q}\right)^n + a_1 \left(\frac{p}{q}\right)^{n-1} + \cdots + a_{n-1}\left(\frac{p}{q}\right) + a_n = 0.$$

Multiplying by q^n, you obtain

(*) $a_0 p^n + a_1 p^{n-1} q + \cdots + a_{n-1} p q^{n-1} + a_n q^n = 0;$

$\therefore a_n q^n = -p(a_0 p^{n-1} + a_1 p^{n-2} q + \cdots + a_{n-1} q^{n-1}).$

By fact (1) above, $a_n q^n$ is an integer having p as a factor. Hence, by fact (2), a_n must have p as a factor. Thus, $p \in \{\text{integral factors of } a_n\}$.

To complete the proof, transform the starred equation (*) above to

$$a_0 p^n = -q(a_1 p^{n-1} + \cdots + a_{n-1} p q^{n-2} + a_n q^{n-1}).$$

Then, reasoning as before, you can conclude that $q \in \{\text{integral factors of } a_0\}$.

An equation such as $x^2 - 2 = 0$, whose coefficients are integers and whose leading coefficient is 1, can have only integers as rational roots (Why?). We state this fact as a corollary of the Rational Root Theorem.

COROLLARY.   If $x^n + a_1 x^{n-1} + \cdots + a_{n-1} x + a_n = 0$ has integral coefficients, its rational roots, if any, must be integral factors of a_n.

Do you see how to apply this corollary to the equation $x^2 - 2 = 0$ to deduce that $\sqrt{2}$ must be an irrational number?

Exercises

Find the rational zeros of the given functions.

A

1. $\{[x, P(x)]: P(x) = x^3 + 4x^2 + 9x + 6\}$
2. $\{[x, Q(x)]: Q(x) = x^3 - 9x^2 + 26x - 24\}$
3. f, where $f(x) = \frac{3}{2}x^3 + x^2 + x - \frac{1}{2}$
4. g, where $g(x) = x^3 - x^2 - \dfrac{x}{4} + \dfrac{1}{4}$

5. $I^3 + 2I^2 - 13I + 10$ **7.** $2I^4 + 13I^3 - 13I^2 + 15I$
6. $I^3 - 9I^2 + 14I + 24$ **8.** $12I^4 + 20I^3 - I^2 - 6I$

The given number is a root of the equation. Use this fact to prove that the number is irrational.

9. $\sqrt{2} + \sqrt[3]{3}$; $x^6 - 6x^4 - 6x^3 + 12x^2 - 36x + 1 = 0$
10. $\sqrt{2} + \sqrt{5}$; $y^4 - 14y^2 + 9 = 0$

Use the Rational Root Theorem to prove that the following numbers are irrational.

B **11.** $-\sqrt{3}$ **13.** $\sqrt[3]{\frac{1}{2}}$ **15.** $1 - \sqrt[4]{2}$
   12. $\sqrt{7}$ **14.** $\sqrt[5]{6}$ **16.** $1 + \sqrt[3]{5}$

17. Determine all integers n so that $x^3 + 2x^2 + nx - 3 = 0$ shall have at least one rational root.

18. Determine all integers n so that $y^3 - y^2 + ny + 4 = 0$ shall have at least one rational root.

C **19.** Prove that $x^n - 1 = 0$ has exactly two rational roots if n is an even positive integer, but just one rational root if n is an odd positive integer.

20. Let a_1, a_2, and a_3 denote integers each having the prime number c as an integral factor. (**a**) Prove that any integral root of the equation $x^3 + a_1x^2 + a_2x + a_3 = 0$ must have c as an integral factor. (**b**) Use the result of part (a) to find the rational roots of $x^4 + 24x^3 - 52x^2 + 26x - 52 = 0$.

6-9 Bounds for Real Roots; Descartes' Rule

In applying the Rational Root Theorem, you often have many rational numbers to test as possible roots. You can eliminate some of those possibilities by finding a real number M that is greater than or equal to every real root of the equation, and another real number L less than or equal to every real root. For, then only rational numbers between L and M need be tested. M and L are called **upper** and **lower bounds** for the real roots. The following theorem tells how to find bounds for the roots.

THEOREM Let $P(x)$ be a polynomial with real coefficients and with positive leading coefficient. Let M be a nonnegative real number and L a nonpositive real number. If the coefficients of the quotient and remainder obtained on dividing $P(x)$ by $x - M$ are all positive numbers or zero, then $P(x) = 0$ has no roots greater than M. If the coefficients obtained on dividing $P(x)$ by $x - L$ are alternately nonnegative and nonpositive numbers, then $P(x) = 0$ has no roots less than L.

EXAMPLE. Find the least positive integer that the theorem on page 244 shows to be an upper bound and the greatest negative integer that the same theorem shows to be a lower bound of the zeros of the function $P = \{(x, y): y = 2x^3 - 2x^2 + x + 8\}$.

Solution: Use synthetic substitution with $x = 1, 2, 3, \ldots$, until an upper bound is reached, and with $x = -1, -2, -3, \ldots$ until a lower bound is reached.

$$
\begin{array}{r|rrrr}
 & 2 & -2 & 1 & 8 \\
\hline
1 & 2 & 0 & 1 & 9 \rightarrow \text{no negative coefficient} \\
\hline
-1 & 2 & -4 & 5 & 3 \\
-2 & 2 & -6 & 13 & -18 \rightarrow \text{alternating positive and negative}
\end{array}
$$

∴ 1 is an upper bound and -2 is a lower bound of the real zeros, **Answer.**

To see why 1 is an upper bound for the real zeros of the function P in the preceding example, note that

$$2x^3 - 2x^2 + x + 8 = (x - 1)(2x^2 + 1) + 9.$$

For $x > 1$, $x - 1$, $2x^2 + 1$, and 9 all denote positive numbers, so that $2x^3 - 2x^2 + x + 8$ represents a positive number. Hence, for no $x > 1$ can $P(x) = 0$. Therefore, 1 is an upper bound of the zeros of P.

On the other hand,

$$2x^3 - 2x^2 + x + 8 = (x + 2)(2x^2 - 6x + 13) - 18.$$

For $x < -2$, $x + 2 < 0$, whereas $2x^2 - 6x + 13 > 0$. (Why?) Hence, $(x + 2)(2x^2 - 6x + 13) < 0$, so that $(x + 2)(2x^2 - 6x + 13) - 18$ represents numbers *less than 0*. Thus, for no $x < -2$ can $P(x) = 0$. Therefore, -2 is a lower bound of the zeros of P.

The argument showing that 1 and -2 are upper and lower bounds of the real zeros of P illustrates the reasoning to use in proving the theorem in general. (Exercises 13 and 14, page 247.)

The theorem stated on page 244 indicates how to find bounds for the *magnitude* of the real roots of a polynomial equation. A proposition known as **Descartes' Rule of Signs** gives bounds for the *number* of real roots of the equation. If, as you view a polynomial with real coefficients and with terms in order of decreasing degree, the signs associated with the coefficients of two successive terms are opposite, a **variation in sign** is said to occur. Thus,

$$2x^3 - 2x^2 + x + 8$$
$$\qquad\;\; 1 \qquad\; 2$$

contains two variations in sign. Descartes' Rule, which is stated below and accepted without proof, implies that $2x^3 - 2x^2 + x + 8 = 0$ has either two or no positive real roots. In general:

> **THEOREM** The number of positive real roots of $P(x) = 0$, where $P(x)$ is a polynomial with real coefficients, is equal to the number of variations in sign occurring in $P(x)$, or else is less than this number by a positive even integer.

Since every negative root of $P(x) = 0$ is a positive root of $P(-x) = 0$ (Why?), you can use Descartes' Rule to investigate the number of negative roots of $2x^3 - 2x^2 + x + 8 = 0$, by replacing x with $-x$:

$$2(-x)^3 - 2(-x)^2 + (-x) + 8$$
$$= -2x^3 \quad - 2x^2 \quad - \quad x + 8$$

By inspection you observe that there is one variation in sign, and the equation has just one negative root.

The preceding discussion together with the results of the Example on page 245 enable you to restrict the rational numbers to be tested as roots of $2x^3 - 2x^2 + x + 8 = 0$ to the set $\{-\frac{1}{2}, \frac{1}{2}\}$. (Why?) Substitution shows that neither $-\frac{1}{2}$ nor $\frac{1}{2}$ satisfies the equation, so the equation has no rational roots. Can you explain why the equation must have exactly one irrational negative root, and has either two or no irrational positive roots?

Exercises

For each of the following equations determine **(a)** the least nonnegative integral upper bound and the greatest nonpositive lower bound of the real roots; **(b)** the possible numbers of positive and negative real roots; **(c)** the rational roots.

1. $x^3 - 4x^2 + 8x - 5 = 0$
2. $2x^3 - 7x^2 - 21x + 54 = 0$
3. $2y^4 - 7y^3 + 4y^2 + 7y - 6 = 0$
4. $6y^4 + 29y^3 + 40y^2 + 7y - 12 = 0$

5. $2t^3 + 3t^2 - 4t - 1 = 0$
6. $2t^3 + 3t^2 - 4t - 4 = 0$
7. $x^4 + x^3 + 16 = 0$
8. $x^4 - 2x^3 - 3 = 0$

Show that each function has exactly one real zero.

9. $\{[x, g(x)]: g(x) = 2x^7 + x^6 + x^2 + 1\}$
10. $\{[x, g(x)]: g(x) = 3x^5 - x^4 - x^2 - 2\}$
11. $\{(x, y): y = x^5 + x^4 + 3x^3 + 3x^2 + 2x + 2\}$
12. $\{(x, y): y = x^5 - x^4 + 5x^3 - 3x^2 + 4x - 6\}$

13. Let $P(x) = (x - M)Q(x) + P(M)$. Prove that if the terms of $Q(x)$ all have positive or zero coefficients, and if M is a nonnegative real number such that $P(M) \geq 0$, then $P(x) = 0$ can have no roots greater than M.

14. Let $P(x) = (x - L)Q(x) + P(L)$. Prove that if L is a nonpositive real number, and if the coefficients of $Q(x)$ and $P(L)$ are alternately nonnegative and nonpositive numbers, then $P(x) = 0$ can have no roots less than L.

Chapter Summary

1. A **relation** is a set of ordered pairs. The set of all first coordinates of the ordered pairs in a relation is called the **domain**, and the set of all second coordinates the **range**, of the relation. Every relation in $\Re \times \Re$ is a subset of $\Re \times \Re$.

2. A relation defined by an open sentence in which one member is an expression of the form $ax + by$ (a and b constants and not both zero), and the other member is a constant, is called a **linear relation**. The graph of a linear relation is either a straight line or an **open** or **closed half-plane**.

3. A **function** is a relation in which no two different ordered pairs have the same first coordinate. The **value** of the function f at x is denoted by $f(x)$.

4. You can set up an **arithmetic of functions**. Two functions f and g with the same domain D, and for which $f(x) = g(x)$ for each $x \in D$, are **equal**. The sum, difference, and product of two functions f and g are defined over a domain that is the intersection S of the domains of f and g, and

$$f + g = \{[x, [f + g](x)] : [f + g](x) = f(x) + g(x)\}$$

$$f - g = \{[x, [f - g](x)] : [f - g](x) = f(x) - g(x)\}$$

$$fg = \{[x, [fg](x)] : [fg](x) = f(x) \cdot g(x)\}$$

Those elements of S for which $g(x) \neq 0$ constitute the domain of the quotient of f and g, and

$$\frac{f}{g} = \left\{ \left[x, \left[\frac{f}{g}\right](x)\right] : \left[\frac{f}{g}\right](x) = \frac{f(x)}{g(x)}, g(x) \neq 0 \right\}$$

A function whose range contains just one element is called a **constant function**. The function that pairs each element in the domain with itself is called the **identity function** and is denoted by I.

5. A function defined by an equation of the form $y = P(x)$, where $P(x)$ is a polynomial, is called a **polynomial function**. The **degree of the function** is the same as the degree of the polynomial. The **zero polynomial**, 0, is not assigned a degree. You can use **synthetic substitution** to find values $P(x)$ for given values of x.

6. There is an **arithmetic of polynomials** with which you became very familiar in your earlier study of algebra. Given $P(x)$ and $Q(x)$, you can find $P(x) + Q(x)$, $P(x) - Q(x)$, $P(x)Q(x)$, and $\dfrac{P(x)}{Q(x)}$ where $Q(x) \neq 0$. The **Remainder Theorem** asserts that for every polynomial $P(x)$ of nonzero degree over a field F, and every $c \in F$, there exists a unique polynomial $Q(x)$ such that $P(x) = (x - c)Q(x) + P(c)$.

7. The **Factor Theorem**, "For every polynomial $P(x)$ over a field F, and every $c \in F$, $x - c$ is a factor of $P(x)$ if and only if c is a root of $P(x) = 0$," helps you find the **zeros** of a polynomial function P. If n is the greatest integer for which it is true that $(x - c)^n$ is a factor of $P(x)$, then c is an **n-fold zero** or a **zero of multiplicity n** of P.

8. The theorem, "If p and q denote integers ($q \neq 0$) such that $\dfrac{p}{q}$ is in lowest terms and represents a rational root of a polynomial equation with integral coefficients, then p must be an integral factor of the constant term, and q an integral factor of the leading coefficient," is called the **Rational Root Theorem**. You can use it to help you find rational roots of polynomial equations.

9. Bounds on the number and magnitude of the real roots of a polynomial equation over $\mathcal{R}$ are given by **Descartes Rule of Signs** (page 246) and the theorem stated on page 244.

Chapter Test

handwritten: $x \leq 2$, $y \geq 0$

6-1   1. State the domain and range of the relation $\{(x, y): y = \sqrt{2 - x}\}$.

2. Specify by roster: $\{(x, y): |x|^3 + y^2 < 8\}$, and $x \in J, y \in J$.
handwritten: $(0,0)(0,1)(0,-1)(0,2)(0,-2)(1,0)(-1,0)(1,1)(1,-1)(-1,1)(-1,-1)(1,2)(1,-2)(-1,2)(-1,-2)$

6-2   Sketch the graph of the relation defined by each open sentence.

3. $2x + y \leq 4$ 4. $0 \leq y \leq |x|$

6-3   5. Let $f(x) = 2x^2 - 3x + 1$ and find $f(3) - f(2)$. *handwritten: 7*

6. How many functions are there with domain $\{-1, 0, 1\}$ and range a subset of $\{0, 1\}$? *handwritten: 8*

6-4   If $f = \{(-2, 1), (-1, 2), (0, 3), (1, -4), (2, 3)\}$ and $g = \{(-2, 3), (0, 0), (2, 5)\}$, specify each function.

7. $f + g$ 8. fg *handwritten: $(-2,3)(0,8)(2,15)$*
handwritten: $(-2,4)(0,3)(2,8)$

6-5   9. If $P(x) = 2x^4 - x^2 + 3x - 1$, find $P(2)$ by synthetic substitution. *handwritten: 33*

6-6   10. If $P(x) = x^5 + 1$, use synthetic division to find the quotient and remainder when $P(x)$ is divided by $x + 1$. *handwritten: $Q(x) = x^4 - x^3 + x^2 - x + 1$ $r = 0$*

6-7   11. Determine $k \in J$ so that, over J, $x - 1$ will be a factor of the polynomial $2x^3 + (2 - k)x^2 - (k - 2)$. *handwritten: $k = 3$*

12. Show that $x - 3$ is a multiple factor of the polynomial

$$3x^4 - 37x^3 + 147x^2 - 207x + 54,$$

and find its multiplicity. *handwritten: $= 2$*

6-8   13. Find all rational zeros of the following polynomial function:

$$\{[x, P(x)]: P(x) = 5x^3 + 16x^2 - 18x - 8\}. \quad \text{—4}$$

14. Given that $-1 + \sqrt{2}$ is a root of $x^2 + 2x - 1 = 0$, prove that $-1 + \sqrt{2}$ is an irrational number.

6-9   15. **a.** State the possibilities for the number of positive roots and the number of negative roots of $x^3 + x^2 + 10x - 6 = 0$. *handwritten: 1 pos 3 neg or 1 pos once*

b. Find the least nonnegative integral upper bound and the greatest nonpositive lower bound of the real roots of this equation.

handwritten: $m = 1 =$ upper $-1 =$ lower

Reading List

BIRKOFF, GARRETT and SAUNDERS MAC LANE. *A Brief Survey of Modern Algebra.* New York: The Macmillan Co., 1953.

FINE, HENRY B. *College Algebra.* New York: Dover, 1961.

MCCOY, NEAL H. *Introduction to Modern Algebra.* Boston: Allyn and Bacon Inc., 1960.

MOSTOW, GEORGE D., JOSEPH H. SAMPSON, and JEAN-PIERRE MEYER. *Fundamental Structures of Algebra.* New York: McGraw-Hill Book Co., Inc. 1963.

WEISS, MARIE J., and R. DUBISCH. *Higher Algebra for the Undergraduate.* New York: John Wiley & Sons, Inc., 1962.

Karl Weierstrass

It has been said, half jokingly, that in mathematics a method is a trick that works more than once. Of course this is an exaggeration, but it is true that sometimes mathematicians are more interested in finding methods that produce desired results than in proving exactly why these methods work. This practical orientation was common during the 17th and early 18th centuries, when the work of Newton, Leibniz, and Euler inspired mathematicians to concentrate on making new discoveries rather than on constructing rigorous proofs for existing theorems. With time, however, calculus and mathematical analysis became well established, and mathematicians turned their attention to the logical foundations of these fields. A mathematician who initiated and carried through many of the investigations into the foundations of analysis was Karl Weierstrass (German, 1815–1897).

Weierstrass was sent by his father to study law, but he was not interested in his studies and came home after four years without a degree. To redeem himself in the eyes of his family, he earned a teacher's certificate and began a career of teaching mathematics in secondary schools, while spending many of his nights in mathematical research. About fifteen years after this, one of his articles came to the attention of the top mathematicians of the day, and he was awarded a university position at Berlin.

In his work, Weierstrass was concerned with the fundamental concepts of such topics as calculus, function theory, irrational numbers, and infinite series. He developed the frequently used theorem, known as the Weierstrass M-test, for establishing the convergence of certain infinite series. This theorem states that if the absolute value of each term of an infinite series, I, is less than or equal to the corresponding term of a convergent series of positive constants, I is convergent. For example, consider the series $I = 1 + x + x^2 + \cdots + x^n + \cdots$, where $-\frac{1}{2} < x < \frac{1}{2}$. The series of constants $1 + \frac{1}{2} + \frac{1}{4} + \cdots + (\frac{1}{2})^{n-1} + \cdots$ is a geometric series with ratio $\frac{1}{2}$, and is, therefore, convergent. Moreover, the absolute value of each term of I is less than or equal to the corresponding term of this series, and thus I is convergent. See if you can use this theorem to establish the convergence of the series

$$\frac{\sin x}{1^2} + \frac{\sin 2x}{2^2} + \cdots + \frac{\sin nx}{n^2} + \cdots.$$

251

7

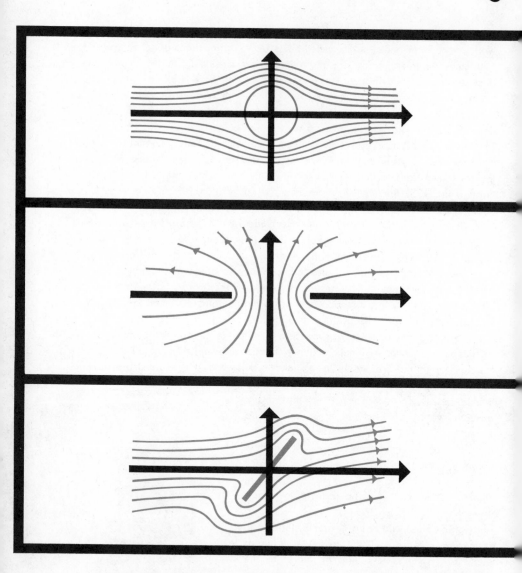

The theory of complex numbers has many applications in science and engineering. Equations involving complex numbers and complex variables can be used to describe the two-dimensional flow of an incompressible fluid, such as water. The flow diagrams above illustrate flow around a circular cylinder perpendicular to the plane, flow through an aperture, and flow around a flat plate.

The Field of
Complex Numbers

Although the field $\mathcal{R}$ of real numbers has properties of great utility, it still is not extensive enough to provide solutions for many kinds of polynomial equations, even one as simple as $x^2 + 1 = 0$. In this chapter, you will study a field that is rich enough in numbers to supply solutions for every polynomial equation with coefficients in $\mathcal{R}$.

FACTORIZATION OF A POLYNOMIAL

7-1 Reducibility over a Field

A polynomial over a field F is **reducible** over F if it is the product of two or more polynomials over F, none of which is a constant. A polynomial that is not reducible over F is called **irreducible** over F.

For example, $x^2 - 3x + 2$ is reducible over the field of rational numbers because $x^2 - 3x + 2 = (x - 1)(x - 2)$. On the other hand, since a product of nonconstant polynomials is of degree two or more (Why?), it follows that $2x + 1$ is irreducible over the field of rational numbers. Can you explain why every linear polynomial over a field is irreducible over the field?

A polynomial irreducible over a field is called **prime** if its leading coefficient is 1. Thus, over the field of rational numbers, $2x + 1$ is irreducible but not prime; on the other hand, $x + \frac{1}{2}$ is a prime polynomial over this field. Notice that you can always express an irreducible polynomial over a field as the product of its leading coefficient and a prime polynomial; for example, $2x + 1 = 2(x + \frac{1}{2})$.

An important proposition is that every nonconstant polynomial over a field can be expressed as a product of a constant and prime polynomials over the field in one and essentially only one way. This assertion, like its analogue, the Fundamental Theorem of Arithmetic (page 62), will be accepted without proof. It is stated as follows:

253

THEOREM Every nonconstant polynomial $P(x)$ over a field F is representable in the form

$$P(x) = a_0[f_1(x)]^{m_1}[f_2(x)]^{m_2} \cdots [f_k(x)]^{m_k},$$

where $f_1(x), f_2(x), \ldots, f_k(x)$ are different prime polynomials over F, $m_1, m_2, \ldots, m_k$ are positive integers, and a_0 is the leading coefficient of $P(x)$. The representation is unique except for the order of the factors.

To find the factorization of a polynomial, you may use the Factor Theorem, synthetic substitution, Descartes' Rule, and the Rational Root Theorem, as well as inspection based on the following familiar "factor patterns":

$$x^2 - a^2 = (x + a)(x - a)$$
$$x^2 + 2ax + a^2 = (x + a)^2$$
$$x^2 + (a + b)x + ab = (x + a)(x + b)$$
$$x^3 - a^3 = (x - a)(x^2 + ax + a^2)$$
$$x^3 + a^3 = (x + a)(x^2 - ax + a^2)$$
$$x^3 + 3ax^2 + 3a^2x + a^3 = (x + a)^3$$

EXAMPLE 1. Factor $\frac{1}{2}y^3 - \frac{3}{2}y^2 - 2y + 6$ over the field of rational numbers.

Solution: 1. $\frac{1}{2}y^3 - \frac{3}{2}y^2 - 2y + 6 = \frac{1}{2}(y^3 - 3y^2 - 4y + 12)$.

2. Test $y^3 - 3y^2 - 4y + 12 = 0$ for rational roots.

	1	−3	−4	12
1	1	−2	−6	6
2	1	−1	−6	0

$\therefore \frac{1}{2}y^3 - \frac{3}{2}y^2 - 2y + 6 = \frac{1}{2}(y - 2)(y^2 - y - 6)$
$= \frac{1}{2}(y - 2)(y - 3)(y + 2)$, **Answer.**

Notice that you discuss the reducibility or factorization of a polynomial only with reference to a specific field containing the coefficients of the polynomial. You can easily find polynomials that are irreducible over one field, but reducible over another.

EXAMPLE 2. Discuss the reducibility of $5z^2 - 1$ over the field (**a**) R of rational numbers; (**b**) $\Re$ of real numbers.

Solution: **a.** $1, -1, \frac{1}{5}, -\frac{1}{5}$ are the only rational numbers to test as roots of $5z^2 - 1 = 0$. Since $5(1)^2 - 1 = 5(-1)^2 - 1 \neq 0$, and $5\left(\frac{1}{5}\right)^2 - 1 = 5\left(-\frac{1}{5}\right)^2 - 1 \neq 0, 5z^2 - 1 = 0$ has no rational root. Hence $5z^2 - 1$ has no linear factor with rational coefficients and is not reducible over R, **Answer.**

b. $5z^2 - 1 = 5(z^2 - \frac{1}{5}) = 5\left(z + \dfrac{1}{\sqrt{5}}\right)\left(z - \dfrac{1}{\sqrt{5}}\right).$

$\therefore 5z^2 - 1$ is reducible over $\mathcal{R}$, and

$\therefore 5z^2 - 1 = 5\left(z + \dfrac{\sqrt{5}}{5}\right)\left(z - \dfrac{\sqrt{5}}{5}\right)$, **Answer.**

A field F over which *every* nonconstant polynomial is a product of a number and one or more prime *linear* polynomials over F is said to be **algebraically complete.** Example 2 shows that the field of rational numbers is not algebraically complete.

Can you explain why $5z^2 + 1$ is irreducible over both the field of rational numbers and the field of real numbers? Recall that for every replacement of z by a real number, $5z^2 \geq 0$. Thus, even the real number system is not algebraically complete.

Exercises

Determine the prime factors of the given polynomial over R.

A

1. $x^4 - 6x^3 + 7x - 2$
2. $x^3 - 3x^2 + x + 1$
3. $x^3 - 7$ *prime*
4. $x^2 + 3x + 5$

5. $y^4 - 18y^2 + 81$
6. $y^4 - 4y^2 + 4$
7. $y^8 - 16y^5 + 64y^2$
8. $y^9 + 16y^6 + 64y^3$

Determine the prime factors of the given polynomial over $\mathcal{R}$.

B

9. $x^3 - 7$
10. $x^3 + 4$
11. $t^4 - 6t^2 + 9$
12. $t^4 + 10t^2 + 25$

13. $9x^3 + 9\sqrt{3}x^2 + 9x + \sqrt{3}$
14. $\sqrt{2}x^3 + 6x^2 + 6\sqrt{2}x + 4$
15. $v^6 + 2v^3 + 1$
16. $v^6 - 16v^3 + 64$

C

17. Prove that for every integer k, $x^2 + (k + 1)x + k$ is reducible over the field of rational numbers.

18. Prove that for every integer k, $x^2 + 6kx + 1$ is irreducible over the field of rational numbers.

19. Prove that if $P(x)$ is an irreducible polynomial over a field F and there exists in F a number r such that $P(r) = 0$, then $P(x)$ is a linear polynomial.

20. Show that every number of the form $a + b\sqrt{2}$ where a and b are integers satisfies either a linear or an irreducible quadratic equation over the field of rational numbers.

OPERATIONS WITH COMPLEX NUMBERS

7-2 Addition of Complex Numbers

The fact that the real number system is not algebraically complete may prompt you to wonder whether any field containing the real numbers is algebraically complete. To obtain such a field, we define a new number system, denoted by C and called the complex number system. Its elements are all the ordered pairs of real numbers such as $(2, 1)$, $(0, 0)$, $(-\sqrt{2}, 3)$ and are termed **complex numbers**. Notice that C consists of the same elements as the set of vectors discussed in Chapter 4.

Equality and addition are defined for complex numbers just as they are for vectors.

If (a, b) and (c, d) denote complex numbers:

1. $(a, b) = (c, d)$ if and only if $a = c$ and $b = d$.
2. $(a, b) + (c, d) = (a + c, b + d)$.

Consequently, the same arguments that demonstrate the properties of vector addition (page 134) prove the corresponding closure, substitution, commutative, associative, and existence of identity and inverse properties of addition of complex numbers. For example, $(0, 0)$ is the identity for addition in C. Also for any complex number (c, d), the complex number $(-c, -d)$ is the additive inverse. You compute the difference of two complex numbers just as you compute the difference of two vectors:

$$(a, b) - (c, d) = (a, b) + (-c, -d) = (a - c, b - d).$$

A complex number, such as $(-5, 0)$, $(1, 0)$, or $(0, 0)$, in which the second entry is 0, is frequently denoted simply by its first element: $-5, 1, 0$. This means that in practice we identify the subset of complex numbers of the form $(a, 0)$ with the set $\mathfrak{R}$ of real numbers, and we write $(a, 0) = a$. Since $(a, 0) + (c, 0) = (a + c, 0)$, this identification is consistent with addition in C and in $\mathfrak{R}$ because it pairs the sum of two complex numbers with the sum of the corresponding real numbers.

The complex number $(0, 1)$ is usually denoted by the letter i or by $1i$. Similarly, $2i$ stands for $(0, 2)$, $-3i$ for $(0, -3)$, and, in general, bi for $(0, b)$.

It is easy to see that every complex number (a, b) can be written in the **standard form** $a + bi$, for

$$(a, b) = (a, 0) + (0, b) = a + bi.$$

We call a the **real part**, and b the **imaginary*** part, of $a + bi$. Thus, you add

---

* The term "imaginary" is a relic of seventeenth-century uneasiness about complex numbers; it does not imply nonexistence. Any complex number $a + bi$ in which $b \neq 0$ is called an **imaginary number**.

and subtract complex numbers by adding or subtracting their real parts and imaginary parts separately. Note that to simplify notation the symbol $a + (-bi)$ is written $a - bi$.

EXAMPLE. If $r = -2 + i$, $s = 4 - 7i$, and $t = -2 - i$, find $r + s, r - s, r + t$.

Solution:
$$r + s = (-2 + i) + (4 - 7i)$$
$$= (-2 + 4) + (1 - 7)i = 2 - 6i$$
$$r - s = (-2 + i) - (4 - 7i)$$
$$= (-2 - 4) + [1 - (-7)]i = -6 + 8i$$
$$r + t = (-2 + i) + (-2 - i)$$
$$= (-2 - 2) + (1 - 1)i = -4 + 0i = -4$$

The representation of vectors by points or by arrows in standard position in a plane suggests a similar geometric representation of complex numbers. Figure 7–1 represents $-2 + i$ and $4 - 7i$ by the points **R**(−2, 1) and **S**(4, −7). Can you suggest why, as shown in the figure, the horizontal axis is called the *axis of reals* (or the *real axis*), and the vertical axis, the *axis of imaginaries* (or the *imaginary axis*)?

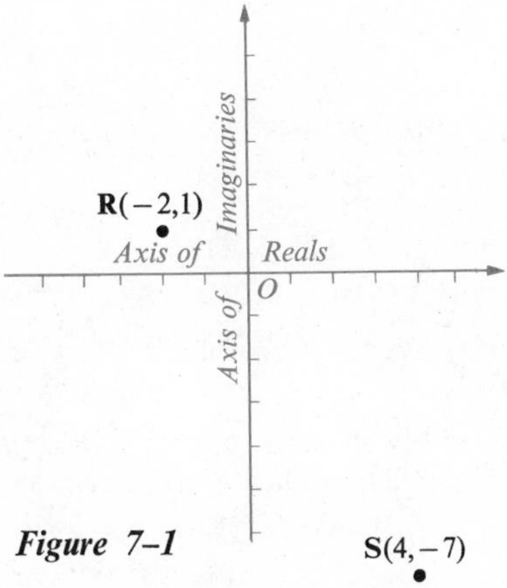

Using the triangle (or parallelogram) law of vector addition, you can represent the sum and difference of complex numbers graphically. Figures 7–2 and 7–3 show the constructions for $r + s$ and $r - s$, where $r = -2 + i$ and $s = 4 - 7i$.

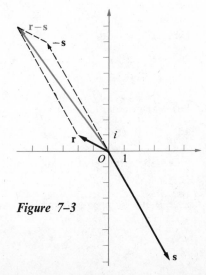

Figure 7–1

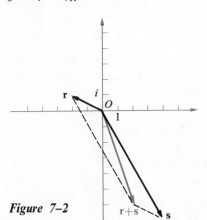

Figure 7–2

Figure 7–3

The concept of absolute value, or norm, of a vector (page 138) suggests a similar concept for complex numbers. We define the **absolute value**, or **modulus**, of $a + bi$ (in symbols, $|a + bi|$) to be the nonnegative real number $\sqrt{a^2 + b^2}$. You can restate for absolute values of complex numbers the theorems given on page 139 for norms of vectors.

> **THEOREM** Let $a + bi$ and $c + di$ denote complex numbers. Then:
>
> 1. $|a + bi| \geq 0$;
> 2. $|a + bi| = 0$ if and only if $a + bi = 0$;
> 3. $|(a + bi) + (c + di)| \leq |a + bi| + |c + di|$ (triangle inequality).

Exercises

Let r be the first complex number and s the second. Compute (a) $r + s$; (b) $r - s$; (c) $s - r$.

1. $2 + 3i, i$
2. $-i, 4 - 7i$
3. $1 - i, -1 - 6i$
4. $-2i, 3 + 5i$
5. $-3, 1 - 2i$
6. $-2 - 4i, -1 + i$

7–12. Verify the results in Exercises 1–6 by performing the indicated operations graphically.

13. Prove that the points representing the following complex numbers lie on the circle of radius 1 with center at the origin:

$$1, -1, i, -i, \frac{1}{2} - \frac{\sqrt{3}}{2} i, -\frac{\sqrt{2}}{2} - \frac{\sqrt{2}}{2} i.$$

14. Show that the points representing $1 + 5i, 1 - 5i, -1 + 5i, -1 - 5i$ are the vertices of a rectangle.

15–20. Verify that $\left| |r| - |s| \right| \leq |r + s| \leq |r| + |s|$ for r and s in Exercises 1–6.

Express in standard form.

21. $(7 - 2i) + (3 - 2i) - (7 + 8i)$
22. $(-2 - 5i) - (8 + i) + (4 + 5i)$
23. $-(-1 + i) + 5 - (i - 11)$
24. $(3 - 2i) + 5i - (7 - i)$

Solve each equation over C.

25. $(3 - 5i) + z = -7 + 2i$
26. $(-7 - 3i) - z = 5 - 9i$

Prove each statement for all complex numbers z and v.

27. $|-z| = |z|$
28. If the points representing z and v are **P** and **T**, then $|z - v| = d(\mathbf{P}, \mathbf{T})$.

29. Prove that the set of complex numbers of the form $(0, b)$ is closed under addition.

30. Prove that the set of complex numbers of the form (a, b), $b \neq 0$, is not closed under addition.

7-3 Multiplication of Complex Numbers

The identification of complex numbers such as $3 + 0i$, $1 + 0i$, $-1 + 0i$ with their real parts 3, 1, -1 suggests choosing a definition for multiplication in C that will preserve the validity of statements like $1 \cdot 3 = 3 \cdot 1 = 3$, $(-1)3 = 3(-1) = -3$. Figure 7–4 pictures these products and indicates that multiplying a complex number by $1 + 0i$, or 1, leaves the arrow representing the number unchanged; but multiplication by $-1 + 0i$, or -1, rotates the arrow counterclockwise through $180°$.

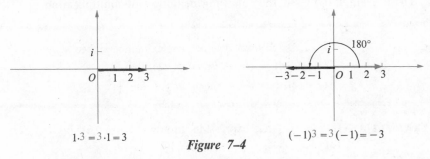

$$1 \cdot 3 = 3 \cdot 1 = 3 \qquad\qquad (-1)3 = 3(-1) = -3$$

Figure 7–4

To maintain this pattern, multiplication of a number by $0 + i$, or i, should rotate the arrow picturing the number through $90°$. Thus, the examples in Figure 7–5 suggest these special definitions:

1. $i \cdot i = -1$; that is, $i^2 = -1$.

2. $a \cdot i = ai$.

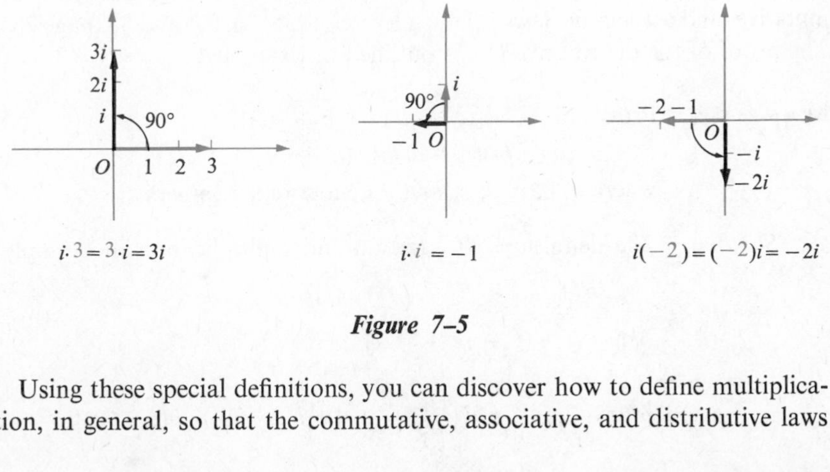

$$i \cdot 3 = 3 \cdot i = 3i \qquad\qquad i \cdot i = -1 \qquad\qquad i(-2) = (-2)i = -2i$$

Figure 7–5

Using these special definitions, you can discover how to define multiplication, in general, so that the commutative, associative, and distributive laws will be preserved in C. Notice that these laws have been obeyed in evaluating the following products.

$$-4(7i) = (-4 \cdot 7)i = -28i; \quad 3i(2) = (3 \cdot 2)i = 6i$$

$$(3i)(7i) = (3 \cdot 7)(i \cdot i) = 21i^2 = 21(-1) = -21$$

$$(-\tfrac{1}{2}i)(10i) = (-\tfrac{1}{2} \cdot 10)i^2 = -5(-1) = 5$$

$$(-4 + 3i)(2 + 7i) = -4(2 + 7i) + 3i(2 + 7i)$$
$$= (-4 \cdot 2 + (-4)7i) + (3i \cdot 2 + 3i \cdot 7i)$$
$$= (-8 - 28i) + (6i - 21)$$
$$= (-8 - 21) + (-28 + 6)i$$

$$\therefore (-4 + 3i)(2 + 7i) = -29 - 22i$$

These examples suggest the following definition of multiplication in C.

> If (a, b) and (c, d) denote complex numbers, then
> $(a, b)(c, d) = (ac - bd, ad + bc)$; that is,
> $(a + bi)(c + di) = (ac - bd) + (ad + bc)i$.

EXAMPLE 1. If $z = 3 + 2i$, express in standard form (**a**) $7z$; (**b**) $5iz$; (**c**) $(3 - 2i)z$.

Solution: **a.** $7z = 7(3 + 2i) = 21 + 14i$

b. $5iz = 5i(3 + 2i) = -10 + 15i$

c. $(3 - 2i)z = (3 - 2i)(3 + 2i)$
$$= (9 + 4) + (6 - 6)i = 13 + 0i = 13$$

Verifying that multiplication in C obeys the closure, substitution, commutative, and associative laws is left as Exercises 35, 36, 37, and 38, page 264. The proof of the distributive law is outlined in Example 2.

EXAMPLE 2. Prove: $(a + bi)[(c + di) + (e + fi)]$
$$= (a + bi)(c + di) + (a + bi)(e + fi)$$
where a, b, c, d, e, and f denote real numbers.

Solution: The definitions of addition and multiplication in C imply:
$$(c + di) + (e + fi) = (c + e) + (d + f)i$$

$$\therefore (a + bi)[(c + di) + (e + fi)]$$
$$= (a + bi)[(c + e) + (d + f)i]$$
$$= [a(c + e) - b(d + f)] + [a(d + f) + b(c + e)]i$$

Also
$$(a + bi)(c + di) = (ac - bd) + (ad + bc)i$$
$$(a + bi)(e + fi) = (ae - bf) + (af + be)i$$

$\therefore (a + bi)(c + di) + (a + bi)(e + fi)$
$$= [(ac - bd) + (ae - bf)] + [(ad + bc) + (af + be)]i$$

But the properties of real numbers ensure that

$$(ac - bd) + (ae - bf) = a(c + e) - b(d + f)$$

and

$$(ad + bc) + (af + be) = a(d + f) + b(c + e). \quad \text{(Why?)}$$

$\therefore$ by the definition of equality in C,

$(a + bi)[(c + di) + (e + fi)]$
$$= (a + bi)(c + di) + (a + bi)(e + fi).$$

Complex numbers such as $3 + 2i$ and $3 - 2i$, which have standard form $a + bi$ and $a - bi$, are called **conjugates** of each other (in symbols, it is customary to write $\overline{a + bi} = a - bi$). You can readily see that

$$(a + bi)(a - bi) = a^2 + b^2.$$

Thus, the product of a complex number z and its conjugate $\bar{z}$ is the square of the absolute value of the number: $z\bar{z} = |z|^2$.

It is also easy to verify that if $a + bi \neq 0$,

$$(a + bi)\left(\frac{a}{a^2 + b^2} - \frac{b}{a^2 + b^2}i\right) = 1 + 0i = 1.$$

Since $1 + 0i$, or 1, is the **multiplicative identity** in C (Exercise 39, page 264), we call $\dfrac{a}{a^2 + b^2} - \dfrac{b}{a^2 + b^2}i$ the **reciprocal** or **multiplicative inverse** of $a + bi$ and we write

$$\frac{1}{a + bi} = \frac{a}{a^2 + b^2} - \frac{b}{a^2 + b^2}i \quad (a + bi \neq 0).$$

Do you see that every nonzero number in C has a unique reciprocal in C? For example, $\dfrac{1}{7 - i} = \dfrac{7}{50} + \dfrac{1}{50}i$.

The basic properties of addition and multiplication of complex numbers can be summarized by stating that *C is a field*. As in any field, we define division of any number by a nonzero number to be the product of the first number and the reciprocal of the second. Thus,

$$\frac{c + di}{a + bi} = (c + di) \frac{1}{a + bi} \qquad (a + bi \neq 0).$$

Because the familiar "laws of fractions"

$$\frac{x}{u} \cdot \frac{y}{v} = \frac{xy}{uv}, \frac{xv}{uv} = \frac{x}{u}, \frac{x}{u} + \frac{y}{u} = \frac{x + y}{u}, \frac{x}{u} + \frac{y}{v} = \frac{xv + uy}{uv}, \qquad (u \neq 0, v \neq 0)$$

are valid in any field (Exercises 9, 33, 34, 37, pages 45–46), you can use them to simplify expressions involving quotients in C.

EXAMPLE 3. Express $\dfrac{-2 + 3i}{1 - i}$ in standard form.

Solution: *Plan:* Multiply numerator and denominator by the conjugate of the denominator.

$$\frac{-2 + 3i}{1 - i} = \frac{(-2 + 3i)(1 + i)}{(1 - i)(1 + i)} = \frac{-5 + i}{2}$$

$$\therefore \frac{-2 + 3i}{1 - i} = -\frac{5}{2} + \frac{1}{2}i, \textbf{ Answer.}$$

EXAMPLE 4. If $z = 2 - 11i$ and $v = 1 + 2i$, verify:

(a) $|zv| = |z| |v|$; (b) $\left|\dfrac{z}{v}\right| = \dfrac{|z|}{|v|}$.

Solution: $|z| = \sqrt{2^2 + (-11)^2} = \sqrt{125} = \sqrt{25 \cdot 5} = 5\sqrt{5}$

$\qquad\quad |v| = \sqrt{1 + 2^2} = \sqrt{5}$

(a)	(b)
$zv = (2 - 11i)(1 + 2i)$	$\dfrac{z}{v} = \dfrac{(2 - 11i)(1 - 2i)}{(1 + 2i)(1 - 2i)}$
$zv = 24 - 7i$	$\dfrac{z}{v} = \dfrac{-20 - 15i}{5} = -4 - 3i$
$|zv| = \sqrt{(24)^2 + (-7)^2} = 25$	$\left|\dfrac{z}{v}\right| = \sqrt{(-4)^2 + (-3)^2}$
$25 \overset{?}{=} 5\sqrt{5} \cdot \sqrt{5}$	$\qquad = 5$
$25 = 25$	$5 \overset{?}{=} \dfrac{5\sqrt{5}}{\sqrt{5}}$
	$5 = 5$

Example 4 illustrates the following theorem, whose proof is left as Exercises 43 and 44, page 264.

THEOREM If z and v denote complex numbers, then

1. $|zv| = |z| |v|$;

2. $\left|\dfrac{z}{v}\right| = \dfrac{|z|}{|v|}$, provided $v \neq 0$.

Exercises

Express in standard form.

1. $5(-2 + 4i)$

2. $-3(6 - 7i)$

3. $-4i(5 + 11i)$

4. $2i(-8 - 10i)$

5. $\dfrac{-6 - 12i\sqrt{2}}{3}$

6. $\dfrac{-15 + 35i\sqrt{3}}{5}$

7. $(2 - i)(1 + i)$

8. $(-3 - i)(4 + i)$

9. $(7 - 2i)(7 + 2i)$

10. $(5 + 8i)(5 - 8i)$

11. $(-2 + 5i)^2$

12. $(3 - 4i)^2$

13. $i^4 + i^3 + i^2 + i$

14. $i - i^2 + i^3 - i^4$

15. $(1 - i)^3$

16. $(1 + i)^4$

17. $i^5(2 + 3i)(-2 + 3i)$

18. $i^7(3 - 4i)(-3 + 4i)$

Determine the reciprocal and conjugate of each complex number.

19. i

20. i^3

21. $3 - i$

22. $1 - 2i$

23. $i - 2$

24. $2i - 1$

Express in standard form.

25. $\dfrac{5 - i}{i}$

26. $\dfrac{3 + 4i}{-i}$

27. $\dfrac{2i}{i + 4}$

28. $\dfrac{-4i}{i - 3}$

29. $\dfrac{2 - i}{7 + 5i}$

30. $\dfrac{-2 - 3i}{4 + 3i}$

Solve each equation over C.

B **31.** $(1 - 7i)z = i$

32. $(2 + i)z = -i$

33. $(3 + i)z + 4 - i = 2i$

34. $iz + 1 - 8i = 5$

Prove that multiplication in C obeys the indicated law.

35. Closure Law

37. Commutative Law

36. Substitution Law

38. Associative Law

39. Prove: $1 + 0i$ is the multiplicative identity in C.

40. Prove: The sum of a complex number and its conjugate is a real number.

41. Prove: **(a)** The conjugate of the sum of two complex numbers is the sum of the conjugates of the numbers. **(b)** For every positive integer n the conjugate of the sum of n complex numbers is the sum of the conjugates of the numbers. (*Hint:* Use mathematical induction.)

42. Prove: **(a)** The conjugate of the product of two complex numbers is the product of the conjugates of the numbers. **(b)** For every positive integer n, the conjugate of the product of n complex numbers is the product of the conjugates of the numbers. (*Hint:* Use mathematical induction.)

43. Prove: For all complex numbers z and v, $|zv| = |z| |v|$.

44. Prove: For all complex numbers z and v, with $v \neq 0$, $\left|\dfrac{z}{v}\right| = \dfrac{|z|}{|v|}$.

7–4 Square Roots

You recall that if r denotes a nonnegative real number, $\sqrt{r}$ denotes the principal square root of r; that is, $\sqrt{r}$ is the nonnegative real number whose square is r.

The statement $i^2 = -1$ suggests that you write $i = \sqrt{-1}$ and call i a *square root of* -1. Notice also that $(i\sqrt{2})^2 = 2i^2 = -2$, so that it is reasonable to write $\sqrt{-2} = i\sqrt{2}$. In general, for every positive real number r, we agree on the following definition:

$$\sqrt{-r} = i\sqrt{r}, \quad r > 0.$$

Do you see that if d is a nonzero real number, $x^2 = d$ has exactly two roots in C? If $d > 0$, the roots are the real numbers $\sqrt{d}$ and $-\sqrt{d}$; if $d < 0$, they are the conjugate imaginary numbers $i\sqrt{|d|}$ and $-i\sqrt{|d|}$. Thus, the two roots of $x^2 = 2$ are $\sqrt{2}$ and $-\sqrt{2}$, while the two roots of $x^2 = -2$ are $i\sqrt{2}$ and $-i\sqrt{2}$.

EXAMPLE 1. Solve $(y - 3)^2 = -16$ over C.

Solution: $(y - 3)^2 = -16$ is equivalent to the sentence

$$y - 3 = \sqrt{-16} \text{ or } y - 3 = -\sqrt{-16}$$
$$y - 3 = i\sqrt{16} \quad \bigg| \quad y - 3 = -i\sqrt{16}$$
$$y = 3 + 4i \quad \bigg| \quad y = 3 - 4i$$

$\{3 + 4i, 3 - 4i\}$, **Answer.**

To simplify a square-root radical whose radicand is a negative number, *first* express the radical as the product of a real number and *i*. *Then* use the properties of real roots of real numbers (page 114) to simplify this product.

EXAMPLE 2. $\sqrt{-25} + \sqrt{-36} = i\sqrt{25} + i\sqrt{36} = 5i + 6i = 11i$

EXAMPLE 3. $\sqrt{-27} \cdot \sqrt{-3} = i\sqrt{27} \cdot i\sqrt{3}$

$$= \sqrt{27 \cdot 3} \cdot i^2 = \sqrt{81}(-1) = -9$$

Note that if you wrote $\sqrt{-27} \cdot \sqrt{-3} = \sqrt{-27 \cdot -3} = \sqrt{81} = 9$, you would obtain an incorrect result because you would have applied properties proved only for radicals denoting *real numbers*. This is why it is important to follow the order of operations indicated above.

Can you solve the equation $x^2 = d$ if d denotes an imaginary number? The next example indicates a procedure for finding the square roots of any complex number. In Chapter 12 you will learn another method.

EXAMPLE 4.   Determine in C the square roots of $5 - 12i$.

Solution: Let a and b denote real numbers. Then, $a + bi$ is a square root of $5 - 12i$ if and only if

$$(a + bi)^2 = 5 - 12i.$$

$$\therefore (a^2 - b^2) + 2abi = 5 - 12i$$

$$\therefore (1) \qquad a^2 - b^2 = 5$$

$$(2) \qquad\qquad 2ab = -12$$

Also, $|(a + bi)^2| = |5 - 12i| = \sqrt{5^2 + (-12)^2} = 13$

But, by the theorem stated on page 263,

$$|(a + bi)^2| = |a + bi|^2 = a^2 + b^2.$$

$$\therefore (3) \qquad a^2 + b^2 = 13$$

Adding (1) and (3), you obtain

$$2a^2 = 18$$

$$\therefore \qquad\qquad a^2 = 9$$

Since $ab = -6$, $a = 3$ and $b = -2$ or $a = -3$ and $b = 2$.
Check: $(3 - 2i)^2 = (-3 + 2i)^2 = (9 - 4) - 12i = 5 - 12i$.
$3 - 2i$ and $-3 + 2i$, **Answer.**

Exercises

Express in standard form.

A

1. $(i\sqrt{2})^2$

2. $(i\sqrt{5})^2$

3. $5\sqrt{-72}$

4. $-3\sqrt{-98}$

5. $2\sqrt{-5} \cdot 3\sqrt{-2}$

6. $-\sqrt{-6} \cdot \sqrt{-1}$

7. $\sqrt{-12} \cdot \sqrt{-15}$

8. $\sqrt{-8} \cdot \sqrt{-10}$

9. $\sqrt{-125} \cdot \sqrt{-5}$

10. $\sqrt{-216} \cdot \sqrt{-6}$

11. $\sqrt{-\frac{1}{3}} \cdot \sqrt{27}$

12. $\sqrt{-343} \cdot \sqrt{\frac{1}{7}}$

13. $\dfrac{\sqrt{-8}}{\sqrt{-2}}$

14. $\dfrac{12\sqrt{-10}}{4\sqrt{-5}}$

15. $\dfrac{8}{4\sqrt{-2}}$

16. $\dfrac{-12}{2\sqrt{-3}}$

17. $\sqrt{-9} - \sqrt{-25} + \sqrt{-49}$

18. $\sqrt{-4} + \sqrt{-1} - \sqrt{-36}$

19. $\sqrt{-2} - i^2\sqrt{-8} + i^3\sqrt{32}$

20. $i\sqrt{-5} + i^5\sqrt{-125}$

21. $\dfrac{\sqrt{2} + \sqrt{-3}}{\sqrt{2} - \sqrt{-3}}$

22. $\dfrac{\sqrt{-5} - \sqrt{-6}}{\sqrt{-5} + \sqrt{-6}}$

Solve each equation over C.

23. $(x + 1)^2 = -36$

24. $(y + 4)^2 = -49$

25. $(z - 2i)^2 + 25 = 0$

26. $(3z - i)^2 + 4 = 0$

B

27. $y^2 - 6y + 10 = 0$

28. $x^2 + 10x + 34 = 0$

29. $z^2 = i$

30. $z^2 = -2i$

31. $z^2 = 7 + 24i$

32. $z^2 = -(21 + 20i)$

C

33. Prove: If $a, b, c,$ and d denote real numbers, $d \neq 0$, and $(a + bi)^2 = c + di$, then $a^2 = \dfrac{\sqrt{c^2 + d^2} + c}{2}, b^2 = \dfrac{\sqrt{c^2 + d^2} - c}{2}$, and ab and d are both positive or both negative numbers.

34. Prove the converse of the theorem stated in Exercise 33.

35. Let $a, b,$ and c denote real numbers, $a \neq 0$, and let $D = b^2 - 4ac$. Prove that $ax^2 + bx + c = 0$ is equivalent to $\left(x + \dfrac{b}{2a}\right)^2 = \dfrac{D}{4a^2}$.

36. Use the result of Exercise 35 to prove that the roots of $ax^2 + bx + c = 0$, $a \neq 0$, are (1) $\dfrac{-b \pm \sqrt{D}}{2a}$ if $D \geq 0$; (2) $\dfrac{-b \pm i\sqrt{|D|}}{2a}$ if $D < 0$.

SOLUTION OF EQUATIONS

7-5 Fundamental Theorem of Algebra

Because C contains the square roots of each of its elements, you can prove that every quadratic polynomial has exactly two prime linear factors over C. Study and justify the following steps in factoring the polynomial $a_0 x^2 + a_1 x + a_2$ $(a_0 \neq 0)$.

$$a_0 x^2 + a_1 x + a_2 = a_0 \left(x^2 + \frac{a_1}{a_0} x + \frac{a_2}{a_0} \right)$$

But $x^2 + \dfrac{a_1}{a_0} x$ comprises the first two terms in the expansion of

$$\left(x + \frac{a_1}{2a_0} \right)^2, \text{ since } \left(x + \frac{a_1}{2a_0} \right)^2 = x^2 + \frac{a_1}{a_0} x + \frac{a_1^2}{4a_0^2}$$

$$\therefore \qquad x^2 + \frac{a_1}{a_0} x = \left(x + \frac{a_1}{2a_0} \right)^2 - \frac{a_1^2}{4a_0^2} \quad \text{(Why?)}$$

$$\therefore \qquad a_0 x^2 + a_1 x + a_2 = a_0 \left[\left(x + \frac{a_1}{2a_0} \right)^2 - \frac{a_1^2}{4a_0^2} + \frac{a_2}{a_0} \right]$$

$$= a_0 \left[\left(x + \frac{a_1}{2a_0} \right)^2 - \frac{a_1^2 - 4a_0 a_2}{4a_0^2} \right]$$

For all complex numbers a_0, a_1, and a_2 $(a_0 \neq 0)$, $\dfrac{a_1^2 - 4a_0 a_2}{4a_0^2}$ denotes a complex number (Why?) whose square roots

$$\frac{\sqrt{a_1^2 - 4a_0 a_2}}{2a_0} \quad \text{and} \quad -\frac{\sqrt{a_1^2 - 4a_0 a_2}}{2a_0}$$

belong to C. Hence,

$$a_0 x^2 + a_1 x + a_2$$

$$= a_0 \left[\left(x + \frac{a_1}{2a_0} \right) - \frac{\sqrt{a_1^2 - 4a_0 a_2}}{2a_0} \right] \times \left[\left(x + \frac{a_1}{2a_0} \right) + \frac{\sqrt{a_1^2 - 4a_0 a_2}}{2a_0} \right]$$

$$\therefore \; a_0 x^2 + a_1 x + a_2$$

$$= a_0 \left(x + \frac{a_1 - \sqrt{a_1^2 - 4a_0 a_2}}{2a_0} \right) \times \left(x + \frac{a_1 + \sqrt{a_1^2 - 4a_0 a_2}}{2a_0} \right)$$

EXAMPLE 1.   Factor $3x^2 - 2x + 1$ over C.

Solution: $a_0 = 3, a_1 = -2, a_2 = 1;$

$a_1^2 - 4a_0a_2 = (-2)^2 - 4 \cdot 3 \cdot 1 = -8$

$3x^2 - 2x + 1$

$$= 3\left(x + \frac{-2 + \sqrt{-8}}{2 \cdot 3}\right)\left(x + \frac{-2 - \sqrt{-8}}{2 \cdot 3}\right)$$

$$= 3\left(x - \frac{2 - 2i\sqrt{2}}{2 \cdot 3}\right)\left(x - \frac{2 + 2i\sqrt{2}}{2 \cdot 3}\right)$$

$\therefore 3x^2 - 2x + 1$

$$= 3\left[x - \left(\frac{1}{3} - \frac{\sqrt{2}}{3}i\right)\right]\left[x - \left(\frac{1}{3} + \frac{\sqrt{2}}{3}i\right)\right],$$ **Answer.**

The result of Example 1 together with the Factor Theorem and the theorem stated on page 239 implies that the solution set of $3x^2 - 2x + 1 = 0$ is

$$\left\{\frac{1}{3} + \frac{\sqrt{2}}{3}i, \frac{1}{3} - \frac{\sqrt{2}}{3}i\right\}.$$

In general, the roots of $a_0x^2 + a_1x + a_2 = 0$ $(a_0 \neq 0)$ are given by

$$\frac{-a_1 + \sqrt{a_1^2 - 4a_0a_2}}{2a_0} \text{ and } \frac{-a_1 - \sqrt{a_1^2 - 4a_0a_2}}{2a_0}. \quad \text{(Why?)}$$

These expressions for the roots comprise what is called the **quadratic formula.**

EXAMPLE 2.   Solve $x^2 + ix + 2 = 0$ over C.

Solution: $a_0 = 1, a_1 = i, a_2 = 2;$

$a_1^2 - 4a_0a_2 = i^2 - 4 \cdot 1 \cdot 2 = -9$

$$\frac{-a_1 \pm \sqrt{a_1^2 - 4a_0a_2}}{2a_0} = \frac{-i \pm \sqrt{-9}}{2 \cdot 1} = \frac{-i \pm 3i}{2}$$

$\therefore$ the roots are i and $-2i$, **Answer.**

Having proved that every quadratic polynomial is reducible over C, you may ask whether *every* polynomial of degree two or more is reducible over C. In 1799 the eminent German mathematician Karl Friedrich Gauss proved the following Fundamental Theorem of Algebra.

THEOREM Every polynomial of positive degree over C has at least one prime linear factor over C.

On the basis of this assertion, whose proof will not be given here, you can use mathematical induction to prove that C is algebraically complete.

THEOREM Every polynomial of positive degree n over C is the product of a constant and n prime linear polynomials over C.

Proof: Let S be the set of positive integers n for which the theorem is true.

(1) $1 \in S$; for $a_0 x + a_1 = a_0 \left(x + \dfrac{a_1}{a_0} \right)$, $a_0 \neq 0$; and $x + \dfrac{a_1}{a_0}$ is a prime linear polynomial over C. (Why?)

(2) Suppose $k \in S$; that is, suppose every polynomial of degree k is the product of a constant and k prime linear polynomials over C.

Now, let $P(x)$ be a polynomial of degree $k + 1$ over C. By the Fundamental Theorem of Algebra, $P(x)$ has a prime linear factor $x - r$ over C. Therefore, $P(x) = (x - r)Q(x)$ where $Q(x)$ is of degree k over C (Why?).

By the induction hypothesis, there exists a complex number a_0, and k complex numbers $r_1, r_2, \ldots, r_k$ such that $Q(x) = a_0(x - r_1)(x - r_2) \cdots (x - r_k)$.

Hence, $P(x) = a_0(x - r)(x - r_1)(x - r_2) \cdots (x - r_k)$; that is, $P(x)$ is the product of a constant and $k + 1$ prime linear polynomials over C. Thus, if $k \in S$, $(k + 1) \in S$.

Together, parts (1) and (2) and the principle of mathematical induction guarantee that S contains every positive integer, and therefore they prove the theorem.

Deducing the following corollary of this theorem is left as an exercise for you. (Exercise 23, page 271.)

COROLLARY. Every polynomial equation of positive degree n over C has exactly n roots if a root of multiplicity k is counted as k roots.

The formulas for the roots of a quadratic equation, synthetic substitution, the Rational Root Theorem, and familiar factor patterns are useful aids in factoring polynomials or solving equations of higher degree over C.

EXAMPLE 3. Factor $x^4 - 16$ over C.

Solution: $\qquad x^4 - 16 = (x^2 - 4)(x^2 + 4)$

$\qquad \therefore x^4 - 16 = (x - 2)(x + 2)(x - 2i)(x + 2i)$, **Answer.**

EXAMPLE 4. Solve $y^3 - y^2 + 3y - 10 = 0$ over C.

Solution: 1. Because the coefficients are integers, use the Rational Root Theorem to identify possible rational roots, $\dfrac{p}{q}$. Note that no negative roots are possible. (Why?)

$$a_0 = 1; a_3 = -10$$

$$\frac{p}{q} \in \{1, 2, 5, 10\}$$

2. Use synthetic substitution and the Factor Theorem to test the possibilities.

$$
\begin{array}{r|rrrr}
 & 1 & -1 & 3 & -10 \\
\hline
1 & 1 & 0 & 3 & -7 \\
2 & 1 & 1 & 5 & 0\checkmark
\end{array}
$$

$\qquad \therefore y^3 - y^2 + 3y - 10 = (y - 2)(y^2 + y + 5)$

3. Use the quadratic formula. The roots of $y^2 + y + 5 = 0$ are

$$\frac{-1 + \sqrt{1^2 - 4 \cdot 1 \cdot 5}}{2 \cdot 1} \quad \text{and} \quad \frac{-1 - \sqrt{1^2 - 4 \cdot 1 \cdot 5}}{2 \cdot 1},$$

or $\qquad \dfrac{-1 + \sqrt{-19}}{2} \quad \text{and} \quad \dfrac{-1 - \sqrt{-19}}{2}$

$\therefore$ the solution set of the given equation is

$$\left\{2, -\frac{1}{2} + \frac{i\sqrt{19}}{2}, \quad -\frac{1}{2} - \frac{i\sqrt{19}}{2}.\right\}, \text{ **Answer.**}$$

Exercises

Solve each equation over C.

A

1. $x^2 + x + 3 = 0$
2. $x^2 + 5x - 3 = 0$

3. $y^2 - 7y + 1 = 0$
4. $y^2 - 9y - 11 = 0$

5. $9 - t - 3t^2 = 0$

6. $2 - t - 2t^2 = 0$

7. $\dfrac{x^2}{2} + \dfrac{13}{5}x = \dfrac{29}{10}$

8. $\dfrac{x}{2} = \dfrac{x^2}{4} + 2$

9. $v^3 + v^2 + v = 0$

10. $v^3 - v^2 + 3v = 0$

11. $2w^3 + 13w^2 - 13w + 15 = 0$

12. $8w^3 - 16w^2 + 16w - 5 = 0$

13. $6x^4 - 17x^3 + 8x^2 + 8x - 3 = 0$

14. $x^4 + x^3 + 7x^2 - x - 8 = 0$

15. $4y^5 - 4y^4 - 15y^3 - 6y^2 + 2y + 1 = 0$

16. $y^5 - 2y^4 - 6y^3 + 15y^2 - 4y - 4 = 0$
    1, 2, 2, ±1 nou

B 17. $ix^2 - 3x - 2i = 0$

18. $x^2 - x + 1 - i = 0$
    $-i, 1+i$

Given the indicated root(s), find the other roots of the equation.

19. $iz^3 - 2z^2 - 1 = 0; -i$

20. $z^3 + 2iz^2 + z + 2i = 0; i$ $-i, -2i$

21. $x^4 + (2 - i)x^3 + (1 - i)x^2 - 2x = 2 - 2i; 1 \text{ and } -1 + i$

22. $x^4 - (2 + i)x^3 + (1 + 2i)x^2 - (2 + i)x + 2i = 0; -i \text{ and } i$ $2, i$

C 23. Prove that every polynomial equation of positive degree n over C has exactly n roots if a root of multiplicity k is counted as k roots.

24. Prove that a polynomial of degree n has no more than $\dfrac{n}{2}$ multiple linear factors.

7–6 Relationships Among Roots and Coefficients

Writing the polynomial $a_0x^n + a_1x^{n-1} + \cdots + a_n \ (a_0 \neq 0)$ over C in factored form $b(x - r_1)(x - r_2) \cdots (x - r_n)$, you can derive relationships among the coefficients of the polynomial and the roots $r_1, r_2, \ldots, r_n$.

Consider, for example, a cubic polynomial. You have

$$a_0x^3 + a_1x^2 + a_2x + a_3 = b(x - r_1)(x - r_2)(x - r_3).$$

Multiplying the factors in the right member of this equation, you find that

$$a_0x^3 + a_1x^2 + a_2x + a_3$$
$$= bx^3 - b(r_1 + r_2 + r_3)x^2 + b(r_1r_2 + r_1r_3 + r_2r_3)x - b(r_1r_2r_3).$$

Because polynomials are equal if and only if their corresponding coefficients are equal, you deduce that

$$a_0 = b, \ a_1 = -b(r_1 + r_2 + r_3), \ a_2 = b(r_1r_2 + r_1r_3 + r_2r_3),$$
$$a_3 = -b(r_1r_2r_3)$$

$$\therefore r_1 + r_2 + r_3 = -\frac{a_1}{a_0}, \ r_1r_2 + r_1r_3 + r_2r_3 = \frac{a_2}{a_0}, \ r_1r_2r_3 = -\frac{a_3}{a_0}.$$

You can use the foregoing relationships to find a cubic equation whose roots are given.

EXAMPLE 1. Find a cubic equation having the roots 1, -2, and 3.

Solution: Let the equation be $x^3 + a_1x^2 + a_2x + a_3 = 0$ and let $r_1 = 1, r_2 = -2, r_3 = 3$. Then $a_0 = 1$, and

$$r_1 + r_2 + r_3 = 1 - 2 + 3 = 2 = -a_1$$

$$r_1r_2 + r_1r_3 + r_2r_3 = 1(-2) + 1 \cdot 3 + (-2)3 = -5 = a_2$$

$$r_1r_2r_3 = 1(-2)3 = -6 = -a_3$$

$\therefore$ the equation is $x^3 - 2x^2 - 5x + 6 = 0$, **Answer.**

Check: Use synthetic substitution to verify that 1, -2, and 3 satisfy $x^3 - 2x^2 - 5x + 6 = 0$. The check is left for you to complete.

The results derived for cubic polynomials can be generalized to polynomials of any positive degree over C. Let $r_1, r_2, \ldots, r_n$ be the roots of the equation $a_0x^n + a_1x^{n-1} + \cdots + a_n = 0$. Define $S_1, S_2, \ldots, S_n$ as follows:

$$S_1 = r_1 + r_2 + \cdots + r_n$$

$$S_2 = r_1r_2 + r_1r_3 + r_2r_3 + \cdots + r_{n-1}r_n$$

$$\cdots \cdots$$

$$S_n = r_1r_2 \ldots r_n$$

Thus, S_k is the sum of all products formed by multiplying exactly k of the roots $r_1, r_2, \ldots, r_n$. The following assertion can be proved by induction on n. (Exercise 22, page 274.)

THEOREM　If $a_0x^n + a_1x^{n-1} + \cdots + a_n = 0$ $(a_0 \neq 0)$ has the n roots $r_1, r_2, \ldots, r_n$ in C, then $S_k = (-1)^k \dfrac{a_k}{a_0}$; that is, the sum of the products of the roots taken k at a time is $(-1)^k$ times the product of the coefficient of x^{n-k} and the reciprocal of the leading coefficient.

EXAMPLE 2. Determine positive numbers a and b so that $x^4 + ax^3 + bx^2 + 4x + 4 = 0$ will have one pair of equal roots and two other roots that are reciprocals of each other.

Solution: Let the roots be denoted by $r, r, s, \dfrac{1}{s}$. In the equation:

$a_0 = 1, a_1 = a, a_2 = b, a_3 = 4, a_4 = 4$.

$\therefore r \cdot r \cdot s \cdot \dfrac{1}{s} = \dfrac{a_4}{a_0} = 4$

$$r^2 = 4$$

$\therefore r = 2$ or $r = -2$

Since $a > 0$ and $b > 0$, $x^4 + ax^3 + bx^2 + 4x + 4 = 0$ has no positive root. (Why?)

$\therefore r = -2$

Also $r^2 s + r^2 \dfrac{1}{s} + rs \dfrac{1}{s} + rs \dfrac{1}{s} = -\dfrac{a_3}{a_0} = -4$

$\therefore r^2 s + \dfrac{r^2}{s} + 2r = -4$

$$4s + \dfrac{4}{s} - 4 = -4$$

$$s^2 + 1 = 0$$

$$s = i \quad \text{or} \quad s = -i$$

$$\dfrac{1}{s} = -i \quad \Big| \quad \dfrac{1}{s} = i$$

$\therefore$ the roots are $-2, -2, i$ and $-i$.

$r + r + s + \dfrac{1}{s} = -\dfrac{a_1}{a_0} = -a;$

$\therefore -a = -2 - 2 + i + (-i) = -4; a = 4$, **Answer.**

$r^2 + rs + \dfrac{r}{s} + rs + \dfrac{r}{s} + s \cdot \dfrac{1}{s} = \dfrac{a_2}{a_0} = b$

$\therefore b = r^2 + 2rs + \dfrac{2r}{s} + 1 = 4 - 4i + 4i + 1; b = 5$, **Answer.**

Check: Verifying the results by synthetic substitution is left to you.

Exercises

Use the theorem on page 272 to determine an equation having the given solution set or a polynomial having the indicated factors.

A

1. $\{0, 2, -3\}$ 3. $\{1 + i, 1 - i, 2\}$

2. $\{1, i, -i\}$ 4. $\{2 - i, 0, i\}$

5. $x + 1$ and $x - 3$ as double factors.

6. $y - 1$ as a factor and $y + 2$ as a triple factor.

$y^4 + 5y^3 + 6y^2 - 4y - 8$

Using the given information, determine the roots and the unspecified coefficient(s) of each equation.

7. One root of $x^3 - 3x^2 + kx + 75 = 0$ is the negative of another.

8. One root of $x^3 - 63x + k = 0$ is half another and $k > 0$.

9. $3x^3 + kx^2 + 8x + 4 = 0$ has a pair of equal real roots.

10. The sum of two roots of $3x^3 + kx^2 - 3x + 2 = 0$ is 0.

(B)

11. One root of $2z^4 - 5z^3 + kz - 2 = 0$ is the reciprocal of another.

12. One root of $z^3 - 11z^2 + kz + 132 = 0$ is the sum of the others.

13. The reciprocal of each root of $z^3 + kz^2 + hz + 3 = 0$ is a root.

14. The roots of $z^4 + hz^3 - 54z^2 + kz + 81 = 0$ are all equal.

15. The roots of $x^3 - 6x^2 + kx + 64 = 0$ are in geometric progression. (*Hint:* Let the roots be $\dfrac{a}{r}$, a, ra.)

16. The roots of $x^3 + kx^2 - x - 3 = 0$ are rational numbers in arithmetic progression. (*Hint:* Let the roots be $a - d$, a, $a + d$.)

17. Find an equation whose roots are twice the roots of

$$x^4 - 3x^3 + 2x^2 + 4x - 1 = 0.$$

18. Find an equation whose roots are 1 more than the roots of

$$x^5 - 11x^3 + 5x^2 + x - 3 = 0.$$

(C)

19. Determine an equation whose roots are the reciprocals of the roots of

$$a_0x^4 + a_1x^3 + a_2x^2 + a_3x + a_4 = 0, \ a_0 \neq 0, \ a_4 \neq 0.$$

20. Determine an equation whose roots are the squares of the roots of

$$x^3 + a_1x^2 + a_2x + a_3 = 0.$$

21. If r_1, r_2, and r_3 are the roots of $x^3 + a_1x^2 + a_2x + a_3 = 0$, evaluate:

(a) $\dfrac{1}{r_1} + \dfrac{1}{r_2} + \dfrac{1}{r_3}$, if $a_3 \neq 0$; **(b)** $r_1^3 + r_2^3 + r_3^3$.

22. Prove the theorem stated on page 272.

7-7 Polynomials with Real Coefficients

Using the quadratic formula or the relationships among roots and coefficients, you can verify that the roots of $x^2 - 6x + 13 = 0$ are $3 + 2i$ and $3 - 2i$. This example illustrates a property of all polynomial equations with *real* coefficients: imaginary roots occur in conjugate pairs.

| THEOREM | If a polynomial equation $P(x) = 0$ with real coefficients has $a + bi$ as a root (a and b real, $b \neq 0$), then $a - bi$ is also a root. |

Proof: The polynomial

$$S(x) = [x - (a + bi)][x - (a - bi)] = x^2 - 2ax + (a^2 + b^2)$$

has real coefficients. (Why?) Therefore, the division algorithm for polynomials over the field $\Re$ guarantees that there exist polynomials $Q(x)$ and $R(x)$ over $\Re$ such that

$$P(x) = S(x)Q(x) + R(x)$$

where $R(x)$ is either the zero polynomial or of degree at most 1. Thus, for some real numbers c and d, $R(x) = cx + d$. Hence,

$$P(a + bi) = S(a + bi)Q(a + bi) + c(a + bi) + d.$$

By hypothesis, $P(a + bi) = 0 + 0i$. Also, $S(a + bi) = 0 + 0i$. Therefore,

$$0 + 0i = c(a + bi) + d = (ca + d) + cbi.$$

Because equal complex numbers have equal real and imaginary parts, you have: $\quad 0 = ca + d, \quad$ and $\quad 0 = cb.$

Since $b \neq 0$, the last two equations imply that $c = 0$ (Why?), and therefore, that $d = 0$. Thus, $P(x) = S(x)Q(x)$. Also $S(a - bi) = 0$. Hence, $P(a - bi) = 0$.

EXAMPLE 1. One root of $x^3 - 8x^2 + kx + g = 0$ is $3 - i$. If k and g denote real numbers, determine **(a)** the other roots; **(b)** the values of k and g.

Solution: **a.** Since the equation has real coefficients, *both* $3 - i$ and $3 + i$ are roots. Let r denote the third root.

Then: $(3 - i) + (3 + i) + r = 8$ (Why?)
$$6 + r = 8$$
$$r = 2$$

$\therefore$ the roots are $3 - i$, $3 + i$, and 2, **Answer.**

b. $\quad k = (3 - i)(3 + i) + 2(3 - i) + 2(3 + i)$
$$= 10 + 6 - 2i + 6 + 2i = 22$$
$$-g = (3 - i)(3 + i)2 = 20$$
$\therefore k = 22; g = -20,$ **Answer.**

You know that any polynomial $P(x)$ with real coefficients is the product of a real number (its leading coefficient) and prime linear factors over C. Some of these linear factors may have real coefficients. For those with imaginary coefficients, (1) the theorem stated on page 275 tells you that every factor of the form $x - (a + bi)$ ($b \neq 0$) can be paired with another linear factor $x - (a - bi)$; and (2) the product of these paired linear factors is a quadratic polynomial over $\mathcal{R}$ that is irreducible over $\mathcal{R}$. These facts are summarized in the following proposition.

THEOREM   Every polynomial of n ($n > 0$) degree over $\mathcal{R}$ is the product of a real number and one or more prime linear or quadratic polynomials over $\mathcal{R}$.

Because the irreducible quadratic polynomials over $\mathcal{R}$ play an important role in factoring over $\mathcal{R}$, it is useful to be able to identify such polynomials quickly. You know that the roots of $a_0 x^2 + a_1 x + a_2 = 0$ ($a_0 \neq 0$) are given by $\dfrac{-a_1 + \sqrt{a_1^2 - 4a_0 a_2}}{2a_0}$ and $\dfrac{-a_1 - \sqrt{a_1^2 - 4a_0 a_2}}{2a_0}$.

If a_0, a_1, and a_2 denote real numbers, these formulas designate different real numbers, the same real number, or conjugate imaginary numbers according as $a_1^2 - 4a_0 a_2$ denotes a positive number, 0, or a negative number. We call $\mathbf{a_1^2 - 4a_0 a_2}$ the **discriminant** of $a_0 x^2 + a_1 x + a_2$. Thus, for real numbers a_0, a_1, and a_2, the polynomial $a_0 x^2 + a_1 x + a_2$ is reducible over $\mathcal{R}$ if its discriminant is a nonnegative number, but is irreducible over $\mathcal{R}$ if its discriminant is a negative number.

EXAMPLE 2. Determine whether $x^2 - 10x + 32$ is irreducible over $\mathcal{R}$.

Solution: $a_1^2 - 4a_0 a_2 = (-10)^2 - 4 \cdot 1 \cdot 32 = 100 - 128 < 0$.

$\therefore x^2 - 10x + 32$ is irreducible over $\mathcal{R}$, **Answer.**

Exercises

Let P be a function whose domain is C and whose values are given by a poly-nominal P(x) with real coefficients and leading coefficient 1. Determine P(x), if P has the indicated number of zeros.

1. Three zeros, two of which are 1 and $2i$.
2. Three zeros, two of which are -1 and $3i$.
3. Three zeros, including -3 and $1 + 5i$.
4. Three zeros, including 2 and $3 - i$.
5. Four zeros, including i and $1 + i$.
6. Four zeros, including $-i$ and $-1 + i$.

Over C determine the solution set of the equation having the given roots.

7. $2y^3 + 11y^2 + 28y + 24 = 0;\ -2 - 2i$

8. $y^3 - 3y^2 + 4y - 2 = 0;\ 1 - i$

9. $x^7 - x = 0;\ \dfrac{1 + \sqrt{3}i}{2}$ **10.** $x^5 + x^3 - x^2 - 1 = 0;\ \dfrac{-1 + \sqrt{3}i}{2}$

Given the indicated factor, express each polynomial as a product of a constant and one or more prime polynomials over the field of (**a**) rational numbers; (**b**) real numbers; (**c**) complex numbers.

B

11. $t^4 - t^3 - t - 1;\ t - i$

12. $t^4 + 2t^3 + 2t - 1;\ t + i$

13. $x^4 - 2x^3 + x^2 + 4x - 6;\ (x - 1) + \sqrt{2}i$

14. $x^4 + 4x^3 + 10x^2 + 12x + 21;\ (x + 2) - \sqrt{3}i$

15. $z^4 + 5z^3 + 12z^2 + 22z - 40;\ z + (1 - 3i)$

16. $z^4 - 6z^3 + 11z^2 - 6z + 10;\ z + (i - 3)$

State whether each assertion is true. Justify your answer.

17. If $2 + 3i$ is a root of a polynomial equation, then so is $2 - 3i$.

18. If $2 + 3i$ is a root of a polynomial equation with real coefficients, then so is $-2 + 3i$.

19. Every polynomial with real coefficients and of odd degree has at least one real root.

20. Every polynomial equation with real coefficients has an even number of imaginary roots.

If the given equation has the indicated root and if a and b denote real numbers, determine a and b.

C

21. $x^3 - x^2 + x + a = 0;\ b - i$ **22.** $x^3 + ax^2 - 9x - b = 0;\ a + i$

23. **a.** Prove: If $a + b\sqrt{r}$ is an irrational root of a polynomial equation with rational coefficients where a, b, and r denote rational numbers, then $a - b\sqrt{r}$ is also a root.

   b. Use the theorem stated in (**a**) to solve $y^4 - y^3 - 4y^2 + 5y - 5 = 0$ over C, given that $\sqrt{5}$ is a root.

24. Prove or disprove: Every polynomial equation with rational coefficients has an even number of irrational roots.

Let c denote a real constant. Show that over $\Re$ the solution set of each of the following equations is $\emptyset$.

25. $\dfrac{c}{x + c} = \dfrac{c}{x} + 1$ **26.** $\dfrac{1}{c - x} = \dfrac{1}{c} - \dfrac{1}{x}$

Chapter Summary

1. A polynomial over a field F is **reducible** over F if it is a product of two or more polynomials over F, none of which is a constant. If the leading coefficient of an **irreducible** polynomial over F is 1, the polynomial is called **prime**.

2. The set $\mathcal{R} \times \mathcal{R}$ of ordered pairs of real numbers, with the operations of addition and multiplication defined by

$$(a, b) + (c, d) = (a + c, b + d)$$
$$(a, b) \cdot (c, d) = (ac - bd, ad + bc),$$

is called the set C of **complex numbers**. You can prove that C is a field and that it is **algebraically complete** in the sense that every nonconstant polynomial over C is a product of a constant and one or more prime linear polynomials over C. The set $\mathcal{R}$ of real numbers can be considered as a subset of the set C of complex numbers.

3. The symbol i is defined to denote $\sqrt{-1}$, a **square root** of -1, and every complex number (a, b) can also be denoted by $a + bi$. The **absolute value**, or **modulus**, of $a + bi$ is $|a + bi| = \sqrt{a^2 + b^2}$, and the **conjugate** of $a + bi$ is $a - bi$. The product of any complex number and its conjugate is a real number.

4. The **fundamental theorem of algebra** asserts that every nonconstant polynomial with complex coefficients has at least one prime linear factor over C. This theorem implies that every polynomial equation of positive degree n over C has exactly n solutions.

5. If $a + bi$ is a solution of a polynomial equation with real coefficients, then so is its conjugate, $a - bi$. Also, every polynomial of positive degree over $\mathcal{R}$ is the product of a real number and one or more prime linear or quadratic factors over $\mathcal{R}$.

Chapter Test

7-1   **1.** Determine the prime factors of $x^4 - 14x^2 + 49$ over the field of (**a**) rational numbers, (**b**) real numbers.

     2. Determine the prime factors of $x^4 - 64 = 0$ over the field of (**a**) rational numbers; (**b**) real numbers; (**c**) complex numbers.

7-2   **3.** Express $(4 - 2i) + (2i - 11) - (i - 7)$ in standard form.

     4. Solve $(3 - 2i) + (4 - i) = z - (2 + i)$ over C.

7-3   **5.** Express $(1 - i)^2(1 + i)^2$ in standard form.

     6. Express $\dfrac{3 + i}{i^2 - 3i}$ in standard form.

7-4   **7.** Express $\frac{1}{2}\sqrt{-128} - \frac{1}{5}\sqrt{-200} + 7\sqrt{-8}$ in standard form.

     8. Solve $z^2 - 4z + 7 = 0$ over C.

7-5   **9.** Solve $x^3 - 4x^2 + 9x - 36 = 0$ over C, given that $3i$ is one solution.

    10. Solve $x^2 + ix - x - i = 0$ over C.

7-6   **11.** Determine an equation having the solution set $\{3, 1 + i, 1 - i\}$.

    12. Determine the solution set and unspecified coefficient if 2 is one solution of $x^3 + 6x^2 + kx + 8 = 0$.

7-7   **13.** Find the polynomial equation $P(x) = 0$ with real coefficients and leading coefficient 1 which has exactly three solutions, two of which are 2 and $-3i$.

    14. Determine the solution set over C of

$$x^4 - 3x^3 + 3x^2 - 2 = 0,$$

given that $1 + i$ is one solution.

1. a) x^2-7
   b) $x+\sqrt{7}, x-\sqrt{7}$

2. a) $x^2+8, x-8$
   b) $x^2+8, x+2\sqrt{2}, x-2\sqrt{2}$
   c) $x+2i\sqrt{2}, x-2i\sqrt{2}, x+2\sqrt{2}, x-2\sqrt{2}$

3. $-i$

4. $9-2i$

5. 4

6. $-3/5 + 4/5 i$

7. $16i\sqrt{2}$

8. $2+\sqrt{3}i, 2-\sqrt{3}i$

9. $3i, -3i, 4$

10. $1, -i$

11. $x^3 - 5x^2 - 4x - 6$

12. $K=-20$ $\{2, -4+2\sqrt{5}, -4-2\sqrt{5}\}$

13. $x^3 - 2x^2 + 9x - 18$

14. $\{1+i, 1-i, \dfrac{1+\sqrt{5}}{2}, \dfrac{1-\sqrt{5}}{2}\}$

Reading List

BECKENBACH, EDWIN F., *Complex Variable Theory*.   Mathematics Magazine, vol. 24, pp. 7–28, 1951.

CAJORI, F., *Historical Note on the Graphic Representation of Imaginaries before the Time of Wessel*.   American Mathematical Monthly, vol. 19, pp. 167–171, 1912.

COURANT, RICHARD, and HERBERT ROBBINS, *What Is Mathematics?*   New York: Oxford University Press, Inc., 1941.

DIAMOND, LOUIS E., *Introduction to Complex Numbers*.   Mathematics Magazine, vol. 30, pp. 233–249, 1957.

FINE, HENRY B., *College Algebra*.   New York: Dover, 1961.

Kelley, John L., *Introduction to Modern Algebra*.   Princeton, N.J.: D. Van Nostrand Co., Inc., 1960.

MCCLENON, R. B., *A Contribution of Leibnitz to the History of Complex Numbers*.   American Mathematical Monthly, vol. 30, pp. 369–374, 1923.

ROSENBLOOM, P. C., *An Elementary Construction Proof of the Fundamental Theorem of Algebra*.   American Mathematical Monthly, vol. 52, pp. 562–570, 1945.

SCHELKUNOFF, S. A., *A Note on the Geometrical Applications of Complex Numbers*.   American Mathematical Monthly, vol. 37, pp. 301–303, 1930.

SCHOOL MATHEMATICS STUDY GROUP, *Introduction to Matrix Algebra*.   New Haven, Conn.: Yale University Press, 1961.

SCHOOL MATHEMATICS STUDY GROUP, *Complex Number System*.   School Mathematics Study Group, Stanford, California, 1964.

TAYLOR, HOWARD E., and THOMAS L. WADE, *University Freshman Mathematics*.   New York: John Wiley and Sons, Inc., 1963.

C. G. J. Jacobi

The German mathematician C. G. J. Jacobi (1804–1851) has been called "the Great Algorist" because of his unusual insight and skill in developing and manipulating formulas and computational schemes in such fields as the theory of elliptic functions, higher algebra, and mathematical physics. The word "algorist" and the related word "algorithm" have an interesting history. In the 9th century A.D. there was an Islamic mathematician, astronomer, and geographer named al-Khowarizmi, who wrote a number of important works on arithmetic and algebra. In the 12th century his books were translated into Latin, bearing the name "Algorismus." Consequently, during the Middle Ages any mathematician who calculated by the methods of these books, that is, by means of "algorisms" instead of with an abacus, was called an "algorist." Today, an algorithm is a method or computational procedure for solving a specific type of problem, and an algorist is anyone who develops or uses these algorithms. Jacobi devised algorithms which led to advances in modern analysis.

Most of Jacobi's life was spent in teaching and in mathematical research. He was an inspiring teacher who presented the results of his own work to his students and encouraged them to explore mathematics for themselves. His research covered many fields. His most important work in analysis was in the field of elliptic functions.

An elliptic function is a function of a complex variable with certain special properties. One of these, which was discovered by Jacobi and Abel independently, is double-periodicity. You have seen that a trigonometric function such as the sine function has one fundamental period, namely, 2π. Any other period of this function must be an integral multiple of 2π. An elliptic function, on the other hand, has two different fundamental periods, say p_1 and p_2, where p_1 and p_2 are complex numbers, so that if E is an elliptic function, and z, a complex variable, $E(z + p_1) = E(z)$ and $E(z + p_2) = E(z)$. Jacobi proved many useful theorems concerning elliptic functions and related topics and was the first to apply the results of elliptic function theory to the theory of numbers.

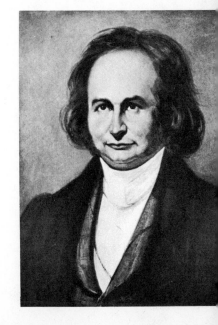

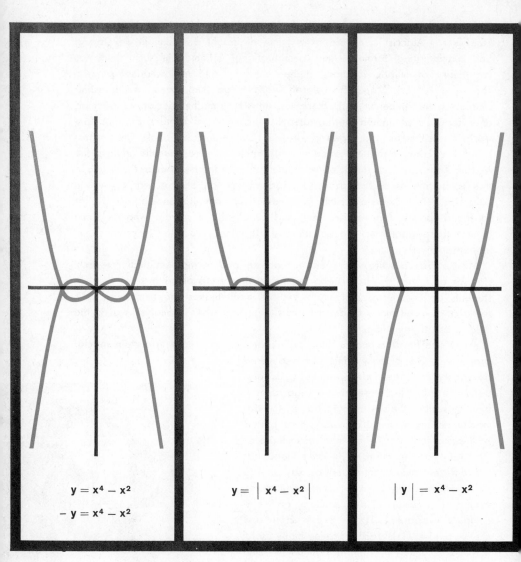

$y = x^4 - x^2$

$-y = x^4 - x^2$

$y = \left| x^4 - x^2 \right|$

$\left| y \right| = x^4 - x^2$

The first diagram shows the graphs of the polynomial equations $y = x^4 - x^2$ and $-y = x^4 - x^2$. The following diagrams show the graphs of the equations formed by replacing the right-hand member of $y = x^4 - x^2$ by its absolute value and the left-hand member of $y = x^4 - x^2$ by its absolute value.

raphs of
Polynomial Functions

In Chapter 3 the discussion of limits of infinite sequences introduced concepts that are fundamental in calculus. Using these concepts, you will now study a basic problem in calculus: determining lines tangent to the graph of a given function. Although the functions whose graphs will be analyzed are restricted to polynomial functions with domain $\Re$, the present chapter, nevertheless, gives a convincing view of the power of calculus methods.

LIMITS AND CONTINUITY

8-1 Plotting Points in Curve Sketching

To sketch the graph of a polynomial function with domain $\Re$ such as $f = \{(x, y): y = x^3 + 3x^2 - 9x - 10\}$, you usually begin by using synthetic substitution to compute a table of selected values. Then you plot the corresponding points. Note that for convenience different scales have been used on the coordinate axes in Figure 8–1.

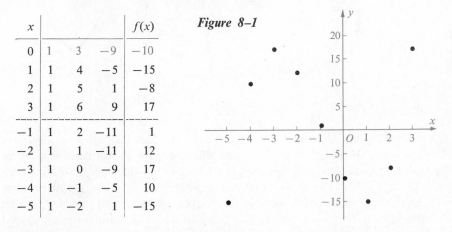

x				$f(x)$
0	1	3	−9	−10
1	1	4	−5	−15
2	1	5	1	−8
3	1	6	9	17
−1	1	2	−11	1
−2	1	1	−11	12
−3	1	0	−9	17
−4	1	−1	−5	10
−5	1	−2	1	−15

Figure 8–1

Notice also that the synthetic substitution computation indicates that 3 is an upper bound for the real zeros of f. (Why?) Similarly, you can see that −5 is a lower bound for the zeros. (Why?)

283

The next step in sketching the graph is drawing a curve through the plotted points. But, as Figure 8–2 suggests, there are many curves that contain those points.

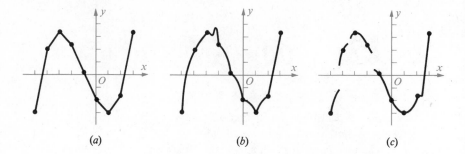

(a)   (b)   (c)

Figure 8–2

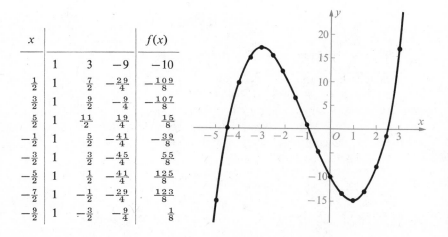

x				$f(x)$
	1	3	-9	-10
$\frac{1}{2}$	1	$\frac{7}{2}$	$-\frac{29}{4}$	$-\frac{109}{8}$
$\frac{3}{2}$	1	$\frac{9}{2}$	$-\frac{9}{4}$	$-\frac{107}{8}$
$\frac{5}{2}$	1	$\frac{11}{2}$	$\frac{19}{4}$	$\frac{15}{8}$
$-\frac{1}{2}$	1	$\frac{5}{2}$	$-\frac{41}{4}$	$-\frac{39}{8}$
$-\frac{3}{2}$	1	$\frac{3}{2}$	$-\frac{45}{4}$	$\frac{55}{8}$
$-\frac{5}{2}$	1	$\frac{1}{2}$	$-\frac{41}{4}$	$\frac{125}{8}$
$-\frac{7}{2}$	1	$-\frac{1}{2}$	$-\frac{29}{4}$	$\frac{123}{8}$
$-\frac{9}{2}$	1	$-\frac{3}{2}$	$-\frac{9}{4}$	$\frac{1}{8}$

Figure 8–3

Plotting additional points (Figure 8–3) provides further evidence about the shape of the graph and suggests that the curve shown there is a better approximation of the graph than the curves in (a), (b), or (c) of Figure 8–2. To verify that Figure 8–3 really is a good picture of the graph requires methods to be discussed later in this chapter. Meanwhile, you may assume that the graph of any polynomial function whose domain is the set of real numbers is a smooth unbroken curve, although you can only guess its shape by plotting a reasonably large subset of its points.

Exercises

Sketch the graph of the function whose domain is $\mathcal{R}$ and whose values are given by the indicated formula.

A

1. $f(x) = x^3$
2. $f(x) = 2x^3$
3. $g(x) = x^3 + 2$
4. $g(x) = x^3 - 2$
5. $h(x) = x^3 - 3x$
6. $h(x) = x^3 + 6x$

7. $p(x) = x^3 + 2x^2 - 1$
8. $p(x) = x^3 - 2x^2 + 1$
9. $r(x) = x^4 + x^2$
10. $r(x) = x^4 - x^2$
11. $s(x) = x^4 - 6x^2 + 2$
12. $s(x) = x^4 + 4x^2 - 20$

B

13. Show that if the graph of $\{(x, y): y = ax^6 + bx^4 + cx^2 + d\}$ contains the point $\mathbf{P}(x_1, y_1)$, then it also contains the point $\mathbf{P}'(-x_1, y_1)$.

14. Show that if $\mathbf{P}(x_1, y_1)$ is a point of the graph of $\{(x, y): y = ax^5 + bx^3 + cx\}$, then $\mathbf{P}''(-x_1, -y_1)$ also is a point of the graph.

15. On the basis of Exercise 13, state and prove a property of the graph of every function with domain $\mathcal{R}$ whose values are given by a polynomial in x in which every term is of even degree in x.

16. On the basis of Exercise 14, state and prove a property of the graph of every function with domain $\mathcal{R}$ whose values are given by a polynomial in x in which every term is of odd degree in x.

8–2 Limits of Functions; Continuity

Figure 8–4 shows partial graphs of the functions

(a) $t = \left\{(x, y): y = \dfrac{2(x - 1)}{x - 1}, x \neq 1\right\}$,

(b) $g = \{(x, y): y = 2[x]\}$, and

(c) $s = \{(x, y): y = 2x^2\}$.

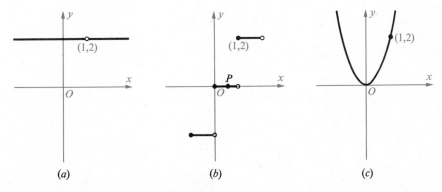

(a)   (b)   (c)

Figure 8–4

Both t and g (preceding page) have graphs with a "break" at $(1, 2)$. The break occurs in the graph of t because t does not have a value at 1. Although g does have a value at 1 [in fact, $g(1) = 2$], the graph of g has a break at $(1, 2)$ because the graph contains points like **P** with x-coordinate close to 1 but with y-coordinate not correspondingly close to $g(1)$.

On the other hand, in the vicinity of $(1, 2)$ the graph of s is a smooth unbroken curve. This property is due to the fact that when x denotes a number close to 1, $s(x)$ is a number close to $s(1)$.

To describe more precisely the behavior of t, g, and s near $(1, 2)$, we will extend to functions the concept of limit developed in Section 3–6 for infinite sequences. A function $f = \{(x, y): y = f(x)\}$ with domain D is said to have the **limit** l as x approaches c provided that whenever x is replaced by the successive terms of an infinite sequence of elements of D, $x_1, x_2, \ldots$, $x_n, \ldots$ whose limit is c but whose terms all differ from c, the corresponding values of f, namely, $f(x_1), f(x_2), \ldots, f(x_n), \ldots$, form a convergent sequence whose limit is l. Thus,

$$\lim_{x \to c} f(x) = l$$

if and only if whenever $\lim\limits_{n \to \infty} x_n = c \quad (x_n \neq c), \quad \lim\limits_{n \to \infty} f(x_n) = l.$

Notice that this definition means that the sequence $f(x_1), f(x_2), \ldots$, $f(x_n), \ldots$ must converge to the *same number l* for *every* sequence $x_1, x_2, \ldots$, $x_n, \ldots$ converging to c. Note also that the restriction to sequences x_1, $x_2, \ldots, x_n, \ldots$ with c as a limit but with *terms different from c* means that $\lim\limits_{x \to c} f(x)$ depends on the behavior of $f(x)$ for x *near* c, not *at* c.

EXAMPLE 1. For each function t, s, and g defined above, determine whether the limit as x approaches 1 exists. If the limit exists, find it.

Solution: (1) Let $x_1, x_2, \ldots, x_n, \ldots$ be an *arbitrary* sequence such that $\lim\limits_{n \to \infty} x_n = 1, (x_n \neq 1).$

(**a**) Since $x_n \neq 1$, $t(x_n) = \dfrac{2(x_n - 1)}{x_n - 1} = 2.$ (Why?)

$\therefore \lim\limits_{n \to \infty} t(x_n) = \lim\limits_{n \to \infty} 2 = 2.$

$\therefore \lim\limits_{x \to 1} t(x) = 2,$ **Answer.**

(**b**) $s(x_n) = 2x_n^2.$

$\therefore$ Using part (3) and the corollary of the theorem stated on page 97, you find the following:

$$\lim_{n \to \infty} s(x_n) = 2(\lim_{n \to \infty} x_n)(\lim_{n \to \infty} x_n) = 2 \cdot 1 \cdot 1 = 2.$$

$$\therefore \lim_{x \to 1} s(x) = 2, \textbf{ Answer.}$$

(2) Let $x_1, x_2, \ldots, x_n, \ldots$ be the sequence for which $x_n = 1 + (-\frac{1}{10})^n$. Then, $\lim_{n \to \infty} x_n = 1$. (Why?) Since the terms of this sequence are alternately less than 1 and greater than 1, and $g(x_n) = 2[1 + (-\frac{1}{10})^n]$, the successive terms $g(x_n)$ are $0, 2, 0, 2, \ldots$ (Why?) Hence, the sequence $g(x_1), g(x_2), \ldots, g(x_n), \ldots$ diverges.

$$\therefore \lim_{x \to 1} g(x) \text{ does not exist, } \textbf{Answer.}$$

The preceding example suggests how the limit concept enables you to contrast the behaviors of t, s, and g near $(1, 2)$. In the case of s, we have proved that $\lim_{x \to 1} s(x)$ exists and equals 2, or $s(1)$. On the other hand, $\lim_{x \to 1} t(x)$ exists and is 2; but the limit does not equal $t(1)$ because t is not defined at 1. For g, $\lim_{x \to 1} g(x)$ does not even exist. We call s a *continuous function at 1*, while we describe t and g as *discontinuous functions* at 1. In general, a function is said to be **continuous at c** if and only if $\lim_{x \to c} f(x) = f(c)$. This definition requires that

1. f must have a value *at c*;
2. f must have a limit as x *approaches c*;
3. the value of f at c must equal the limit of f as x approaches c.

EXAMPLE 2. Prove that $f = \{(x, y): y = x^3 + 3x^2 - 7x + 3\}$ is continuous at 2.

Solution: Let $x_1, x_2, \ldots, x_n, \ldots$ be an arbitrary sequence such that $\lim_{n \to \infty} x_n = 2$. Then: $\lim_{n \to \infty} f(x_n) = \lim_{n \to \infty} (x_n^3 + 3x_n^2 - 7x_n + 3)$. Hence, using the theorem stated on page 97, you find $\lim_{n \to \infty} f(x_n) = 2^3 + 3 \cdot 2^2 - 7 \cdot 2 + 3 = f(2)$.

$$\therefore \lim_{x \to 2} f(x) = f(2); \text{ so that } f \text{ is continuous at 2.}$$

A function is called **continuous** if it is continuous at each element of its domain. Example 2 illustrates an argument that can be generalized to prove the following fact. (See also Exercises 29 and 30, page 289.)

THEOREM   A polynomial function whose domain is $\Re$ is continuous.

Exercises

(a) For $f(x)$ and c, as indicated, find $\lim\limits_{x \to c} f(x)$ or show that the limit does not exist. (b) In each case state whether the function $\{(x, y): y = f(x), x \in \Re\}$ is continuous at c.

A

1. $f(x) = 3x^2 + 2x - 1; c = 5$
2. $f(x) = 7x^2 - x - 1; c = -2$
3. $f(x) = x^4 - x^2 + x; c = 0$
4. $f(x) = x^5 - x^2 + 3x; c = 0$
5. $f(x) = 2(x - 1)^2 + 3(x - 1) + 7; c = 1$
6. $f(x) = 6(x + 3)^3 - (x + 3)^2 + 2; c = -3$
7. $f(x) = 7 - (x + 2) + 2(x + 2)^2 - (x + 2)^5; c = -2$
8. $f(x) = -3 + (x - 4)^2 - (x - 4)^3 + 3(x - 4)^4; c = 4$

B

9. $f(x) = \begin{cases} \dfrac{x}{x}, & \text{if } x \neq 0 \\ 1, & \text{if } x = 0 \end{cases}; c = 0$

10. $f(x) = \begin{cases} 1, & \text{if } x > 0 \\ 0, & \text{if } x = 0 \\ -1, & \text{if } x < 0 \end{cases}; c = 0$

11. $f(x) = \begin{cases} \dfrac{x^3 - 1}{x - 1}, & \text{if } x \neq 1 \\ 1, & \text{if } x = 1 \end{cases}; c = 1$

12. $f(x) = \begin{cases} \dfrac{x^3 + 8}{x + 2}, & \text{if } x \neq -2 \\ 12, & \text{if } x = -2 \end{cases}; c = -2$

Evaluate each limit or show that it does not exist.

13. $\lim\limits_{x \to 0} \dfrac{f(x) - f(0)}{x}; f(x) = x^2 + x + 1$

14. $\lim\limits_{x \to 0} \dfrac{f(x) - f(0)}{x}; f(x) = x^3 - 2x + 6$

15. $\lim\limits_{x \to 1} \dfrac{g(x) - g(1)}{x - 1}; g(x) = 2x^2 + 3x + 2$

16. $\lim\limits_{x \to 2} \dfrac{g(x) - g(2)}{x - 2}; g(x) = 3x^2 - 2x - 7$

17. $\lim\limits_{t \to -3} \dfrac{f(t) - f(-3)}{t + 3}; f(t) = t^3 - 10$

18. $\lim\limits_{t \to -1} \dfrac{f(t) - f(-1)}{t + 1}; f(t) = 2t^4$

19. $\lim\limits_{x \to 1} \dfrac{h(x) - h(1)}{x - 1}$; $h(x) = |x - 1|$

20. $\lim\limits_{x \to 1} \dfrac{m(x) - m(1)}{x - 1}$; $m(x) = \sqrt{|x|}$

Let f and g be functions such that $\lim\limits_{x \to c} f(x) = l$ and $\lim\limits_{x \to c} g(x) = k$. Prove each of the following statements. (*Hint:* See Section 6–4 and the theorem stated on page 97.)

21. $\lim\limits_{x \to c} [f + g](x) = l + k$

22. $\lim\limits_{x \to c} [f - g](x) = l - k$

23. $\lim\limits_{x \to c} [fg](x) = lk$

24. $\lim\limits_{x \to c} \left[\dfrac{f}{g}\right](x) = \dfrac{l}{k}$, provided $k \neq 0$.

Let f and g be continuous functions at c. Prove that each of the following functions is also continuous at c. (*Hint:* Use Exercises 21–24.)

25. $f + g$ **26.** $f - g$ **27.** fg **28.** $\dfrac{f}{g}$, if $g(c) \neq 0$.

29. Prove that if I is the identity function over $\Re$, a and c are any real numbers, and n any positive integer, then the function aI^n is continuous at c. (*Hint:* Use Exercise 27 and the principle of mathematical induction.)

30. Prove that every polynomial function over $\Re$ is continuous. (*Hint:* Use Exercises 25 and 29 and the principle of mathematical induction.)

8–3 The Location Principle

Consider the following statements:

1. A certain polynomial function f with domain $\Re$ contains $(-2, -3)$ and $(1, 4)$.

2. f is continuous so that its graph is an unbroken curve.

3. Any line parallel to the vertical axis intersects the graph of f in at most one point.

Do you see that these facts imply that f must have a zero between -2 and 1? Fact 1 means that the graph of f must contain the points $(-2, -3)$ and $(1, 4)$, as in Figure 8–5a, page 290. Fact 2 assures you that the graph cannot be broken like the one shown in Figure 8–5b. Fact 3 guarantees that the graph cannot pass outside the black lines as does the graph in Figure 8–5c. Therefore, the graph must intersect the x-axis in at least one point with abscissa between -2 and 1. Figure 8–6 shows several possibilities.

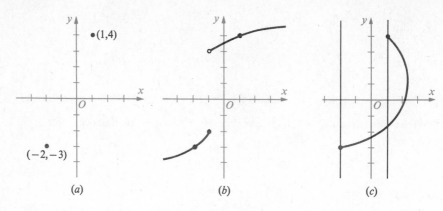

Figure 8–5

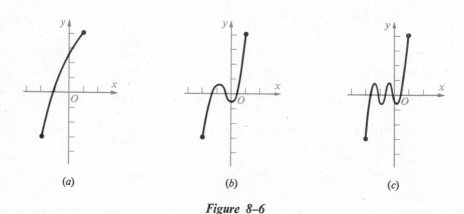

Figure 8–6

Facts 2 and 3, page 289, imply the following theorem, called the **Location Principle**. Its proof is part of calculus.

> **THEOREM** If *f* is a function that is continuous at every number between two real numbers *a* and *b*, and if $f(a)$ and $f(b)$ denote numbers one of which is positive and the other negative, then *f* has at least one zero between *a* and *b*.

In case *f* is a polynomial function, the Location Principle can be restated to assert that *f* has an odd number of zeros between *a* and *b*, if a zero of multiplicity *m* is counted *m* times.

The Location Principle and theorems discussed in Chapters 6 and 7 together provide useful clues to the number and location of the zeros of a polynomial function.

EXAMPLE.   Locate consecutive integers between which there are zeros of

$$p = \{(x, y): \ y = x^4 - 3x^2 + 5x - 6\}.$$

Solution: Use synthetic substitution to compute values of p.

x					$p(x)$	
0	1	0	−3	5	−6	
1	1	1	−2	3	−3	2 is an upper bound of the
2	1	2	1	7	8	zeros. (Why?)
−1	1	−1	−2	7	−13	
−2	1	−2	1	3	−12	−3 is a lower bound of the
−3	1	−3	6	−13	33	zeros. (Why?)

∴ p has at least one zero between 1 and 2, and at least one
zero between −3 and −2. By Descartes' Rule, p has 3 or 1
positive zeros (Why?); also, because $p(-x) = x^4 - 3x^2 - 5x + 6$, p has exactly one negative zero. (Why?)
Thus, p has exactly one zero between −3 and −2, and
either three zeros or one zero between 1 and 2, **Answer.**

Beware of assuming the converse of the Location Principle. That is, do not assume that if
$f(c) = 0$ and $a < c < b$, then one of the numbers $f(a)$ and $f(b)$ must be positive and the other
negative. Figure 8–7 shows part of the graph of
a polynomial function where $a < c < b$, $f(c) = 0$, but where $f(a)$ and $f(b)$ are both positive
numbers.

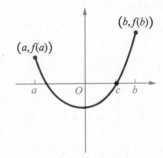

Figure 8–7

Exercises

Show that the function whose domain is $\mathcal{R}$ and whose values are specified by
the given polynomial has real zeros, as indicated. Find consecutive integers
between which each such zero lies.

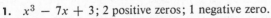

A

1. $x^3 - 7x + 3$; 2 positive zeros; 1 negative zero.

2. $7x^3 + 4x^2 - 12x - 8$; 2 negative zeros; 1 positive zero.

3. $5x^3 + 2x^2 + 7$; 1 negative zero; no positive zeros.

4. $2x^3 - x^2 - 3$; 1 positive zero; no negative roots.

5. $x^4 + 4x + 1$; 2 negative zeros; no positive zeros.

6. $x^4 - 5x + 2$; 2 positive zeros; no negative zeros.

7. $x^4 - 3x^2 + x - 6$; 1 positive and 1 negative zero.

8. $x^4 - 5x^3 - 5x^2 - 4$; 1 positive and 1 negative zero.

9. Determine the set of positive integers k for which $x^3 + 3x^2 + 2x = k^2$ has an odd number of roots between -2 and 2.

K=all k's between −2+10

10. Determine the values of the real number k for which $x^4 + 8x^3 - 5x^2 - 2x + k = 0$ has an odd number of roots between -1 and 1.

11. **a.** Verify that if $f(x) = 3x^3 - 6x^2 - x - 2$, then $f(1) = -6$ and $f(4) = 90$.

    b. Use this fact and the Location Principle to state why every equation of the form $3x^3 - 6x^2 - x - 2 = d$, where $-6 < d < 90$, has at least one root between 1 and 4.

12. Show that if k is a nonzero real number such that the polynomial function $\{(x, y): y = x^3 - 2x^2 - 2x + k\}$ has no multiple zeros and exactly one zero between -1 and 0, then the function also has one zero between 0 and 1.

Let f be a continuous function having domain $\Re$ and $\{1, 5\}$ as its set of real zeros. If x_1 is a real number for which $f(x_1) > 0$, state whether each assertion is necessarily true. Justify your answer.

13. If $1 < x_1 < 5$ and $1 < x_2 < 5$, then $f(x_2) > 0$.

14. If $1 < x_1 < 5$ and $x_2 > 5$, then $f(x_2) < 0$.

15. If $x_1 < 1$ and $x_2 < 1$, then $f(x_2) > 0$.

16. If $x_1 > 5$ and $x_2 > 5$, then $f(x_2) > 0$.

Prove each statement.

17. If f is a continuous function at all numbers between the real numbers a and b and if d is a real number between $f(a)$ and $f(b)$, then there is at least one real number c between a and b such that $f(c) = d$.

18. Every nonconstant polynomial of even degree over $\Re$ whose leading coefficient and constant term are opposite in sign has at least one positive zero and at least one negative zero.

19. **a.** If M is the greatest real zero of a continuous function f with domain $\Re$, then $f(c)$ has the same sign for all real numbers $c > M$.

    b. State an analogous theorem for L, the least real zero of f.

20. If a and b are consecutive zeros of a continuous function f with domain $\Re$, then $f(c)$ has the same sign for all real numbers c between a and b. (*Hint:* Real numbers a and b are called consecutive zeros of f if $a \neq b$, $f(a) = f(b) = 0$, and f has no zero between a and b.)

SLOPES AND DERIVATIVES

8-4 Tangents to Curves

To learn how to describe the direction of a curve at one of its points, consider the point $P(1, 2)$ on the graph of $s = \{(x, y): y = 2x^2\}$. (Figure 8–8.) Let $x_1, x_2, \ldots, x_n, \ldots$ be an arbitrary sequence of real numbers whose limit is 1, but whose terms are all different from 1. Then, $S_1(x_1, 2x_1^2)$, $S_2(x_2, 2x_2^2), \ldots, S_n(x_n, 2x_n^2)$, $\ldots$ is a sequence of points all on the graph of s, but all different from P. (Why?) Because

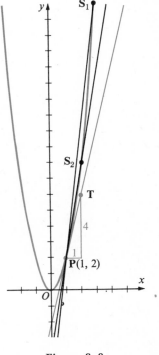

$$\lim_{n\to\infty} x_n = 1 \text{ and } \lim_{n\to\infty} 2x_n^2 = 2,$$

you can think of $S_1, S_2, \ldots, S_n, \ldots$ as a sequence of points having $P(1, 2)$ as "limit point."

Now consider the sequence of lines PS_1, PS_2, $\ldots, PS_n, \ldots$. A direction vector of PS_n is $(x_n - 1, 2x_n^2 - 2)$. (Why?). In fact, since $x_n \neq 1$ (Why?), you can choose

$$\frac{1}{x_n - 1}(x_n - 1, 2x_n^2 - 2) = [1, 2(x_n + 1)]$$

as direction vector of PS_n. But

$$\lim_{n\to\infty} 2(x_n + 1) = 2(1 + 1) = 4.$$

Figure 8–8

Therefore, as Figure 8–8 suggests, you can regard $PS_1, PS_2, \ldots, PS_n, \ldots$ as a sequence of lines having the line PT with direction vector $(1, 4)$ as "limit line." We call this line the *tangent* to the graph of s at P. Its slope 4 is called the *slope of the graph* at P. Notice that

$$2(x_n + 1) = \frac{2x_n^2 - 2}{x_n - 1} = \frac{s(x_n) - s(1)}{x_n - 1}.$$

This means that we have defined the slope of the graph of s at P to be $\lim_{n\to\infty} \dfrac{s(x_n) - s(1)}{x_n - 1}$, where $x_1, x_2, \ldots, x_n, \ldots$ is any sequence whose limit is 1, but whose terms are real numbers different from 1. But the definition of limit discussed in Section 8–2 implies that

$$\lim_{n\to\infty} \frac{s(x_n) - s(1)}{x_n - 1} = \lim_{x\to 1} \frac{s(x) - s(1)}{x - 1}.$$ Thus,

the slope of the graph of s at $\mathbf{P}$ is $\lim\limits_{x \to 1} \dfrac{s(x) - s(1)}{x - 1}$.

The preceding discussion illustrates how we define tangents to the graph of any function. Let f be a continuous function and c be a number in its domain, and let $\lim\limits_{x \to c} \dfrac{f(x) - f(c)}{x - c}$ be a real number. The **tangent** to the graph of f at $\mathbf{P}[c, f(c)]$ is the line through $\mathbf{P}$ with slope equal to

$$\lim_{x \to c} \frac{f(x) - f(c)}{x - c}.$$

We call this limit the **slope** of the graph of f at $\mathbf{P}$.

EXAMPLE 1. **a.** Determine the slope of the graph of the function $f = \{(x, y): y = 3x^2 - 5x + 1\}$ at the point $\mathbf{P}$, whose abscissa is 2.

b. State an equation of the tangent to the graph at $\mathbf{P}$.

Solution: **a.** $\quad f(x) = 3x^2 - 5x + 1$

$\qquad\qquad f(2) = 3 \cdot 2^2 - 5 \cdot 2 + 1$

$\qquad \therefore\ f(x) - f(2) = 3(x^2 - 2^2) - 5(x - 2)$

$\qquad\qquad\qquad\quad = 3(x^2 - 4) - 5(x - 2)$

For $x \neq 2$, you have:

$$\frac{f(x) - f(2)}{x - 2} = 3(x + 2) - 5$$

$$\lim_{x \to 2} \frac{f(x) - f(2)}{x - 2} = 3(2 + 2) - 5 = 7$$

$\therefore$ the slope of the graph at $\mathbf{P}$ is 7, **Answer.**

b. Since $f(2) = 3$, $\mathbf{P} = (2, 3)$. The tangent through $\mathbf{P}(2, 3)$ has slope 7. Its equation is
$y - 3 = 7(x - 2)$; $y = 7x - 11$, **Answer.**

The following example shows that not every continuous function has a graph with a tangent at each of its points.

EXAMPLE 2. Prove that the graph of $f = \{(x, y): y = |x|\}$ does not have a tangent at $\mathbf{P}(0, 0)$.

Solution: $f(x) = |x| = \begin{cases} x \text{ if } x \geq 0 \\ -x \text{ if } x < 0 \end{cases}$

$f(0) = 0$

$\therefore f(x) - f(0) = \begin{cases} x \text{ if } x > 0 \\ -x \text{ if } x < 0 \end{cases}$

$\therefore \dfrac{f(x) - f(0)}{x - 0} = \begin{cases} 1 \text{ if } x > 0 \\ -1 \text{ if } x < 0 \end{cases}$

Let $x_1, x_2, \ldots, x_n, \ldots$ be the sequence whose nth term is $(-\frac{1}{10})^n$. Then, $\lim\limits_{n \to \infty} x_n = \dfrac{(-1)^n}{10^n} = 0$. Because the terms of this sequence are alternately negative and positive numbers, you find the following:

$$\frac{f(x_n) - f(0)}{x_n - 0} = \begin{cases} -1 \text{ if } n \text{ is odd} \\ 1 \text{ if } n \text{ is even} \end{cases}$$

Since the terms of the sequence whose nth term is

$$\frac{f(x_n) - f(0)}{x_n}$$

are alternately -1 and 1, the sequence diverges. Hence, $\lim\limits_{x \to 0} \dfrac{f(x) - f(0)}{x - 0}$ does not exist (Why?) so that the graph of f does not have a tangent at $\mathbf{P}(0, 0)$.

Figure 8–9 pictures the situation near $\mathbf{P}(0, 0)$. If $\mathbf{S}_1, \mathbf{S}_2, \ldots, \mathbf{S}_n, \ldots$ is the sequence of points on the graph which have abscissas $-\frac{1}{10}, \frac{1}{100}, \ldots,$ $\dfrac{(-1)^n}{10^n}, \ldots$, the sequence of the lines $\mathbf{PS}_1, \mathbf{PS}_2, \ldots$ cannot have a single "limit line" because its terms have slopes alternately -1 and 1.

Figure 8–9

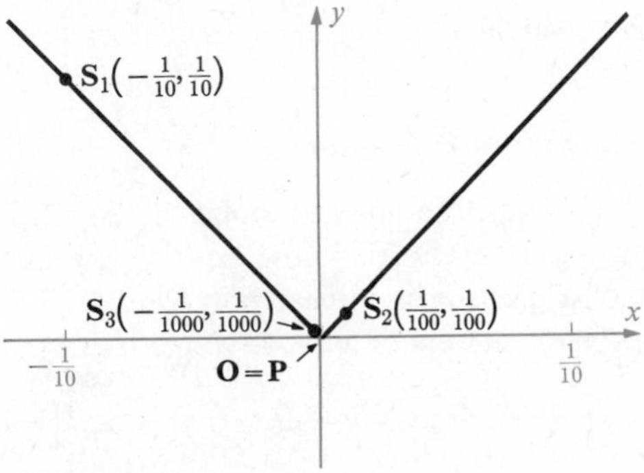

Exercises

If the slope of the graph of the given function exists at the point **P** with given abscissa, determine: (**a**) the slope; (**b**) an equation of the line tangent to the graph at **P**.

A

1. $\{(x, y): y = -7x + 2\}$; 3
2. $\{(x, y): y = 5x - 7\}$; -2
3. $\{(x, y): y = x^2 + 2x + 3\}$; -1
4. $\{(x, y): y = x^2 - 6x + 4\}$; 3
5. $\{[x, p(x)]: p(x) = 2x^2 - x - 6\}$; -4
6. $\{[x, p(x)]: p(x) = 3x^2 + x - 10\}$; 2
7. f, where $f(x) = 4x^3$; 1
8. f, where $f(x) = 2x^3$; -1
9. g, where $g(x) = x^2 - x^3$; 0
10. g, where $g(x) = x - 2x^3$; 0

B

11. $\left\{(x, y): y = \dfrac{1}{x}\right\}$; 1
12. $\left\{(x, y): y = \dfrac{2}{x}\right\}$; 1
13. $\{(x, y): y = [x]\}$; 2
14. $\{(x, y): y = [x]\}$; $\frac{1}{2}$
15. $\{(x, y): y = |x|\}$; -2
16. $\{(x, y): y = |x - 1|\}$; 1
17. $\{(x, y): y = x|x|\}$; 0
18. $\{(x, y): y = |x|^3\}$; 0

If a and c denote real numbers and f is the function defined over $\mathcal{R}$ by the given polynomial, prove that the slope m of the graph of f at $[c, f(c)]$ has the value indicated.

C

19. $f(x) = ax^2$; $m = 2ac$
20. $f(x) = ax^3$; $m = 3ac^2$

Let m and M be the slopes of the graphs of the functions f and g at the points $[c, f(c)]$ and $[c, g(c)]$, respectively. Prove each statement.

21. The slope of the graph of $f + g$ at $[c, f(c) + g(c)]$ is $m + M$.
22. The slope of the graph of $f - g$ at $[c, f(c) - g(c)]$ is $m - M$.
23. If b denotes a real number and $f = \{(x, y): y = b\}$, then for every real number c, $\lim\limits_{x \to c} \dfrac{f(x) - f(c)}{x - c} = 0$.
24. If m and b denote real numbers and $f = \{(x, y): y = mx + b\}$, then for every real number c, $\lim\limits_{x \to c} \dfrac{f(x) - f(c)}{x - c} = m$.

8–5 Polynomial Expansions

In computing the slope at a point of the graph of a polynomial function, you will find it useful to know how to express a polynomial as a sum of powers of a given prime linear polynomial. To write a power of x such as x^2 in terms of powers of $x - 4$, you can use the Binomial Theorem. Thus,

$$x = (x - 4) + 4; \therefore x^2 = [(x - 4) + 4]^2 = (x - 4)^2 + 8(x - 4) + 16.$$

Similarly,

$$x^3 = [(x - 4) + 4]^3 = (x - 4)^3 + 12(x - 4)^2 + 48(x - 4) + 64.$$

Using these results, you can write $P(x) = x^3 + x^2 - 5x + 1$ as a sum of powers of $x - 4$:

$$P(x) = [(x - 4) + 4]^3 + [(x - 4) + 4]^2 - 5[(x - 4) + 4] + 1$$
$$= (x - 4)^3 + 12(x - 4)^2 + 48(x - 4) + 64$$
$$+ (x - 4)^2 + 8(x - 4) + 16$$
$$- 5(x - 4) - 20 + 1$$

$$\therefore P(x) = 1(x - 4)^3 + 13(x - 4)^2 + 51(x - 4) + 61 \qquad (*)$$

Express the right member of the starred $(*)$ statement in the nested form

$$P(x) = \{[1(x - 4) + 13](x - 4) + 51\}(x - 4) + 61$$

and you can verify the entries in the following table.

When you divide $x - 4$ into	the quotient is	the remainder is
(1) $P(x)$	$[(x - 4) + 13](x - 4) + 51$	$61 = P(4)$
(2) the quotient obtained in Step (1)	$(x - 4) + 13$	51
(3) the quotient obtained in Step (2)	1	13

Thus, you can compute the coefficients in the right member of the starred statement by starting with $x^3 + x^2 - 5x + 1$ and repeatedly dividing by $x - 4$. Doing the addition steps in the synthetic division process mentally, you can conveniently arrange the work as shown.

$$
\begin{array}{r|rrrr}
4 & 1 & 1 & -5 & 1 \\
  & 1 & 5 & 15 & 61 \\
  & 1 & 9 & 51 \\
  & 1 & 13 \\
\end{array}
$$

EXAMPLE 1. Let f be the function whose values are given by

$$f(x) = 2x^4 - x^3 + x^2 + 3.$$

a. Express $f(x)$ in powers of $x + 1$.

b. Determine the slope of the graph of f at the point with abscissa -1.

(*Solution on page 298*)

Solution: Note that $x + 1 = x - (-1)$

a.

$$\begin{array}{r|rrrrr} -1 & 2 & -1 & 1 & 0 & 3 \\ & & 2 & -3 & 4 & -4 & 7 \\ & & 2 & -5 & 9 & -13 \\ & & 2 & -7 & 16 \\ & & 2 & -9 \end{array}$$

$\therefore f(x) = 2(x + 1)^4 - 9(x + 1)^3 + 16(x + 1)^2 - 13(x + 1) + 7,$
Answer.

b. $f(-1) = 7.$ (Why?) Therefore, using the answer to part (**a**), you find:

$$f(x) - f(-1) = 2(x + 1)^4 - 9(x + 1)^3 + 16(x + 1)^2 - 13(x + 1)$$

$$\therefore f(x) - f(-1) = -13(x + 1) + 16(x + 1)^2 - 9(x + 1)^3 + 2(x + 1)^4$$

For $x \neq -1$, you have

$$\frac{f(x) - f(-1)}{x + 1} = -13 + 16(x + 1) - 9(x + 1)^2 + 2(x + 1)^3$$

$$\therefore \lim_{x \to -1} \frac{f(x) - f(-1)}{x + 1} = -13 + 16(0) - 9(0)^2 + 2(0)^3 = -13$$

$\therefore$ the slope of the graph of f at $(-1, 7)$ is -13, **Answer.**

You know that the constant term in the expansion of any polynomial $f(x)$ in powers of $x - c$ is $f(c)$. (Why?) Example 1 suggests that the coefficient of $(x - c)^1$ in this expansion is the slope of the graph of the function f at $[c, f(c)]$. Because this conjecture is correct (Exercise 24, page 299), you can determine the slope of the graph by using synthetic division.

EXAMPLE 2. Determine an equation of the tangent to the graph of $f = \{(x, y): y = 2x^3 - 8x^2 + 5x + 1\}$ at the point whose abscissa is 3.

Solution: *Plan:* Determine the first and second remainders on dividing twice by $x - 3$.

$$\begin{array}{r|rrrr} 3 & 2 & -8 & 5 & 1 \\ & & 2 & -2 & -1 & -2 = f(3) \\ & & 2 & 4 & 11 & = \text{slope at } (3, -2) \end{array}$$

$\therefore$ an equation of the tangent at $(3, -2)$ is
$y - (-2) = 11(x - 3)$, or $y = 11x - 35$, **Answer.**

Exercises

(a) Use synthetic division to express each polynomial in powers of $x - c$ where c denotes the indicated real number. **(b)** What is the slope of the tangent at the point with abscissa c on the graph of the function specified by the given polynomial?

A

1. $3x^2 - 7x + 2$; -1
2. $5x^2 + 11x - 3$; 2
3. $x^3 - 3x^2 + x - 2$; 3
4. $2x^3 + x^2 - 3x + 4$; -2

5. $2x^3 - 1$; 5
6. $x^3 + x$; 3
7. $1 - x + 2x^2 + 6x^3 + 12x^4$; $-\frac{1}{2}$
8. $2 + x + 3x^2 - 6x^3 - 18x^4$; $-\frac{1}{3}$

Determine an equation of the tangent to the graph of the indicated function at the point whose abscissa is given.

9. $f = \{(x, y): y = 7x^3 - 2\}$; 0
10. $f = \{(x, y): y = 2x^3 - 3x + 1\}$; 0
11. $g = \{[x, g(x)]: g(x) = x^4 - x^3 + 3x^2 + 1\}$; -1
12. $g = \{[x, g(x)]: g(x) = x^4 + 5x^2 + x - 2\}$; 1

B Expand in powers of $x - c$.

13. $x^4 + 3x - 2$; $c = i$
14. $x^4 - 2x^2 + 2$; $c = -i$

15. $x^3 - x - 1$; $c = 2 - i$
16. $x^3 + x^2 - 3$; $c = 1 + i$

By the binomial theorem the coefficient of $(x - c)^1$ in the expansion of $kx^m = k[(x - c) + c]^m$ in powers of $x - c$ is $k\begin{pmatrix} m \\ m - 1 \end{pmatrix} c^{m-1} = mkc^{m-1}$. Use this fact to determine the coefficient of $(x - c)^1$ in the expansion of the given polynomial in powers of $x - c$.

17. $5x^7$
18. $4x^4$

19. a_0x^n
20. a_1x^{n-1}

21. $a_0x^2 + a_1x + a_2$
22. $a_0x^3 + a_1x^2 + a_2x + a_3$

Prove each statement. In Exercises 24–26 assume that $b_n, b_{n-1}, b_{n-2}, \ldots, b_0$ are constants, and $f(x) = b_n + b_{n-1}(x - c) + b_{n-2}(x - c)^2 + \cdots + b_0(x - c)^n$, $n \in N$.

C

23. In the expansion of $a_0x^n + a_1x^{n-1} + \cdots + a_{n-2}x^2 + a_{n-1}x + a_n$ in powers of $x - c$, the coefficient of the term in which the exponent of $x - c$ is 1 is $na_0c^{n-1} + (n - 1)a_1c^{n-2} + \cdots + 2a_{n-2}c + a_{n-1}$. (*Hint:* The coefficient is the sum of the coefficients of $(x - c)^1$ in the expansions of $a_0x^n, a_1x^{n-1}, \ldots a_{n-2}x^2, a_{n-1}x$.)

24. $b_n = f(c)$ and $\lim\limits_{x \to c} \dfrac{f(x) - f(c)}{x - c} = b_{n-1}$.

25. The zeros of $b_n + b_{n-1}y + b_{n-2}y^2 + \cdots + b_0y^n$ are the zeros of $f(x)$ each decreased by c.

26. If b_n, b_{n-1}, b_{n-2}, ..., b_0 and c denote nonnegative real numbers, then $f(x)$ has no real zero greater than c.

27. Use the result of Exercise 25 and synthetic division to find polynomials whose zeros are the zeros of $x^3 - 2x^2 + x + 5$ each decreased or increased as indicated.

   a. decreased by 1   c. increased by 2

   b. decreased by i d. increased by i

28. Determine c so that 0 is the coefficient of the term of degree 2 in the polynomial whose zeros are the zeros of $a_0x^3 + a_1x^2 + a_2x + a_3$ each decreased by c. (*Hint:* Use Exercise 25.)

8–6 Derivatives of Polynomials

If c denotes a constant, you know that the coefficient of $(x - c)^1$ in the expansion of any polynomial $f(x)$ in powers of $x - c$ is the slope of the graph of f at $[c, f(c)]$ (page 298). Therefore, it is useful to find a simple expression for this coefficient.

Can you state the term in which the exponent of $x - c$ is 1 in the expansion of kx^m in powers of $x - c$, where $m \geq 1$? Since $kx^m = k[(x - c) + c]^m$, the binomial theorem (Section 3–5) implies that the term is

$$k \binom{m}{m-1} (x - c)^1 c^{m-1} = mkc^{m-1}(x - c).$$

Using this fact, you can verify the entries in the following table.

In the expansion of	the coefficient of $(x - c)^1$ is
$4x^3$	$3 \cdot 4c^2 = \quad 12c^2$
$-5x^2$	$2(-5)c^1 = \quad -10c$
$7x^1$	$1 \cdot 7c^0 = \quad 7$

To determine the coefficient of $(x - c)^1$ in the expansion of $g(x) = 4x^3 - 5x^2 + 7x - 3$, you simply add the coefficients of $(x - c)^1$ in the expansions of the terms $4x^3$, $-5x^2$, and $7x$. (Why?) Thus, using the entries in the preceding table, you find that the coefficient of $(x - c)^1$ in the proposed expansion of $g(x)$ is $12c^2 - 10c + 7$. This means that at the point with abscissa c on the graph of the function g

$$\text{the ordinate} = g(c) = \quad 4c^3 - 5c^2 + 7c - 3,$$
$$\text{the slope of the graph} = 12c^2 - 10c + 7.$$

The preceding discussion illustrates the following theorem (Exercises 23 and 24, page 299).

THEOREM   If c denotes a real number and if f is a function with domain $\mathcal{R}$ whose values are given by the polynomial

$$f(x) = a_0 x^n \quad + \qquad a_1 x^{n-1} + \cdots + \; a_{n-2} x^2 + a_{n-1} x + a_n,$$

then the slope of the graph of f at $[c, f(c)]$ is

$$na_0 c^{n-1} + \quad (n-1)a_1 c^{n-2} + \cdots + 2a_{n-2} c \; + a_{n-1}.$$

The function whose value at c is the slope of the graph of f at $[c, f(c)]$ is called the **slope function** derived from f, or the **derivative** of f, and is denoted by the symbol f'. Thus, the domain of f' is the set of real numbers c for which $\lim\limits_{x \to c} \dfrac{f(x) - f(c)}{x - c}$ is a real number, $f'(c)$.

For a polynomial function f, you can apply the preceding theorem to assert that if

$$f(x) = \quad a_0 x^n \quad + \qquad a_1 x^{n-1} + \cdots + \; a_{n-2} x^2 + a_{n-1} x + a_n;$$

then

$$f'(x) = na_0 x^{n-1} + (n-1)a_1 x^{n-2} + \cdots + 2a_{n-1} x \; + a_{n-1}.$$

EXAMPLE.   If $f(x) = 2x^3 + 3x^2 - 12x + 1$, determine: **(a)** $f'(x)$; **(b)** the points on the graph of $\{(x, y): y = f(x)\}$ where the slope of the tangent is 0.

Solution: **a.** $f(x) = \qquad 2x^3 + \qquad 3x^2 - 12x^1 + 1$

$f'(x) = 3 \cdot 2x^2 + 2 \cdot 3x^1 + 1(-12)$

$f'(x) = \qquad 6x^2 + \qquad 6x \; - 12,$ **Answer.**

b. The slope of the tangent is 0 if and only if x satisfies the equation $f'(x) = 0$, or

$$6x^2 + 6x - 12 = 0$$
$$\therefore \quad x^2 + x - 2 = 0$$
$$(x + 2)(x - 1) = 0$$

$x + 2 = 0$ *or* $x - 1 = 0$

$x = -2$ $x = 1$

$f(-2) = 21$ (Why?) $f(1) = -6$ (Why?)

$\therefore$ The slope of the tangent is 0 at $(-2, 21)$ and $(1, -6)$, **Answer.**

As a partial check of the answer to part **(b)** preceding, you can verify that the first and second remainders on dividing $f(x)$ twice by $x + 2$, and twice by $x - 1$ are 21 and 0, and -6 and 0, respectively:

$$\begin{array}{r|rrrr} -2 & 2 & 3 & -12 & 1 \\ & & 2 & -1 & -10 \quad 21 \checkmark \\ \hline & 2 & -5 & 0 \checkmark \end{array} \qquad \begin{array}{r|rrrr} 1 & 2 & 3 & -12 & 1 \\ & & 2 & 5 & -7 \quad -6 \checkmark \\ \hline & 2 & 7 & 0 \checkmark \end{array}$$

The derivative of f', in symbols, $(f')'$, is usually denoted by f'' and is called the **second derivative** of f. Using the fact that $f''(c)$ is the slope of the graph of f' at the point $[c, f'(c)]$, you can verify that:

If $f(x) = a_0x^n + a_1x^{n-1} + \cdots + a_{n-2}x^2 + a_{n-1}x + a_n$, then

1. $f''(x) = n(n - 1)a_0x^{n-2} + (n - 1)(n - 2)a_1x^{n-3} + \cdots + 2 \cdot 1a_{n-2}$.

2. $\dfrac{f''(c)}{2!} = \dfrac{f''(c)}{2}$ is the coefficient of $(x - c)^2$ in the expansion of $f(x)$

in powers of $x - c$. (See Exercises 22 and 23, page 303.)
For example, if $f(x) = 2x^4 - x^3 + x^2 + 3$, then:

$$f'(x) = 8x^3 - 3x^2 + 2x;$$
$$f''(x) = 24x^2 - 6x + 2;$$
$$f''(-1) = 24(-1)^2 - 6(-1) + 2 = 32.$$

Notice that $\dfrac{f''(-1)}{2} = 16$, which is the coefficient of $(x + 1)^2$ in the expansion of $f(x)$ obtained in the Example above.

Exercises

Let $f(x)$ be the given polynomial. **(a)** Find $f'(x)$. **(b)** Find $f''(x)$. **(c)** Use your answer to **(a)** to determine the slope of the tangent at $[c, f(c)]$ on the graph of $f = \{(x, y): y = f(x)\}$.

A

1. $6x - 1; c = \frac{2}{3}$

2. $4x + 5; c = \frac{3}{2}$

3. $6x^2 + 3x + 1; c = 0$

4. $x^2 - 7x - 9; c = -1$

5. $2x^3 - 7x + x^2; c = 1$

6. $2x + 4 - x^3; c = 0$
   a) $2 - 3x^2$
   b) $-6x$
   c) 2

7. $5 - x + 2x^2 - x^4; c = -2$

8. $1 + x + x^2 + x^3 + x^4; c = -3$
   a) $4x^3 + 3x^2 + 2x + 1$
   b) $12x^2 + 6x + 2$
   c) -86

Determine an equation of (a) the tangent to the graph of the function g at the point whose abscissa is given; (b) an equation of the line perpendicular to the tangent at this point.

9. $g = \{(x, y): y = 2x^2 + 4x - 1\}; 0$

10. $g = \{(x, y): y = 5x^2 - 2x + 4\}; 1$

11. $g = \{(x, y): y = x^3 - 5x^2 + 3x + 1\}; -1$

12. $g = \{(x, y): y = 2x^3 + x^2 + 4x + 10\}; -2$

B   13–16. For the graph of the function g in Exercises 9–12, find the coordinates of the point(s) at which the tangent is a horizontal line.

17. Find the coordinates of each point in which the tangent to the graph of $\{(x, y): y = x^3 - 2x^2 + 1\}$ at $(2, 1)$ intersects the graph.

18. Find equations of the two lines, each of which is tangent to the graph of $\{(x, y): y = x^2 - 3x + 5\}$ and each of which passes through $(0, 1)$.

Prove each statement. Assume that $\mathcal{R}$ is the domain of f.

19. If $f(x)$ is a constant, then $f'(x)$ is the zero polynomial.

20. If $f(x)$ is a linear polynomial, then $f''(x)$ is the zero polynomial.

Prove each statement.

Let $f = \{(x, y): y = a_0x^n + a_1x^{n-1} + \cdots + a_{n-2}x^2 + a_{n-1}x + a_n\}$.

C   21. If $f''(x)$ is the zero polynomial, then $f(x)$ is either a constant or a linear polynomial.

22. $f''(x) = n(n - 1)a_0x^{n-2} + (n - 1)(n - 2)a_1x^{n-3} + \cdots + 2 \cdot 1a_{n-2}.$

23. $\dfrac{f''(c)}{2!}$ is the coefficient of $(x - c)^2$ in the expansion of $f(x)$ in powers of $x - c$.

24. If $n \geq 2$ and c is a multiple zero of f, then c is a zero of f'. (*Hint:* Expand $f(x)$ in powers of $x - c$.)

25. If $n > 2$ and c is a zero of multiplicity 3 or more of f, then c is a zero of f''. (*Hint:* Use Exercise 23 above.)

26. (a) If $n \geq 2$, c is a root of at least multiplicity 2 of the equation

$$f(x) = f(c) + f'(c) \cdot (x - c).$$

(b) Interpret this fact in terms of the intersection of the tangent to the graph of f at $[c, f(c)]$.

Determine the polynomial $f(x)$ satisfying the given conditions.

27. $f'(x)$ is the zero polynomial and $f(3) = 5$.

28. $f'(x) = 2$ and $f(3) = 1$.

Let $f(x)$ and $g(x)$ denote polynomials over $\mathcal{R}$. Prove each statement.

29. The derivative of $f + g$ is $f' + g'$.

30. The derivative of $f - g$ is $f' - g'$.

APPLICATIONS OF THE DERIVATIVE

8-7 Using Derivatives in Graphing

Since $(1, m)$ is a direction vector of any straight line of slope m in the coordinate plane, you know that a line of negative slope falls from left to right, a line with slope 0 is horizontal, while a line of positive slope rises from left to right. (Figure 8–10).

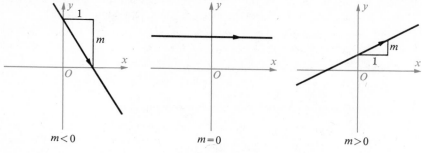

Figure 8–10

Figure 8–11 suggests similar properties of the graph of a polynomial function f.

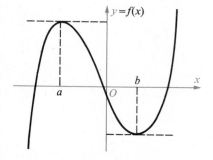

1. At each point where $x < a$ or $x > b$ the slope of the tangent is a positive number, so that $f'(x) > 0$, $f(x)$ increases, and the graph of f rises as x increases.

2. At each point where $a < x < b$, the slope of the tangent is negative, so that $f'(x) < 0$, $f(x)$ decreases, and the graph of f falls as x increases.

Figure 8–11

3. At the points where $x = a$ or $x = b$ the tangent is horizontal and $f'(x) = 0$. On the graph, points where $f'(x) = 0$ are called **critical points**.

Notice that a and b, the zeros of f', separate the rest of $\mathcal{R}$ into three subsets: $\{x : x < a\}$, $\{x : a < x < b\}$; $\{x : x > b\}$. Because f' is a continuous function having no zero in these subsets, the Location Principle insures that over any one of these subsets the values of f' are *consistently negative* or *consistently positive*. Thus, to test whether $f'(x)$ denotes a positive number or whether it denotes a negative number for *every* value of x in one of these subsets, you need only know the nature of $f'(x)$ for *one particular* value of x in the subset.

Proving that the values of f' indicate where the graph of f falls, rises, and may turn must be postponed until you study calculus thoroughly. Meanwhile, however, you may use the derivative as an aid in graphing.

EXAMPLE 1. Sketch the graph of f, where $f(x) = x^4 - x^3 - 5x^2 - 1$.

Solution:

1. Find the zeros of f'. These are the x-coordinates of the points where the graph has horizontal tangents.

$$f(x) = x^4 - x^3 - 5x^2 - 1$$
$$f'(x) = 4x^3 - 3x^2 - 10x$$
$$4x^3 - 3x^2 - 10x = 0$$
$$x(4x^2 - 3x - 10) = 0$$
$$x(4x + 5)(x - 2) = 0$$
$$\therefore -\tfrac{5}{4}, 0, \text{ and } 2 \text{ are the zeros of } f'.$$

2. From each subset into which the zeros of f' separate $\mathfrak{R}$, choose a particular number c at which to evaluate $f'(x)$, and thereby determine whether f rises or falls over the subset.

Subset	c	$f'(c)$	Over the subset the graph of f
$\{x:\ x < -\tfrac{5}{4}\}$	-2	negative	falls
$\{x:\ -\tfrac{5}{4} < x < 0\}$	-1	positive	rises
$\{x:\ 0 < x < 2\}$	1	negative	falls
$\{x:\ x > 2\}$	3	positive	rises

3. Use the data obtained in Steps 1 and 2 together with a table of values of f to plot points and sketch the graph. Be sure to include the critical points on the graph.

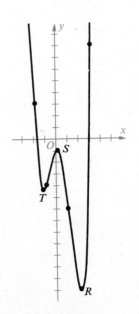

x					$f(x)$
0	1	-1	-5	0	-1
1	1	0	-5	-5	-6
2	1	1	-3	-6	-13
3	1	2	1	3	8
-1	1	-2	-3	3	-4
$-\tfrac{5}{4}$	1	$-\tfrac{9}{4}$	$-\tfrac{35}{16}$	$\tfrac{175}{64}$	$-\tfrac{1091}{216} \doteq -5$
-2	1	-3	1	-2	3

The point **S** on the graph of the function f in Example 1 is called a *relative maximum point* of the graph and its ordinate $f(0)$ is a *relative maximum* of the function. **S** is a relative maximum because its ordinate equals or exceeds the ordinate of every point in its *immediate vicinity*. Notice that the ordinate of **S** is *not* the greatest value of f. Can you explain why **T** and **R** are called *relative minimum points* of the graph?

These observations suggest the following definitions: $f(c)$ is a **relative maximum [minimum]** of a function f with domain $\mathfrak{R}$ provided there exist distinct real numbers a and b, $a < c < b$, such that if x is between a and b, then $f(c) \geq f(x)[f(c) \leq f(x)]$. It can be proved that a *necessary* condition for $f(c)$ to be a relative maximum [minimum] of a *polynomial* function over $\mathfrak{R}$ is that $f'(c) = 0$. Example 2 shows that this condition is *not sufficient*.

EXAMPLE 2. Sketch the graph of $g = \{(x, y): y = x^3\}$.

Solution: $g(x) = x^3$

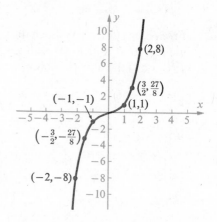

1. Determine the critical points.

    $g'(x) = 3x^2$; $3x^2 = 0$ if and only if $x = 0$.

    $g(0) = 0$; $\therefore$ $(0, 0)$ is the only critical point.

2. If $x \neq 0, g'(x) > 0$. (Why?) Hence, the graph is the ascending curve drawn through the plotted points shown.

Note that at each point to the left of the origin the graph of the function in Example 2 lies below the tangent at the point (*is concave downward*), whereas to the right of $(0, 0)$ it lies above each tangent (*is concave upward*). In calculus it is proved that at points of the graph of a polynomial function where the second derivative is negative, the graph is concave downward; but at points where the second derivative is positive, the graph is concave upward. You can verify this fact for the function g in Example 2 by noting that $g''(x) = 6x$, so that $g''(x) < 0$ for $x < 0$, but $g''(x) > 0$ for $x > 0$.

Notice also that at the origin the tangent (which happens to be the x-axis) cuts across the graph of g. We call $(0, 0)$ an *inflection point* of the graph. A point **P** on a curve is an **inflection point** if the curve is concave upward in an interval on one side of **P** and concave downward in an interval on the other side of **P**. A *necessary but not sufficient* condition for $[c, f(c)]$ to be an inflection point of the graph of a *polynomial* function f is that $f''(c) = 0$. You can verify that the graph of the function in Example 1 has inflection points whose abscissas are $\dfrac{3 \pm \sqrt{129}}{12} \doteq \frac{7}{6}, -\frac{2}{3}$ by showing that at those points $f''(x) = 12x^2 - 6x - 10 = 0$ *and* by testing the sign of $f''(x)$ over the subsets of $\Re$ indicated in the following table.

Subset	c	$f''(c)$	Over the subset the graph of f is
$\left\{x: x < \dfrac{3 - \sqrt{129}}{12}\right\}$	-1	positive	concave upward
$\left\{x: \dfrac{3 - \sqrt{129}}{12} < x < \dfrac{3 + \sqrt{129}}{12}\right\}$	0	negative	concave downward
$\left\{x: x > \dfrac{3 + \sqrt{129}}{12}\right\}$	2	positive	concave upward

Exercises

For the function whose values are given by the indicated polynomial, determine (a) the intervals in which the function is increasing and those in which it is decreasing; (b) the relative maximum, relative minimum, and inflection points (if any) of its graph; (c) the slope of the tangent to the graph at each inflection point; (d) sketch the graph.

A

1. $2x^2 - 8x + 1$
2. $3x^2 + 12x - 5$
3. $-x^2 - 6x + 2$
4. $-x^2 + 10x - 15$
5. $x^3 + 3x - 1$
6. $x^3 - 3x + 1$

7. $2x^3 - x^2 - 4x$
8. $2x^3 - 4x^2 + 3x + 1$
9. $1 - 12x^2 - x^4$
10. $2x^3 - x^4$
11. $(x - 1)(x + 2)^2$
12. $(x + 1)^2(x - 5)$

Let $f = \{(x, y): y = x^3 - 3x^2 - 9x + k\}$ where k is a real constant. Prove each statement.

B

13. If $-5 < k < 27$, f has 3 different real zeros.
14. If $k < -5$, f has exactly 1 real zero.
15. If $k > 27$, f has exactly 1 real zero.
16. If $k = -5$ or $k = 27$, f has 1 double real zero and 1 other real zero.

Let $g = \{(x, y): y = x^4 - 4x + h\}$, where h is a real constant. Prove each statement.

17. If $h < 3$, g has exactly 2 different real zeros.
18. If $h > 3$, g has no real zero.

19. If $h = 3$, g has 1 real zero and it is a double zero.

20. The graph of g contains no inflection points.

Determine the numbers of real and of imaginary roots of each equation.

21. $z^3 - 3z^2 - 9z + 28 = 0$

22. $z^3 - 12z + 17 = 0$

23. $3x^4 - 4x^3 - 12x^2 + 24x + 20 = 0$

24. $3x^4 + 8x^3 - 6x^2 + 31 = 0$

C **25.** Show by an example that if f is not a polynomial function, its graph may fail to have a horizontal tangent at a relative maximum or minimum point. (*Hint:* See Example 2, page 295.)

26. Explain why a straight line can intersect the graph of a polynomial function of degree $n \geq 2$ in at most n points.

27. Prove that the graph of a quadratic polynomial function has exactly one critical point and no inflection point.

28. Prove that the graph of a cubic polynomial function has at most two critical points and exactly one inflection point.

29. Prove that the graph of a polynomial function of degree $n \geq 2$ has at most $n - 1$ critical points and at most $n - 2$ inflection points.

30. Prove that if c is a multiple zero of a polynomial function f, then the point $(c, 0)$ is either a relative maximum or minimum point or an inflection point of the graph of f. (*Hint:* Use Exercises 24 and 25, page 303.)

Sketch the graph of each relation.

31. $\{(x, y): |y| = x^2\}$

32. $\{(x, y): |y| = x^3\}$

33. $\{(x, y): y = |x|^3 - 3|x|^2 + 1\}$

34. $\{(x, y): |y| = x^3 - 3x^2 + 1\}$

8–8 Applications of Maxima and Minima

In applied mathematics many problems require finding numbers described in such terms as "the largest area," "the lowest cost," "the least volume," "the shortest distance," "the greatest profit." If you can translate the problem into finding the maximum or minimum value of a polynomial function, then you can use the methods of this chapter to solve it. The following examples illustrate the procedure.

EXAMPLE 1. A missile fired from a launching pad followed a path whose equation was $y = x - \dfrac{3.125}{10^6} x^2$, x and y being measurements in feet. Determine the maximum altitude attained by the missile.

Solution: *Plan:*   Use the methods of Section 8–7 to determine the maximum value of

$$f = \left\{ (x, y): \ y = x - \frac{3.125}{10^6} x^2 \right\} .$$

$$f(x) = x - \frac{3.125}{10^6} x^2$$

$$f'(x) = 1 - 2 \left(\frac{3.125}{10^6} \right) x = 0$$

$$\therefore f'(x) = 0 \text{ if and only if: } \frac{6.250x}{10^6} = 1$$

$$6.250x = 10^6 = 1000000$$

$$x = 160,000 = 16 \cdot 10^4$$

If $x < 16 \cdot 10^4$, $f'(x) > 1 - \dfrac{6.250}{10^6} \cdot 16 \cdot 10^4 > 1 - 1 = 0$, and $f(x)$ is increasing; if $x > 16 \cdot 10^4$, $f'(x) < 1 - 1 = 0$, and $f(x)$ is decreasing. Therefore, the maximum value of f is $f(16 \cdot 10^4) = 16 \cdot 10^4 - \dfrac{3.125}{10^6} (16 \cdot 10^4)^2 = 80,000.$

$\therefore$ the maximum altitude attained by the missile is 80,000 feet, **Answer.**

EXAMPLE 2.   Find the dimensions of the rectangular field of largest area which can be enclosed by a fence 500 yards long. What is the area of this field?

Solution:

1. Draw a figure illustrating the problem. Then, choose a variable such as x to represent one dimension, say the width, of the rectangle; express the other dimension in terms of x also. Note the 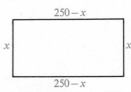 domain of x. Since the perimeter of the rectangle is 500 yards (Why?), twice the length is $500 - 2x$.

$\therefore$ length $= 250 - x$. Since the width and length of a rectangle must be positive numbers, $0 < x < 250$.

(*cont. on p. 310*)

2. Express $A(x)$, the area of the rectangle, in terms of x.

$A(x) = $ length $\times$ width
$\therefore A(x) = x(250 - x)$
$A(x) = 250x - x^2$

3. Use the method of Section 8–6 to find the relative maximum value.

$A'(x) = 250 - 2x = 0$
$\therefore 2x = 250$
$x = 125$

If $x < 125$, $A'(x) > 0$ and $A(x)$ is increasing; if $x > 125$, $A'(x) < 0$, and $A(x)$ is decreasing (Why?).

$\therefore$ over the interval $0 < x < 250$, the maximum value of $A(x)$ is $A(125)$.

4. Use the results of Step 3 to determine the required dimensions and area.

The rectangle of largest area with a perimeter of 500 yd. has:
width $(x) = 125$ yd.
length $(250 - x) = 250 - 125$, or 125 yd.
area $= (125)^2 = 15{,}625$ sq. yd., **Answer.**

As a check, note that the perimeter is $125 + 125 + 125 + 125 = 500$, as given.

The result of Example 2 illustrates a well-known fact: *the rectangle of greatest area with perimeter a is the square whose side has length $\dfrac{a}{4}$.* Can you guess which rectangle of given area has the smallest perimeter?

EXAMPLE 3. Determine the point on the graph of $s = \{(x, y): y = 2x^2\}$ which is nearest $T(9, 0)$.

Solution: 1. Let $P(x, 2x^2)$ be any point on the graph of s.

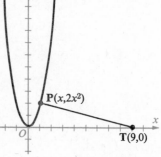

2. $d(\mathbf{P}, \mathbf{T})$
$= \sqrt{(x - 9)^2 + (2x^2)^2}$
$= \sqrt{4x^4 + x^2 - 18x + 81}$

3. $d(\mathbf{P}, \mathbf{T})$ will be least when its square is least; we locate the minimum of

$D(x) = [d(\mathbf{P}, \mathbf{T})]^2 = 4x^4 + x^2 - 18x + 81$
$D'(x) = 16x^3 + 2x - 18.$

Using synthetic substitution and the Factor Theorem, you find: $D'(x) = (x - 1)(16x^2 + 16x + 18).$

The single *real* value of x for which $D'(x) = 0$ is 1. (Why?)
If $x < 1$, $D'(x) < 0$, and $D(x)$ is decreasing; if $x > 1$,
$D'(x) > 0$, and $D(x)$ is increasing.

∴ the minimum value of $D(x)$ is $D(1)$.

4. $d(\mathbf{P}, \mathbf{T})$ is least when $\mathbf{P}$ is the point $(1, 2 \cdot 1^2)$, or $(1, 2)$,
Answer.

EXAMPLE 4. A bus company charging a 20-cent fare carries 8000 riders
daily. In anticipation of a fare rise, the management con-
ducts a survey which reveals that the line would lose 800
riders for each 5 cents added to the fare. Under these conditions what fare should be charged to maximize passenger-
revenue?

Solution: 1. Let x denote the number of 5-cent increases in the fare
($x \geq 0$).
Then, $20 + 5x = $ the resulting fare.
$8000 - 800x = $ the number of riders when the fare is
$20 + 5x$ cents.
The domain of x is $0 \leq x \leq 10$. (Why?)

2. Passenger-revenue, $p(x)$, is given by the formula:

$$p(x) = (20 + 5x)(8000 - 800x) \quad \text{(Why?)}$$
$$= 4000(4 + x)(10 - x)$$
$$p(x) = 4000(40 + 6x - x^2)$$

Proving that the maximum of $p(x)$ is $p(3)$ is left to you.

∴ the optimal fare is $20 + 3 \cdot 5$, or 35 cents, **Answer.**

The examples suggest the following steps in solving maximum-minimum
problems.

1. If appropriate, draw a figure to illustrate the problem. Then, select
a variable to use in expressing the quantities described in the
problem. Note restrictions on the values of the variable.

2. Express the quantity whose maximum or minimum is to be found in
terms of a function whose values are given by an expression in the
selected variable.

3. Use the methods of Section 8–6 to obtain the desired maximum or
minimum.

4. Use the result of Step 3 to obtain the number or numbers required in
the problem and verify that the proposed answer satisfies the given
conditions.

Exercises

1. If a stone is tossed upward with an initial velocity of 112 feet per second from a height of 700 feet above the surface of Mars, its height h above the surface t seconds later is given by $h = -5.6t^2 + 112t + 700$. Determine the maximum height reached by the stone.

2. In a 110-volt circuit having a resistance of 11 ohms, the power W in watts when a current I is flowing is given by $W = 110I - 11I^2$. Determine the maximum power that can be delivered in this circuit.

3. A real-estate operator estimates that the monthly profit p in dollars from a building s stories high is given by $p = -2s^2 + 92s$. What height building would he consider most profitable?

4. If a stone is tossed upward with an initial velocity of 72 feet per second from a height of 800 feet above the surface of the earth, its height h above the ground t seconds later is $-16t^2 + 72t + 800$. What is the maximum height reached by the stone?

5. Determine two numbers whose sum is 120 such that the product of the first and the square of the second is a maximum.

6. Determine two numbers whose sum is 36 such that the product of the first and the cube of the second is a maximum.

7. A rectangular field is to be enclosed by a fence and divided into two smaller rectangular fields by another fence. Find the dimensions of the field of greatest area that can be thus enclosed and partitioned with 1200 feet of fencing.

8. A homesteader is offered as much land as he can enclose in a rectangular plot, one side of which is to lie along the straight bank of river. Find the area of the largest such plot he can obtain, if he has 2400 feet of fencing to use and does not fence the river side of his plot.

9. The power W in watts developed in an electric circuit in which a current I is flowing is given by $W = EI - RI^2$, where E is the voltage and R the resistance. Determine the maximum power which can be delivered by a 220-volt circuit through a resistance of 5.5 ohms.

10. A fruit grower wishes to ship early in the season when prices are high and spoilage is low. He now has 15 tons on hand and estimates he can add 3 tons per week by waiting. His present profit is $300 per ton; and he estimates this will reduce by $20 per ton for each week he delays. In how many weeks should he ship to maximize his profit?

11. A set consists of the segments passing through the point $Q(3, 4)$, each having one endpoint on the x-axis and the other on the y-axis. Determine a function whose minimum is the length of the shortest segment in the set.

12. Of segments extending from the negative ray of the x-axis to the positive ray of the y-axis, let l be the length of the shortest which contains the point $(-2, 5)$. Find a function whose minimum is l.

13. What is the ratio of the height to the diameter of a right circular cylindrical can of greatest volume having a total surface area of 96π sq. cm.?

14. A rectangular sheet of aluminum measures 8' by 12'. Find the length of the sides of congruent squares to be cut from each corner so that an open box formed by turning up the flaps will have maximal volume.

15. What is the minimum velocity of a particle whose velocity with respect to time is given by $v = t(t - 6)$?

16. The velocity of a particle is expressed by $v = 2t^3 - 5t^2 + 6t - 15$. **(a)** What is the nonnegative time at which velocity is minimal? **(b)** What is the velocity at this time? Assume $0 \le t \le 5$.

C 17. Let **P** be a point on the positive x-axis, **Q** on the positive y-axis, and **O** the origin. Determine **P** and **Q** so that $\overline{PQ}$ contains the point (3, 5) and $\triangle POQ$ has maximum area.

18. Solve Exercise 17 if $\triangle POQ$ has minimum area.

19. Find the point **P**(x, y) of the graph of $p = \{(x, y): y = x^2 + 6\}$ which is nearest the point **Q**(21, 12). What is the length of $\overline{PQ}$?

20. What is the minimum distance from the point **Q**(15, 20) to the graph of $f = \{(x, y): y = x^2 - 4\}$? What is the slope of the line tangent to the graph of f at **P** if **P** is on f such that $d(\mathbf{P}, \mathbf{Q})$ is minimal?

21. The number n of units of a certain commodity sold at price p is given by $n = -0.1p^2 + 18p$. The revenue is the product of the selling price and the number of units sold. If production is limited to 100 units, find the maximum revenue for this commodity.

22. An airplane whose capacity is 100 passengers is to be chartered for a flight to Europe. The fare is to be $150 per person, if 60 people buy tickets. However, the airline agrees to reduce the fare for every passenger by $1 for each additional ticket sold. How many tickets should be sold to maximize the ticket revenue for this flight?

8–9 Approximating Zeros

If $f(x) = 2x^3 - 6x^2 + 6x - 3$, the Location Principle ensures that f has at least one zero between 1 and 2 because $f(1) = -1$ while $f(2) = 1$. However, since $f'(x) = 6x^2 - 12x + 6 = 6(x - 1)^2$ has no negative value, the graph of f rises from left to right (Figure 8–12), so that f has just one zero (call it r) between 1 and 2.

To discover how to find a better approximation of r, notice that Figure 8–12 indicates that the tangent line to the graph of f at **A**(2, 1) intersects the x-axis in the point **T**, which is near the point where the graph itself crosses the axis. This suggests that starting with the abscissa 2 of **A** as a first approximation of r, you can obtain a closer approximation by computing the abscissa of **T**, that is, the x-intercept of the tangent to the graph at **A**.

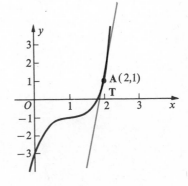

Figure 8–12

Now the line tangent to the graph of a function f at any of its points $[x_1, f(x_1)]$ has $f'(x_1)$ as its slope. (Why?) Hence, an equation of the tangent line is $y - f(x_1) = f'(x_1)[x - x_1]$. If you let x_2 denote the x-intercept of the tangent, you find

$$0 - f(x_1) = f'(x_1)[x_2 - x_1].$$

Therefore, provided $f'(x_1) \neq 0$,

$$x_2 = x_1 - \frac{f(x_1)}{f'(x_1)}.$$

Applying the preceding result to the polynomial $f(x) = 2x^3 - 6x^2 + 6x - 3$ with $x_1 = 2$, you find

$$x_2 = 2 - \frac{f(2)}{f'(2)} = 2 - \frac{1}{6} \doteq 1.8,$$

where $f(2)$ and $f'(2)$ have been computed by repeated synthetic division:

$$
\begin{array}{r|rrrr}
2 & 2 & -6 & 6 & -3 \\
  &   & 2 & -2 & 2 \quad 1 = f(2) \\
\hline
  & 2 & 2 & 6 = f'(2) &
\end{array}
$$

Accordingly, as a second approximation of r, we take $x_2 = 1.8$.

To obtain a third approximation x_3, or r, you can repeat the procedure with x_2 in place of x_1. You have

$$x_3 = x_2 - \frac{f(x_2)}{f'(x_2)} = 1.8 - \frac{f(1.8)}{f'(1.8)}.$$

$$
\begin{array}{r|rrrr}
1.8 & 2 & -6 & 6 & -3 \\
    &   & 3.6 & -4.32 & 3.024 \\
\hline
    & 2 & -2.4 & 1.68 & 0.024 = f(1.8) \\
    &   & 3.6 & 2.16 & \\
\hline
    & 2 & 1.2 & 3.84 = f'(1.8) &
\end{array}
$$

$$x_3 = 1.8 - \frac{0.024}{3.84} \doteq 1.7938.$$

Another repetition of the process yields x_4 with

$$x_4 = x_3 - \frac{f(x_3)}{f'(x_3)} = 1.7938 - \frac{f(1.7938)}{f'(1.7938)}.$$

The computation yields $x_4 = 1.7937005$, an approximation of r correct to eight significant figures.

The foregoing example illustrates a general procedure, called Newton's method, of approximating the irrational zeros of a function. The method is based on the assumption that starting with a fairly good estimate (call it x_1) of a zero r, you obtain successively closer approximations x_2, x_3, x_4, ... by using the recursion formula

$$x_{n+1} = x_n - \frac{f(x_n)}{f'(x_n)} \quad (n = 1, 2, 3, \ldots).$$

Figure 8–13 illustrates the repetitive pattern in the procedure. Notice that the process requires $f'(x)$ to be different from zero for x near r. In fact, as Figure 8–14 indicates, Newton's method may fail to give a better approximation to r if either f' or f'' has a zero near r.

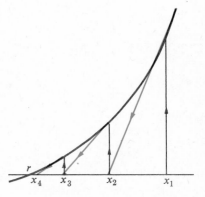

Figure 8–13

Therefore, in using Newton's method, you first find an interval which contains a zero of a given function f, but which does not contain a zero of f' or f''. Then, after selecting one of the endpoints of the interval to be x_1, you use the recursion formula to obtain successive approximations of r. A common practice is to repeat the procedure until two successive approximations agree to the required number of figures.

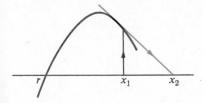

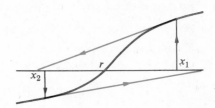

Figure 8–14

EXAMPLE. Find $\sqrt{3}$ to three decimal places.

Solution: *Plan:* Use Newton's method to approximate the positive root of $f(x) = x^2 - 3 = 0$.

$$f(x) = x^2 - 3,$$
$$f'(x) = 2x,$$
$$f''(x) = 2.$$

(cont. on p. 316)

Since $f(1.7) = (1.7)^2 - 3 = -0.11$ and $f(1.8) = (1.8)^2 - 3 = 0.24$, $1.7 < \sqrt{3} < 1.8$. Between 1.7 and 1.8, f' and f'' have no zeros. (Why?) Therefore, let $x_1 = 1.8$.

$$x_2 = x_1 - \frac{f(x_1)}{f'(x_1)} = x_1 - \frac{x_1^2 - 3}{2x_1}.$$

$$x_2 = \frac{1}{2}\left(x_1 + \frac{3}{x_1}\right) = \frac{1}{2}\left(1.8 + \frac{3}{1.8}\right) \doteq 1.733.$$

Similarly, $x_3 = \frac{1}{2}\left(x_2 + \frac{3}{x_2}\right)$

$$= \frac{1}{2}\left(1.733 + \frac{3}{1.733}\right) \doteq 1.73205.$$

Because $\dfrac{3}{1.73205} \doteq 1.73205161$, x_3 approximates $\sqrt{3}$ to at least six figures. (Why?) Hence, to three decimal places, $\sqrt{3} \doteq 1.732$, **Answer.**

$Kx^n = nkx^{n-1} = f'(x)$

Exercises

Use Newton's method to find the indicated root to four significant figures.

A
1. $\sqrt{5}$ 3. $\sqrt[3]{2}$ 5. $\sqrt[5]{-3}$
2. $\sqrt{17}$ 4. $\sqrt[3]{-7}$ 6. $\sqrt[4]{6}$

Find the indicated zero(s) of the given function to three decimal places.

7. $\{(x, y): y = x^3 - 3x + 1\}$, between 1 and 2.
8. $\{(x, y): y = x^3 + 2x - 20\}$, between 2 and 3.
9. $\{(x, y): y = x^3 - 3x^2 - 9x - 4\}$, between 0 and -1.
10. $\{(x, y): y = x^3 + 3x^2 - 2x - 5\}$, between -2 and -1.

B
11. All real zeros of $\{(x, y): y = x^3 + x^2 + 1\}$
12. All real zeros of $\{(x, y): y = x^3 + 7x - 7\}$
13. Prove that for any positive real number a, the recursion formula used in Newton's method of approximating $\sqrt{a}$ can be written in the form

$$x_{n+1} = \frac{1}{2}\left(x_n + \frac{a}{x_n}\right).$$

14. Prove that for any real number a, the recursion formula used in Newton's method of approximating $\sqrt[3]{a}$ can be written in the form

$$x_{n+1} = \frac{1}{3}\left(2x_n + \frac{a}{x_n^2}\right).$$

Chapter Summary

1. Information about a function may be obtained by plotting selected points of its graph. Synthetic substitution is useful in this process. However, this information is not complete since the graphs of many different functions contain any given finite set of points.

2. An important characteristic of functions is **continuity** at a point. A function continuous at each point for which it is defined is said to be a continuous function. Every polynomial function with domain $\mathcal{R}$ is **continuous**. A function f is continuous at c if and only if (1) f has a value at c, and (2) for *every* sequence $x_1, x_2, x_3, \ldots$ in its domain having c as its limit, the corresponding sequence $f(x_1), f(x_2), f(x_3), \ldots$ has $f(c)$ as its limit.

3. The **location principle** asserts that a continuous function f which is positive at a and negative at b has at least one zero between a and b. The fact that a polynomial function has an odd number of zeros between numbers a and b for which $f(a) > 0$ and $f(b) < 0$ is a conclusion based on the *location principle*. (Zeros of multiplicity m must be counted m times.) The converse of the location principle is not always true. The location principle, the rules for determining upper and lower bounds, synthetic substitution, and Descartes' Rule provide information about the existence of roots of a polynomial equation and suggest intervals in which they may be found.

4. The graph of every polynomial function has a tangent line at each of its points. If the graph of a continuous function has a tangent at $(c, f(c))$, then its **slope** is given by

$$\lim_{x \to c} \frac{f(x) - f(c)}{x - c}.$$

5. Every polynomial, $f(x)$, can be expanded in powers of $(x - c)$ through the use of the binomial theorem or repeated division by $x - c$. The coefficient of $(x - c)^1$ in this expansion is denoted by $f'(c)$ and gives the slope of the tangent to the graph of f at the point $(c, f(c))$. The **derivative** of the polynomial function f, where $f(x) = a_0 x^n + a_1 x^{n-1} + a_2^{n-2} + \cdots + a_{n-1}x + a_n$ is the polynomial function f', where $f'(x) = na_0 x^{n-1} + (n-1)a_1 x^{n-2} + (n-2)a_2 x^{n-3} + \cdots + a_{n-1}$. In particular, (1) if $f(x)$ is a constant, $f'(x) = 0$, the zero polynomial; (2) if $f(x) = a_0 x^n$, then $f'(x) = na_0 x^{n-1}$; and (3) the derivative of a polynomial function is the sum of the derivatives of each of its terms.

The **second derivative** f is denoted by f''. $\dfrac{f''(c)}{2}$ is the coefficient of $(x - c)^2$ in the expansion of $f(x)$ in powers of $x - c$.

6. On the graph of a continuous function f a point $(c, f(c))$ at which a horizontal tangent line exists, $(f'(c) = 0)$ is called a **critical point**. A necessary but not sufficient condition for $(c, f(c))$ to be a **relative maximum [minimum]** is $f'(x) = 0$. A function is said to be **concave downward [upward]** at a maximum [minimum]. A necessary but not sufficient condition for a point $(c, f(c))$ to be an **inflection point** is $f''(c) = 0$.

7. The relationships of relative maxima and minima to the derivatives of a function are useful in many applied problems.

8. Newton's method can be used to approximate irrational zeros of a function.

Chapter Test

8-1   1.   Sketch the graph of the function whose domain is $\Re$ and whose values
           are given by $f(x) = x^3 - 4x^2 - 5$.

8-2   2.   Show that the function whose domain is $\Re$ and whose values are given
           by $f(x) = \dfrac{x^2 + x - 12}{x + 4}$ is continuous at $x = 2$ but is discontinuous
           at $x = -4$.

8-3   3.   Show that the function defined in $\Re$ by $f(x) = -x^3 - 2x^2 + x - 3$
           has at most one real zero; find two consecutive integers between which
           it lies.

8-4   4.   By using the expression $\lim\limits_{x \to c} \dfrac{f(x) - f(c)}{x - c}$ determine (**a**) the slope, and

           (**b**) the equation, of the line tangent to the graph of

           $$f = \{(x, y): y = 3x^2 - 10x\}$$

           at the point with abscissa -2 on the graph.

8-5   5.   Expand the polynomial $p(x) = 5x^3 - 3x^2 + 2$ in powers of $x - 4$.

8-6   6.   **a.** Find f' for the function defined by $f(x) = x^4 - 4x^3 - 20x^2 + 17$.

           b. Determine the equation of the tangent to the graph of f at the
           point whose abscissa is 1.

In exercises 7–9 let values of f with domain $\Re$ be defined by the polynomial
$f(x) = x^4 - 4x^3 - 20x^2 + 17$.

8-7   7.   Find the numbers x for which f has critical points and tell whether
           each critical point is a relative maximum, relative minimum, or neither.

      8.   Find the inflection points of f.

      9.   Sketch the graph of f, indicating each critical point, each point of
           inflection, and each real zero. For each real zero that is not an integer
           give a pair of consecutive integers between which it lies.

8-8   10. A bullet is fired vertically with a velocity of $v_0 = 1440$ ft. per second.
           Find the maximum altitude reached by the bullet and the time in seconds
           required to reach this altitude if the formula $s = v_0 t - 16t^2$ gives the
           vertical distance the bullet travels.

8-9   11. Approximate to the nearest hundredth the greatest real root of
           $x^3 - 2x - 5 = 0$.

Reading List

DICKSON, L. E. *New First Course in the Theory of Equations.* New York: John Wiley & Sons, Inc., 1939.

HESSE, ALLEN R. *Iterative Methods in High School Algebra.* The Mathematics Teacher, vol. 57, pp. 16–19, 1964.

HIGHT, DONALD W. *The Limit Concept in the SMSG Revised Sample Textbooks.* The Mathematics Teacher, vol. 57, pp. 194–199, April, 1964.

JOHNSON, RICHARD E., and FRED L. KIOKEMEISTER. *Calculus.* Boston: Allyn and Bacon, Inc., 1959.

KATTSOFF, LOUIS O. *Polynomials and Functions.* Mathematics Magazine, vol. 33, pp. 157–160, 1960.

KENT, JAMES R. F. *Differential and Integral Calculus.* Boston: Houghton Mifflin Co., 1960.

KRISHNAIAH, P. V. *A Simple Proof of Descartes' Rule of Signs.* Mathematics Magazine, vol. 36, p. 190, 1963.

LEAKE, LOWELL, JR. *An Iterative Application for Elementary Algebra.* The Mathematics Teacher, vol. 57, pp. 12–15, 1964.

NYGAARD, P. H. *Iteration Solution Methods.* The Mathematics Teacher, vol. 57, pp. 8–11, 1964.

PROTTER, M. H., and C. B. MORREY, JR. *Calculus with Analytic Geometry: A First Course.* Reading, Mass.: Addison-Wesley Publishing Co., Inc., 1963.

SAWYER, W. W. *What Is Calculus About?* New York: Random House, Inc., 1961.

SPRAGUE, ATHERTON, H. *A Note on δ and ε.* American Mathematical Monthly, vol. 67, pp. 576–578, 1960.

THOMAS, GEORGE B., JR. *Elements of Calculus and Analytic Geometry.* Reading, Mass.: Addison-Wesley Publishing Co., Inc., 1959.

Niels Henrik Abel

Today, because of the enormous expense of many of our important research projects, the social responsibility of the government toward scientists and scientific development has become generally accepted. Moreover, there has been a growing tendency for scientists of different nations to share their knowledge in working toward common goals. These conditions, however, did not exist during the lifetime of the Norwegian mathematician Niels Henrik Abel (1802–1829), who fought throughout his working years against poverty and professional jealousies.

At eighteen, after the death of his father, Abel was faced with the support of his mother and six brothers and sisters. He was able to finish his university studies, though, and a few years later was sponsored by the Norwegian government on a trip to talk with European mathematicians and to establish his own mathematical reputation. Unfortunately this trip proved disappointing to Abel, for his works were largely ignored or dismissed by leading mathematicians of the day, among them Gauss and Cauchy. He returned penniless and ill to Kristiania, Norway, to find that he had not been appointed to a university position there as he had expected. He died a short time later, before receiving word that he had been appointed to a professorship at the University of Berlin.

It has been said that Abel left mathematicians enough to keep them busy for 500 years. One of his important fields of research was group theory. A group, you may remember, is an abstract system consisting of undefined elements, $a, b, c, \ldots$, of a set S and a binary operation $\circ$, such that for all $a, b, c \in S$, (1) $a \circ b \in S$; (2) $(a \circ b) \circ c = a \circ (b \circ c)$; (3) there is a unique element e, such that $a \circ e = e \circ a = a$; (4) for each element a, there is an element a', such that $a \circ a' = a' \circ a = e$.

For example, the set $G = \{1, -1, i, -i\}$, with the operation of multiplication, forms a group. Check to see that conditions 1–4 are satisfied. Groups which are commutative, that is, which have the property that $a \circ b = b \circ a$ for all $a, b \in S$, are called Abelian groups. Is G Abelian? Can you think of a group which is not Abelian?

321

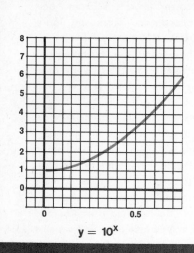

$$y = 10^x$$

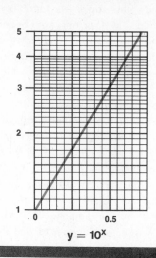

$$y = 10^x$$

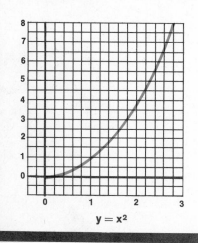

$$y = x^2$$

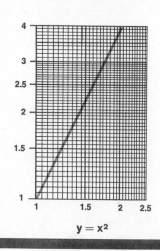

$$y = x^2$$

On semilogarithmic graph paper, the vertical axis has a logarithmic scale and the horizontal axis has a uniform scale. On logarithmic graph paper, both axes have logarithmic scales. Plotted on semilogarithmic and logarithmic paper, respectively, the graphs of $y = 10^x$ and $y = x^2$ are straight lines.

Exponential and Logarithmic Functions

You are already familiar with the definition and laws of operations of powers of real numbers in case the exponents involved are nonnegative integers. Now you will see how the definition can be extended to include all real numbers as exponents. It is interesting to note that the laws of exponents remain valid after the extension. No less important, though, is the fact that the extension leads to functions that are extremely useful in mathematical models of the physical world.

EXPONENTIAL FUNCTIONS

9-1 Rational Exponents

In Chapter 3, you studied the laws of exponents for nonnegative integral exponents and real bases. These laws, which are summarized below, will now guide you in defining b^x, first for the remaining integral exponents x ($b \neq 0$), and then for all rational exponents x ($b > 0$).

1. $b^m b^n = b^{m+n}$

2. $(ab)^m = a^m b^m$

3. $(b^m)^n = b^{mn}$

4. $\dfrac{b^m}{b^n} = b^{m-n}, \quad b \neq 0$

5. $\dfrac{b^m}{b^n} = \dfrac{1}{b^{n-m}}, \quad b \neq 0$

6. $\left(\dfrac{a}{b}\right)^m = \dfrac{a^m}{b^m}, \quad b \neq 0.$

7. If $b \notin \{-1, 0, 1\}$, then $b^m = b^n$ if and only if $m = n$.

8. If $a > 0$, $b > 0$, and $m \neq 0$, then $a^m = b^m$ if and only if $a = b$.

9. If $b \neq 0$, $b^0 = 1$.

Now consider the fraction $\dfrac{3^2}{3^7} = \dfrac{1}{3^{7-2}} = \dfrac{1}{3^5}$. If Law 4 were to hold

for $m < n$, then you would have $\dfrac{3^2}{3^7} = 3^{2-7} = 3^{-5}$. This suggests that

you write $3^{-5} = \dfrac{1}{3^5}$ and that you make the following general definition.

If $n \in N$ and $b \in \mathcal{R}, b \neq 0$, then $b^{-n} = \dfrac{1}{b^n}$; that is, b^{-n} is the reciprocal of b^n.

Under this definition, the laws of exponents hold for *all* integral powers, in accordance with the following theorem.

THEOREM   For all nonzero real numbers a and b and for all integers m and n, Laws 1–9 (page 323) are valid.

Proof of Law 2: You already know that Law 2 holds in case $m \geq 0$ (Why?). If $m < 0$, $-m > 0$; and

$$(ab)^m = \frac{1}{(ab)^{-m}} \qquad \text{Definition of a negative power.}$$

$$= \frac{1}{a^{-m}b^{-m}} \qquad \text{Law 2 for positive exponents.}$$

$$= \frac{1}{a^{-m}}\frac{1}{b^{-m}} \qquad \text{Corollary 4, page 42.}$$

$$= a^m b^m \qquad \text{Definition of a negative power.}$$

You will be asked to prove the other laws in the exercises on page 327. If both m and n are involved in a law, then several cases must be treated, for m and n can separately be positive, zero, or negative.

Let us turn now to a consideration of rational exponents, in general. If Law 1 were to hold for all rational exponents, then it would have to be true, for example, that $5^{\frac{3}{2}} \cdot 5^{\frac{3}{2}} = 5^{\frac{3}{2}+\frac{3}{2}} = 5^3$. On the other hand, you know that $(\sqrt{5})^3(\sqrt{5})^3 = 5^3$. This suggests that you write $5^{\frac{3}{2}} = (\sqrt{5})^3$. Of course, for every positive integer q and every positive real number b, you know that $\sqrt[q]{b}$ denotes a unique positive real number (Theorem, page 114). These considerations lead to the following general definition in which the symbol $\mathcal{R}^+$ designates *the set of positive real numbers.*

If $p \in J, q \in N,$ and $b \in \mathcal{R}^+$, then $b^{\frac{p}{q}} = (\sqrt[q]{b})^p$.

Because $(\sqrt[q]{b})^p = \sqrt[q]{b^p}$ (Theorem, page 114), you can also write

$$b^{\frac{p}{q}} = \sqrt[q]{b^p}, \quad \text{or} \quad (b^{\frac{p}{q}})^q = b^p.$$

Furthermore, because $\sqrt[q]{b^q} = b$ (Why?), $(\sqrt[q]{b^q})^p = b^p$; or

$$(b^q)^{\frac{p}{q}} = b^p.$$

These facts have been restated as part 1 of the following theorem.

THEOREM   If b denotes a positive real number, p and m denote integers, and q denotes a positive integer, then

1. $(b^{\frac{p}{q}})^q = b^p = (b^q)^{\frac{p}{q}}$;

2. $(b^{\frac{p}{q}})^{qm} = b^{pm} = (b^{qm})^{\frac{p}{q}}$.

Part 2 of this theorem results from using part 1 and the laws of integral exponents. Thus:

$$(b^{\frac{p}{q}})^{qm} = [(b^{\frac{p}{q}})^q]^m = [b^p]^m = b^{pm};$$

$$[b^{qm}]^{\frac{p}{q}} = [(b^m)^q]^{\frac{p}{q}} = (b^m)^p = b^{mp} = b^{pm}.$$

As asserted in the following theorem, the laws of exponents hold also for rational powers.

THEOREM   For all positive real numbers a and b, all integers m and p, and all positive integers n and q:

1. $b^{\frac{m}{n}}b^{\frac{p}{q}} = b^{\frac{mq+np}{nq}}$

4. $\dfrac{b^{\frac{m}{n}}}{b^{\frac{p}{q}}} = b^{\frac{mq-np}{nq}}$

2. $(ab)^{\frac{m}{n}} = a^{\frac{m}{n}}b^{\frac{m}{n}}$

5. $\dfrac{b^{\frac{m}{n}}}{b^{\frac{p}{q}}} = \dfrac{1}{b^{\frac{np-mq}{nq}}}$

3. $(b^{\frac{m}{n}})^{\frac{p}{q}} = b^{\frac{mp}{nq}}$

6. $\left(\dfrac{a}{b}\right)^{\frac{m}{n}} = \dfrac{a^{\frac{m}{n}}}{b^{\frac{m}{n}}}$

7. If $b \neq 1$, then $b^{\frac{m}{n}} = b^{\frac{p}{q}}$ if and only if $\dfrac{m}{n} = \dfrac{p}{q}$.

8. If $\dfrac{p}{q} \neq 0$, then $a^{\frac{p}{q}} = b^{\frac{p}{q}}$ if and only if $a = b$.

Proof of Law 1: Since $b > 0$, the definition of a rational power implies that $b^{\frac{m}{n}}$, $b^{\frac{p}{q}}$ and $b^{\frac{mq+np}{nq}}$ all denote positive real numbers. (Why?) Hence, by Law 8 for integral exponents, Law 1 for rational exponents is valid if and only if

$$(b^{\frac{m}{n}}b^{\frac{p}{q}})^{nq} = (b^{\frac{mq+np}{nq}})^{nq}.$$

Proving the validity of the preceding equation constitutes Exercise 28, page 327.

EXAMPLE. Verify that (a) $25^{\frac{2}{4}} = 25^{\frac{1}{2}}$; and (b) $(8^{-\frac{2}{3}})^3 = \frac{1}{64}$.

Solution: (a) $25^{\frac{2}{4}} = (\sqrt[4]{25})^2 = (\sqrt{5})^2 = 5$, $25^{\frac{1}{2}} = (\sqrt{25})^1 = 5^1 = 5$.

(b) $(8^{-\frac{2}{3}})^3 = [(\sqrt[3]{8})^{-2}]^3 = (2^{-2})^3 = (\frac{1}{4})^3 = \frac{1}{64}$.

∴ (a) $25^{\frac{2}{4}} = 25^{\frac{1}{2}}$; (b) $(8^{-\frac{2}{3}})^3 = \frac{1}{64}$, **Answer.**

In the definition of $b^{\frac{p}{q}}$ notice that b has been restricted to being a positive number. Without this restriction, some of the laws of exponents fail to hold. (See Exercise 36, page 327.)

Exercises

Express as a numeral or as a numeral times a product of powers of variables. State replacement sets for any variables involved.

A

1. $3^5 \cdot 3^{-2}$

2. $4^0 \cdot 2^3$

3. $\dfrac{5^2}{5^3}$

4. $7^m \cdot 7^{-n}$

5. $(x^3)(2x)(xy^2)^{-1}$

6. $(t^2)(2t)^3(2^2t^0)$

7. $\dfrac{(-r^2s)^3}{(2rs^{-1})^2}$

8. $(x^{-2}y^{-3})^{-4}$

Using only positive exponents, restate each expression.

9. $(x^2y^{-3})^{-1}$

10. $\dfrac{2^{-1}r^{-2}s}{3r^2s^3}$

11. $(x + y)^{-1} - x^{-1} - y^{-1}$

12. $1 + r^{-1} - \dfrac{1}{1 + r}$

Evaluate.

13. $8^{-\frac{2}{3}}$

14. $0.25^{\frac{3}{2}}$

15. $9^{\frac{1}{2}} - 9^{-\frac{1}{2}}$

16. $(5^{-\frac{1}{2}})^2 + 3^{\frac{0}{2}}$

Solve for x.

17. $2^x = 4^{2x-1}$

19. $2^x = 2^{-x}$

18. $x^{-\frac{2}{3}} = 4$

20. $(x + 3)^{\frac{1}{2}} = (\frac{1}{8})^{\frac{1}{3}}$

Assume that, for all nonzero real numbers a and b, the following statements are true for all nonnegative integers m and n. Prove that they are true for all integers m and n.

B

21. $b^m b^n = b^{m+n}$

22. $(b^m)^n = b^{mn}$

24. $\dfrac{b^m}{b^n} = \dfrac{1}{b^{n-m}}$

23. $\dfrac{b^m}{b^n} = b^{m-n}$

25. $\left(\dfrac{a}{b}\right)^m = \dfrac{a^m}{b^m}$

26. If $b \notin \{-1, 1\}$, then $b^m = b^n$ if and only if $m = n$.

27. If $a > 0$, $b > 0$, $m \neq 0$, and $a^m = b^m$, then $a = b$.

Assume that, for all positive real numbers a and b, and for all integers m and p, the following statements are true for $n = 1$ and $q = 1$. Prove that they are true for all positive integers n and q. (*Hint:* Consider appropriate powers of the two members of each equation.)

28. $b^{\frac{m}{n}} b^{\frac{p}{q}} = b^{\frac{mq+np}{nq}}$

32. $\dfrac{b^{\frac{m}{n}}}{b^{\frac{p}{q}}} = \dfrac{1}{b^{\frac{np-mq}{nq}}}$

29. $(ab)^{\frac{m}{n}} = a^{\frac{m}{n}} b^{\frac{m}{n}}$

30. $(b^{\frac{m}{n}})^{\frac{p}{q}} = b^{\frac{mp}{nq}}$

33. $\left(\dfrac{a}{b}\right)^{\frac{m}{n}} = \dfrac{a^{\frac{m}{n}}}{b^{\frac{m}{n}}}$

31. $\dfrac{b^{\frac{m}{n}}}{b^{\frac{p}{q}}} = b^{\frac{mq-np}{nq}}$

34. If $b \neq 1$, then $b^{\frac{m}{n}} = b^{\frac{p}{q}}$ if and only if $\dfrac{m}{n} = \dfrac{p}{q}$.

$\left(\textit{Hint:} \dfrac{m}{n} = \dfrac{p}{q} \text{ if and only if } mq = np.\right)$

35. If $\dfrac{p}{q} \neq 0$, then $a^{\frac{p}{q}} = b^{\frac{p}{q}}$ if and only if $a = b$.

36. If $(-1)^{\frac{1}{2}} = \sqrt{-1} = i$, prove that $(-1 \cdot -1)^{\frac{1}{2}} \neq (-1)^{\frac{1}{2}}(-1)^{\frac{1}{2}}$.

9–2 The Function $\{(x, y): y = 2^x\}$

For every rational number x, you can identify the unique real number denoted by 2^x. For example, $2^{-2} = \dfrac{1}{2^2} = \dfrac{1}{4}$, $2^{-0.5} = \dfrac{1}{2^{\frac{1}{2}}} = \dfrac{1}{\sqrt{2}}$, $2^{1.5} = 2^{\frac{3}{2}} = 2\sqrt{2}$, and so on. This means that you have defined a function $f = \{(x, y): y = 2^x\}$ whose domain is the set R of *rational numbers*.

x	-2	-1.5	-1	-0.5	0	0.5	1	1.5	2
2^x	0.250	0.354	0.500	0.707	1.000	1.414	2.000	2.828	4.000

Using the approximation $\sqrt{2} \doteq 1.414$, you can verify that the accompanying table gives the values of this function to three decimal places for values of x from -2 to 2 at intervals of length 0.5.

Figure 9–1 shows the ordered pairs in this table as coordinates of points of the plane and suggests several properties of f.

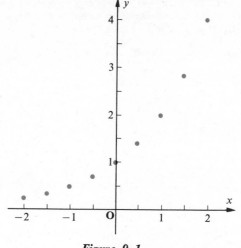

Figure 9–1

1. If $x \in R$, $2^x > 0$.
2. If $x \in R$ and $x > 0$, then $2^x > 1$.
3. If $x_1 \in R$, $x_2 \in R$, and $x_2 > x_1$, then $2^{x_2} > 2^{x_1}$.

To prove that these properties hold for f, let $x = \dfrac{p}{q}$ where p denotes an integer, and q, a positive integer.

1. Since $2 > 0$, $2^p > 0$. (Why?) Hence, by definition, $\sqrt[q]{2^p} > 0$. Therefore, since $2^{\frac{p}{q}} = \sqrt[q]{2^p}$, $2^{\frac{p}{q}} > 0$.

2. Because $\dfrac{p}{q} > 0$, $p > 0$. (Why?) Now, suppose that $\sqrt[q]{2} \leq 1$. Then (Exercise 8, page 73), $2 = (\sqrt[q]{2})^q \leq 1$. But the statement "$2 \leq 1$" contradicts the fact that $2 > 1$. Hence, $\sqrt[q]{2} > 1$, and, by Exercise 6, page 73, $2^{\frac{p}{q}} = (\sqrt[q]{2})^p > 1$.

3. This property is a consequence of (1) and (2); for the distributive property and Law 4 of exponents ensures that

$$2^{x_2} - 2^{x_1} = 2^{x_1}(2^{x_2 - x_1} - 1)$$

where $x_2 - x_1 > 0$.

By (1), $2^{x_1} > 0$. Property 2 implies that

$$2^{x_2-x_1} > 1,$$

so that

$$2^{x_2-x_1} - 1 > 0.$$

Hence,

$$2^{x_2} - 2^{x_1} > 2^{x_1} \cdot 0,$$

or

$$2^{x_2} > 2^{x_1}.$$

Any function f having the property that $f(x_2) > f(x_1)$ whenever x_1 and x_2 are elements in its domain such that $x_2 > x_1$ is called an **increasing function**. Thus, $\{(x, y): y = 2^x, x \in R\}$ is an increasing function all of whose values are positive numbers. By plotting additional points of the graph of f (Figure 9–2), you may guess still another property of f.

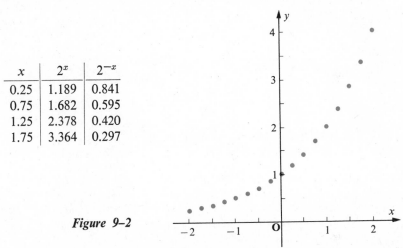

x	2^x	2^{-x}
0.25	1.189	0.841
0.75	1.682	0.595
1.25	2.378	0.420
1.75	3.364	0.297

Figure 9–2

4. If $r_1, r_2, r_3, \ldots$ is a convergent sequence of rational numbers whose limit is the rational number r, then the sequence $2^{r_1}, 2^{r_2}, 2^{r_3}, \ldots$ is a convergent sequence with 2^r as its limit. In symbols, **if $\lim_{n \to \infty} r_n = r$, then $\lim_{n \to \infty} 2^{r_n} = 2^r$**; or, more briefly, **$\lim_{r_n \to r} 2^{r_n} = 2^r$**. For example, if this property holds, then $\lim_{n \to \infty} 2^{\frac{1}{n}} = 2^0 = 1$ and $\lim_{n \to \infty} 2^{(1-10^{-n})} = 2^1 = 2$.

Proving Property 4 will be postponed until Section 9–3. Meanwhile, however, this property suggests how to define 2^x in case x is an irrational number. To illustrate the definition, let us consider $2^{\sqrt{3}}$. Suppose that $r_1, r_2, r_3, \ldots$ is the sequence of rational numbers

$$1, 1.7, 1.73, 1.732, 1.7320, 1.73205, \ldots$$

whose successive terms are obtained by taking more and more places in the decimal representing $\sqrt{3}$. This sequence is nondecreasing, its terms are all less than the rational number 3, and it has $\sqrt{3}$ as its limit.

Now consider the infinite sequence

$$2^{r_1}, 2^{r_2}, 2^{r_3}, \ldots.$$

Property 3 (page 328) implies that this sequence of powers of 2 is non-decreasing, and that each of its terms is less than 2^3. (Why?) Hence, the Axiom of Completeness guarantees that $\lim\limits_{n\to\infty} 2^{r_n}$ is a real number. You define $2^{\sqrt{3}}$ to be this limit.

In general, if c is *any* irrational number, and $r_1, r_2, r_3, \ldots$ is a nondecreasing convergent sequence of rational numbers whose limit is c, then 2^{r_1}, $2^{r_2}, 2^{r_3}, \ldots$ is a bounded nondecreasing sequence which, by the Axiom of Completeness, has a limit. You identify this limit with 2^c. Thus,

$$\text{if } \lim_{n\to\infty} r_n = c$$

where $r_1 \le r_2 \le r_3 \ldots$ and $r_n \in R$ for $n = 1, 2, 3, \ldots$, then

$$2^c = \lim_{n\to\infty} 2^{r_n}.$$

It can be proved (Section 9–3) that if $s_1, s_2, s_3, \ldots$ is any other convergent sequence of rational numbers with c as limit, then $\lim\limits_{s_n\to c} 2^{s_n}$ also exists and equals 2^c. Hence, in defining 2^c, you can actually use any sequence of rational numbers converging to c.

You have now associated a unique real number 2^x with each real number x. This means that you have defined a function which is denoted by $\exp_2$ (read "exponential to the base 2") where

$$\exp_2 = \{(x, y)\colon y = 2^x, x \in \mathcal{R}\}.$$

Thus, $\exp_2(x) = 2^x$.

Are the laws of exponents valid for the values 2^x of $\exp_2$? To show that they are, you use the limit theorem stated on page 97.

EXAMPLE 1. Prove that for every pair of real numbers x and v, $2^x 2^v = 2^{x+v}$.

Proof: Let $r_1, r_2, r_3, \ldots$ and $s_1, s_2, s_3, \ldots$ be nondecreasing convergent sequences of rational numbers such that

$$\lim_{n\to\infty} r_n = x \quad \text{and} \quad \lim_{n\to\infty} s_n = v.$$

Then

$$2^x 2^v = (\lim_{n\to\infty} 2^{r_n})(\lim_{n\to\infty} 2^{s_n}) \qquad \text{Definition of } 2^c.$$

$$= \lim_{n\to\infty} (2^{r_n} 2^{s_n}). \qquad \text{Theorem, page 97.}$$

$$\therefore 2^x 2^v = \lim_{n\to\infty} 2^{r_n + s_n}. \qquad \text{Law 1 of rational exponents.}$$

But $\lim_{n\to\infty} (r_n + s_n) = x + v.$ Theorem, page 97.

$$\therefore 2^x 2^v = 2^{x+v}. \qquad \text{Definition of } 2^c.$$

Exercises 15–18, page 333, require you to prove other laws of exponents for the values of $\exp_2$.

You can also verify that properties 1–3 (page 328) hold for $\exp_2$.

EXAMPLE 2. Prove that if x denotes a positive real number, then $2^x > 1$.

Proof: Since $x > 0$, you can determine a nondecreasing sequence $r_1, r_2, r_3, \ldots$ of *positive* rational numbers having x as its limit. (Why?) Since $r_1 \le r_n$, $2^{r_1} \le 2^{r_n}$ for $n = 1, 2, 3, \ldots$ (Why?) Hence, $2^{r_1} \le \lim_{n\to\infty} 2^{r_n} = 2^x$. Because $0 < r_1$,

$$0 < \frac{r_1}{2} < r_1. \quad \text{(Why?)} \quad \text{Hence, } 1 < 2^{\frac{r_1}{2}} < 2^{r_1}. \quad \text{(Why?)}$$

Therefore, by the transitive property of order, $1 < 2^x$.

Proving that $2^x > 0$ for every real number x and, therefore, that $\exp_2$ is an increasing function is left to you. Property 4 (page 329) can also be extended to $\exp_2$; thus, $\exp_2$ is continuous at each point of its domain $\mathcal{R}$. (See Section 9–3.)

Figure 9–3 on the following page shows the graph of $\exp_2$ over part of its domain and illustrates the properties of $\exp_2$ that we have already recognized. It also suggests that the range of $\exp_2$ is $\mathcal{R}^+$ (Exercise 21, page 333), and that at each of its points the graph is concave upward.

The following theorem summarizes the facts you now know about $\exp_2$.

THEOREM The function $\exp_2 = \{(x, y): y = 2^x, x \in \mathcal{R}\}$ is continuous and increasing. Its range is $\mathcal{R}^+$. Its values satisfy the laws of exponents; and if $x > 0$, $\exp_2 (x) > 1$.

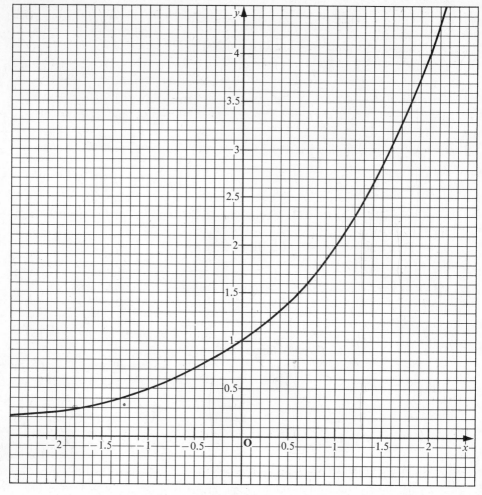

Figure 9–3

Exercises

In Exercises 1–8, use the graph of $\exp_2 = \{(x, y): \; y = 2^x\}$ shown in Figure 9–3 above.

Estimate to one decimal place:

1. $2^{0.6}$ **3.** $2^{1.9}$ **5.** $2^{\sqrt{2}}$

2. $2^{-1.8}$ **4.** $2^{-0.1}$ **6.** $2^{\sqrt{3}}$

Estimate z to one decimal place:

7. $2^z = 2.5$ **8.** $2^z = 0.8$

B　**9.** Using the fact that $2^{4.6} = 2^4 \cdot 2^{0.6}$, compute $2^{4.6}$ to one decimal place.

10. Using the fact that $4^{0.8} = (2^2)^{0.8}$, compute $4^{0.8}$ to one decimal place.

In Exercises 11–14, use the entries in the tables on pages 328 and 329 to determine several ordered pairs of the given function; then, sketch its graph.

11. $\{(x, y): y = 2^{2x}, -1 \le x \le 1\}$

12. $\{(x, y): y = 2 \cdot 2^x, -2 \le x \le 2\}$

13. $\{(x, y): y = 2^{x+2}, -2 \le x \le 2\}$

14. $\left\{(x, y): y = \dfrac{2^x}{2}, -2 \le x \le 2\right\}$

Given that each statement is true for all rational numbers x and v, prove that it is also true for all real numbers x and v.

C　**15.** $(2^x)^v = 2^{xv}$　　　　**16.** $\dfrac{2^x}{2^v} = 2^{x-v}$　　　　**17.** $\dfrac{2^x}{2^v} = \dfrac{1}{2^{v-x}}$

18. $2^x = 2^v$ if and only if $x = v$.

19. $2^x > 0$.

20. If $v > x$, then $2^v > 2^x$.

21. Prove: (**a**) If M is any positive number, there exist real numbers x and v such that $2^x \ge M$ and $2^v \le M$. (*Hint:* See Exercises 22 and 26, page 74).

　　　　(**b**) Use the result of (**a**) and the fact that $\exp_2$ is a continuous function to explain why $\mathcal{R}^+$ is the range of $\exp_2$.

22. The number of bacteria in a certain culture was observed to double every day. If there were 10^5 present at the first count, how many were there (**a**) after two days, (**b**) after five days, (**c**) one day before the first count?

In Exercises 23 and 24, assume the number of bacteria in the culture of Exercise 22 to be given by the formula $N = 10^5 \cdot 2^t$, where t is measured in days.

23. Approximately how many bacteria were present after $\frac{3}{2}$ days?

24. If there were N_0 bacteria after t_0 days, how many were present t days later?

C　**9–3 Continuity of Exp₂ (*Optional*)**

An important assertion to be used in proving that $\exp_2$ is a continuous function is the following proposition. You will recognize its first corollary as a statement that we guessed in Section 9–2 (Property 4, page 329).

| THEOREM | If $r_1, r_2, r_3, \ldots$ is a convergent sequence of rational numbers such that $\lim\limits_{n \to \infty} r_n = 0$, then $\lim\limits_{n \to \infty} 2^{r_n} = 1$. |

Proof: *Plan:* Show that for every positive number h, $0 < h < 1$, you can choose a positive integer M such that

$$|2^{r_n} - 1| < h \quad \text{whenever } n > M.$$

Let h be any positive real number less than 1. The theorem stated and proved on page 72 ensures that, for every positive integer p, $(1 + h)^p \geq 1 + ph$. When you apply this result with $p \geq \dfrac{1}{h}$, you discover that

$$(1 + h)^p \geq 1 + \frac{1}{h} \cdot h = 2;$$

$\therefore$ if $0 < h < 1, p \in J,$ and $p \geq \dfrac{1}{h}$,

then

$$2 \leq (1 + h)^p.$$

$$\therefore 2^{\frac{1}{p}} \leq 1 + h. \quad \text{(Ex. 2, page 337.)}$$

Now since $\lim\limits_{n \to \infty} r_n = 0$, the terms in the sequence $r_1, r_2, r_3, \ldots$ must all eventually lie within an interval of length $\dfrac{2}{p}$ centered at 0; that is, there must exist a positive integer M so great that

$$-\frac{1}{p} < r_n < \frac{1}{p} \qquad \text{for all } n > M.$$

Because $2^0 = 1$, and r_n and $\dfrac{1}{p}$ denote rational numbers, you can use Properties 2 and 3, page 328, in case $r_n \geq 0$, to discover that $1 \leq 2^{r_n} < 2^{\frac{1}{p}} \leq 1 + h$, for $n > M$. Thus, if $r_n \geq 0$, then

$$1 \leq 2^{r_n} < 1 + h, \qquad\qquad n > M.$$

In case $r_n < 0, -r_n > 0$, and you find

$$1 < 2^{-r_n} < 1 + h, \qquad\qquad n > M.$$

$$\therefore \frac{1}{1 + h} < 2^{r_n} < 1, \qquad\qquad n > M.$$

But

$$1 - h < \frac{1}{1 + h} \cdot \quad \text{(Why?)}$$

Thus, if $r_n < 0$, then

$$1 - h < 2^{r_n} < 1, \qquad\qquad n > M.$$

Since $1 - h < 1 < 1 + h$, the two inequalities printed in red imply that for each r_n such that $n > M$,

$$1 - h < 2^{r_n} < 1 + h.$$

Hence, for every positive real number $h < 1$, you can find a positive integer M such that

$$|2^{r_n} - 1| < h, \qquad\qquad n > M.$$

This fact means that $\lim\limits_{n \to \infty} 2^{r_n} = 1$.

COROLLARY 1. If r is a rational number and if $r_1, r_2, r_3, \ldots$ is any convergent sequence of rational numbers such that

$$\lim_{n \to \infty} r_n = r, \quad \text{then} \quad \lim_{n \to \infty} 2^{r_n} = 2^r.$$

Proof: Since $\quad \lim\limits_{n \to \infty} r_n = r, \lim\limits_{n \to \infty} (r_n - r) = 0. \quad$ (Why?)

Hence, $\quad \lim\limits_{n \to \infty} 2^{r_n - r} = 1.$

But $\qquad 2^{r_n - r} = \dfrac{2^{r_n}}{2^r} \quad$ (Why?)

and $\qquad \lim\limits_{n \to \infty} 2^{r_n - r} = \dfrac{\lim\limits_{n \to \infty} 2^{r_n}}{2^r}$

$\therefore \dfrac{\lim\limits_{n \to \infty} 2^{r_n}}{2^r} = 1, \quad$ and

$$\lim_{n \to \infty} 2^{r_n} = 2^r.$$

COROLLARY 2. Let c be an irrational number and $r_1, r_2, r_3, \ldots$ a nondecreasing sequence of rational numbers such that

$$\lim_{n \to \infty} r_n = c \quad \text{and} \quad \lim_{n \to \infty} 2^{r_n} = 2^c.$$

If $s_1, s_2, s_3, \ldots$ is any other sequence of rational numbers such that

$$\lim_{n \to \infty} s_n = c, \quad \text{then} \quad \lim_{n \to \infty} 2^{s_n} = 2^c.$$

Proof: Since $\lim_{n\to\infty} s_n = \lim_{n\to\infty} r_n = c$, $\lim_{n\to\infty} (s_n - r_n) = 0$.

Therefore, $\lim_{n\to\infty} 2^{s_n-r_n} = 1$. (Why?)

Now, $\qquad\qquad\qquad s_n = (s_n - r_n) + r_n$.

$\qquad\qquad \therefore\ 2^{s_n} = 2^{s_n-r_n} \cdot 2^{r_n}$. (Why?)

$\qquad \therefore\ \lim_{n\to\infty} 2^{s_n} = \lim_{n\to\infty} 2^{s_n-r_n} \cdot \lim_{n\to\infty} 2^{r_n}$. (Why?)

$\qquad\qquad\qquad\qquad = 1 \cdot 2^c$.

$\qquad \therefore\ \lim_{n\to\infty} 2^{s_n} = 2^c$.

Knowing that $\exp_2$ is an increasing function, you can now prove that $\exp_2$ is continuous. The result follows from the next theorem whose proof uses the fact that given any real number x, you can find rational numbers as close to x as you may wish.

THEOREM   If $x_1, x_2, x_3, \ldots$ is any convergent sequence of real numbers whose limit is c, then $\lim_{n\to\infty} 2^{x_n} = 2^c$.

Proof: Suppose $x_1, x_2, x_3, \ldots$ is a sequence of real numbers such that $\lim_{n\to\infty} x_n = c$. Choose *rational* numbers $r_1, r_2, r_3, \ldots$ and $s_1, s_2, s_3, \ldots$ according to the following plan:

$$r_1 \leq x_1 \leq s_1 \quad \text{and} \quad 0 \leq s_1 - r_1 < 1,$$
$$r_2 \leq x_2 \leq s_2 \quad \text{and} \quad 0 \leq s_2 - r_2 < \tfrac{1}{2},$$

and, in general,

$$r_n \leq x_n \leq s_n \quad \text{and} \quad 0 \leq s_n - r_n < \frac{1}{n}, \quad n = 1, 2, 3, \ldots$$

Then $\qquad 0 \leq s_n - x_n < \dfrac{1}{n} \quad \text{and} \quad 0 \leq x_n - r_n < \dfrac{1}{n}$.

Hence, $\qquad 0 \leq \lim_{n\to\infty} (s_n - x_n) \leq \lim_{n\to\infty} \dfrac{1}{n} = 0$, and

$$0 \leq \lim_{n\to\infty} (x_n - r_n) \leq \lim_{n\to\infty} \frac{1}{n} = 0.$$

$$\therefore\ \lim_{n\to\infty} (s_n - x_n) = 0 = \lim_{n\to\infty} (x_n - r_n).$$

But, by hypothesis, $\lim\limits_{n\to\infty} x_n = c$. Hence,

$$0 = \lim_{n\to\infty} (s_n - x_n) = \lim_{n\to\infty} s_n - \lim_{n\to\infty} x_n.$$

$$\therefore\ 0 = \lim_{n\to\infty} s_n - c,\ \text{or}$$

$$\lim_{n\to\infty} s_n = c.$$

Similarly,
$$\lim_{n\to\infty} r_n = c.$$

Therefore,
$$\lim_{n\to\infty} 2^{s_n} = \lim_{n\to\infty} 2^{r_n} = 2^c.\quad \text{(Why?)}$$

Now,
$$2^{r_n} \le 2^{x_n} \le 2^{s_n}, \qquad n = 1, 2, 3, \ldots \text{(Why?)}$$

$$\therefore\ \lim_{n\to\infty} 2^{r_n} \le \lim_{n\to\infty} 2^{x_n} \le \lim_{n\to\infty} 2^{s_n},\quad \text{and}$$

$$2^c \le \lim_{n\to\infty} 2^{x_n} \le 2^c.$$

$$\therefore\ \lim_{n\to\infty} 2^{x_n} = 2^c.$$

COROLLARY. Exp_2 is a continuous function.

Proof: $\mathrm{Exp}_2\,(c)$ denotes a real number for every real number c. The theorem just proved implies that $\lim\limits_{x\to c} \exp_2\,(x) = \exp_2\,(c)$. Therefore, $\exp_2$ is a continuous function.

Exercises

Prove each statement.

1. For all positive real numbers a and b and all positive integers p, if $a < b$, then $a^{\frac{1}{p}} < b^{\frac{1}{p}}$.

2. If h denotes a positive real number and p, a positive integer, such that $2 \le (1 + h)^p$, then $2^{\frac{1}{p}} \le 1 + h$.

3. For all positive real numbers a and b, and all positive integers p and q, $a^{\frac{p}{q}} < b^{\frac{p}{q}}$ if and only if $a < b$.

4. For all positive numbers a and b, all negative integers p, and all positive integers q, $a^{\frac{p}{q}} < b^{\frac{p}{q}}$ if and only if $b < a$.

Evaluate each of the following limits.

5. $\lim\limits_{x\to 3} 2^{1-x}$

6. $\lim\limits_{x\to 1} 2^{x^2+3x-5}$

7. $\lim\limits_{x \to \sqrt{7}} 2^{x^2-4}$

8. $\lim\limits_{x \to \sqrt{3}} (2^{x^4} - 2^{x^2+1})$

9. Prove that if k denotes a real number, then $\{(x, y): y = 2^{x+k}, x \in \mathcal{R}\}$ is a continuous function.

10. Prove that if k denotes a real number, then $\{(x, y): y = 2^{kx}, x \in \mathcal{R}\}$ is a continuous function.

9–4 Exponential Functions

You can define $10^{\sqrt{3}}$, $(\frac{1}{15})^{\sqrt[3]{6}}$, π^{π}, and, in general, b^x, for any positive real number b by following the pattern used in defining 2^x. However, you can avoid the limiting process for each separate base by employing your knowledge of $\exp_2$ to define b^x.

Because $\exp_2$ is an increasing function with $\mathcal{R}^+$ as its range, you know that for any positive real number b, there is a unique real number k for which $2^k = b$ (Figure 9–4).

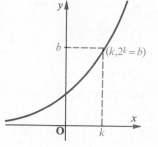

For example, referring to Figure 9–3 (page 332), you can verify that $3 \doteq 2^{1.6}$. It is quite natural, then, for you to define the power b^x by

(1) $$b^x = 2^{kx},$$

and the function $\exp_b$ by

(2) $$\exp_b = \{(x, y): y = b^x\}.$$

Figure 9–4

Using these definitions, you can now readily show that the laws of exponents are true in general.

THEOREM   For all positive real numbers a and b and all real numbers x and v:

1. $b^x b^v = b^{x+v}$.

2. $(ab)^x = a^x b^x$.

3. $(b^x)^v = b^{xv}$.

4. $\dfrac{b^x}{b^v} = b^{x-v}$.

5. $\dfrac{b^x}{b^v} = \dfrac{1}{b^{v-x}}$.

6. $\left(\dfrac{a}{b}\right)^x = \dfrac{a^x}{b^x}$.

7. If $b \neq 1$, then $b^x = b^v$ if and only if $x = v$.

8. If $x \neq 0$, then $a^x = b^x$ if and only if $a = b$.

The following example illustrates how to deduce the various parts of this theorem from the corresponding properties of 2^x. (See Exercises 17–23, page 342.)

EXAMPLE. Prove: If a and b denote positive real numbers and x denotes any real number, then $(ab)^x = a^x b^x$.

Proof: Let k_1 and k_2 denote real numbers such that

$$a = 2^{k_1} \quad \text{and} \quad b = 2^{k_2}.$$

Using the laws of exponents for 2^x, you find

$$(ab)^x = (2^{k_1} \cdot 2^{k_2})^x$$
$$= (2^{k_1+k_2})^x$$
$$= 2^{(k_1+k_2)x}$$
$$= 2^{k_1 x + k_2 x}.$$
$$\therefore (ab)^x = 2^{k_1 x} \cdot 2^{k_2 x}$$

But $a^x = 2^{k_1 x}$ and $b^x = 2^{k_2 x}$.

$$\therefore (ab)^x = a^x b^x.$$

Because $\exp_2$ is a continuous function, it follows that $\exp_b$ is also a continuous function (Exercise 10, page 338). Now can you guess how the graph of $\exp_b$ compares with that of $\exp_2$ for various positive real numbers b?

First, consider the real numbers b such that $b > 2$. In this case, if $b = 2^k$, then $k > 1$. (Why?) Therefore, if $x_2 > x_1$, then $kx_2 > kx_1$, and $2^{kx_2} > 2^{kx_1}$. This means $b^{x_2} > b^{x_1}$ so that $\exp_b$ is an increasing function. Furthermore, $kx > x$ or $kx < x$ according as $x > 0$ or $x < 0$; hence, $b^x > 2^x$ or $b^x < 2^x$ according as $x > 0$ or $x < 0$ (Why?) (Figure 9–5).

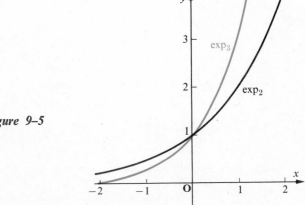

Figure 9–5

Secondly, suppose that $1 < b < 2$, so that $0 < k < 1$. In this case, $\exp_b$ is still an increasing function (Why?), but its graph lies below that of $\exp_2$ for $x > 0$, and above that of $\exp_2$ for $x < 0$ (Why?) (Figure 9–6).

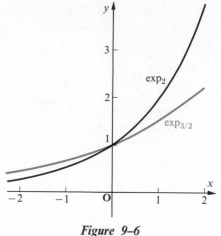

Figure 9–6

Thirdly, let $b = 1$. Now, $k = 0$ and $b^x = 2^{0 \cdot x} = 2^0 = 1$. Thus, $\exp_1$ is the constant function $\{(x, y): y = 1, x \in \Re\}$ (Figure 9–7).

Lastly, suppose that $0 < b < 1$. In this situation, $k < 0$. Hence, if $x_2 > x_1$, then $kx_2 < kx_1$. As a consequence, $\exp_b$ is now a *decreasing function;* that is, if $x_2 > x_1$, then $b^{x_2} < b^{x_1}$ (Why?). In fact, since $b^x = \left(\dfrac{1}{b}\right)^{-x}$, the graph of $\exp_b$ is the mirror image (*reflection*) of the graph of $\exp_{\frac{1}{b}}$ in the y-axis (Figure 9–8).

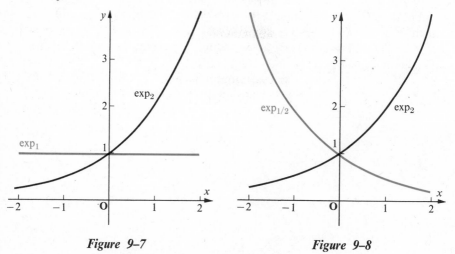

Figure 9–7   **Figure 9–8**

Notice that, for each real number $b > 0$,

$$\exp_b 0 = 1 \quad \text{and} \quad \exp_b 1 = b.$$

You can summarize the results of this discussion as follows:

> **THEOREM**   For each $b \in \Re^+$, $b \neq 1$, the function
> $$\exp_b = \{(x, y): y = b^x, x \in \Re\}$$
> is continuous and has $\Re^+$ as its range; it is increasing or decreasing according as $b > 1$ or $0 < b < 1$.

An irrational number that plays a prominent role in mathematical analysis is denoted by the letter e and is defined by

$$e = \lim_{x \to 0} (1 + x)^{\frac{1}{x}}, \quad x \in \Re.$$

Although the proof that the indicated limit exists and equals an irrational number will not be given here, you can approximate e by evaluating $(1 + x)^{\frac{1}{x}}$ for values of x close to 0. Thus, the following table suggests that to four decimal places $e \doteq 2.7183$.

x	1	0.1	0.01	0.001	0.0001	0.00001
$(1 + x)^{\frac{1}{x}}$	2	2.594	2.705	2.717	2.7182	2.7183

The function

$$\exp_e = \{(x, y): y = e^x, x \in \Re\}$$

has a central position in the study of exponential functions. Consequently, it is often called *the* exponential function. A table of selected values of $\exp_e$ is given in Table 5 at the end of the book.

Exercises

A

1. Complete the following table, giving entries to three decimal places.

x	-1	-0.5	0	0.5	1
3^x	?	?	?	1.732	?
$(\frac{1}{3})^x$	?	?	?	?	?

2. Using your completed table in Exercise 1, sketch the graph of
   (a) $f = \{(x, y): y = 3^x, -1 \leq x \leq 1\}$,
   (b) $g = \{(x, y): y = (\frac{1}{3})^x, -1 \leq x \leq 1\}$.

In Exercises 3–8, sketch the graph of $\exp_b = \{(x, y)\colon y = b^x\}$ on the domain $-2 \leq x \leq 2$ for the given value of b.

3. $b = 4$

4. $b = \frac{1}{4}$

5. $b = 0.6$

6. $b = 1$

7. $b = \frac{10}{11}$

8. $b = \frac{11}{10}$

B

9. Using the data in Table 5, sketch the graph of $\exp_e = \{(x, y)\colon y = e^x\}$ for $-2 \leq x \leq 2$. Draw a tangent to your graph at $P(0, 1)$ and estimate its slope.

10. Argue that if $0 < a < e$, then at $P(0, 1)$ the slope of the tangent to the graph of $\exp_a = \{(x, y)\colon y = a^x\}$ is less than or equal to that of the graph of $\exp_e = \{(x, y)\colon y = e^x\}$.

In Exercises 11–14, solve for x, given that $4 \doteq e^{1.386}$.

11. $16 = e^x$

12. $x = e^{-1.386}$

13. $x = e^{0.693}$

14. $x = e^0$

C

15. Show that if
$$f = \{(x, y)\colon y = f(x), x \in \mathcal{R}\}$$
is increasing, then
$$g = \{(x, y)\colon y = f(2x), x \in \mathcal{R}\}$$
is increasing.

16. Show that if
$$f = \{(x, y)\colon y = f(x), x \in \mathcal{R}\}$$
is increasing, then
$$h = \{(x, y)\colon y = f(-x), x \in \mathcal{R}\}$$
is decreasing.

In Exercises 17–24, a and b denote positive real numbers, and x and v denote real numbers. Prove each statement.

17. $b^x b^v = b^{x+v}$

18. $(b^x)^v = b^{xv}$

19. $\dfrac{b^x}{b^v} = b^{x-v}$

20. $\dfrac{b^x}{b^v} = \dfrac{1}{b^{v-x}}$

21. $\left(\dfrac{a}{b}\right)^x = \dfrac{a^x}{b^x}$

22. If $b \neq 1$, then $b^x = b^y$ if and only if $x = y$.

23. If $x \neq 0$, then $a^x = b^x$ if and only if $a = b$.

24. Show that if $0 < a < b$ then $0 < a^x < b^x$ or $0 < b^x < a^x$ according as $x > 0$ or $x < 0$.

9-5 Linear Interpolation

Can you find $e^{0.27}$? Table 5 at the end of the book contains entries for $e^{0.25}$ and $e^{0.30}$ but not for $e^{0.27}$. In fact, in the table you find $e^{0.25} \doteq 1.2840$ and $e^{0.30} \doteq 1.3499$.

⟍ To see how to approximate $e^{0.27}$, con-sider Figure 9–9, which is a schematic diagram comparing part of the graph of $\exp_e$ between $\mathbf{P}(0.25, 1.2840)$ and $\mathbf{Q}(0.30, 1.3499)$ with the straight line joining $\mathbf{P}$ and $\mathbf{Q}$. The diagram suggests that you might use the ordinate h of the point $\mathbf{C'}$ on the line $\mathbf{PQ}$ as an acceptable approximation of $e^{0.27}$, the ordinate of $\mathbf{C}$ on the curve. Because $\mathbf{P}$, $\mathbf{C'}$, and $\mathbf{Q}$ are collinear, you know that

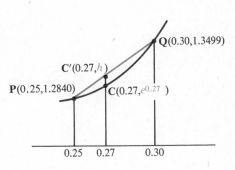

Figure 9–9

the slope of segment $\overline{PC'}$ = the slope of segment $\overline{PQ}$

$$\frac{h - 1.2840}{0.27 - 0.25} = \frac{1.3499 - 1.2840}{0.30 - 0.25}$$

$$\frac{h - 1.2840}{0.02} = \frac{0.0659}{0.05}$$

$$h - 1.2840 = \tfrac{2}{5}(0.0659)$$

$$h - 1.2840 \doteq 0.026 \text{ (to three places)}$$

$$h \doteq 1.310 \doteq e^{0.27}$$

Denoting $e^{0.27} - e^{0.25}$ by d, you can arrange the work as follows:

x	e^x
$0.05\begin{bmatrix} 0.30 \\ 0.02\begin{bmatrix} 0.27 \\ 0.25 \end{bmatrix} \end{bmatrix}$	$\begin{bmatrix} 1.3499 \\ e^{0.27} \\ 1.2840 \end{bmatrix}d \Big] 0.0659$

$$d = \tfrac{2}{5}(0.0659) \doteq 0.026$$

$$e^{0.27} \doteq 1.2840 + 0.026 \doteq 1.310, \textbf{ Answer.}$$

This process, called *linear interpolation*, enables you to use consecutive entries in a table of values of a function to compute an approximation of the value of the function at a number between the consecutive entries. Do you see why, for an exponential function, linear interpolation never gives too small a number as an approximation?

You can also interpolate in reverse to find x if e^x is known and is not an entry in the table.

EXAMPLE 1. A certain radioactive substance disintegrates in time, so that starting with A grams, the number y of grams present t years later is given by $y = Ae^{kt}$. If half of the given substance is left after 10 years (the *half-life* is 10 years), find k.

Solution: Since the half-life is 10, the equation

$$y = Ae^{kt}$$

must be true when y is replaced by $\dfrac{A}{2}$ and t is replaced by 10.

$$\frac{A}{2} = Ae^{10k}$$

$$\therefore \tfrac{1}{2} = e^{10k}, \text{ or}$$

$$0.5000 = e^{10k}$$

In Table 5, in the column headed e^{-x}, find the consecutive entries 0.4966 and 0.5220 between which 0.5000 lies, and note the corresponding exponents of e: -0.70 and -0.65. The computation of an approximation of $10k$ can be arranged as follows:

x	e^x
-0.65	0.5220
$10k$	0.5000
-0.70	0.4966

$$0.05 \left[d \left[\begin{array}{cc} -0.65 & 0.5220 \\ 10k & 0.5000 \\ -0.70 & 0.4966 \end{array} \right] 0.0034 \right] 0.0254$$

$$\frac{d}{0.05} = \frac{0.0034}{0.0254} \,;\, d = (0.05)\,\frac{34}{254} \doteq 0.01$$

$$\therefore 10k = -0.70 + 0.01 \doteq -0.69$$

$$k \doteq -0.069, \textbf{ Answer.}$$

It is not necessary to have a table of values of b^x for every base b. Table 5 is adequate for small numbers b.

EXAMPLE 2. Determine an approximation of $2.117^{0.80}$.

Solution: From Table 5 you find that

$$2.117 \doteq e^{0.75}$$

Hence, $(2.117)^{0.80} \doteq (e^{0.75})^{0.80} \doteq e^{0.60}$

In Table 5, you find $e^{0.60} \doteq 1.8221$

$\therefore 2.117^{0.80} \doteq 1.8221$, **Answer.**

Exercises

In Exercises 1–6, use Table 5 to determine e^x for the given values of x.

A

1. 0.30	**3.** 1.6	**5.** 5
2. 0.95	**4.** 3.2	**6.** 10

7–12. Use Table 5 to determine the value of e^{-x} for x given in Exercises 1–6.

In Exercises 13–18, use Table 5 and linear interpolation to determine e^x for the given value of x.

13. 0.222	**15.** −0.966	**17.** 0.653
14. 0.867	**16.** 0.966	**18.** −0.044

In Exercises 19–22, use Table 5 to approximate the given power.

B   **19.** $5^{1.7}$ **20.** $(\frac{1}{3})^{0.1}$ **21.** $(0.7)^{-2.5}$ **22.** $(3.1)^{-\frac{3}{2}}$

In Exercises 23–28, use Table 5 to find an approximation of the value of x.

23. $e^x = 90.02$	**25.** $e^x = 0.0111$	**27.** $x = 1.5^{2.3}$
24. $e^x = 2.014$	**26.** $e^x = 0.583$	**28.** $2^x = 1.263$

29. When the electromotive force is cut off in a certain electric circuit, the current I, t seconds later, is given by $I = I_0 e^{-kt}$, where I_0 is the intensity of current at the time the EMF is cut off and k is a constant depending on the circuit. If a current of 10 amperes falls to 0.5 ampere in 0.01 sec., determine k.

30. In a room maintained at a constant temperature of 10°C, a certain body cools from 90°C to 80°C in 2 minutes. When will its temperature be 50°C? (Assume that if $h(t)$ is the difference between the temperature of the body at time t and the temperature of the room, $h(t) = Ae^{-kt}$.)

[handwritten: A = original difference in temp. between body + room]

COMPOSITION AND INVERSION OF FUNCTIONS

9-6 Composition of Functions

You can think of a function whose domain is the set D and whose range is the set S as a *mapping* from D to S. Figure 9–10 pictures the function $\{(x_1, y_1), (x_2, y_1), (x_3, y_2)\}$ as a mapping under which two elements, x_1 and x_2, of D are mapped into the same element y_1 of S, while x_3 is mapped into another element, y_2, of S. The function shown in Figure 9–11 is called a **one-to-one function** or **mapping**, because *distinct* elements of D are mapped into *distinct* elements of S.

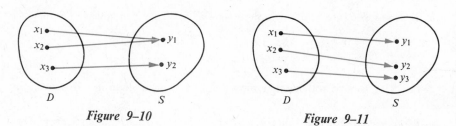

Figure 9–10   *Figure 9–11*

Now suppose that f is the function which maps each real number into its cube, that is, $f = \{(x, y): y = x^3\}$. Do you see that f is a one-to-one mapping with $\mathfrak{R}$ as domain and range? Also, let g be the function which maps each real number into its absolute value; thus, $g = \{(x, y): y = |x|\}$. Notice that g is *not* a one-to-one mapping from its domain, $\mathfrak{R}$, to its range, $\mathfrak{R}^+ \cup \{0\}$. (Why?)

Choose a real number, say -2. You can verify that $g(-2) = |-2| = 2$, and $f(2) = 2^3 = 8$. Thus, if you "apply" the mapping g to the number -2, and then "apply" f to the result, 2, you obtain the number 8; that is, $f[g(-2)] = 8$. If you repeat this procedure for every number x in the domain of g, you obtain a function that maps each x into the element $f[g(x)] = |x|^3$ in the range of g. We call this function the *composition* of f and g, and denote it by $f \circ g$.

In general, the **composition** $f \circ g$ of f and g is defined by

$$f \circ g = \{(x, y): y = f[g(x)]\}.$$

Because "$[f \circ g](x) = f[g(x)]$" is a meaningful statement for those and only those values of x in the domain of g such that $g(x)$ is an element in the domain of f, the domain $D_{f \circ g}$ of $f \circ g$ consists of just those values of x. Thus, $D_{f \circ g}$ is a subset of the domain D_g of g.

EXAMPLE 1. If $f = \{[x, f(x)]: \; f(x) = 3x + 1, x \in \mathfrak{R}\}$ and
$$g = \{[x, g(x)]: \; g(x) = x^2 - 2, x \in \mathfrak{R}\}, \text{ find}$$

(a) $f \circ g$; **(b)** $g \circ f$.

Solution: Let x denote any real number.

(a) $[f \circ g](x) = f[g(x)] = f[x^2 - 2] = 3(x^2 - 2) + 1$
$$= 3x^2 - 5$$

$\therefore f \circ g = \{(x, y): \; y = 3x^2 - 5, x \in \mathfrak{R}\}$, **Answer.**

(b) $[g \circ f](x) = g[f(x)] = g[3x + 1] = (3x + 1)^2 - 2$
$$= 9x^2 + 6x - 1$$

$\therefore g \circ f = \{(x, y): \; y = 9x^2 + 6x - 1, x \in \mathfrak{R}\}$,
Answer.

As Example 1 shows, composition of functions is not a commutative operation; that is, it is not always true that $f \circ g = g \circ f$. In fact, as the following example indicates, $f \circ g$ and $g \circ f$ may have different domains.

EXAMPLE 2. If f is defined by $f(x) = \sqrt{4 - x}$ ($x \in \mathfrak{R}$ and $x \le 4$) and g by $g(x) = x^2$ ($x \in \mathfrak{R}$), find $f \circ g$ and $g \circ f$, and specify their domains, $D_{f \circ g}$ and $D_{g \circ f}$.

Solution: $[f \circ g](x) = f[g(x)] = f(x^2) = \sqrt{4 - x^2}$.

$\therefore f \circ g = \{(x, y): \; y = \sqrt{4 - x^2}\}$;

$D_{f \circ g} = \{x: \; x \in \mathfrak{R} \text{ and } -2 \le x \le 2\}$, **Answer.**

$[g \circ f](x) = g[f(x)] = g(\sqrt{4 - x})$
$$= (\sqrt{4 - x})^2 = |4 - x|.$$

$g \circ f = \{(x, y): \; y = |4 - x|\}$;

$D_{g \circ f} = \{x: \; x \in \mathfrak{R} \text{ and } x \le 4\}$, **Answer.**

Note that in Example 2, $D_{f \circ g}$ is a *proper* subset of D_g. Since $D_{g \circ f} = D_f$, $D_{g \circ f}$ is an *improper* subset of D_f.

Exercises

In Exercises 1–8, find $g \circ f$ and $f \circ g$ and specify their domains. Assume that D_f and D_g consist of the real numbers for which the respective expressions for $f(x)$ and $g(x)$ denote real numbers.

1. $f(x) = 2x + 1; g(x) = x - 6$

2. $f(x) = x^2 - 4; g(x) = x + 2$

3. $f(x) = x^2 + 1; g(x) = \sqrt{x - 1}$

4. $f(x) = 2x^2 - 3; g(x) = \sqrt{x + 1}$

5. $f(x) = \dfrac{1}{1 + x}; g(x) = \dfrac{1}{2 - x}$

6. $f(x) = x^2 - \dfrac{2}{x}; g(x) = \sqrt{x - 1}$

7. $f(x) = 2x - 1; g(x) = \frac{1}{2}x + \frac{1}{2}$

8. $f(x) = 3x^2 - 7; g(x) = c.$

9–16. In Exercises 1–8, determine which, if any, of the functions f, g, $f \circ g$, and $g \circ f$ are one-to-one mappings.

17. Let $f(x) = ax + b$ and $g(x) = cx + d$ define linear functions with domain $\mathfrak{R}$. Find the slopes of the graphs of $f \circ g$ and $g \circ f$.

18. Use the results of Exercise 17 to make a conjecture about the slopes of the graphs of the composites of two linear functions.

19. Let I denote the identity function defined by $I(x) = x$. Show that if g is any function, $g \circ I = I \circ g = g$.

20. Let g be any linear function defined by an equation of the form $g(x) = ax + b$. Show that if $g \circ I = f$, then $f = g$.

21. Let g be defined by $g(x) = ax + b$. Find an expression for $f(x)$ if $f \circ g = I$.

22. Let f, g, and h be linear functions. Show that $(f \circ g) \circ h = f \circ (g \circ h)$.

23. Prove that if g is a constant function, then for every function f, $f \circ g$ is a constant function.

24. Prove that if $0 < b \neq 1$, then $\exp_b$ is a one-to-one mapping from $\mathfrak{R}$ to $\mathfrak{R}^+$.

In Exercises 25 and 26, f, g, and h denote linear functions with domain $\mathfrak{R}$. State whether the given equation is valid for all such functions. Justify your answer.

25. $(f + g) \circ h = f \circ h + g \circ h$

26. $f \circ (g \circ h) = (f \circ g) \circ (f \circ h)$

9–7 Inverses of Functions

Figure 9–12 uses arrows to picture the one-to-one mapping f from a set D_f to a set R_f. It is natural to think of reversing the arrows to obtain a mapping g from R_f to D_f (Figure 9–13).

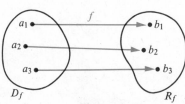

Figure 9–12

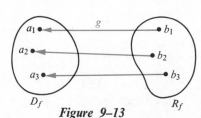

Figure 9–13

Note that $\qquad f = \{(a_1, b_1), (a_2, b_2), (a_3, b_3)\}$ and

$$g = \{(b_1, a_1), (b_2, a_2), (b_3, a_3)\},$$

where the ordered pairs in g are obtained by interchanging the coordinates of each of the ordered pairs in f. Therefore, the range of f is the domain of g, and the range of g is the domain of f. (Why?) Moreover, if you choose any element, say a_1, of D_f you have

$$[g \circ f](a_1) = g[f(a_1)] = g(b_1) = a_1;$$

similarly, for any element, say b_2, of $D_g = R_f$,

$$[f \circ g](b_2) = f[g(b_2)] = f(a_2) = b_2.$$

Thus, if $x \in D_f$, $[g \circ f](x) = x$, and if $x \in D_g$, $[f \circ g](x) = x$. We call f and g *inverse functions*.

In general, if f is a one-to-one function, then the **inverse** of f (in symbols, f^{-1})* is the function whose domain $D_{f^{-1}}$ is the range R_f of f and whose values are defined by $f^{-1}(b) = a$ where $b \in R_f$ and $f(a) = b$. Notice that this definition requires that $(a, b) \in f$ if and only if $(b, a) \in f^{-1}$.

EXAMPLE 1. If $f = \{(x, y): y = 2x - 6, x \in \mathcal{R}\}$, express $f^{-1}(x)$ as a polynomial in x.

Solution: Suppose $(a, b) \in f$. Then:

(1) $b = 2a - 6$, so that $a = \dfrac{b + 6}{2} = \dfrac{1}{2}b + 3$;

(2) $(b, a) \in f^{-1}$, so that $f^{-1}(b) = a = \frac{1}{2}b + 3$.

$\therefore$ replacing the letter b by x in the expression for $f^{-1}(b)$, you find $f^{-1}(x) = \frac{1}{2}x + 3$, **Answer.**

As a check of the work in Example 1, notice that

$$[f^{-1} \circ f](x) = f^{-1}[f(x)] = f^{-1}(2x - 6) = \tfrac{1}{2}(2x - 6) + 3 = x.$$

Checking that $[f \circ f^{-1}](x) = x$ is left to you.

Can you suggest a short-cut for the solution of Example 1? In the equa-

---

* Beware of confusing f^{-1} with $\dfrac{1}{f}$. In this book the symbol f^{-1}, where f is a function, will mean the inverse of f, *not* the reciprocal function $\dfrac{1}{f}$.

tion $y = 2x - 6$ relating the coordinates of each ordered pair (x, y) in f, interchange x and y. Thus,

since $$f = \{(x, y): y = 2x - 6\},$$

$$f^{-1} = \{(x, y): x = 2y - 6\},$$

or $$f^{-1} = \{(x, y): y = \tfrac{1}{2}x + 3\}.$$

The fact that you obtain the ordered pairs in the inverse of a function by interchanging the coordinates of each of the ordered pairs of the function itself has an important graphical significance. Look at Figure 9–14, which shows the graphs of (a, b) and (b, a) in the plane. Do you see that the graph of $y = x$ appears to be the perpendicular bisector of the line segment joining (a, b) and (b, a)? Because you can prove that this is indeed the case (Exercise 28, page 352), you say that (b, a) is the **reflection** of (a, b), and (a, b) is the reflection of (b, a), in the graph of $y = x$. (The situation is also described by saying that (a, b) and (b, a) are *symmetric* with respect to the line.) Accordingly, the graph of f^{-1} must be the reflection of the graph of f in the line with equation $y = x$.

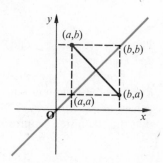

Figure 9–14

EXAMPLE 2. Given the function f in Example 1, page 349, graph f and f^{-1} on the same set of axes.

Solution: Since $f = \{(x, y): y = 2x - 6, x \in \Re\}$ and
$$f^{-1} = \{(x, y): y = \tfrac{1}{2}x + 3, x \in \Re\},$$

the graphs of f and f^{-1} are the straight lines shown in the adjoining figure.

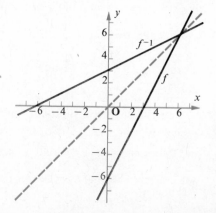

Can you define the inverse of a function that is not one-to-one? Consider the quadratic function $\{(x, y): y = x^2, x \in \mathfrak{R}\}$. Interchanging the variables converts the equation $y = x^2$ into $x = y^2$. For each positive number x, the equation $x = y^2$ is satisfied by two real numbers y. For example, given 4 as the value of x, you can choose 2 *or* -2 as the value of y, since $4 = 2^2$ *and* $4 = (-2)^2$. Thus, as Figure 9–15 shows, $\{(x, y): x = y^2\}$ is a relation that is *not* a function. This situation could be described by saying "the inverse of the function $\{(x, y): y = x^2\}$ is the relation $\{(x, y): x = y^2\}$," and there are, in fact, occasions when it is useful to say this. However, in this book, we shall require the inverse of a function to be a *function*. Therefore,

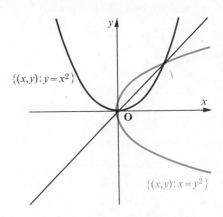

Figure 9–15

you must conclude that any function, such as $\{(x, y): y = x^2, x \in \mathfrak{R}\}$, which is not one-to-one does *not* have an inverse. Can you explain why the function $h = \{(x, y): y = x^2, x \in \mathfrak{R}^+\}$ does have an inverse? In fact, $h^{-1} = \{(x, y): y = \sqrt{x}, x \in \mathfrak{R}^+\}$.

You would be very likely to guess that the following important theorem is true. Although we will not prove it here, we will use it and its corollary in later work.

THEOREM The inverse of every continuous one-to-one function is a continuous function.

COROLLARY. The inverse of a continuous increasing (decreasing) function is continuous.

The corollary follows from the theorem and the fact that an increasing (or a decreasing) function is one-to-one (Exercise 31, page 352).

Exercises

In Exercises 1–8, **(a)** state whether the given function has an inverse; **(b)** if the inverse exists, specify it by roster.

A

1. $\{(1, 2), (2, 3), (3, 4)\}$
2. $\{(1, 3), (2, -3), (0, 0)\}$
3. $\{(0, 1)\}$
4. $\{(-1, 0)\}$

5. $\{(2, 1), (3, 2), (4, 1), (5, 3)\}$
6. $\{(1, -1), (2, -3), (3, -2), (4, -1)\}$
7. $\{(-2, 2), (-1, 1), (0, 0), (1, -1)\}$
8. $\{(-5, 1), (5, 2), (-4, 3), (4, 4)\}$

In Exercises 9–16, (**a**) state whether the function f has an inverse. Assume D_f is the set of real numbers for which the given expression for $f(x)$ denotes real numbers; (**b**) if f^{-1} exists, find an equation for $f^{-1}(x)$ in terms of x.

9. $f(x) = 3x - 6$

10. $f(x) = \dfrac{x - 2}{4}$

11. $f(x) = \sqrt{x^2 - 2}$

12. $f(x) = \sqrt{x^2 + 3}$

13. $f(x) = \sqrt{x} - 3$

14. $f(x) = 2\sqrt{x} + 6$

15. $f(x) = \dfrac{1}{1 - x}$

16. $f(x) = x^2 - 3$

17–24. In Exercises 9–16, graph f and f^{-1} on the same set of axes.

B 25. Describe all functions f with domain and range $\mathcal{R}$ such that $f = f^{-1}$.

26. Prove that if f is a linear function over $\mathcal{R}$, then f^{-1} also is a linear function over $\mathcal{R}$.

27. Find a set of relationships between the constants a, b, c, and d so that the function defined by

$$f(x) = \frac{ax + b}{cx + d} \quad \left(ad - bc \neq 0, x \in \mathcal{R}, x \neq -\frac{d}{c} \right)$$

is its own inverse.

28. Prove that the graph of $y = x$ is the perpendicular bisector of the line segment joining the points (a, b) and (b, a), where $a \neq b$.

C 29. Prove that if f and g have inverses, then $(f \circ g)^{-1} = g^{-1} \circ f^{-1}$.

30. Prove that $\{f_1, f_2, f_3, f_4, f_5, f_6\}$ is a group with respect to composition if the values of the functions are defined by the following equations ($x \in \mathcal{R}$):

$$f_1(x) = x \qquad f_4(x) = \frac{1}{1 - x}, x \neq 1$$

$$f_2(x) = 1 - x \qquad f_5(x) = \frac{x - 1}{x}, x \neq 0$$

$$f_3(x) = \frac{1}{x}, x \neq 0 \qquad f_6(x) = \frac{x}{x - 1}, x \neq 1$$

Prove each statement.

31. An increasing (decreasing) function is one-to-one and has an inverse.

32. The inverse of an increasing function is an increasing function.

33. The inverse of a decreasing function is a decreasing function.

34. A continuous increasing function has a continuous increasing inverse. (*Hint:* Use the theorem on page 351 and Exercises 31 and 32 above.)

35. A continuous decreasing function has a continuous decreasing inverse. (*Hint:* Use the theorem on page 351 and Exercises 31 and 33 above.)

36. If f and g are functions such that $g = f^{-1}$, then $f = g^{-1}$.

LOGARITHMIC FUNCTIONS

9-8 Inverse of an Exponential Function

Does an exponential function have an inverse? In Section 9–4 you saw that $\exp_b$ is increasing if $b > 1$, but is decreasing if $0 < b < 1$. In either case, the function is one-to-one (Exercise 31, page 352) and, hence, has an inverse. Figures 9–16 and 9–17 show the graphs of two exponential functions together with the graphs of their inverses.

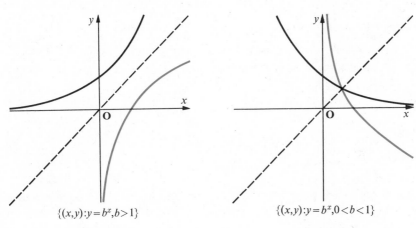

$$\{(x,y):y=b^x,b>1\}$$

Figure 9–16

$$\{(x,y):y=b^x,0<b<1\}$$

Figure 9–17

The inverse of an exponential function $\exp_b$ is called a **logarithmic function** and is denoted by $\log_b$. As Figures 9–16 and 9–17 suggest, $\log_b$ is a continuous increasing function if $b > 1$, but it is a continuous decreasing function if $0 < b < 1$. In each case, the domain of $\log_b$ is $\mathcal{R}^+$.

Also, since $\exp_b = \{(x, y): y = b^x, x \in \mathcal{R}\}$ $\qquad$ $(b > 0, b \neq 1)$,

$\qquad\qquad$ $\log_b = \{(x, y): x = b^y, x \in \mathcal{R}^+\}$ $\qquad$ $(b > 0, b \neq 1)$.

The equation $x = b^y$ is also written

$$y = \log_b x \qquad\qquad (b > 0, b \neq 1),$$

which is read "y equals the logarithm of x to the base b."

Since $\exp_b$ and $\log_b$ are inverse functions,

$$[\exp_b \circ \log_b](x) = x \quad \text{and} \quad [\log_b \circ \exp_b](x) = x; \text{ hence,}$$

$$b^{\log_b x} = x \quad \text{and} \qquad \log_b b^x = x.$$

The foregoing identities are important relationships to keep in mind.

EXAMPLE 1. Determine t if (**a**) $t = \log_3 \frac{1}{27}$; (**b**) $\log_{10} 10^t = 2$.

Solution: (**a**) Since $t = \log_3 \frac{1}{27}$, the first identity above implies that $3^t = \frac{1}{27} = 3^{-3}$.

$\therefore t = -3.$ (Why?)

(**b**) If $\log_{10} 10^t = 2$, the second identity above implies that

$2 = t.$ (Why?)

$\therefore$ (**a**) -3; (**b**) 2, **Answer.**

The identity $b^{\log_b x} = x$ indicates why $\log_b x$ is often described as the exponent needed in the power of b to yield x. Thus, $\log_2 8 = 3$ because $2^3 = 8$ and $\log_{10} 0.1 = -1$ because $10^{-1} = 0.1$.

The foregoing identity also guarantees that

$$b^{\log_b 1} = 1 \qquad\qquad (b > 0, b \neq 1).$$

Also, since $b^0 = 1$ for every positive real number b, you have

$$\log_b 1 = 0.$$

Because $\log_b$ is the inverse of $\exp_b$, you can quickly deduce the properties of logarithms from the laws of exponents. The following theorem states the **Laws of Logarithms**.

THEOREM If a, b, and c are positive real numbers, and $b \neq 1$, then

1. $\log_b ac = \log_b a + \log_b c$.

2. $\log_b \dfrac{a}{c} = \log_b a - \log_b c$.

3. $\log_b a^c = c \log_b a$.

4. $\log_b \sqrt[c]{a} = \dfrac{1}{c} \log_b a$, if c is a positive integer.

5. $\log_b a = \log_b c$ if and only if $a = c$.

Proof of 1: Using the identity $b^{\log_b x} = x$, you have $ac = b^{\log_b ac}$, $a = b^{\log_b a}$, and $c = b^{\log_b c}$. Therefore, Law 1 of exponents (page 323) implies

$$b^{\log_b ac} = ac = b^{\log_b a} \cdot b^{\log_b c}$$
$$= b^{\log_b a + \log_b c}.$$

$\therefore \log_b ac = \log_b a + \log_b c.$ (Why?)

The proofs of the other parts of the theorem are left as Exercises 35, 36, 37, and 38, page 356.

EXAMPLE 2. Given $\log_2 3 \doteq 1.6$, find an approximation of $\log_2 144$.

Solution: Applying the first law of logarithms, you find

$$\log_2 144 = \log_2 (2^4 \cdot 3^2) = \log_2 2^4 + \log_2 3^2.$$

But $\log_2 2^4 = 4.$ (Why?)

Also, using the third law of logarithms, you obtain

$$\log_2 3^2 = 2 \log_2 3 \doteq 2(1.6) = 3.2.$$

$\therefore \log_2 144 \doteq 4 + 3.2 = 7.2$, **Answer.**

Exercises

In Exercises 1–6, write each logarithmic statement in exponential form.

1. $\log_3 9 = 2$
2. $\log_2 32 = 5$
3. $\log_7 7 = 1$
4. $\log_3 1 = 0$
5. $\log_{\frac{1}{2}} 8 = -3$
6. $\log_{\frac{2}{3}} \frac{9}{4} = -2$

In Exercises 7–12, write each exponential statement in logarithmic form.

7. $125 = 5^3$
8. $81 = 3^4$
9. $\frac{2}{3} = \left(\frac{3}{2}\right)^{-1}$
10. $\frac{1}{6} = \left(\frac{1}{36}\right)^{\frac{1}{2}}$
11. $1000 = \left(\frac{1}{10}\right)^{-3}$
12. $\frac{1}{10} = (1000)^{-\frac{1}{3}}$

In Exercises 13–18, find a value for x that makes the given assertion true.

13. $\log_x 8 = 3$
14. $\log_x \frac{1}{4} = -\frac{1}{2}$
15. $\log_3 x = -2$
16. $\log_4 x = -\frac{1}{2}$
17. $\log_3 \frac{1}{9} = x$
18. $\log_{\frac{1}{3}} 27 = x$

In Exercises 19–24, state whether the given statement is true. If it is not, replace the right-hand member with a numeral that makes it true.

19. $\log_2 8 - \log_{\frac{1}{2}} 8 = 6$
20. $\log_5 625 + \log_3 \left(\frac{1}{81}\right) = 1$
21. $4^{2\log_4 3} + 3^{2\log_3 4} = 1$
22. $6^{\frac{1}{2}\log_6 36} \cdot 9^{2\log_9 81} = 6$
23. $3 \log_{10} 4 - 2 \log_{10} 8 = \log_3 1$
24. $\log_2 4 + \log_4 2 = 1$

Write each expression in Exercises 25–30 in simpler form.

B

25. $e^{\log_e e}$ **27.** $8^{\log_2 5}$ **29.** $\exp_e (\log_{e^2} 3)$

26. $e^{2\log_e e}$ **28.** $16^{\log_4 2}$ **30.** $\exp_8 (\log_4 2)$

C

31. Prove part 2 of the theorem on page 354.

32. Prove Part 3 of the theorem on page 354.

33. Prove Part 4 of the theorem on page 354.

34. Prove Part 5 of the theorem on page 354.

35. Prove that if $b > 1$, then $\log_b a < \log_b c$ if and only if $0 < a < c$.

36. Prove that if $b < 1$, then $\log_b a < \log_b c$ if and only if $a > c > 0$.

37. Prove that if $b < c$ and $b > 1$, then $\log_b c > 1$.

38. Prove that if $b > c$ and $b > 1$, then $\log_b c < 1$.

39. Prove that if $1 < c$ and $1 < b < a$, then $\log_a c < \log_b c$.

40. Prove that if $x_1, x_2, \ldots, x_n \ldots$ is a geometric progression, then $\log_b x_1$, $\log_b x_2, \ldots, \log_b x_n, \ldots$ is an arithmetic progression.

9–9 Values for Log₁₀ x

Since you know that $4^3 = 64$, you know that $\log_4 64 = 3$. In general, if you know the exponent u such that $b^u = a$, then you know $\log_b a$. (Why?) How, though, do you find $\log_b a$ when a is not a familiar power of b? The answer is that you use a table of logarithms.

While it would be convenient to have a table of $\log_b$ for every base you encounter, a table for just one base is sufficient for you to find any logarithm, as you will see in the next section. Consequently, you will now learn how to use a table of logarithms to the frequently used base 10. The values of $\log_{10}$ are called **common** or **Briggsian logarithms.***

You obtain common logarithms of integral powers of 10 by writing the power in exponential form and noting the exponent.

Exponential Form	Logarithmic Form
$0.01 = 10^{-2}$	$\log_{10} 0.01 = -2$
$0.1 = 10^{-1}$	$\log_{10} 0.1 = -1$
$1 = 10^0$	$\log_{10} 1 = 0$
$10 = 10^1$	$\log_{10} 10 = 1$
$100 = 10^2$	$\log_{10} 100 = 2$

---

*Another system of logarithms frequently used consists of the *natural or Napierian logarithms*, that is, logarithms to the base e.

To find the common logarithms of numbers that are not integral powers of 10, you can use Table 4 at the end of the book, which gives the first four significant figures in the logarithms of numbers between 1 and 10. The table below is an excerpt from Table 4. To find an approximation for $\log_{10} x$ when $1 \leq x < 10$ and the decimal numeral for x contains three or fewer significant digits, find the first two significant digits of x in the left-hand column, then locate the third digit in the top row, and read the approximation of $\log_{10} x$ at the intersection of the appropriate row and column.

N	0	1	2	3	4	5	6	7	8	9
12	0792	0828	0864	0899	0934	0969	1004	1038	1072	1106
13	1139	1173	1206	1239	1271	1303	1335	1367	1399	1430
14	1461	1492	1523	1553	1584	1614	1644	1673	1703	1732

For example, to find $\log_{10} 1.34$, look for 13 under x and move along row 13 to the column headed 4, where you find 1271. Since $\log_{10} x$ is between 0 and 1 when x is between 1 and 10, each entry in the table is understood to be preceded by a decimal point. Therefore, $\log_{10} 1.34 \doteq 0.1271$. Note that the symbol $\doteq$ is used because, with only one exception (which one?), the logarithms in Table 4 are approximations of irrational numbers.

By expressing each positive real number as the product of a number between 1 and 10 and a power of 10, you can extend the range of the table to include all positive numbers. For example,

$$134 = 1.34 \times 10^2$$
$$\therefore 134 \doteq 10^{0.1271} \times 10^2 = 10^{2.1271}$$
$$\therefore \log_{10} 134 \doteq 2.1271.$$

Additional examples are

$$1340 = 1.340 \times 10^3, \quad \log_{10} 1340 \doteq 3.1271$$
$$13400 = 1.340 \times 10^4, \quad \log_{10} 13400 \doteq 4.1271$$
$$0.134 = 1.34 \times 10^{-1}, \quad \log_{10} 0.134 \doteq -1 + 0.1271$$
$$0.0134 = 1.34 \times 10^{-2}, \quad \log_{10} 0.0134 \doteq -2 + 0.1271$$

Observe that a logarithm is the sum of two parts: an integral part, called the **characteristic**, and a decimal fractional part, called its **mantissa**, which is positive and which can be found in Table 4. To retain this pattern, you usually do not write a logarithm such as $-2 + 0.1271$ in the form -1.8729. Instead, you preserve the positive mantissa by writing $0.1271 - 2$, or more often, since $-2 = 8.0000 - 10$, by stating

$$\log_{10} 0.0134 \doteq -2 + 0.1271 = 8 + 0.1271 - 10 = 8.1271 - 10.$$

EXAMPLE 1. Find $\log_{10} 0.642$.

Solution: $0.642 = 6.42 \times 10^{-1}$, so the characteristic is $-1 = 9.0000 - 10$. Now, in Table 4 look for row 64 and column 2, and find the mantissa 8075.

$$\therefore \log_{10} 0.642 = 9.8075 - 10, \textbf{Answer.}$$

To find the common logarithm of a number with a four-digit numeral, you use linear interpolation.

EXAMPLE 2. Find $\log_{10} 13.74$.

Solution: Using an abbreviated form, you have:

x	$\log_{10} x$
13.80	1.1399
13.74	$\log_{10} 13.74$
13.70	1.1367

$$0.10 \begin{bmatrix} 0.04 \begin{bmatrix} 13.80 \\ 13.74 \\ 13.70 \end{bmatrix} \end{bmatrix} \qquad \begin{bmatrix} 1.1399 \\ \log_{10} 13.74 \\ 1.1367 \end{bmatrix} d \Big] 0.0032$$

$$d \doteq \tfrac{4}{10}(0.0032) \doteq 0.0013 \text{ (rounded to four places)}$$

$$\therefore \log_{10} 13.74 \doteq 1.1367 + 0.0013 = 1.1380, \textbf{Answer.}$$

If $\log_{10} k = x$, then k is called the **antilogarithm to the base 10** of x, and is denoted by **antilog$_{10}$ x**. Given antilog$_{10}$ x, you can find x by reversing the process of finding the common logarithm of a number.

EXAMPLE 3. Find antilog$_{10}$ $(8.2301 - 10)$.

Solution: In the body of Table 4, you find that the mantissa, 0.2301, falls between tabular entries 0.2279 and 0.2304. You have

x	$\log x$
0.01700	$8.2304 - 10$
antilog$_{10}$ $(8.2301 - 10)$	$8.2301 - 10$
0.01690	$8.2279 - 10$

$$0.00010 \begin{bmatrix} d \begin{bmatrix} 0.01700 \\ \text{antilog}_{10}(8.2301-10) \\ 0.01690 \end{bmatrix} \end{bmatrix} \qquad \begin{bmatrix} 8.2304-10 \\ 8.2301-10 \\ 8.2279-10 \end{bmatrix} 0.0022 \Big] 0.0025$$

$$d \doteq \frac{22}{25}(0.00010) \doteq 0.00009.$$

$$\therefore \text{antilog}_{10}(8.2301 - 10) \doteq 0.01690 + 0.00009 = 0.01699, \textbf{Answer.}$$

By virtue of the theorem on page 354, you can use logarithms to help you compute products, quotients, powers, and roots. When using logarithms for such computations, however, you should always remember that your results will be at best only four-significant-figure approximations to actual values, because the logarithms listed in Table 4 are, themselves, approximations with only that accuracy.

EXAMPLE 4. Determine an approximation of $\dfrac{\sqrt[3]{27.31}}{0.1420}$.

Solution: Let $N = \dfrac{\sqrt[3]{27.31}}{0.1420}$.

$$\log_{10} N = \log_{10} \sqrt[3]{27.31} - \log_{10} 0.1420. \quad \text{(Why?)}$$

$$\therefore \log_{10} N = \tfrac{1}{3}\log_{10} 27.31 - \log_{10} 0.1420.$$

Consulting Table 4 (and using interpolation as needed), you obtain:

$$\log_{10} N = \tfrac{1}{3}(1.4364) - (9.1523 - 10)$$

$$\therefore \log_{10} N \doteq \underbrace{\quad 0.4788 \quad} - \underbrace{(9.1523 - 10)}$$

$$\doteq (10.4788 - 10) - (9.1523 - 10)$$

$$\log_{10} N = 1.3265.$$

$$\therefore N = \text{antilog}_{10}\, 1.3265 \doteq 21.21, \textbf{ Answer.}$$

Note that $\dfrac{\sqrt[3]{27.31}}{0.1420} \doteq 21.21$ checks with the rough estimate

$$\frac{\sqrt[3]{27.31}}{0.1420} \doteq \frac{\sqrt[3]{27}}{0.14} = \frac{3}{0.14} = \frac{300}{14} \doteq 21.$$

Exercises

In Exercises 1–12, evaluate the given logarithm or antilogarithm.

1. $\log_{10} 93.5$	**5.** $\log_{10} 98.86$	**9.** antilog$_{10}$ 0.8401
2. $\log_{10} 1140$	**6.** $\log_{10} 0.7023$	**10.** antilog$_{10}$ 3.4200
3. $\log_{10} 0.0201$	**7.** $\log_{10} 0.01543$	**11.** antilog$_{10}$ (8.2210 − 10)
4. $\log_{10} 0.0031$	**8.** $\log_{10} 4.317$	**12.** antilog$_{10}$ (9.8706 − 10)

Use logarithms to the base 10 and the theorem on page 354 to approximate each of the following.

13. $(0.3172)(1.35)$

14. $\dfrac{2.1765}{1.7122}$

15. $\dfrac{482.1}{(83.8)(3.141)}$

16. $\dfrac{(28.1)^2 \cdot (81.23)}{(2.177)^5}$

17. $\sqrt[4]{213.8}$ **19.** $\sqrt[3]{\dfrac{42.71}{\pi^2}}$

18. $\sqrt[3]{(2.17)(8.131)^2}$ **20.** $\dfrac{\sqrt[5]{(28.1)^2}}{\sqrt[4]{(2.172)^3}}$

21. $\sqrt[3]{0.2173}$ (*Hint:* Use $29.0000 - 30$ for the characteristic.)

22. $\sqrt[4]{0.02237}$ (*Hint:* Use $38.0000 - 40$ for the characteristic.)

23. $\dfrac{21.4}{0.0173}$ **24.** $\dfrac{(8.17)^3}{0.0125}$

In Exercises 25–32, state the characteristic of the given logarithm if the mantissa is to be a positive decimal.

25. $\log_3 50$ **27.** $\log_{\frac{1}{2}} \frac{1}{5}$ **29.** $\log_3 \frac{1}{15}$ **31.** $\log_{\frac{1}{4}} 52$

26. $\log_7 104$ **28.** $\log_{\frac{1}{3}} \frac{2}{5}$ **30.** $\log_2 \frac{1}{50}$ **32.** $\log_{\frac{2}{5}} 107$

Use logarithms and their properties to help you find the solution set of each of the following. Check each potential root to ensure that it satisfies the given equation.

33. $\log_7 (x + 1) + \log_7 (x - 5) = 1$

34. $\log_2 (9x + 5) - \log_2 (x^2 - 1) = 2$

35. $\log_{10} (x + 2) + \log_{10} (x - 1) = 1$

36. $\log_{10} (x - 3) - \log_{10} (x + 1) = 1$

37. $3^{x+2} = 10$ **39.** $3^{x^2} = 21$

38. $7^{-x} = 10$ **40.** $3^{x-2} = 16$

9–10 Values for $\text{Log}_b x$

Without having a table of values of $\log_5$, can you determine $\log_5 6$? To see why it is not necessary to have a table of logarithms to the base 5 to solve this problem, study the following argument.

Let $y = \log_5 6$.

Then $5^y = 6$.   (Why?)

Taking common logarithms, you obtain

$$\log_{10} 5^y = \log_{10} 6. \quad \text{(Why?)}$$

$$\therefore y \log_{10} 5 = \log_{10} 6. \quad \text{(Why?)}$$

$$\therefore y = \frac{\log_{10} 6}{\log_{10} 5}.$$

$$\therefore \log_5 6 = \frac{\log_{10} 6}{\log_{10} 5}.$$

Using Table 4, you can verify that

$$\log_5 6 \doteq \frac{0.7782}{0.6990} \doteq 1.1133.$$

The preceding discussion illustrates the relationship that holds, in general, between the logarithms of a number to two different bases.

THEOREM   If a, b, and x denote positive real numbers, $a \neq 1$ and $b \neq 1$, then

$$\log_a x = \frac{\log_b x}{\log_b a}.$$

Proof: *Plan:* The argument parallels the reasoning used to determine $\log_5 6$. Justifying the steps in the proof is left to you.

$$\text{Let} \qquad y = \log_a x.$$

$$\text{Then} \quad a^y = x.$$

$$\therefore \; \log_b a^y = \log_b x$$

$$y \log_b a = \log_b x$$

$$\therefore \; y = \frac{\log_b x}{\log_b a}, \quad \text{or}$$

$$\log_a x = \frac{\log_b x}{\log_b a}$$

In particular, replacing a by e and b by 10, you obtain the following corollary.

COROLLARY 1.   If $x > 0$, $\log_e x = \dfrac{\log_{10} x}{\log_{10} e}$.

Using the fact that $\log_{10} e \doteq 0.4343$, you can apply the corollary to deduce that

$$\log_e x \doteq \frac{\log_{10} x}{0.4343} \doteq 2.3026 \log_{10} x.$$

EXAMPLE.   Find $\log_e 274$.

Solution: $\log_e 274 \doteq 2.3026 \log_{10} 274$.

Therefore, since Table 4 yields $\log_{10} 274 \doteq 2.4378$,

$$\log_e 274 \doteq (2.3026)(2.4378) \doteq 5.613, \textbf{ Answer.}$$

The problem of determining $\log_e 274$ in the preceding Example is equivalent to finding x so that $e^x = 274$. (Why?) Hence, using the method of Section 9–5, you could solve this example by reverse interpolation in Table 5. However, the resulting approximation to $\log_e 274$ would be less accurate than the answer obtained above, because Table 5 contains relatively few entries.

Since $\log_b b = 1$ (Why?), you can also deduce the following assertion from the theorem proved above.

COROLLARY 2.   If $a > 0$, $b > 0$, $a \neq 1$ and $b \neq 1$, then

$$(\log_a b)(\log_b a) = 1.$$

Exercises

In Exercises 1–12, find the required logarithm by using Table 4.

A
1. $\log_2 17$
2. $\log_3 83$
3. $\log_5 927$

4. $\log_6 281$
5. $\log_3 0.2174$
6. $\log_2 0.8192$

7. $\log_5 0.001235$
8. $\log_6 0.002178$
9. $\log_e 12470$

10. $\log_e 0.08172$
11. $\log_e 0.3002$
12. $\log_e 8276$

B
13. Find an $x \neq 2$ such that $\dfrac{\log_e x}{x} = \dfrac{\log_e 2}{2}$.

14. Find an $x \neq 4$ such that $\dfrac{\log_e x}{x} = \dfrac{\log_e 4}{4}$.

15. If $f(x) = \log_e (x + 1)$, find all x such that $f(x) = f(2) + f(3)$.

16. If $g(x) = \log_e \dfrac{x + 1}{x - 1}$, find all x such that $g(x) = g(2) + g(3)$.

17. If $\log_b a = K$, and $c = a^2$, find $\log_b c$ in terms of K.

18. If $\log_b a = K$, and $a = c^2$, find $\log_b c$ in terms of K.

C
19. Prove Corollary 2 above.

20. Prove that if a, b, c, and d are positive real numbers none of which is equal to 1, then
$$\log_a b \cdot \log_b c \cdot \log_c d = \log_a d.$$

21. Prove that if $a > 0$, $x > 0$, and $a \neq 1$, then $\log_a x = -\log_{\frac{1}{a}} x$.

22. Prove that if $a > 0$, $a \neq 1$, and $x > 0$, $\log_a x = \log_{a+1} x$, then $x = 1$.

23. Show that if $\log_a 2 = \log_b 4$, then $b = a^2$.

24. Show that if $\log_a 3 = \log_b 27$, then $b = a^3$.

9–11   Tangents to the Graphs of Log$_b$ and Exp$_b$ (*Optional*)

Let $x_1, x_2, x_3, \ldots$ be any convergent
sequence of positive real numbers
having the real number c as limit and
having all its terms different from c.
Figures 9–18 (a), (b), and (c) show the
graph of log$_b$ near the point $\mathbf{P}(c, \log_b c)$,
together with the line $\mathfrak{I}_n$ (in red) containing $\mathbf{P}$ and the point $\mathbf{S}_n(x_n, \log_b x_n)$
for $n = 1, 2, 3$. (The curvature of the
graph of log$_b$ is exaggerated to show
detail.) The black line, $\mathfrak{I}$, represents the
limiting position of $\mathfrak{I}_n$ as n increases
without bound, and is defined to be the
tangent to the graph of log$_b$ at $\mathbf{P}$.

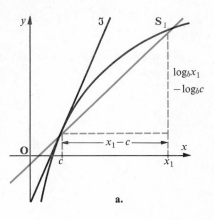

a.

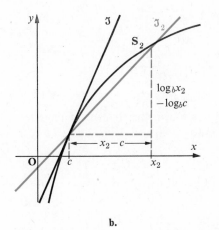

b.

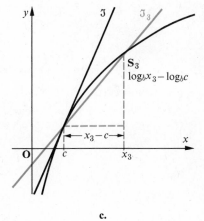

c.

Figure 9–18

The **slope** of the graph of log$_b$ at $\mathbf{P}$ is defined to be the slope of the tangent
to the graph at $\mathbf{P}$, and is, therefore, the limit (if it exists) of the sequence

$$\frac{\log_b x_1 - \log_b c}{x_1 - c}, \frac{\log_b x_2 - \log_b c}{x_2 - c}, \frac{\log_b x_3 - \log_b c}{x_3 - c}, \ldots$$

Thus, if $f = \log_b$, and if, as in Section 8–6, f' denotes the derivative of f,
that is, the function whose value at c is the slope of the graph of f at $[c, f(c)]$,
then you can write the foregoing definition as follows:

If $x_n \in \mathcal{R}^+$, $c \in \mathcal{R}^+$, and $x_n \neq c$, then

$$f'(c) = \lim_{x_n \to c} \frac{\log_b x_n - \log_b c}{x_n - c}.$$

To show that this limit exists for each $c > 0$, and to find an expression for it in terms of c, you can restate the ratio

$$\frac{\log_b x_n - \log_b c}{x_n - c}$$

in slightly different terms. By the second law of logarithms, you can write

$$\frac{\log_b x_n - \log_b c}{x_n - c} = \frac{\log_b \dfrac{x_n}{c}}{x_n - c}$$

$$= \frac{\log_b \left(1 + \dfrac{x_n - c}{c}\right)}{x_n - c}.$$

Therefore,

(1) $$f'(c) = \lim_{x_n \to c} \frac{\log_b \left(1 + \dfrac{x_n - c}{c}\right)}{x_n - c},$$

if this limit exists.

By multiplying and dividing the expression in the right-hand member of (1) by c ($c \neq 0$), you can proceed as follows:

$$f'(c) = \lim_{x_n \to c} \frac{1}{c}\left(\frac{c}{x_n - c}\right)\left[\log_b \left(1 + \frac{x_n - c}{c}\right)\right]$$

$$= \lim_{x_n \to c} \frac{1}{c} \log_b \left(1 + \frac{x_n - c}{c}\right)^{\frac{c}{x_n - c}} \quad \text{(Why?)}$$

$$f'(c) = \frac{1}{c} \lim_{x_n \to c} \log_b \left(1 + \frac{x_n - c}{c}\right)^{\frac{1}{\frac{x_n - c}{c}}} \quad \text{(Why?)}$$

Now, by the continuity of the function $\log_b$,

$$\lim_{x_n \to c} \log_b x_n = \log_b (\lim_{x_n \to c} x_n) = \log_b c.$$

Hence, you can write

$$f'(c) = \frac{1}{c} \log_b \left[\lim_{x_n \to c} \left(1 + \frac{x_n - c}{c}\right)^{\frac{1}{\frac{x_n - c}{c}}}\right],$$

But, if in the assertion $\lim_{t \to 0} (1 + t)^{\frac{1}{t}} = e$ (page 341) you replace t by

$$\frac{x_n - c}{c}, \text{ you find } \lim_{x_n \to c} \left(1 + \frac{x_n - c}{c}\right)^{\frac{1}{\frac{x_n - c}{c}}} = e.$$

$$\therefore \ f'(c) = \frac{1}{c} \log_b e.$$

Since the preceding argument is valid for every c in $\mathcal{R}^+$, you can make the following assertion.

THEOREM   If $x \in \mathcal{R}^+, b \in \mathcal{R}^+, b \neq 1,$ and
$$f = \{(x, y): \ y = \log_b x\}, \text{ then}$$
$$f'(x) = \frac{1}{x} \log_b e.$$

EXAMPLE 1. Find the derivative of $\log_e$.

Solution: Let $f = \log_e$. Then from the foregoing theorem, and the fact that $\log_e e = 1$, you have

$$f'(x) = \frac{1}{x} \log_e e = \frac{1}{x}.$$

$\therefore$ the derivative of $\log_e = \left\{(x, y): \ y = \frac{1}{x}\right\}$, **Answer.**

EXAMPLE 2. Find the equation of the line tangent to the graph of $y = \log_{10} x$ at the point where $x = 1$.

Solution: When $x = 1$, $\log_{10} x = 0$, so that the point of tangency is $(1, 0)$. Also if $y = \log_{10} x$, then

$$y' = \frac{1}{x} \log_{10} e.$$

At $(1, 0)$ the slope is

$$y' \doteq \tfrac{1}{1}(.4343) = .4343.$$

The equation is $y - 0 \doteq .4343(x - 1)$, or with $=$ in place of $\doteq$,
$$y = .4343x - .4343, \textbf{Answer.}$$

Figure 9–19 suggests that the reflection in the line

$$\mathfrak{L} = \{(x, y):\ y = x\}$$

of a line whose slope is m $(m \neq 0)$ is a line whose slope is $\dfrac{1}{m}$. You can use this fact to determine the slope of the graph of $\exp_b$ at the point $\mathbf{T}(a, c)$ $[c \in \mathfrak{R}^+]$, given the slope of the graph of $\log_b$ at $\mathbf{P}(c, a)$. In fact,

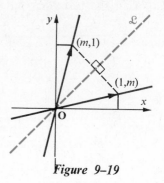

Figure 9–19

$$\text{slope of graph of } \log_b \text{ at } \mathbf{P} = \frac{\log_b e}{c}. \quad \text{(Why?)}$$

Therefore, using the fact suggested by Figure 9–19, you discover that

$$\text{slope of graph of } \exp_b \text{ at } \mathbf{T} = \frac{c}{\log_b e}.$$

But $c = b^a$ (Why?), and $\dfrac{1}{\log_b e} = \log_e b$ (Why?). Hence, the **slope of the graph of $\exp_b$** at the point whose abscissa is a is $b^a \log_e b$. This gives the following theorem.

> **THEOREM**   If $x \in \mathfrak{R}, b \in \mathfrak{R}^+, b \neq 1,$ and $g = \{(x, y):\ y = b^x\}$, then $g'(x) = b^x \log_e b.$

Since $\log_e e = 1$, you also have the following result.

COROLLARY.   If $g = \{(x, y):\ y = e^x,\ x \in \mathfrak{R}\}$,

then $g' = \{(x, y):\ y = e^x,\ x \in \mathfrak{R}\}$;

that is, the derivative of e^x is e^x.

Notice that if $b > 1$, all the values of the derivative $\dfrac{\log_b e}{x}$ of $\log_b x$ $(x \in \mathfrak{R}^+)$, and of the derivative $b^x \log_e b$ of b^x $(x \in \mathfrak{R})$ are positive numbers (Why?). This fact confirms a result that you already know (see page 353): if $b > 1$, $\log_b$ and $\exp_b$ are increasing functions. On the other hand, as x increases, the derivative of $\log_b$ decreases, whereas the derivative of $\exp_b$ increases. (Why?) This fact means that no value of the second derivative of $\log_b$ can be positive, whereas no value of the second derivative of $\exp_b$ can be negative. This observation confirms a result that you have guessed: if $b > 1$, the graph of $\log_b$ is concave downward, whereas the graph of $\exp_b$ is concave upward. In case $0 < b < 1$, you can similarly discuss these functions.

Exercises

Find the derivative f' for each of the functions f whose values are indicated, and evaluate the derivative at the given value for x.

(C)

1. $f(x) = \log_2 x; \; x = 2$
2. $f(x) = \log_3 x; \; x = 3$
3. $f(x) = \log_{10} x; \; x = 10$
4. $f(x) = \log_e x; \; x = \frac{1}{10}$
5. $f(x) = \log_3 x; \; x = 0.21$

6. $f(x) = \log_{\frac{1}{2}} x; \; x = 4$
7. $f(x) = \log_{\frac{2}{3}} x; \; x = 1$
8. $f(x) = \log_{\frac{1}{e}} x; \; x = e$
9. $f(x) = 2^x; \; x = 2$
10. $f(x) = e^x; \; x = 0$

11–20. In each of Exercises 1–10, find the equation of the tangent to the graph of the given equation at the point with given abscissa.

21. Use the definition of the derivative $f'(c) = \lim_{h \to 0} \dfrac{\log_e (c + h) - \log_e c}{h}$ to show that the derivative of $f = \{(x, y): y = \log_e ax\}$ is independent of a; that is, show that if $y = \log_e ax$, then $y' = \dfrac{1}{x}$.

22. Use the definition of the derivative in Exercise 21 to show that if $y = a \log_e x$, then $y' = \dfrac{a}{x}$.

23. Use the result in Exercise 22 and the laws of logarithms to show that if $y = \log_e x^n$, then $y' = \dfrac{n}{x}$.

24. Use the result in Exercise 22 and the laws of logarithms to show that if $y = \log_e \sqrt[n]{x}$, then $y' = \dfrac{1}{nx}$.

Chapter Summary

1. The definition of powers with rational exponents is chosen for consistency with the laws for positive integral exponents. If $b > 0$, the expression $b^{\frac{p}{q}} (p \in J, q \in N)$ denotes the pth power of the nonnegative **qth root** of b.

2. The function $\exp_2$ is defined by an equation of the form $y = 2^x$ for $x \in \mathcal{R}$. It is continuous and increasing, and has as its range the set $\mathcal{R}^+$ of positive real numbers.

3. The **exponential function** with base b is denoted by $\exp_b$ and is defined by an equation of the form $y = b^x$, where $b \in \mathcal{R}^+$ and $x \in \mathcal{R}$. An exponential function is continuous; it is **increasing** if $b > 1$, and **decreasing** if $b < 1$.

4. Powers of a base b can be approximated by the use of a table of $\exp_b$. If the value you seek is not in the table, you can use **linear interpolation** to obtain an approximation.

5. The **composition** $f \circ g$ of two functions f and g is the function such that $[f \circ g](x) = f[g(x)]$. The domain of $f \circ g$ is the subset of D_g such that for each x in the subset, $g(x) \in D_f$.

6. The functions f and f^{-1} are **inverses** if and only if $f \circ f^{-1} = f^{-1} \circ f = I$, where I is the identity function. This implies that $f[f^{-1}(x)] = f^{-1}[f(x)] = x$, for each x in the domain of f. A function has an inverse if and only if it is **one-to-one**. Every continuous function with an inverse has a continuous inverse.

7. The inverse of an exponential function is a **logarithmic function**. You use the important identities

$$b^{\log_b x} = x \quad \text{and} \quad \log_b b^x = x$$

to help you prove the following **laws of logarithms**:

If a, b, and c are positive numbers, and $b \neq 1$, then

1. $\log_b ac = \log_b a + \log_b c$,

2. $\log_b \dfrac{a}{c} = \log_b a - \log_b c, \ (c \neq 0)$

3. $\log_b a^c = c \log_b a$,

4. $\log_b \sqrt[c]{a} = \dfrac{1}{c} \log_b a, \quad (c \text{ a positive integer}),$

5. $\log_b a = \log_b c$ if and only if $a = c$.

8. A logarithm can be viewed as the sum of an integer called the **characteristic** and a decimal fraction called the **mantissa**. The characteristic of the common logarithm of x ($\log_{10} x$) is found by expressing x as the product of a number between 1 and 10 and a power of 10; the exponent in the power of 10 is the characteristic. To find an approximation for the mantissa of $\log_{10} x$ you look in a table of logarithms and use linear interpolation as needed. You can use a table for $\log_{10}$ and the laws of logarithms to compute products, quotients, powers, and roots.

9. If you have a table for $\log_b x$, you can use the relationship

$$\log_a x = \frac{\log_b x}{\log_b a}$$

to find $\log_a x$ for any base a. In particular, you can use the tables for $\log_{10} x$ to find values for $\log_e x$.

10. The derivative of $y = \log_b x$ is $y' = \dfrac{1}{x} \log_b e$; when evaluated at a value $x = c$, it gives you the slope of the tangent to the graph of $y = \log_b x$ where $x = c$. The derivative of $y = \log_e x$ is just $y' = \dfrac{1}{x}$. The derivative of $y = b^x$ is $y' = b^x \log_e b$, and of $y = e^x$ is $y' = e^x$.

Chapter Test

9-1 **1.** Express as a simpler numeral: $\frac{1}{32}$

  a. $8^{-\frac{5}{3}}$, **b.** $(\frac{1}{3})^0$.

  2. Solve for x: $(\frac{1}{2})^{2x-1} = 2(4)^{x-1}$. $x = \frac{1}{2}$

9-2 **3.** Sketch the graph of $y = 2^x$, $-2 \le x \le 2$, and from it read the $x = .4$
  values of x and of t to one decimal place if $2^x = 1.3$ and $2^{1.3} = t$. $t = 2.4$

9-3 *(Optional)*

  4. Find $\lim\limits_{x \to 0.6} 2^{25x^2 - 10x - 1}$.

9-4 **5.** Given that $5 = 3^{1.47}$, solve for x: $25 = 3^x$. $x = 2.94$

9-5 **6.** Given that $e^{0.75} = 2.117$, $e^{0.76} = 2.138$, determine $e^{0.756}$ by linear
  interpolation. 2.13

9-6 **7.** If $f(x) = |x|$ and $g(x) = x^2 - 1$ define the functions f and g with
  domain $\mathcal{R}$, find equations defining $f \circ g$ and $g \circ f$. $f \circ g = |x^2 - 1|$
   $g \circ f = x^2 - 1$

  8. In Exercise 7, what is the domain of $f \circ g$?   all real numbers

9-7 **9.** State an equation defining the inverse of f if f is defined by
  $y = \sqrt{9 - x}$, $x \in \mathcal{R}$, $x \le 9$.

  10. Show that the functions defined by $y = ax + b$ and $y = \dfrac{x - b}{a}$
  ($a \neq 0$, $x \in \mathcal{R}$) are inverses.

9-8 **11.** Find x so that $x = \frac{1}{5}$ $x = 81$

  a. $\log_x 5 = -1$ **b.** $\log_3 x = 4$.

  12. Write $e^{3 \log_e 2}$ in simpler form. 8

9-9 **13.** What is the characteristic of $\log_2 \frac{3}{5}$? -1

  14. Given $\log_{10} 6.75 \doteq 0.8293$ and $\log_{10} 6.76 \doteq 0.8299$, find an
  approximation for $\log_{10} 67.56$. 1.8297

a.ϵ445

9–10   **15.** If $\log_{10} 2 \doteq 0.3010$, find an approximation for $\log_2 100$.

9–11   (*Optional*)

     16. Find the equation of the tangent to the graph of $y = \log_e x$ when $x = e^2$. Leave your result in terms of e.

$$y = \frac{1}{e^2}(x) + 1$$

Reading List

Beckenbach, Edwin F., and Richard Bellman. *An Introduction to Inequalities.* New York: W. L. Singer Co., 1961.

Korovkin, P. P., *Inequalities.* New York: Blaisdell Publishing Co., 1961.

Menger, Karl. *Methods of Presenting e and π.* American Mathematical Monthly, vol. 52, pp. 28–33, 1945.

School Mathematics Study Group. Mathematics for High School: *Intermediate Mathematics, Parts I, II.* New Haven, Conn.: Yale University Press, 1961.

—— Mathematics for High School: *Elementary Functions, Parts I, II.* New Haven, Conn.: Yale University Press, 1961.

Taylor, Howard E., and Thomas L. Wade. *University Freshman Mathematics.* New York: John Wiley and Sons, Inc., 1963.

Titchmark, E. *Mathematics for the General Reader.* Garden City: Doubleday, 1959.

Emmy Noether

If it were necessary to find one or two words to characterize the mathematical work of the last 150 years, "rigorous," "abstract," or "axiomatic" might be likely choices. The success which men such as Abel and Dedekind found with the abstract approach encouraged many mathematicians in the latter half of the 19th century to adopt this point of view. In fact, the methods of generalization and abstraction led to such significant results during these years that by the 1930's mathematicians began to predict that they would soon run out of things to generalize and that these methods would lose their power. Strangely enough, it was during this period that the abstract approach was used most effectively by the German mathematician Emmy Noether to reach important new results in the field of algebra.

Amalie Emmy Noether (1882–1935) grew up in a world of mathematics. Her father was a professor of mathematics at the University of Erlangen, and her younger brother also studied mathematics. She received her degree from Erlangen and then in 1916 moved to the University of Göttingen, where she helped Hilbert and Klein develop the mathematical aspects of the theory of relativity. Since tradition opposed the appointment of women to university positions, only the continual persuasion of the mathematics faculty made her appointment to a minor position possible. In the following years her work gave evidence of her great creative power in abstract algebra. She lectured to classes of enthusiastic students at Göttingen until 1933 when the Nazis came to power and she and other outstanding scientists of Jewish background were denied the right to teach. She then came to the United States and was warmly received at Bryn Mawr College, where she taught until her death.

Korn.

Prof. Emmy Noether

An important phase of Miss Noether's work was concerned with the theory of rings. A commutative ring is an abstract system with two binary operations, addition and multiplication. It has the properties of the real number system except for the existence of an identity element for multiplication and the existence of multiplicative inverses for all elements. The set of all even integers is an example of a commutative ring. Can you think of others?

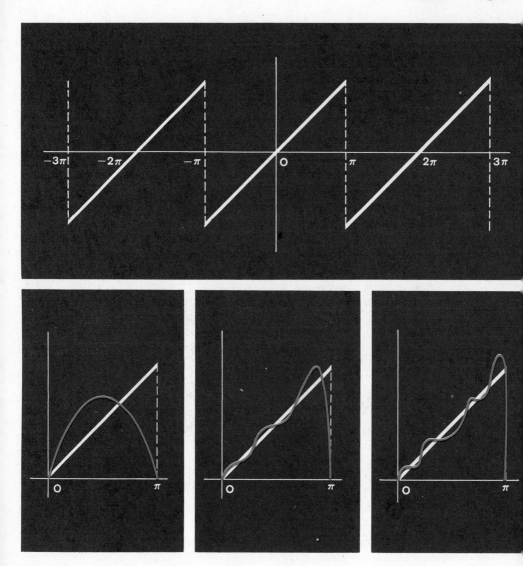

Most periodic functions can be approximated as closely as desired by partial sums of an infinite trigonometric series. The periodic function defined by $y = x$, $-\pi < x < \pi$ (top diagram) can be represented by the series $y = 2\left(\sin x - \dfrac{\sin 2x}{2} + \dfrac{\sin 3x}{3} - \cdots\right)$.

Approximations using the first 1, 4, and 10 terms of the series, respectively, are shown.

The Circular Functions
and Trigonometry

*Many physical phenomena recur in regular patterns, or periods.
For example, the bob of a pendulum swings back and forth in a regular
pattern, the voltage in an alternating-current circuit oscillates con-
stantly between positive and negative values, and the seasons of the
year follow one another in a recurring cycle. We speak of such
phenomena as periodic changes. Mathematical models of periodic
change make use of periodic functions, the most basic of which are the
circular and trigonometric functions you will study in this chapter.*

THE CIRCULAR FUNCTIONS

10–1 The Unit Circle

In geometry you learned that a **circle** is the set
of points in a plane at a given distance from a
given point in the plane. The given point is the
center of the circle and the distance from the
center to each point of the circle is the **radius**.
A **unit circle** is a circle whose radius is one unit.

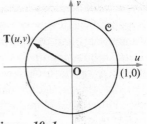

Figure 10–1

Let $\mathcal{C}$ be the unit circle with its center **O** at the origin $(0, 0)$ of a rectangular
coordinate system (Figure 10–1). If $\mathbf{T}(u, v)$ is any point of $\mathcal{C}$, then
$\|\overrightarrow{\mathbf{OT}}\| = 1$. (Why?) Therefore, because $\|\overrightarrow{\mathbf{OT}}\| = \sqrt{u^2 + v^2}$, you have:

$$\sqrt{u^2 + v^2} = 1, \text{ or}$$

$$u^2 + v^2 = 1.$$

We call this equation *the equation of the unit circle with center at the origin
in the uv-plane.*

Notice that if the ordered pair (a, b) satisfies the equation of $\mathcal{C}$, then
$(a, -b)$ also satisfies the equation. (Why?) If a curve has the property
that whenever (a, b) designates a point of the curve, $(a, -b)$ also denotes one
of its points, then the curve is said to be *symmetric with respect to the horizontal axis.* Thus, $\mathcal{C}$ is symmetric with respect to the *u*-axis. But, if (a, b)

373

denotes a point of ℭ, so also does $(-a, b)$. If a curve contains the point $(-a, b)$ whenever it contains the point (a, b), then the curve is called *symmetric with respect to the vertical axis*. Hence, ℭ is also symmetric with respect to the v-axis.

Figure 10–2 summarizes the foregoing symmetry properties of ℭ and indicates that ℭ contains all the points (a, b), $(a, -b)$, $(-a, b)$, $(-a, -b)$ if it contains any one of them.

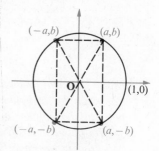

In geometry you take for granted the fact that every circular arc has a length, and, in particular, that the circumference of a circle of radius r is given by $2\pi r$. Thus, the circumference of a unit circle is 2π units. When you study calculus, you will closely examine the problem of defining arc length. Meanwhile, however, we shall assume that it is meaningful to speak of distance along a circle, and we will use this concept to pair every real number with a point of the unit circle ℭ.

Figure 10–2

Figure 10–3 shows ℭ and the vertical line $u = 1$. If you imagine the vertical line to be a flexible number line with origin at **P**$(1, 0)$, you can visualize winding it around ℭ much as you would wind a thread around a spool. Of course, since a line has no thickness, successive windings would fall each exactly upon the others. You can picture both rays of the number line winding around the circle, with the positive ray winding in a counterclockwise direction and the negative ray in a clockwise direction. Do you see that this procedure pairs each real number x of the number line with one and only one point of ℭ?

Because the circumference of ℭ is 2π, the point labeled π on the number line is wound into the point $(-1, 0)$ on ℭ. (Why?) Similarly, the procedure maps $\dfrac{\pi}{2}$ into $(0, 1)$, $\dfrac{3\pi}{2}$ into $(0, -1)$,

and 2π into $(1, 0)$. Also, $-\dfrac{\pi}{2}$ is mapped

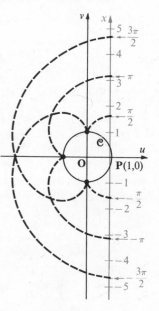

Figure 10–3

into $(0, -1)$, $-\pi$ into $(-1, 0)$, $-\dfrac{3\pi}{2}$ into $(0, 1)$, and -2π into $(1, 0)$. Since one complete counterclockwise winding corresponds to a distance 2π, while each clockwise winding corresponds to a distance -2π, it follows that the process maps all the real numbers $x, x \pm 2\pi, x \pm 4\pi, \ldots, x + 2n\pi$, where $n \in J$, into the same point of ℭ.

Thus, on ℭ the winding process pairs each real number x with the point **T** whose distance along ℭ from **P**$(1, 0)$ is x. If $x > 0$, the distance is measured counterclockwise from **P**; if $x < 0$, the distance is measured clockwise. Notice that the procedure maps 0 into the point **P** itself.

Do you see that the symmetry of $\mathcal{C}$ with respect to the u- and v-axes ensures that if x measures the distance along $\mathcal{C}$ from **P**$(1, 0)$ to the point (a, b), then $-x$ measures the distance along $\mathcal{C}$ to $(a, -b)$? (See Figure 10–4a.) Parts (b) and (c) of Figure 10–4 suggest other consequences of the symmetry of $\mathcal{C}$ and the fact that the length of a semicircle of a unit circle is π.

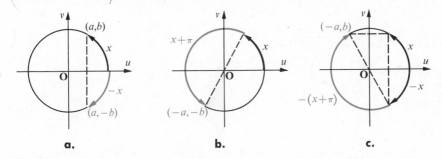

a.   **b.**   **c.**

Figure 10–4

Exercises

1. A long tape measure tacked at its zero point to the rim of a unit disk is wrapped counterclockwise around the disk. The tape mark for $\frac{2}{3}\pi$ falls on point **R** of the disk. Write the positive numbers for five other tape marks that fall on **R**. Write an expression for the positive numbers corresponding to all tape marks that fall on **R**.

2. A long tape measure showing negative numbers is wrapped clockwise around a unit disk. The tape mark for -2 falls on point **Q** of the disk. Write the negative numbers for five other tape marks that fall on **Q**. Write an expression for the negative numbers corresponding to all tape marks that fall on **Q**.

If **T** is the point that is at the given distance on the unit circle $\mathcal{C}$ from **P**$(1, 0)$, name the quadrant in which **T** lies. Assume $k \in J$.

3. $\frac{2}{3}\pi$ **7.** -1 **11.** $4\pi - \frac{1}{3}\pi$

4. 5   **8.** -3 **12.** $\frac{1}{5}\pi + 2k\pi$

5. $-\frac{4}{3}\pi$ **9.** $\dfrac{1000\pi}{6}$ **13.** $-\frac{1}{4}\pi + (2k + 1)\pi$

6. $17\frac{1}{4}\pi$ **10.** $4\pi + \frac{1}{3}\pi$ **14.** $-\frac{2}{3}\pi + \left(\dfrac{4k + 1}{2}\right)\pi$

If on $\mathcal{C}$ the distance from **P**$(1, 0)$ to the point **T** is x, determine the coordinates of the points at the indicated distances on $\mathcal{C}$ from **P**.

15. **T**$(\frac{5}{13}, \frac{12}{13})$; (a) $\pi + x$, (b) $-x$, (c) $\pi - x$, (d) $2\pi + x$.

16. **T**$(\frac{3}{5}, \frac{4}{5})$; (a) $\pi - x$, (b) $\pi + x$, (c) $2\pi - x$, (d) $x - \pi$.

17. $T\left(-\dfrac{1}{3}, \dfrac{2\sqrt{2}}{3}\right)$; (a) $4\pi + x$, (b) $2\pi - x$, (c) $3\pi + x$, (d) $3\pi - x$.

18. $T\left(-\dfrac{8}{17}, -\dfrac{15}{17}\right)$; (a) $6\pi - x$, (b) $5\pi + x$, (c) $5\pi - x$, (d) $8\pi + x$.

The length of the arc of $\mathcal{C}$ from $P(1, 0)$ to T is given. Determine the coordinates of the points at the indicated distances on $\mathcal{C}$ from P.

B   **19.** $T\left(\dfrac{\sqrt{2}}{2}, \dfrac{\sqrt{2}}{2}\right)$, $\dfrac{\pi}{4}$; (a) $-\dfrac{\pi}{4}$; (b) $\dfrac{3\pi}{4}$; (c) $\dfrac{5\pi}{4}$; (d) $\dfrac{7\pi}{4}$.

20. $T\left(\dfrac{1}{2}, \dfrac{\sqrt{3}}{2}\right)$, $\dfrac{\pi}{3}$; (a) $-\dfrac{\pi}{3}$; (b) $\dfrac{2\pi}{3}$; (c) $\dfrac{4\pi}{3}$; (d) $\dfrac{5\pi}{3}$.

21. $T\left(-\dfrac{\sqrt{3}}{2}, -\dfrac{1}{2}\right)$, $-\dfrac{5\pi}{6}$; (a) $\dfrac{\pi}{6}$; (b) $\dfrac{11\pi}{6}$; (c) $\dfrac{7\pi}{6}$; (d) $-\dfrac{7\pi}{6}$.

22. $T\left(\dfrac{1}{\sqrt{2}}, -\dfrac{1}{\sqrt{2}}\right)$, $-\dfrac{\pi}{4}$; (a) $-\dfrac{5\pi}{4}$; (b) $-\dfrac{7\pi}{4}$; (c) $\dfrac{11\pi}{4}$; (d) $\dfrac{9\pi}{4}$.

State whether the graph of the given relation is symmetric with respect to **(a)** the u-axis, **(b)** the v-axis.

23. $\{(u, v): v = 2u^2 + \frac{1}{3}\}$ **26.** $\{(u, v): v^2 = u^4 + 2\}$

24. $\{(u, v): v = 3u^4 - u^2 + 1\}$ **27.** $\{(u, v): 3u^2 + 5v^2 = 15\}$

25. $\{(u, v): v^2 = u^6 - u\}$ **28.** $\{(u, v): u^2 - 9v^2 = 36\}$

10–2 The Sine and Cosine Functions

The winding procedure described in Section 10–1 associates with each real number x one and only one point $T(u, v)$ on the unit circle $\mathcal{C}$. (Figure 10–5.) By assigning to each real number x the first coordinate u of T, you

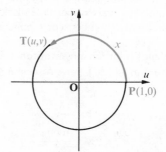

Figure 10–5

can define a function whose domain is $\mathcal{R}$ and whose range is the set of all first coordinates of points on $\mathcal{C}$. This function is called the **cosine function over** $\mathcal{R}$, abbreviated **cos.**

When you pair x with the second coordinate v of T, you obtain the function whose domain is $\mathcal{R}$, whose range is the set of all second coordinates of points on $\mathcal{C}$, and whose name is the **sine function over** $\mathfrak{R}$, abbreviated **sin.** Thus:

If $\mathcal{C}$ is the circle with equation $u^2 + v^2 = 1$ and x is the distance along $\mathcal{C}$ from $\mathbf{P}(1, 0)$ to $\mathbf{T}(u, v)$, then

$$\cos = \{(x, u): u = \cos x\}$$
$$\sin = \{(x, v): v = \sin x\}$$

Figure 10–6 illustrates these definitions.

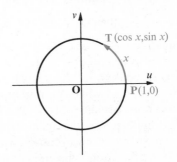

Figure 10–6

Because the unit circle $\mathcal{C}$ is involved in their definitions, we call the cosine and sine functions **circular functions.** Since for every point of $\mathcal{C}$

$$u^2 + v^2 = 1,$$

you have the following basic relationship between the circular functions:

THEOREM For each x in $\mathfrak{R}$, $\sin^2 x + \cos^2 x = 1$.

(The symbols $\sin^2 x$ and $\cos^2 x$ denote $(\sin x)^2$ and $(\cos x)^2$ respectively.)

Do you see that the preceding theorem implies that for every x in $\mathfrak{R}$, $|\sin x| \le 1$ and $|\cos x| \le 1$? (Exercises 27 and 28, page 382.)

You know that if x measures the distance along $\mathcal{C}$ to (u, v), then $-x$ measures the distance to $(u, -v)$. (See Figure 10–4a.) This fact implies the following property of the circular functions.

THEOREM For each x in $\mathfrak{R}$,
$$\cos(-x) = \cos x \text{ and } \sin(-x) = -\sin x.$$

On $\mathcal{C}$ the number π measures the distance counterclockwise from $\mathbf{P}(1, 0)$ to $\mathbf{T}(-1, 0)$. (Why?) Thus, $\cos \pi = -1$ and $\sin \pi = 0$. Because the distance measured clockwise on $\mathcal{C}$ from $\mathbf{P}$ to the point $(0, -1)$ is $-\dfrac{\pi}{2}$, you have $\cos\left(-\dfrac{\pi}{2}\right) = 0$ and $\sin\left(-\dfrac{\pi}{2}\right) = -1$. Numbers such as $\cos \pi$ or

$\sin\left(-\dfrac{\pi}{6}\right)$ which are values of the cosine and sine functions associated with

the points $(1,0)$, $(0, 1)$, $(-1,0)$, or $(0, -1)$ on $\mathcal{C}$ are called **quadrantal values** of these functions. (See Exercises 9 and 10, page 381.)

When x measures the distance on $\mathcal{C}$ from $P(1, 0)$ to a point which lies within a given quadrant, x is said to be *in* that quadrant. For example, if $x = \dfrac{3\pi}{4}$, then x is in the second quadrant. Because $\cos x$ and $\sin x$ are coordinates of points on the unit circle, you can see that for x between 0 and 2π they will be positive or negative in accordance with Figure 10-7.

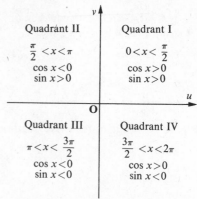

Quadrant II	Quadrant I
$\dfrac{\pi}{2} < x < \pi$	$0 < x < \dfrac{\pi}{2}$
$\cos x < 0$	$\cos x > 0$
$\sin x > 0$	$\sin x > 0$

Quadrant III	Quadrant IV
$\pi < x < \dfrac{3\pi}{2}$	$\dfrac{3\pi}{2} < x < 2\pi$
$\cos x < 0$	$\cos x > 0$
$\sin x < 0$	$\sin x < 0$

Figure 10–7

You can use the relationship $\sin^2 x + \cos^2 x = 1$ together with the symmetry of $\mathcal{C}$ and your knowledge of the geometry of circles to find values for the functions sine and cosine for some special values of x.

EXAMPLE 1. Find values for **(a)** $\cos\dfrac{\pi}{6}$ and $\sin\dfrac{\pi}{6}$; **(b)** $\cos\dfrac{\pi}{3}$ and $\sin\dfrac{\pi}{3}$.

Solution:

a. On $\mathcal{C}$ let $T(a, b)$ be the point at the distance $\dfrac{\pi}{6}$ from $P(1, 0)$. Then, as shown in the figure, the distance from $R(a, -b)$ to P is also $\dfrac{\pi}{6}$.

Since $\dfrac{\pi}{6} + \dfrac{\pi}{3} = \dfrac{\pi}{2}$, the distance from T to $S(0, 1)$ is $\dfrac{\pi}{3}$. Hence, the circular arcs $\overparen{RT}$ and $\overparen{TS}$ have the same length, namely $\dfrac{\pi}{3}$. Because

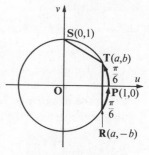

arcs of equal length on a circle are subtended by chords of equal length, you know that $d(R, T) = d(T, S)$. Hence,

$$(1) \qquad 2b = \sqrt{(a - 0)^2 + (b - 1)^2}; \qquad a > 0 \text{ and } b > 0.$$

Squaring each member of the preceding equation, you find:

(2) $$4b^2 = a^2 + b^2 - 2b + 1.$$

Because $T(a, b) \in \mathcal{C}$, $a^2 + b^2 = 1$. Therefore, equation (2) is equivalent to

$$4b^2 = 2 - 2b, \text{ or}$$

$$2b^2 + b - 1 = 0.$$

$$\therefore (2b - 1)(b + 1) = 0$$

$$b = \tfrac{1}{2} \text{ or } b = -1.$$

Since $b > 0$, we reject the possibility $b = -1$. For $b = \tfrac{1}{2}$, you have $a = \sqrt{1 - b^2} = \sqrt{1 - \tfrac{1}{4}} = \dfrac{\sqrt{3}}{2}$. Thus, after verifying that $\left(\dfrac{\sqrt{3}}{2}, \dfrac{1}{2}\right)$ satisfies equation (1), you may conclude that T has coordinates $\left(\dfrac{\sqrt{3}}{2}, \dfrac{1}{2}\right)$.

$$\therefore \cos\frac{\pi}{6} = \frac{\sqrt{3}}{2} \text{ and } \sin\frac{\pi}{6} = \frac{1}{2}, \textbf{ Answer.}$$

b. Let $V(c, d)$ be the point at the distance $\dfrac{\pi}{3}$ along $\mathcal{C}$ from P. Then, $\overset{\frown}{PV}$ and $\overset{\frown}{RT}$ have the same length, so that $d(P, V) = 1$. (Why?) Thus,

$$\sqrt{(c - 1)^2 + (d - 0)^2} = 1;$$

(3) $$c^2 - 2c + 1 + d^2 = 1.$$

Since $c^2 + d^2 = 1$ (Why?), equation (3) is equivalent to $c = \tfrac{1}{2}$. Verifying that $d = \dfrac{\sqrt{3}}{2}$ is left to you. Hence, the coordinates of V are $\left(\dfrac{1}{2}, \dfrac{\sqrt{3}}{2}\right)$, so that

$$\cos\frac{\pi}{3} = \frac{1}{2} \text{ and } \sin\frac{\pi}{3} = \frac{\sqrt{3}}{2}, \textbf{ Answer.}$$

In a similar way, you can prove that $\cos\dfrac{\pi}{4} = \dfrac{\sqrt{2}}{2}$ and $\sin\dfrac{\pi}{4} = \dfrac{\sqrt{2}}{2}$ (Exercise 11, page 381).

EXAMPLE 2. Find $\cos \dfrac{2\pi}{3}$ and $\sin \dfrac{2\pi}{3}$.

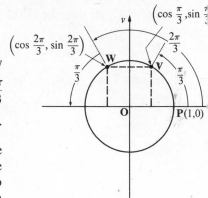

Solution: Sketch $\mathcal{C}$ and locate **V** and **W** such that $\overset{\frown}{PV}$ has length $\dfrac{\pi}{3}$ and $\overset{\frown}{PW}$ has length $\dfrac{2\pi}{3}$.

Notice that **W** has the same v-coordinate as **V**, but the u-coordinates of the two points are negatives of each other. Hence

$$\cos \frac{2\pi}{3} = -\cos \frac{\pi}{3}$$

and

$$\sin \frac{2\pi}{3} = \sin \frac{\pi}{3}.$$

From Example 1, you know that $\cos \dfrac{\pi}{3} = \dfrac{1}{2}$, and $\sin \dfrac{\pi}{3} = \dfrac{\sqrt{3}}{2}$.

$$\therefore \cos \frac{2\pi}{3} = -\frac{1}{2} \quad \text{and} \quad \sin \frac{2\pi}{3} = \frac{\sqrt{3}}{2}, \textbf{ Answer.}$$

EXAMPLE 3. Find $\sin x$.

Solution: Since $\cos x = \frac{4}{5}$, and $\sin^2 x + \cos^2 x = 1$,

you have $\sin^2 x + (\frac{4}{5})^2 = 1$.

$$\therefore \sin x = \frac{3}{5} \quad \text{or} \quad \sin x = -\frac{3}{5}.$$

Because x is in Quadrant I, $\sin x > 0$, and

$$\sin x = \frac{3}{5}, \textbf{ Answer.}$$

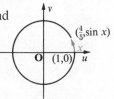

Exercises

In Exercises 1–4, find sin x.

(A) **1.** **2.** **3.** **4.**

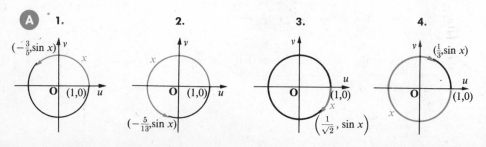

Verify that the following statements are true.

5. $2 \sin \dfrac{\pi}{6} \cos \dfrac{\pi}{6} = \sin \dfrac{\pi}{3}$

7. $\sin \dfrac{\pi}{6} \cos \dfrac{\pi}{3} + \cos \dfrac{\pi}{6} \sin \dfrac{\pi}{3} = \sin \dfrac{\pi}{2}$

6. $\cos \dfrac{\pi}{3} = \cos^2 \dfrac{\pi}{6} - \sin^2 \dfrac{\pi}{6}$

8. $\cos \dfrac{\pi}{2} \cos \dfrac{\pi}{4} + \sin \dfrac{\pi}{2} \sin \dfrac{\pi}{4} = \cos \dfrac{\pi}{4}$

9. Copy and complete the following table of quadrantal values for $\cos x$ and $\sin x$.

x	0	$\dfrac{\pi}{2}$	π	$\dfrac{3\pi}{2}$	2π	$-\dfrac{\pi}{2}$	$-\pi$	$-\dfrac{3\pi}{2}$	-2π
$\cos x$	1	?	?	?	?	?	?	?	?
$\sin x$	0	?	?	?	?	?	?	?	?

10. For what values of x is $\cos x = -1$? $\sin x = -1$?

11. Use the fact that $\dfrac{\pi}{4}$ is one-half of $\dfrac{\pi}{2}$ to prove that $\cos \dfrac{\pi}{4} = \sin \dfrac{\pi}{4} = \dfrac{\sqrt{2}}{2}$.

12. Use Examples 1 and 2 (pages 378–380), Exercise 11 above, and symmetry of the circle to evaluate $\cos x$ and $\sin x$ for the indicated values of x.

a. 0 **e.** $\dfrac{\pi}{2}$ **i.** π **m.** $\dfrac{3\pi}{2}$

b. $\dfrac{\pi}{6}$ **f.** $\dfrac{2\pi}{3}$ **j.** $\dfrac{7\pi}{6}$ **n.** $\dfrac{5\pi}{3}$

c. $\dfrac{\pi}{4}$ **g.** $\dfrac{3\pi}{4}$ **k.** $\dfrac{5\pi}{4}$ **o.** $\dfrac{7\pi}{4}$

d. $\dfrac{\pi}{3}$ **h.** $\dfrac{5\pi}{6}$ **l.** $\dfrac{4\pi}{3}$ **p.** $\dfrac{11\pi}{6}$

Use the symmetry of the circle to test whether the given statement is true for every $x \in \mathcal{R}$. If it is not true, make it into a true statement by changing a sign.

B

13. $\sin(\pi - x) = \sin x$

17. $\cos\left(\dfrac{\pi}{2} - x\right) = \sin x$

14. $\cos(\pi - x) = -\cos x$

18. $\sin\left(\dfrac{\pi}{2} - x\right) = \cos x$

15. $\cos(\pi + x) = \cos x$

19. $\sin(2\pi - x) = -\sin x$

16. $\sin(\pi + x) = \sin x$

20. $\cos(2\pi - x) = -\cos x$

Use the relationship $\sin^2 x + \cos^2 x = 1$ to find y.

21. $\sin x = \tfrac{4}{5}$, $\cos x = y$, x in Quadrant I.

22. $\sin x = \tfrac{5}{13}$, $\cos x = y$, x in Quadrant I.

23. $\cos x = \dfrac{1}{\sqrt{5}}$, $\sin x = y$, x in Quadrant IV.

24. $\cos x = \dfrac{3}{\sqrt{10}}$, $\sin x = y$, x in Quadrant IV.

25. $\sin x = -\dfrac{2\sqrt{6}}{5}$, $\cos x = y$, x in Quadrant III.

26. $\cos x = -\dfrac{\sqrt{15}}{4}$, $\sin x = y$, x in Quadrant II.

27. Prove that for each $x \in \mathcal{R}$, $|\sin x| \le 1$.

28. Prove that for each $x \in \mathcal{R}$, $|\cos x| \le 1$.

29. A function f such that, for each x in its domain, $f(x) = f(-x)$ is called an **even function.** Prove that **cos** is an even function.

30. A function f such that, for each x in its domain, $f(x) = -f(-x)$ is called an **odd function.** Prove that **sin** is an odd function.

Refer to the adjoining figure to prove each of the following statements. Assume $x_1 \in \mathcal{R}$ and $x_2 \in \mathcal{R}$.

31. $|\sin x_1 - \sin x_2| \le |x_1 - x_2|$.
Hint: $|\sin x_1 - \sin x_2| = d(\mathbf{N}, \mathbf{T}_1) \le d(\mathbf{T}_1, \mathbf{T}_2)$.

32. $|\cos x_1 - \cos x_2| \le |x_1 - x_2|$.
Hint: $|\cos x_1 - \cos x_2| \le d(\mathbf{N}, \mathbf{T}_2) \le d(\mathbf{T}_1, \mathbf{T}_2)$.

33. Prove: If $x \in \mathcal{R}$, $|\sin x| \le |x|$.
Hint: Use Exercise 31.

34. Prove: If $x \in \mathcal{R}$, $|1 - \cos x| \le |x|$.
Hint: Use Exercise 32.

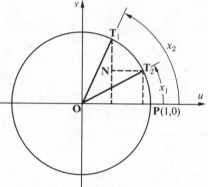

10–3 Graphs of Sine and Cosine

Because the sine and cosine functions are sets of ordered pairs of real numbers, they can be graphed in the plane. Figure 10–8 shows the ordered

Figure 10–8

pairs listed in the following table. If you connect these points from left

x	0	$\dfrac{\pi}{6}$	$\dfrac{\pi}{3}$	$\dfrac{\pi}{2}$	$\dfrac{2\pi}{3}$	$\dfrac{5\pi}{6}$	π	$\dfrac{7\pi}{6}$	$\dfrac{4\pi}{3}$	$\dfrac{3\pi}{2}$	$\dfrac{5\pi}{3}$	$\dfrac{11\pi}{6}$	2π
$y = \sin x$	0	$\frac{1}{2}$	$\dfrac{\sqrt{3}}{2}$	1	$\dfrac{\sqrt{3}}{2}$	$\frac{1}{2}$	0	$-\frac{1}{2}$	$-\dfrac{\sqrt{3}}{2}$	-1	$-\dfrac{\sqrt{3}}{2}$	$-\frac{1}{2}$	0

to right with a smooth curve, the result will be the graph of $\{(x, y) : y = \sin x\}$ over the interval $0 \leq x \leq 2\pi$ (Figure 10-9). This fact will be justified in Chapter 12, when we discuss the continuity of the sine and cosine functions.

Figure 10-9

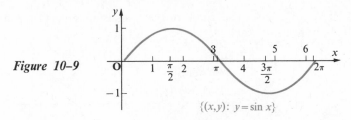

$\{(x,y): y = \sin x\}$

You know that the winding process described in Section 10-1 maps the numbers x and $x + 2n\pi$ for n in J into the same point on the unit circle $\mathcal{C}$. This fact implies the following property of the circular functions.

THEOREM For each x in $\mathcal{R}$ and each n in J,

1. $\sin x = \sin(x + 2n\pi)$;

2. $\cos x = \cos(x + 2n\pi)$.

Therefore, in the graph of the sine function, the points with abscissas x and $x + 2n\pi$ have the same ordinates. Hence, the graph of $\{(x, y): y = \sin x\}$ repeats the pattern shown in Figure 10-9 endlessly along the x-axis in both directions from the origin. Figure 10-10 shows three such intervals of length 2π. Do you see why the graph of the sine function is called a **sine wave**? A synonym for sine wave is **sinusoid**.

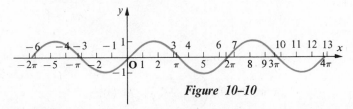

Figure 10-10

A function such as sine whose values recur at a regular interval is called a **periodic function**, and its **period** is the length of the shortest such interval. Thus, the period of the sine function is 2π. On a sine wave an arc with end points $(x, \sin x)$ and $[x + 2\pi, \sin(x + 2\pi)]$ is called a **cycle** of the wave.

Now consider the cosine function. Plotting points for the ordered pairs listed in the following table leads to the curve shown in Figure 10-11.

x	0	$\dfrac{\pi}{6}$	$\dfrac{\pi}{3}$	$\dfrac{\pi}{2}$	$\dfrac{2\pi}{3}$	$\dfrac{5\pi}{6}$	π	$\dfrac{7\pi}{6}$	$\dfrac{4\pi}{3}$	$\dfrac{3\pi}{2}$	$\dfrac{5\pi}{3}$	$\dfrac{11\pi}{6}$	2π
$y = \cos x$	1	$\dfrac{\sqrt{3}}{2}$	$\dfrac{1}{2}$	0	$-\dfrac{1}{2}$	$-\dfrac{\sqrt{3}}{2}$	-1	$-\dfrac{\sqrt{3}}{2}$	$-\dfrac{1}{2}$	0	$\dfrac{1}{2}$	$\dfrac{\sqrt{3}}{2}$	1

You can see a distinct resemblance to the graph of the sine function, a resemblance that is even more pronounced when you focus attention on the cosine curve over the interval $-\dfrac{\pi}{2} \leq x \leq \dfrac{3\pi}{2}$ and the sine curve over the interval $0 \leq x \leq 2\pi$. The graph of the cosine function, like that of the sine function, is a sine wave, or sinusoid, with period 2π.

Figure 10–11

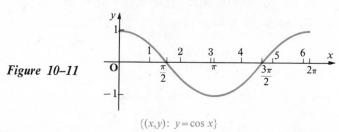

$$\{(x,y): y = \cos x\}$$

Knowing the general shape of the sine wave, you can sketch the curve quickly in any particular interval by finding values of the function at integral multiples of $\dfrac{\pi}{2}$.

EXAMPLE. Sketch the sine curve in the interval $\pi \leq x \leq 4\pi$.

Solution:

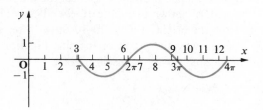

1. Find the value of $\sin x$ for $x = \pi$, $\dfrac{3\pi}{2}$, 2π. Plot the points $(\pi, 0)$, $\left(\dfrac{3\pi}{2}, -1\right)$, $(2\pi, 0)$.

2. Use your knowledge of the general shape of the sine curve to plot the other points shown. Sketch the curve.

Exercises

Over the given interval, graph the function f for $f(x)$ as indicated.

A

1. $f(x) = \sin x$, $-\dfrac{\pi}{2} \leq x \leq 2\pi$

2. $f(x) = \sin x$, $-\pi \leq x \leq 2\pi$

3. $f(x) = \sin x$, $-3\pi \leq x \leq 0$

4. $f(x) = \sin x$, $-2\pi \leq x \leq 2\pi$

5. $f(x) = \cos x, \dfrac{\pi}{2} \leq x \leq \dfrac{5\pi}{2}$ **7.** $f(x) = \cos x, \dfrac{3\pi}{2} \leq x \leq \dfrac{7\pi}{2}$

6. $f(x) = \cos x, -\pi \leq x \leq \pi$ **8.** $f(x) = \cos x, -2\pi \leq x \leq 2\pi$

Using one pair of coordinate axes, draw the sine curve and the cosine curve over the interval $0 \leq x \leq 2\pi$. Indicate the values of x, if any, in that interval for which the given equality or inequality is a true statement.

9. $\sin x = \cos x$

10. $\sin x = -\cos x$

11. $\sin x > \cos x$

12. $\sin x \leq \cos x$

13. $\sin x + \cos x = 1$

14. $\sin x + \cos x = 2$

15. $|\sin x + \cos x| = 1$

16. $\cos x - \sin x = 1$

17. $\sin x \cdot \cos x > 1$

18. $\sin x \cdot \cos x < 0$

19. $\sin x + \cos x = 0.$

20. $\sin x - \cos x = 0.$

Graph the function over the interval $-2\pi \leq x \leq 2\pi$.

21. $\{(x, y): y = |\sin x|\}$ **22.** $\{(x, y): y = |\cos x|\}$

23. Sketch the sine curve and the cosine curve lightly, using one pair of coordinate axes. Draw the graph of $\{(x, y): y = \sin x + \cos x\}$ by finding points for the function by means of adding ruler or compass measurements of ordinates on the preliminary graphs.

24. Follow the procedure for Exercise 23 and draw the graph of

$$\{(x, y): y = \sin x - |\cos x|\}.$$

10-4 Amplitude and Period

For both the sine and cosine functions, the maximum value is 1 and the minimum value is -1. When a periodic function has M as its maximum value and m as its minimum value, the positive number $\dfrac{M - m}{2}$ is called the **amplitude** of the function. Thus, the amplitude of sine and cosine is $\dfrac{1 - (-1)}{2} = 1.$

To draw the graph of $\{(x, y): y = 2 \sin x\}$, notice that the ordinate of each point of this graph is 2 times the ordinate of the corresponding point of the graph of sine. Therefore, as suggested in Figure 10–12, this function has period 2π and amplitude 2. In general, the graph of any function of the form $\{(x, y): y = A \sin x\}$ or $\{(x, y): y = A \cos x\}$, $A \neq 0$, is a sinusoid with period 2π and amplitude $|A|$.

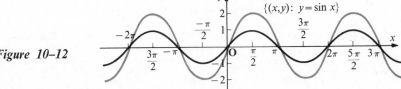

Figure 10–12

To draw the graph of $\{(x, y): y = \sin 2x\}$, notice that as x increases in value from 0 to π, $2x$ increases from 0 to 2π. Therefore, $\sin 2x$ runs through a complete cycle of sine values as x runs from 0 to π. This fact is also apparent in the following table. Thus, as Figure 10–13 indicates, the function has period π and amplitude 1.

x	0	$\dfrac{\pi}{12}$	$\dfrac{\pi}{6}$	$\dfrac{\pi}{4}$	$\dfrac{\pi}{3}$	$\dfrac{5\pi}{12}$	$\dfrac{\pi}{2}$	$\dfrac{7\pi}{12}$	$\dfrac{2\pi}{3}$	$\dfrac{3\pi}{4}$	$\dfrac{5\pi}{6}$	$\dfrac{11\pi}{12}$	π
$2x$	0	$\dfrac{\pi}{6}$	$\dfrac{\pi}{3}$	$\dfrac{\pi}{2}$	$\dfrac{2\pi}{3}$	$\dfrac{5\pi}{6}$	π	$\dfrac{7\pi}{6}$	$\dfrac{4\pi}{3}$	$\dfrac{3\pi}{2}$	$\dfrac{5\pi}{3}$	$\dfrac{11\pi}{6}$	2π
$y = \sin 2x$	0	0.5	0.87	1	0.87	0.5	0	-0.5	-0.87	-1	-0.87	-0.5	0

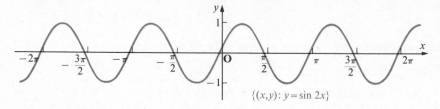

$\{(x,y): y = \sin 2x\}$

Figure 10–13

In general, the graph of a function of the form $\{(x, y): y = A \sin Bx\}$, or $\{(x, y): y = A \cos Bx\}$, $A \neq 0$, $B \neq 0$, is a sinusoid with amplitude $|A|$ and period $\dfrac{2\pi}{|B|}$. By using this fact, you can quickly sketch the graph by locating its maximum and minimum points and the points where it crosses the x-axis.

EXAMPLE 1. Sketch the graph of $\{(x, y): y = 2 \cos \frac{1}{3}x\}$ over one period.

Solution:

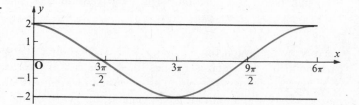

Amplitude $= |2| = 2$; period $= \dfrac{2\pi}{\frac{1}{3}} = 6\pi$.

Over the interval $0 \le x \le 6\pi$:

1. The maximum points occur at the ends of the interval and are $(0, 2)$ and $(6\pi, 2)$.

2. The minimum point occurs at the middle of the interval and is $(3\pi, -2)$.

3. The curve crosses the x-axis at the quarter and three-quarter points: $\left(\dfrac{3\pi}{2}, 0\right)$ and $\left(\dfrac{9\pi}{2}, 0\right)$.

With this information you sketch the curve, as shown.

EXAMPLE 2. If f is the function for which $f(x) = -3\sin 4x$, sketch the graph of f over the interval $-\pi \leq x \leq \pi$.

Solution: Amplitude $= |-3| = 3$; period $= \dfrac{2\pi}{4} = \dfrac{\pi}{2}$.

$\therefore$ the interval $0 \leq x \leq \dfrac{\pi}{2}$ contains one cycle of the graph.

In this interval,

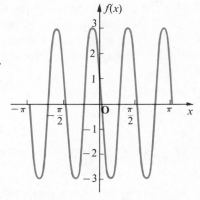

1. The points with zero ordinate are:

$(0, 0)$, $\left(\dfrac{\pi}{4}, 0\right)$, $\left(\dfrac{\pi}{2}, 0\right)$.

2. The minimum point is

$\left(\dfrac{\pi}{8}, -3\right)$.

3. The maximum point is

$\left(\dfrac{3\pi}{8}, 3\right)$.

$\therefore$ the interval $-\pi \leq x \leq \pi$ contains the four cycles shown in the figure.

Exercises

Write an equation of a sine wave with the given characteristics.

1. Period $= 2\pi$; amplitude $= 5$
2. Period $= 2\pi$; amplitude $= \frac{1}{3}$
3. Period $= 2\pi$; amplitude $= \frac{1}{2}$
4. Period $= 2\pi$; amplitude $= 2$
5. Period $= \pi$; amplitude $= \frac{1}{4}$

6. Period $= 3\pi$; amplitude $= 3$
7. Period $= \frac{1}{3}\pi$; amplitude $= 2$
8. Period $= 5\pi$; amplitude $= \frac{1}{3}$
9. Period $= 4$; amplitude $= \frac{1}{2}$
10. Period $= \frac{12}{5}$; amplitude $= 13$

Determine the amplitude and period p of each function f whose values are given by the indicated equation, and then sketch the graph of f over the interval $-p \leq x \leq p$.

11. $f(x) = 3 \cos x$

12. $f(x) = \frac{1}{2} \sin x$

13. $f(x) = -\sin x$

14. $f(x) = -2 \cos x$

15. $f(x) = \sin 3x$

16. $f(x) = \cos 2x$

17. $f(x) = \cos \frac{1}{2}x$

18. $f(x) = \sin \frac{1}{3}x$

19. $f(x) = 2 \sin 6x$

20. $f(x) = 4 \cos 4x$

21. $f(x) = -3 \cos \frac{1}{4}x$

22. $f(x) = -2 \sin \frac{1}{2}x$

B

23. $f(x) = \sin \pi x$

24. $f(x) = \cos \pi x$

25. $f(x) = \cos \frac{\pi}{2} x$

26. $f(x) = \sin \frac{\pi}{2} x$

27. $f(x) = 3 + \sin x$

28. $f(x) = 1 - \cos x$

Over the given interval, (a) draw the graphs of f and g in the same coordinate system; (b) from the graphs estimate to the nearest tenth the values of x for which $f(x) = g(x)$; (c) by adding ruler or compass measurements of ordinates of points of the graphs of f and g, determine points and sketch the graph of $f + g$.

C

29. $f(x) = \cos x; g(x) = 2 \sin x; 0 \leq x \leq 2\pi$

30. $f(x) = 3 \cos x; g(x) = \sin x; 0 \leq x \leq 2\pi$

31. $f(x) = \sin x; g(x) = \sin 2x; 0 \leq x \leq 2\pi$

32. $f(x) = \cos x; g(x) = 2 \sin \frac{x}{2}; 0 \leq x \leq 2\pi$

By the **frequency** of a wave with equation $y = A \sin Pt$ or $y = A \cos Pt$, where t denotes time in seconds, is meant the number of cycles per second. It is equal to the reciprocal of the period. (Why?) Find the frequency of the wave whose equation is given.

33. $y = \sin 40t$

34. $y = \cos 60t$

35. $y = 5 \sin 120\pi t$

36. $y = \sin 30\pi t$

37. The sound wave generated by a tuning fork can be described by an equation of the form $w = a \sin \alpha t$. Write the equation for a fork that vibrates at 440 cycles per second and yields an amplitude of .002 inch.

38. A generator yields electrical current described by the equation $I = a \sin \alpha t$. For a particular generator the amplitude is 3 and the current is the common 60-cycle current. Write the equation and draw its graph.

10–5 Phase Shift

To draw the graph of $f = \left\{(x, y): y = \sin\left(x - \dfrac{\pi}{3}\right)\right\}$, observe that as

x increases from $\dfrac{\pi}{3}$ to $2\pi + \dfrac{\pi}{3}$, $x - \dfrac{\pi}{3}$ increases from 0 to 2π. Therefore,

a cycle of f begins with $x - \dfrac{\pi}{3} = 0$, or $x = \dfrac{\pi}{3}$. The cycle ends with

$x - \dfrac{\pi}{3} = 2\pi$, or $x = \dfrac{7\pi}{3}$. Thus, as indicated in Figure 10–14, the graph

of f is obtained by "shifting" the graph of $\{(x, y): y = \sin x\}$, $\dfrac{\pi}{3}$ units

to the right. We call $\dfrac{\pi}{3}$ the *phase shift* of f.

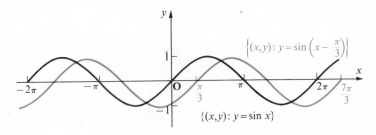

Figure 10–14

Figure 10–15 shows the graph of $\left\{(x, y): y = \sin\left(x + \dfrac{\pi}{3}\right)\right\}$. Because

the sine wave has been shifted $\dfrac{\pi}{3}$ *to the left*, $-\dfrac{\pi}{3}$ is called the *phase shift*.

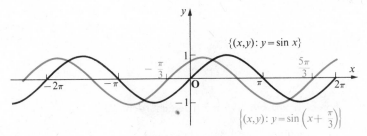

Figure 10–15

In general, the graphs of the equations $y = \sin(x + C)$ and $y = \cos(x + C)$ are sinusoids having **phase shift** equal to $-C$. If $C > 0$, the sinusoid has been "shifted" C units to the left, while if $C < 0$, the wave is "shifted" to the right.

In sketching the graph of the function $\left\{(x, y): y = 3\cos\left(2x - \dfrac{\pi}{2}\right)\right\}$, you should determine the phase shift as well as the amplitude and period. Since

$$3\cos\left(2x - \frac{\pi}{2}\right) = 3\cos 2\left(x - \frac{\pi}{4}\right),$$

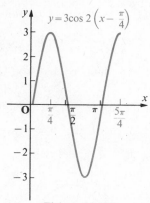

it follows that a cycle of the graph begins with $2\left(x - \dfrac{\pi}{4}\right) = 0$, or $x = \dfrac{\pi}{4}$; it ends with $2\left(x - \dfrac{\pi}{4}\right) = 2\pi$, or $x = \pi + \dfrac{\pi}{4} = \dfrac{5\pi}{4}$.

Thus, the graph has amplitude 3, period $\dfrac{2\pi}{2}$, or π, and phase shift $\dfrac{\pi}{4}$. The curve over the interval $0 \le x \le \dfrac{5\pi}{4}$ is shown in Figure 10–16.

Figure 10–16

The general sine wave $y = A\sin(Bx + C)$ or $y = A\cos(Bx + C)$ where $A \ne 0$ and $B \ne 0$ has:

$$\textbf{amplitude} = |A|; \quad \textbf{period} = \frac{2\pi}{|B|}; \quad \textbf{phase shift} = -\frac{C}{B}$$

The curve is shifted $\left|\dfrac{C}{B}\right|$ units to the left if $\dfrac{C}{B} > 0$, and $\left|\dfrac{C}{B}\right|$ units to the right if $\dfrac{C}{B} < 0$.

Exercises

Write an equation of a sinusoid with the given characteristics.

A

1. Period $= 2\pi$; amplitude $= 4$; phase shift $= 0$.
2. Period $= 2\pi$; amplitude $= 3$; phase shift $= 0$.
3. Period $= \pi$; amplitude $= \frac{1}{2}$; phase shift $= \pi$.
4. Period $= 3\pi$; amplitude $= \frac{1}{10}$; phase shift $= \dfrac{\pi}{2}$.
5. Period $= \dfrac{\pi}{2}$; amplitude $= 1$; phase shift $= -\dfrac{\pi}{2}$.

6. Period $= \dfrac{\pi}{3}$; amplitude $= 6$; phase shift $= -\dfrac{\pi}{4}$.

7. Period $= 4\pi$; amplitude $= 10$; phase shift $= -\pi$.

8. Period $= \dfrac{2\pi}{3}$; amplitude $= 7$; phase shift $= -\dfrac{\pi}{3}$.

Determine the amplitude, period, and phase shift of the graph of each equation. Then sketch the graph.

9. $y = \sin\left(x + \dfrac{\pi}{2}\right)$

10. $y = \sin(x - \pi)$

11. $y = 3\cos\left(x - \dfrac{\pi}{2}\right)$

12. $y = \frac{1}{2}\cos(x + \pi)$

13. $y = \sin(2x - \pi)$

14. $y = \sin\left(4x + \dfrac{\pi}{4}\right)$

B

15. $y = 2\cos\left(\dfrac{x}{2} + \pi\right)$

16. $y = -3\sin(6x - \pi)$.

17. $y = -\frac{1}{3}\sin\left(2x + \dfrac{\pi}{4}\right)$

18. $y = \frac{1}{2}\cos\left(\dfrac{x}{2} - \pi\right)$

19. $y = 3 + \cos\left(x - \dfrac{\pi}{4}\right)$

20. $y = -2 + \sin\left(x + \dfrac{\pi}{6}\right)$

21. $y + 1 = 2\sin\left(2x - \dfrac{\pi}{3}\right)$

22. $y - 1 = 2\cos\left(3x + \dfrac{\pi}{2}\right)$

On one pair of coordinate axes sketch at least one cycle of the graph of each of the following equations.

C

23. $y = \sin x$; $y = \sin\left(x - \dfrac{\pi}{4}\right)$; $y = \sin x + \sin\left(x - \dfrac{\pi}{4}\right)$

24. $y = \cos x$; $y = \cos\left(x + \dfrac{\pi}{2}\right)$; $y = \cos x + \cos\left(x + \dfrac{\pi}{2}\right)$

10-6 Other Circular Functions

Certain combinations of the sine and cosine functions occur so often that we give them special names. The functions *tangent* (tan), *cotangent* (cot), *secant* (sec), and *cosecant* (csc) are defined as follows:

Let $x \in \mathfrak{R}$. Then:

$$\tan = \left\{(x, y): \ y = \tan x = \frac{\sin x}{\cos x}, \quad \cos x \neq 0\right\}$$

$$\cot = \left\{(x, y): \ y = \cot x = \frac{\cos x}{\sin x}, \quad \sin x \neq 0\right\}$$

$$\sec = \left\{(x, y): \ y = \sec x = \frac{1}{\cos x}, \quad \cos x \neq 0\right\}$$

$$\csc = \left\{(x, y): \ y = \csc x = \frac{1}{\sin x}, \quad \sin x \neq 0\right\}$$

Can you suggest why the functions cos and sec are called *reciprocal functions*? Similarly, sin and csc, as well as tan and cot, are pairs of reciprocal functions.

To study the domain and range of the tangent function, we shall find the coordinates of the point **G** of intersection of ray **OT** (Figure 10–17) and the line $u = 1$ which is tangent to the unit circle. Since ray **OT** has slope $\dfrac{\sin x}{\cos x}$, or tan x, it is contained in the line $v = (\tan x)u$. Therefore, for **T** in the first or fourth quadrant, the ray intersects the line $u = 1$ at the point **G**(1, tan x).

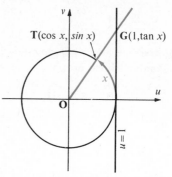

Figure 10–17

This means you can visualize the variation in the value of tan x as x varies from $-\dfrac{\pi}{2}$ to $\dfrac{\pi}{2}$ by noting the change in the ordinate of **G** as **T** moves counterclockwise on the circle from **S**(0, -1). For **T** at **S**, that is, $x = -\dfrac{\pi}{2}$, there is no value of tan x. (Where is **G**?) As x varies from $-\dfrac{\pi}{2}$ to 0, tan x increases through all negative numbers to zero. As x goes from 0 to $\dfrac{\pi}{2}$, tan x increases from zero through all positive numbers.

To see the variation in tan x for $\dfrac{\pi}{2} < x < \dfrac{3\pi}{2}$, consider Figure 10–18, which indicates that for **T** in the second or third quadrant, ray **OT** intersects the line $u = -1$ in the point $(-1, -\tan x)$. Can you explain why tan x runs through all negative numbers, 0, and then all positive numbers as x increases from $\dfrac{\pi}{2}$ to

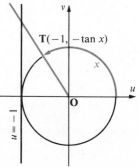

Figure 10–18

$\dfrac{3\pi}{2}$? This suggests that the tangent function has period π (see formula 12, page 421).

The graph of $\{(x, y): y = \tan x\}$ pictures the variation described above and is obtained by repeating the pattern indicated by plotting points over one period such as $-\dfrac{\pi}{2} < x < \dfrac{\pi}{2}$ (Figure 10–19). Note that the entries in the table following are computed by using the values of sin x and cos x. Blank spaces in the table correspond to values of x for which cos $x = 0$ and, consequently, for which tan x is not defined.

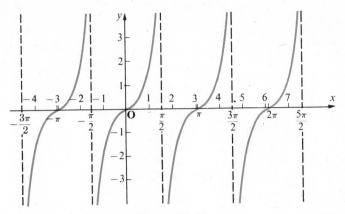

Figure 10–19

x	$-\dfrac{\pi}{2}$	$-\dfrac{\pi}{3}$	$-\dfrac{\pi}{4}$	$-\dfrac{\pi}{6}$	0	$\dfrac{\pi}{6}$	$\dfrac{\pi}{4}$	$\dfrac{\pi}{3}$	$\dfrac{\pi}{2}$
$y = \tan x$		$-\sqrt{3}$	-1	$-\dfrac{\sqrt{3}}{3}$	0	$\dfrac{\sqrt{3}}{3}$	1	$\sqrt{3}$	

You should now be able to explain why the domain of tan is

$$\left\{x:\ x \in \mathcal{R}, x \neq \frac{\pi}{2} + k\pi, k \in J\right\}.$$

The range of tan is $\mathcal{R}$. The dash lines shown in Figure 10–19 all have equations of the form $x = (2k + 1)\dfrac{\pi}{2}$, $k \in J$, and are called *asymptotes* of the graph.

You can discuss the variations and draw the graphs of cot, sec, and csc by referring to tables of values or to the known graphs of their reciprocal functions. Figures 10–20, 10–21, and 10–22 picture the graphs of each pair of reciprocal functions.

Figure 10–20

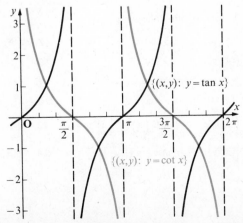

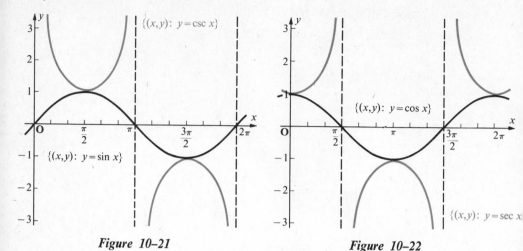

Figure 10–21   Figure 10–22

Exercises

Use the values of cos and sin to compute a table of values of the indicated function for

$$x \in \left\{ 0, \frac{\pi}{6}, \frac{\pi}{4}, \frac{\pi}{3}, \frac{\pi}{2}, \frac{2\pi}{3}, \frac{3\pi}{4}, \frac{5\pi}{6}, \pi, \frac{7\pi}{6}, \frac{5\pi}{4}, \frac{4\pi}{3}, \frac{3\pi}{2}, \frac{5\pi}{3}, \frac{7\pi}{4}, \frac{11\pi}{6}, 2\pi \right\}.$$

Leave blank spaces in the table for values of x not in the domain of the functions.

 1. tan   **2.** cot   **3.** csc   **4.** sec

State the domain, range, and period of each function.

5. cot   **6.** tan   **7.** sec   **8.** csc

State the quadrants in which x lies for the given statement to be true.

9. **a.** $\tan x > 0$; **b.** $\tan x < 0$ **11.** **a.** $\csc x \geq 1$; **b.** $\csc x \leq -1$

10. **a.** $\cot x > 0$; **b.** $\cot x < 0$ **12.** **a.** $\sec x \geq 1$; **b.** $\sec x \leq -1$

Graph each of the following.

13. $\{(x, y): y = 3 \tan x\}$ **17.** $\{(x, y): y = 2 \sec 2x\}$

14. $\{(x, y): y = 3 \sec x\}$ **18.** $\{(x, y): y = 3 \tan 2x\}$

15. $\{(x, y): y = -\cot 2x\}$ **19.** $\{(x, y): y = 2 \csc \frac{1}{2}x\}$

16. $\{(x, y): y = -\csc \frac{1}{2}x\}$ **20.** $\{(x, y): y = \frac{1}{2} \cot \frac{1}{3}x\}$

21. $\left\{(x, y): y = \tan \left(x + \frac{\pi}{3}\right)\right\}$ **23.** $\left\{(x, y): y = \sec \left(2x - \frac{\pi}{6}\right)\right\}$

22. $\left\{(x, y): y = \cot \left(x - \frac{\pi}{4}\right)\right\}$ **24.** $\left\{(x, y): y = \csc \left(\frac{1}{2}x + \frac{\pi}{3}\right)\right\}$

25. $\left\{(x, y): y = 2\cot\left(\frac{1}{2}x - \frac{\pi}{4}\right)\right\}$

26. $\left\{(x, y): y = -\tan\left(2x + \frac{\pi}{3}\right)\right\}$

Prove that each of the following functions is an odd function or prove that it is an even function. (Hint: See Exercises 29 and 30, page 382.)

27. tan **28.** cot **29.** sec **30.** csc

31. Explain how the graph of $\{(x, y): y = a\tan x, a \neq 0\}$ differs from the graph of $\{(x, y): y = \tan x\}$ when

a. $a > 1$ **c.** $-1 < a < 0$

b. $0 < a < 1$ **d.** $a < -1$

32. Explain how the graph of $\{(x, y): y = \sec bx, b \neq 0\}$ differs from the graph of $\{(x, y): y = \sec x\}$ when

a. $b > 1$ **c.** $-1 < b < 0$

b. $0 < b < 1$ **d.** $b < -1$

33. Use the definition $\tan x = \dfrac{\sin x}{\cos x}$, $x \in \mathcal{R}$, $\cos x \neq 0$, to prove that $|\tan x| \geq |\sin x|$ for all $x \in \mathcal{R}$ for which $\tan x$ is defined.

34. Use the definition $\cot x = \dfrac{\cos x}{\sin x}$, $x \in \mathcal{R}$, $\sin x \neq 0$, to prove that $|\cot x| \geq |\cos x|$ for all $x \in \mathcal{R}$ for which $\cot x$ is defined.

35. Prove that $|\sec x| \geq |\tan x|$ for all $x \in \mathcal{R}$ for which both are defined.

36. Prove that $|\csc x| \geq |\cot x|$ for all $x \in \mathcal{R}$ for which both are defined.

10–7 Identities

Because the relationship $\sin^2 x + \cos^2 x = 1$ is true for every $x \in \mathcal{R}$, it is an *identity over* $\mathcal{R}$. An **identity** is any equation that is true for every element in the replacement sets of the variables involved. Some identities result from the form of an expression and the field properties. For example, the open sentence

$$x(x + 1) = x^2 + x$$

is an identity over any field, because of the distributive law. In particular, it is true for, say, $\sin 2$, because $\sin 2 \in \mathcal{R}$, and $\mathcal{R}$ is a field. Thus,

$$\sin 2(\sin 2 + 1) = \sin^2 2 + \sin 2.$$

Other identities involving values of circular functions depend for their validity on the definitions of the functions.

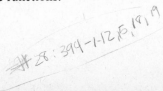

EXAMPLE 1. Prove that, for each x in D, the intersection of the domain of the tangent and cotangent functions, $\cot x \cdot \tan x = 1$.

Solution: D consists of all real numbers except $\frac{\pi}{2} + k\pi$, $k \in J$, where $\tan x$ is not defined, and $k\pi$, $k \in J$, where $\cot x$ is not defined. For every x in D: $\sin x \neq 0$ and $\cos x \neq 0$; also, $\cot x = \frac{\cos x}{\sin x}$ and $\tan x = \frac{\sin x}{\cos x}$. Therefore, using the field properties, you have:

$$\cot x \cdot \tan x = \frac{\cos x}{\sin x} \cdot \frac{\sin x}{\cos x}$$

$$= \frac{\cos x}{\cos x} \cdot \frac{\sin x}{\sin x}$$

$$= 1 \cdot 1.$$

$\therefore \cot x \cdot \tan x = 1.$

The statement of a proposed identity in a given variable often does not include explicit mention of the subset of $\mathcal{R}$ over which the identity is meaningful. However, in proving the identity, you must restrict your argument to those values of the variable for which each member of the identity is defined. Subject to this restriction, you may use the field properties, the definitions of the circular functions, and previously verified identities to prove the proposed identity.

EXAMPLE 2. Prove the identity: $\tan^2 x + 1 = \sec^2 x.$

Solution: By the definition of $\tan x$ and of $\sec x$, the given equation is meaningful for all real numbers x for which $\cos x \neq 0$. For $\cos x \neq 0$, you have:

$$\tan x = \frac{\sin x}{\cos x}$$

$$\therefore \tan^2 x + 1 = \frac{\sin^2 x}{\cos^2 x} + 1$$

$$\therefore \tan^2 x + 1 = \frac{\sin^2 x + \cos^2 x}{\cos^2 x}$$

Since for all x in $\mathcal{R}$, $\sin^2 x + \cos^2 x = 1$, you find:

$$\tan^2 x + 1 = \frac{1}{\cos^2 x} \quad (\cos x \neq 0).$$

$\therefore \tan^2 x + 1 = \sec^2 x$, provided $\cos x \neq 0$.

Another identity similar to that proved in Example 2 is

$$\cot^2 x + 1 = \csc^2 x$$

which you are asked to prove in Exercise 21, page 399.

Identities can be used to express functional values of one circular function in terms of functional values of another.

EXAMPLE 3. Express $\sin x$ in terms of $\cos x$.

Solution: $\sin^2 x + \cos^2 x = 1$

$$\sin^2 x = 1 - \cos^2 x$$

Since $\sin x > 0$ in Quadrants I and II, and

$\sin x < 0$ in Quadrants III and IV,

$\sin x = \sqrt{1 - \cos^2 x}$ in Quadrants I and II,

$\sin x = -\sqrt{1 - \cos^2 x}$ in Quadrants III and IV,
Answer.

EXAMPLE 4. Express $\cot x$ in terms of $\sec x$.

Solution: This can be done, of course, only for values of x for which $\cot x$ and $\sec x$ are defined. (What, then, are the exceptional values?) Except for these values, you can proceed as follows:

$$\cot x = \frac{1}{\tan x}$$

∴ Using Example 2 above, you find:

$$\cot x = \frac{1}{\pm\sqrt{\sec^2 x - 1}} \cdot$$

Since $\cot x > 0$ for $0 < x < \dfrac{\pi}{2}$ or $\pi < x < \dfrac{3\pi}{2}$, and

$\cot x < 0$ for $\dfrac{\pi}{2} < x < \pi$ or $\dfrac{3\pi}{2} < x < 2\pi$,

$\cot x = \dfrac{1}{\sqrt{\sec^2 x - 1}}$ when x is in Quadrants I or III,

$\cot x = -\dfrac{1}{\sqrt{\sec^2 x - 1}}$ when x is in Quadrants II or IV,
Answer.

Often it is convenient to transform each member of a proposed identity to the same expression in terms of sine, cosine, or other function values. The transitive property of equality then permits you to deduce the validity of the identity. Example 5 is an illustration.

EXAMPLE 5. Prove the identity: $\dfrac{\sec x}{1 + \csc x} = \dfrac{\tan x}{1 + \sin x}$.

Solution: Using L.M. (left member) and R.M. (right member) to refer to the members of the identity, you have:

$$\text{L.M.} = \frac{\dfrac{1}{\cos x}}{1 + \dfrac{1}{\sin x}} \qquad \bigg| \qquad \text{R.M.} = \frac{\dfrac{\sin x}{\cos x}}{1 + \sin x}$$

$$= \frac{\sin x}{\cos x(\sin x + 1)} \qquad \bigg| \qquad = \frac{\sin x}{\cos x(1 + \sin x)}$$

$$\therefore \frac{\sec x}{1 + \csc x} = \frac{\tan x}{1 + \sin x}$$

In Example 5 the numerator and denominator of the left member of the identity were multiplied by $\cos x \sin x$. This transformation is valid provided $\cos x \cdot \sin x \neq 0$. The original open sentence, involving both $\sec x$ and $\csc x$, is meaningful if and only if $\cos x \neq 0$, $\sin x \neq 0$, and $\sin x \neq -1$. Thus, the transformation introduced no additional restriction on x and is therefore permissible. What other transformations were used in the proof?

EXAMPLE 6. Prove the identity: $\csc t + \cot t = \dfrac{\sin t}{1 - \cos t}$.

Solution: (Explaining why the following steps in the solution are consistent with the restrictions implicit in the identity is left to you.)

$$\text{L.M.} = \frac{1}{\sin t} + \frac{\cos t}{\sin t} \quad \bigg| \quad \text{R.M.} = \frac{\sin t(1 + \cos t)}{(1 - \cos t)(1 + \cos t)}$$

$$= \frac{1 + \cos t}{\sin t} \qquad \bigg| \qquad = \frac{\sin t(1 + \cos t)}{\sin^2 t}$$

$$\bigg| \qquad = \frac{1 + \cos t}{\sin t}$$

$$\therefore \csc t + \cot t = \frac{\sin t}{1 - \cos t}$$

Exercises

Simplify, reducing each expression to a real number or to a value of one of the six circular functions. State any restrictions on the variables involved.

1. $\tan x \cdot \cos x$
2. $\tan x \cdot \cot x$
3. $\sec^2 t - \tan^2 t$
4. $3\sqrt{\csc^2 t - \cot^2 t}$
5. $\frac{1}{2}\cos x \cdot \sec x$
6. $\sin x \cdot \cos x \cdot \csc x$

7. $\sin^2 x + \sin x + \cos^2 x - 1$
8. $\cos x(\tan x + \cot x)$
9. $\sqrt{\cot^2 t + 1}$
10. $\sqrt{1 - \cos^2 t}$
11. $\dfrac{\sqrt{1 - \sin^2 t}}{\sin t}$
12. $\sqrt{\dfrac{\tan^2 t + 1}{\cot^2 t + 1}}$

13. Express in terms of $\sin x$: **(a)** $\cos x$; **(b)** $\tan x$; **(c)** $\csc x$.
14. Express in terms of $\cos x$: **(a)** $\sin x$; **(b)** $\tan x$; **(c)** $\cot x$.
15. Express in terms of $\tan t$: **(a)** $\cot t$; **(b)** $\sec t$; **(c)** $\cos t$.
16. Express in terms of $\sec t$: **(a)** $\cos t$; **(b)** $\tan t$; **(c)** $\sin t$.

Express in terms of $\sin x$ and $\cos x$ and simplify.

17. $\dfrac{1}{\sec x}(\tan x + \cot x)$
18. $\dfrac{\sin x - \csc x}{\csc x} + \sin^2 x \cot^2 x$

19. $\dfrac{\tan^2 x \csc^2 x - 1}{\csc x \tan^2 x \sin x}$
20. $\dfrac{\csc x(\sin^2 x + \cos^2 x \tan x)}{\sin x + \cos x}$

Prove the identities.

21. $\cot^2 t + 1 = \csc^2 t$
22. $\tan t + \cot t = \sec t \csc t$
23. $1 - 2\cos^2 r = 2\sin^2 r - 1$
24. $\sin r(\sec r - \csc r) = \tan r - 1$
25. $(1 + \sin p)^2 = 2(1 + \sin p) - \cos^2 p$
26. $\dfrac{\tan q + 1}{\cot q + 1} = \dfrac{\sec q}{\csc q}$
27. $\dfrac{1 - \tan x}{1 + \tan x} = \dfrac{\cot x - 1}{\cot x + 1}$
28. $\tan x \sin x = \sec x - \cos x$

29. $\dfrac{1}{1 + \sin m} + \dfrac{1}{1 - \sin m} = 2\sec^2 m$
30. $\dfrac{1 + \tan^2 n}{\tan^2 n} = \csc^2 n$
31. $\dfrac{1 + \sin x}{\cos x} + \dfrac{\cos x}{1 + \sin x} = 2\sec x$
32. $\dfrac{\sin^2 x}{1 - \cos x} = 1 + \cos x$
33. $\sin^4 t - \cos^4 t = \sin^2 t - \cos^2 t$
34. $\dfrac{\sin t + \cos t}{\sec t + \csc t} = \dfrac{\cos t}{\csc t}$
35. $\dfrac{\tan^3 q + 1}{\tan q + 1} = \sec^2 q - \tan q$
36. $\sqrt{\dfrac{1}{1 - \cos x}} = \dfrac{1}{|\sin x|} \cdot \sqrt{1 + \cos x}$

37. $\dfrac{1}{\sqrt{1 + \sin x}} = |\sec x| \sqrt{1 - \sin x}$

38. $\dfrac{1 - \sin t}{\cos t} = \dfrac{\cos t}{1 + \sin t}$

39. $\dfrac{1 + \cos x}{1 - \cos x} = \csc^2 x + 2 \csc x \cot x + \cot^2 x$

40. $\dfrac{\tan x + 1}{\tan x - 1} = \dfrac{1 + 2 \sin x \cos x}{\sin^2 x - \cos^2 x}$

41. $\dfrac{\sin t + \cot t}{\sin t - \cot t} = \dfrac{\sec^2 t - 1 + \sec t}{\sec^2 t - 1 - \sec t}$

42. $\sin^2 t \cos t \cot t = \dfrac{1 - \sin^2 t - \cos^2 t + \sin^2 t \cos^2 t}{\sin t}$

43. $\tan^4 p - 1 = \sec^4 p - 2 \sec^2 p$

44. $\dfrac{\sec q + \tan q}{\cos q - \tan q - \sec q} = -\csc q$

45. $\sqrt{\dfrac{1 - \sin t}{1 + \sin t}} = |\sec t - \tan t|$

46. $\sqrt{\dfrac{\sec t - 1}{\sec t + 1}} = \left| \dfrac{\sin t}{1 + \cos t} \right|$

TRIGONOMETRY

10–8 Angles and their Measure

In geometry you learned that an **angle** is the union of two rays with a common endpoint, called the **vertex** of the angle. The rays are often called the **sides** of the angle. For example, in Figure 10–23, rays **OP** and **OQ** determine an angle, denoted by the symbol $\angle POQ$, read "angle POQ." Because the vertex of this angle is the center of the circle shown in the figure, we call $\angle POQ$ a **central angle** of the circle. Also, on the circle each arc with **P** and **Q** as endpoints is said to **subtend** $\angle POQ$.

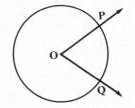

Figure 10–23

It is often convenient to designate one side of an angle as the **initial ray (side)** of the angle, and the other side as its **terminal ray (side)**. In a Cartesian coordinate system angles having the origin as vertex and the positive ray of the horizontal axis as initial side are said to be in **standard position**. Because every angle in the plane is congruent to an angle in standard position, we shall usually restrict our discussion to angles in standard position.

To see how angle measure is related to circular arc measure, consider, as in Section 10–1, the unit circle ℰ and the vertical line through the point $P(1, 0)$. (Figure 10–24.) As before, imagine the vertical line to be a flexible number line with origin at $P(1, 0)$. However, unlike our procedure in Section 10–1, we will not necessarily scale the number line in units of length equal to the radius of ℰ. When you visualize the rays of the number line winding around ℰ, you can see that every number on the line will be paired with a point of ℰ. Moreover, if the unit segment on the number line is selected so that h units are contained in the circle, then the length of the unit segment on

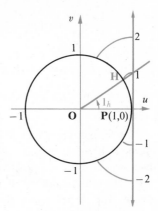

Figure 10–24

the line (or the *unit arc* on ℰ) is $\dfrac{2\pi}{h}$ because the circumference of ℰ is 2π.

Now suppose that **H** is the point of ℰ paired with the number 1 on the number line. We select $\angle POH$ to be the *unit angle* and assign to it the measure 1_h. In these units the measure assigned to any other angle θ in standard position is a number x_h on the number line which is paired with the point in which the terminal side of θ intersects ℰ. (Figure 10–25.) Notice that the measure of θ in "h-units" is not unique. As suggested by Figure 10–25, you can measure the angle by making more than one revolution on ℰ, and by measuring in the negative direction (clockwise) as well as in the positive direction (counterclockwise). However, if each of two numbers measures angle θ, the numbers must differ by an integral multiple of h.

When $h = 360$, the unit of angle measure is called a **degree**, $1°$. Thus, $1°$ is the measure of the central angle subtended by an arc whose length is $\frac{1}{360}$ of the circumference of the circle. $\frac{1}{60}$ of a degree is called a **minute**, $1'$; and $\frac{1}{60}$ of a minute is a **second**, $1''$. Thus, $1° = 60'$ and $1' = 60''$. (Figure 10–26, page 402 shows an angle of $3°$.)

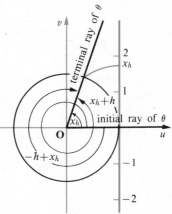

Figure 10–25

When $h = 2\pi$, the unit of angle measure is called a **radian**, 1^R. Hence, 1^R is the measure of the central angle subtended by an arc of length 1 on a circle of radius 1. (Figure 10–27, page 402.) In general, on a unit circle an arc of length x subtends a central angle whose radian measure is x.

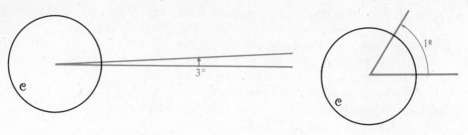

Figure 10–26   *Figure 10–27*

The measure of an angle in one unit is directly related to its corresponding measure in another unit. (Two measures of an angle are called **corresponding measures** if both are positive or both are negative numbers and if each contains the same number of revolutions on ℮.) For example, let $m°\angle \text{AOC}$ denote the degree measure of $\angle \text{AOC}$ and let $m^R\angle \text{AOC}$ denote its radian measure. Because the measures of an angle in different units are proportional to the numbers of corresponding unit arcs contained in the circumference of ℮, you have:

$$\frac{m°\angle \text{AOC}}{360} = \frac{m^R\angle \text{AOC}}{2\pi}.$$

1. $m°\angle \textbf{AOC} = \dfrac{180}{\pi}\, m^R\angle \textbf{AOC}$

2. $m^R\angle \textbf{AOC} = \dfrac{\pi}{180}\, m°\angle \textbf{AOC}$

Statements 1 and 2 are called *conversion equations* because they enable you to convert from measures in radians to measures in degrees and vice versa.

EXAMPLE 1. **a.** If $m^R\angle \theta = \dfrac{5\pi^R}{6}$, find $m°\angle \theta$.

b. If $m°\angle \alpha = -42°$, find $m^R\angle \alpha$.

Solution: **a.** Use equation **1**: $m°\angle \theta = \dfrac{180}{\pi} \cdot \dfrac{5\pi}{6}$, or 150°, **Answer.**

b. Use equation **2**: $m^R\angle \alpha = \dfrac{\pi}{180} \cdot (-42)$, or $-\dfrac{7\pi^R}{30}$, **Answer.**

Note: Since $\pi \doteq 3.1416$, $m^R\angle \alpha \doteq -0.73304^R$.

Figure 10–28 shows $\angle \textbf{AOC}$ as the central angle of two concentric circles, one being a unit circle and the other having radius r. Since the corresponding lengths of arc on concentric circles subtending a given central angle are proportional to the circumferences of the circles, you have:

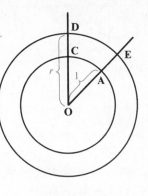

$$\frac{l(\overset{\frown}{ED})}{2\pi r} = \frac{l(\overset{\frown}{AC})}{2\pi}$$

where $l(\overset{\frown}{ED})$ stands for "length of arc **ED**" and $l(\overset{\frown}{AC})$ for "length of arc **AC**." If $m^R\angle AOC$ is x^R, then $x = l(\overset{\frown}{AC})$. (Why?). Hence,

$$l(\overset{\frown}{ED}) = rx.$$

This result is stated in the following theorem.   ***Figure 10–28***

THEOREM   In a circle of radius r, a central angle whose radian measure is x subtends an arc whose length is rx.

EXAMPLE 2. What is the speed in inches per minute of a point on the rim of a record of diameter 10 inches, turning at the rate of 45 RPM (revolutions per minute)?

Solution: 45 RPM $= 45(2\pi) = 90\pi$ radians per minute.

∴ In one minute, the point travels an arc with central angle measuring 90π radians. Hence, the distance traveled in one minute is the length of this arc:
$rx = 5 \cdot 90\pi = 450\pi \doteq 1414$.

1414 inches per minute, **Answer.**

Exercises ·

Copy each table and supply the missing entries.

1.

$m^R\angle AOC$	0^R	$\frac{\pi^R}{6}$	$\frac{\pi^R}{4}$	$\frac{\pi^R}{3}$	$\frac{\pi^R}{2}$	?	?	?	?
$m^\circ\angle AOC$	?	?	?	?	?	120°	135°	150°	180°

2.

$m^R\angle AOC$	?	?	?	?	$\frac{5\pi^R}{3}$	$\frac{7\pi^R}{4}$	$\frac{11\pi^R}{6}$	$2\pi^R$
$m^\circ\angle AOC$	210°	225°	240°	270°	?	?	?	?

3.

$m^R\angle AOC$	$\frac{1}{2}^R$	1^R	$\frac{3}{2}^R$	-2^R	$-\frac{5}{2}^R$	-3^R	$\frac{7}{2}^R$	4^R
$m^\circ\angle AOC$	?	?	?	?	?	?	?	?

4.

$m^R\angle AOC$	?	?	?	?	?	?	?	?
$m^\circ\angle AOC$	-10°	-20°	-40°	80°	160°	320°	640°	1280°

Convert the given degree measure to radian measure. Assume $k \in J$.

5. $(30 + k \cdot 360)^\circ$ **7.** $(-60 + k \cdot 180)^\circ$

6. $(45 + k \cdot 360)^\circ$ **8.** $(-30 + k \cdot 180)^\circ$

Convert the given radian measure to degree measure. Assume $k \in J$.

9. $(\pi + 2k\pi)^R$ **11.** $\left(\dfrac{4k - 1}{2}\pi\right)^R$

10. $\left(\dfrac{\pi}{2} + k\pi\right)^R$ **12.** $\left(\dfrac{4k + 1}{6}\pi\right)^R$

In Exercises 13–20, the first measure listed is a measure of angle θ. State which, if either, of the other given measures is also a measure of θ.

13. $210^\circ;\ -150^\circ,\ -\dfrac{7\pi}{6}^R$ **17.** $-540^\circ;\ 540^\circ,\ 3\pi^R$

14. $100^\circ;\ \dfrac{5\pi}{9}^R,\ -260^\circ$ **18.** $-730^\circ;\ 350^\circ,\ -\dfrac{\pi}{9}^R$

15. $-\pi^R;\ 180^\circ,\ 6\pi^R$ **19.** $\dfrac{\pi}{6}^R;\ \dfrac{25\pi}{6}^R,\ -330^\circ$

16. $\dfrac{\pi}{2}^R;\ -270^\circ,\ \dfrac{5\pi}{2}^R$ **20.** $-\dfrac{\pi}{4}^R;\ \dfrac{7\pi}{4}^R,\ -315^\circ$

21. A wheel turns through 10 revolutions. Through how many radians does any given spoke turn? How many degrees?

22. A wheel turns through $n\pi$ radians. Through how many revolutions does any given spoke turn? How many degrees?

23. A wheel turns 200 revolutions per minute. How fast does it turn in radians per second?

24. A circular gear turns 30 degrees per hour. Through how many radians does it turn in a 24-hour day?

25. Find the length of the arc cut off in a circle with 6-inch radius by a central angle of the given measure.

     a. 2^R **b.** $\frac{1}{3}^R$ **c.** -1^R **d.** n^R

26. Find the length of the arc cut off in a circle with 11-inch radius by a central angle of the given measure.

   a. 3^R **b.** -5^R **c.** $\frac{1}{4}^R$ **d.** $\frac{g^R}{k}$

27. Find the radian measure of a central angle, in a circle of radius 1, that cuts off an arc of the given length.

   a. 2π **b.** $-\pi$ **c.** 1   **d.** .01

28. Find the radian measure of a central angle, in a circle of radius 8, that cuts off an arc of the given length.

   a. 12π **b.** 12   **c.** $-\pi$ **d.** -1

B

29. A wheel with a diameter of 4 feet turns at 180 revolutions per hour. What is the speed in feet per minute of a point on the rim of the wheel?

30. A point on the rim of a wheel with a diameter of 10 feet moves at a speed of 900 feet per minute. How fast does the wheel turn in radians per second?

31. A certain satellite goes around the earth in 96 minutes. Through how many radians per day does the satellite turn, relative to the earth?

32. Show that the speed of a point on the rim of a circular wheel of radius r feet turning at w revolutions per minute is approximately $\frac{1}{14} rw$ miles per hour.

Let the circumference of a circle be divided into 100 arcs of equal length, and call each of these unit arcs a "centangle." Let $m^C\angle AOC$ denote the measure of $\angle AOC$ in centangles.

C

33. Find a conversion equation to convert degree measure to centangle measure; centangle measure to degree measure.

34. Find a conversion equation to convert radian measure to centangle measure; centangle measure to radian measure.

Copy each table and supply the missing entries.

35.

$m^C\angle AOC$	$\frac{25}{3}^C$	?	?	?	$\frac{250}{3}^C$	125^C	170^C
$m°\angle AOC$	30°	40°	100°	200°	?	?	?

36.

$m^C\angle AOC$	10^C	?	?	?	50^C	80^C	90^C
$m^R\angle AOC$	$\frac{\pi}{5}^R$	$\frac{3\pi}{5}^R$	$\frac{7\pi}{10}^R$	$\frac{21\pi}{25}^R$	?	?	?

37. Let $m^C\angle AOC = 10^C$, and write an expression for all centangle measures of $\angle AOC$.

38. Let $m^C\angle AOC = -38^C$, and write an expression for all centangle measures of $\angle AOC$.

10-9 The Trigonometric Functions

You recall that a ray is determined by specifying its endpoint and its direction vector **d**. For example, given that ray q shown in Figure 10–29 has O as endpoint and $(-3, 4)$ as direction vector, you know that

$$q = \{(u, v): \ (u, v) = t(-3, 4) \text{ and } t \geq 0\}.$$

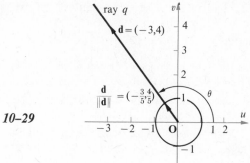

Figure 10–29

Rays with the same endpoint coincide when their direction vectors are positive scalar multiples of each other. Thus, ray q in Figure 10–29 can be described as the ray whose endpoint is O and whose direction vector is the *unit vector* $\frac{1}{5}(-3, 4) = (-\frac{3}{5}, \frac{4}{5})$. In general, if **d** is a direction vector of a ray, then the *unit vector* $\frac{\mathbf{d}}{\|\mathbf{d}\|}$ is also a direction vector of the ray.

Do you see that every ray q having the origin as endpoint is the terminal ray of an angle in standard position? We call the angle θ in standard position having ray q as terminal side the **direction angle** of q. If **d** is a direction vector of q, θ is also called the **vectorial angle**, the **direction angle**, or simply the **direction** of **d**. For example, in Figure 10–29, θ is the direction angle of the vectors $(-3, 4)$, $(-\frac{3}{5}, \frac{4}{5})$, and, in fact, of each vector $t(-3, 4)$ where t denotes a positive real number.

Now let θ be any angle in standard position and let $\mathbf{d} = (u, v)$ be a direction vector of the terminal ray of θ (Figure 10–30). We propose the following definitions:

the trigonometric cosine of angle θ =

$$\frac{u}{\|\mathbf{d}\|} = \frac{u}{\sqrt{u^2 + v^2}}, \text{ and}$$

the trigonometric sine of angle θ =

$$\frac{v}{\|\mathbf{d}\|} = \frac{v}{\sqrt{u^2 + v^2}}$$

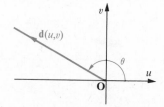

Figure 10–30

You usually write **cos θ** as an abbreviation for "cosine of angle θ" and **sin θ** for "sine of angle θ." Notice that

$$(\cos\theta, \sin\theta) = \frac{\mathbf{d}}{\|\mathbf{d}\|}$$

is the unit vector having θ as direction angle. Thus, cos θ and sin θ are the coordinates of the point 1 unit from the origin on the ray whose direction angle is θ.

EXAMPLE 1. If θ is the direction angle of the vector $\mathbf{d} = (-24, -7)$, sketch θ and find cos θ and sin θ.

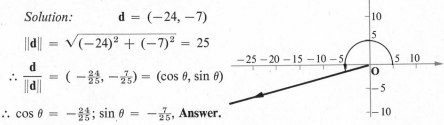

Solution: $\mathbf{d} = (-24, -7)$

$\|\mathbf{d}\| = \sqrt{(-24)^2 + (-7)^2} = 25$

$\therefore \dfrac{\mathbf{d}}{\|\mathbf{d}\|} = (-\frac{24}{25}, -\frac{7}{25}) = (\cos\theta, \sin\theta)$

$\therefore \cos\theta = -\frac{24}{25}; \sin\theta = -\frac{7}{25},$ **Answer.**

The set of all ordered pairs $(\theta, \cos\theta)$ where the domain of θ is the set of angles in standard position is called the **trigonometric cosine function**. We call the set of ordered pairs $(\theta, \sin\theta)$ the **trigonometric sine function**.

Can you explain the relationship between the trigonometric functions and the circular functions defined in Section 10–2? Radian measure provides the link between these functions. Suppose the radian measure of angle θ is x. Then, x is also the measure of the circular arc from **P** to **T** on ℰ (Figure 10–31). Hence, in terms of circular functions the coordinates of **T** are:

Figure 10–31

$(\cos x, \sin x).$

But $\|\mathbf{OT}\| = 1$; therefore, in terms of trigonometric functions the coordinates of **T** are:

$(\cos\theta, \sin\theta).$

Hence, $(\cos\theta, \sin\theta) = (\cos x, \sin x);$ *or*

$\cos\theta = \cos x$ and $\sin\theta = \sin x.$

Thus, if θ is the central angle of the unit circle such that $m^R\angle\theta = x^R$, then each trigonometric function at angle θ has the same value as the corresponding circular function at the number x.

You frequently identify an angle by stating its measure. Thus, you write sin 20° in place of "sine of an angle whose measure is 20°" and $\cos\dfrac{\pi^R}{3}$ in place of "cosine of an angle whose measure is $\dfrac{\pi^R}{3}$." Thus, because of the relationship between the trigonometric and circular functions, you may write $\cos \dfrac{\pi^R}{3} = \cos \dfrac{\pi}{3}$, but $\sin 20° = \sin \dfrac{\pi}{9} \cdot$ (Why?)

In terms of the trigonometric cosine and sine functions, you can define the *trigonometric tangent* (tan), *cotangent* (cot), *secant* (sec), and *cosecant* (csc) functions, each having a set of angles in standard position as domain. In analogy with the definitions in Section 10–6, we state the following definitions.

$$\tan = \left\{ (\theta, \tan \theta): \ \tan \theta = \frac{\sin \theta}{\cos \theta}, \cos \theta \neq 0 \right\}$$

$$\cot = \left\{ (\theta, \cot \theta): \ \cot \theta = \frac{\cos \theta}{\sin \theta}, \sin \theta \neq 0 \right\}$$

$$\sec = \left\{ (\theta, \sec \theta): \ \sec \theta = \frac{1}{\cos \theta}, \cos \theta \neq 0 \right\}$$

$$\csc = \left\{ (\theta, \csc \theta): \ \csc \theta = \frac{1}{\sin \theta}, \sin \theta \neq 0 \right\} \cdot$$

These definitions together with the meaning of $\cos \theta$ and $\sin \theta$ imply the following proposition.

THEOREM   If θ is the direction angle of the nonzero vector (u, v), then:

$$\tan \theta = \frac{v}{u} \ \ (u \neq 0), \quad \sec \theta = \frac{\sqrt{u^2 + v^2}}{u} \ \ (u \neq 0)$$

$$\cot \theta = \frac{u}{v} \ \ (v \neq 0), \quad \csc \theta = \frac{\sqrt{u^2 + v^2}}{v} \ \ (v \neq 0).$$

Using this theorem, you can state the values of $\tan \theta$, $\cot \theta$, $\sec \theta$, and $\csc \theta$ for the angle θ in Example 1, page 407. You have:

$$\tan \theta = \frac{-7}{-24} = \frac{7}{24} \qquad \sec \theta = \frac{25}{-24} = -\frac{25}{24}$$

$$\cot \theta = \frac{-24}{-7} = \frac{24}{7} \qquad \csc \theta = \frac{25}{-7} = -\frac{25}{7}$$

If the terminal ray of an angle in standard position lies in a quadrant, the angle is said to be *in* that quadrant. An angle whose terminal ray lies on one of the coordinate axes is called a **quadrantal angle.**

EXAMPLE 2. If θ is the second-quadrant angle for which $\cos \theta = -\frac{2}{5}$, sketch θ and determine the values of the trigonometric functions at θ.

Solution: Let (u, v) be a direction vector of the terminal ray of θ.

1. Since $\cos \theta = \dfrac{u}{\sqrt{u^2 + v^2}} = \dfrac{-2}{5}$, you can choose $u = -2$ and $\sqrt{u^2 + v^2} = 5$.

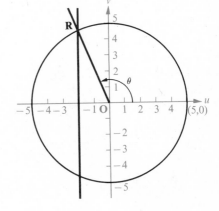

Then, u and v are the coordinates of the point **R** in which the vertical line two units to the left of the vertical axis intersects the circle with center **O** and radius 5.

2. Show θ with terminal ray **OR**.

3. To determine v:

$$\sqrt{(-2)^2 + v^2} = 5$$
$$4 + v^2 = 25$$
$$v^2 = 21; \text{ but } v > 0 \text{ (Why?)}$$
$$\therefore v = \sqrt{21}$$

4. Use the definitions and theorem stated on pages 406 and 408 to obtain:

$$\cos \theta = -\tfrac{2}{5} \qquad \sec \theta = -\tfrac{5}{2}$$

$$\sin \theta = \frac{\sqrt{21}}{5} \qquad \csc \theta = \frac{5}{\sqrt{21}} = \frac{5\sqrt{21}}{21}$$

$$\tan \theta = -\frac{\sqrt{21}}{2} \qquad \cot \theta = -\frac{2}{\sqrt{21}} = -\frac{2\sqrt{21}}{21}$$

Exercises

An angle θ in standard position is the direction angle of the given vector. Find the values of all the trigonometric functions that are defined for θ.

1. $(3, 4)$ 4. $(20, -21)$ 7. $(-1, 1)$ 10. $(-1, -\sqrt{3})$

2. $(4, 3)$ 5. $(5, -12)$ 8. $(0, 3)$ 11. $(-8, -15)$

3. $(0, 5)$ 6. $(3, 0)$ 9. $(-2, 0)$ 12. $(0, -7)$

Name the quadrant in which $\angle\theta$ lies, given that:

13. $\sin \theta > 0$ and $\cos \theta > 0$.   15. $\sin \theta > 0$ and $\cos \theta < 0$.

14. $\sin \theta < 0$ and $\cos \theta < 0$.   16. $\sin \theta < 0$ and $\cos \theta > 0$.

17. $\sin \theta > 0$ and $\tan \theta < 0$.

18. $\cos \theta > 0$ and $\csc \theta < 0$.

19. $\sec \theta < 0$ and $\csc \theta < 0$.

20. $\tan \theta > 0$ and $\cos \theta > 0$.

The quadrant in which $\angle \theta$ lies and the value of one of the trigonometric functions of θ are given. Find the value of the other five functions.

21. II; $\tan \theta = -1$

22. III; $\cos \theta = -\frac{11}{61}$

23. IV; $\sec \theta = \frac{29}{21}$

24. IV; $\csc \theta = -2$

25. III; $\cot \theta = 0.75$

26. III; $\tan \theta = \frac{j}{k}$

27. I; $\sin \theta = \frac{1}{100}$

28. II; $\cos \theta = -\frac{7}{10}$

In Exercises 29–36 the degree measure of $\angle \theta$ is given. **(a)** State the radian measure of $\angle \theta$. **(b)** Using the corresponding values of the circular functions, state the values of all the trigonometric functions that are defined at θ.

29. $0°$

30. $90°$

31. $180°$

32. $360°$

33. $30°$

34. $45°$

35. $270°$

36. $60°$

Prove that each of the following statements is true for every angle θ for which both members of the equation are defined.

37. $\sin^2 \theta + \cos^2 \theta = 1$

38. $\sec^2 \theta - \tan^2 \theta = 1$

39. $\csc^2 \theta - \cot^2 \theta = 1$

40. $\sin \theta \csc \theta = \tan \theta \cot \theta$

41. $\cos \theta \sec \theta = \tan \theta \cot \theta$

42. $\csc^2 \theta (1 - \sin^2 \theta) = \cot^2 \theta$

43. $\sin^2 \theta (\sec^2 \theta + \csc^2 \theta) = \sec^2 \theta$

44. $\tan^2 \theta (\cot^2 \theta + \cot^4 \theta) = \csc^2 \theta$

I rev. =

Chapter Summary

1. The **circular functions sine** and **cosine** are defined by means of the unit circle. The domain of each function is ℛ, and the range of each is the set of all first (cosine) or second (sine) coordinates of the ordered pairs corresponding to the points on the unit circle. These functions are **periodic** with **period** 2π.

2. The graphs of both the sine and cosine functions are **sine waves**, or **sinusoids**.

3. The functions defined by $y = A\sin(Px + C)$ or $y = A\cos(Px + C)$ have **amplitude** $|A|$, period $\dfrac{2\pi}{|P|}$, and **phase shift** $-\dfrac{C}{P}$.

4. Four other circular functions, **tangent, cotangent, secant,** and **cosecant** are defined in terms of sine and cosine. Tangent and cotangent have period π, whereas secant and cosecant have period 2π.

5. An **identity** over a set is a sentence that is true for every element in the replacement sets of the variables involved. To **prove** a given identity, you show that it is equivalent to a known identity or to a universally true statement.

6. An **angle** is the union of two rays with a common end point. To **measure** an angle, you use a circle to assign a number to the angle in terms of arc length on the circle. The length corresponding to a unit of angle measure is $\dfrac{2\pi r}{h}$, where r is the radius of the circle, and h is the number of units in the circumference. If $h = 360$, then the unit is called a **degree**, and if $h = 2\pi$, the unit is called a **radian**. An angle in **standard position** is an angle with the positive u-axis as **initial side**.

7. **Trigonometric functions** are functions whose domains are sets of angles and whose ranges are either ℛ or a subset of ℛ. The trigonometric functions sine, cosine, tangent, cotangent, secant, and cosecant are defined in terms of ratios involving the coordinates of an ordered pair (a, b) corresponding to a point in the terminal side of an angle.

8. Circular functions are related to trigonometric functions through the medium of angle measure. The value of a trigonometric function of an angle θ is equal to the value of the corresponding circular function of the radian measure of θ.

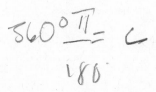

Chapter Test

10–1 **1.** If **T** is the point at distance $\frac{3}{5}\pi$ from **P**$(1, 0)$ on the unit circle, in what quadrant does **T** lie? *II*

10–2 **2.** On a unit circle an arc with initial point $(1, 0)$ and terminal point $(\frac{4}{5}, -\frac{3}{5})$ has length x.
   a. Find $\sin x$. *$-\frac{3}{5}$*   **b.** Find $\cos x$. *$\frac{4}{5}$*

d = all real nu

10–3 **3.** Name the domain and range of the circular function cosine. *$-1 \le y \le 1$*

4. **a.** Using one pair of coordinate axes, draw the sine curve and the cosine curve in the interval $[0 \le x \le \pi]$.
   b. For what value of x in the interval does $\sin x = \cos x$?

10–4 **5.** Name the amplitude and period of the wave with equation $y = 3 \sin 2x$. *3 ; π*

10–5 **6.** Name the phase shift of the function
$$\left\{(x, y): \; y = 5\cos\left(2x - \frac{\pi}{2}\right)\right\}. \quad \frac{\pi}{4}$$

10–6 **7.** Which of the circular functions are not defined for numbers x such that $\sin x = 0$? *$\cot x \;\; \csc x$*

8. What are the domain and range of the circular function tangent?

*d = all real num
except 2k+
r = all real*

10–7 **9.** Prove the identity: $\cos t - \sec t = -\tan t \sin t$.

10. Prove the identity: $1 - \cos x = \dfrac{\sin^2 x}{1 + \cos x}$ $(\cos x \ne -1)$.

10–8 **11.** **a.** Convert $40°$ to radians. *$\frac{2\pi}{9}$*
   b. Convert $-\frac{7}{18}\pi^R$ to degrees. *$-70°$*

12. A wheel turns 900 revolutions per minute. How fast does it turn in radians per second? *30π radians per sec.*

10–9 **13.** Find the values of the six trigonometric functions of θ if θ is an angle in standard position with **T**$(-20, -21)$ on its terminal ray.

$\sin = \frac{-21}{29}$

$\cos = \frac{-20}{29}$

$\tan = \frac{21}{20}$

$\cot \; \frac{20}{21}$

$\sec = \frac{-29}{20}$

$\csc$

Reading List

COMMISSION ON MATHEMATICS. *Appendices* to the *Report of the Commission on Mathematics.* New York: College Entrance Examination Board, 1959.

KING, BRUCE W. *Snowflake Curves.* The Mathematics Teacher, vol. 57, pp. 219–222, 1964.

MANCILL, JULIAN D. *The Sine and Cosine Functions.* Mathematics Magazine, vol. 36, pp. 302–311, 1963.

SCHOOL MATHEMATICS STUDY GROUP. *Elementary Functions, Part II.* New Haven, Conn.: Yale University Press, 1961.

Alfred North Whitehead

Bertrand Russell, who was at one time a student of Alfred North Whitehead and co-author with him of the monumental three-volume *Principia Mathematica*, once related a frightening dream that he had had about this work. It was the year 2100 A.D. and he was standing in a university library watching a library assistant methodically walking along the shelves of books pulling down certain volumes and tossing them into a bucket. The assistant came upon the last remaining copy of *Principia*, took it off the shelf ready to discard it, glanced through it somewhat puzzled by the curious symbols, and then held it in his hand, hesitating . . .

Although the ultimate fate of this work cannot be determined now, it has had a significant influence on the development of scientific thought in the last fifty years, and its authors are recognized as having created a new understanding of logic and the foundations of mathematics. In *Principia*, the English mathematicians Whitehead (1861–1947) and Russell (1872–   ) proposed to develop all mathematical analysis from a formal logical system and to eliminate the inconsistencies and paradoxes that existed in logic at that time. That this proved to be a long, difficult job is confirmed by the fact that they worked for ten years on the three volumes and had not built up the background to introduce the theorem $1 + 1 = 2$ until the second volume.

After finishing his work on *Principia*, Whitehead's interest turned to the philosophy of science, and his ideas on this subject are presented in *Science and the Modern World*. Whitehead explains that the rise of science which has taken place since the 17th century has been made possible in part by a change in attitude characterized by faith in the order and predictability of nature and willingness to experiment and observe details. He sees the role of the scientist as one of formulating general laws from particular situations. To do this, the scientist must have a way of expressing relationships that does not depend upon the observer. He finds the use of mathematics the obvious answer, since mathematics is concerned with patterns of general, abstract relationships.

413

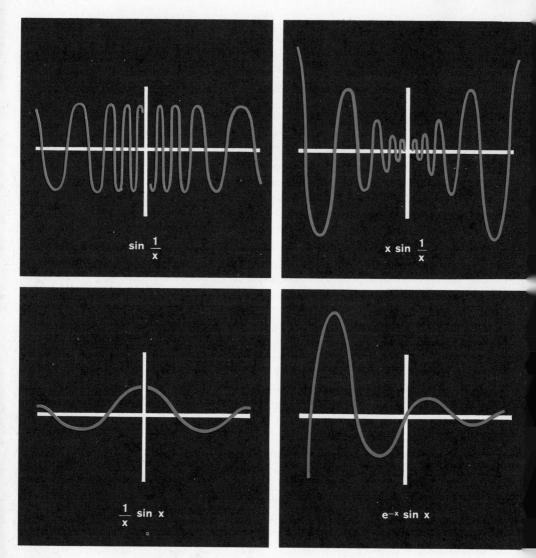

$$\sin \frac{1}{x}$$

$$x \sin \frac{1}{x}$$

$$\frac{1}{x} \sin x$$

$$e^{-x} \sin x$$

All of the curves above retain the undulatory nature of the basic sine wave, but they differ in other characteristics. Of the four formulas, only $e^{-x} \sin x$ is meaningful at $x = 0$, yet all the curves except $\sin \dfrac{1}{x}$ become continuous at $x = 0$ if suitably defined there.

$\sin \dfrac{1}{x}$ is an odd function, $x \sin \dfrac{1}{x}$ and $\dfrac{1}{x} \sin x$ are even functions, and $e^{-x} \sin x$ is neither.

414

Properties of Circular and Trigonometric Functions

The circular and trigonometric functions whose definitions and graphs you studied in Chapter 10 have many interesting interrelationships that are useful in advanced mathematics and in science. In this chapter you will extend your knowledge of identities involving these functions, learn about their inverses, and use these identities and inverses to solve equations.

IDENTITIES

11-1 Cosine of the Sum of Two Numbers

The Greek letters α (alpha), β (beta), and γ (gamma) are frequently used to name angles. They are also used to represent the measures of angles and hence to represent real numbers. In Section 10–9, you saw how values for the circular and trigonometric functions are related through arc length and angle measure. Accordingly, in this chapter you will be using α, β, and γ as variables whose replacement sets will be either a set of real numbers or a set of angles; the results you obtain will apply equally to circular functions or to trigonometric functions.

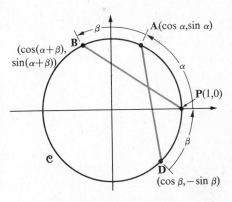

Figure 11–1 pictures the unit circle together with points **P**, **A**, **B**, and **D** on $\mathcal{C}$. Now, $l(\overset{\frown}{DP}) = l(\overset{\frown}{AB})$, because both have measure β. Therefore

Figure 11–1

$l(\overset{\frown}{PB}) = l(\overset{\frown}{DA})$, and since equal arcs on a circle determine equal chords, $d(\mathbf{P}, \mathbf{B}) = d(\mathbf{D}, \mathbf{A})$. You can express this equality using the distance formula:

$$\sqrt{[\cos(\alpha + \beta) - 1]^2 + \sin^2(\alpha + \beta)} = \sqrt{[\cos \alpha - \cos \beta]^2 + [\sin \alpha + \sin \beta]^2}.$$

415

Squaring each member and expanding, you find

$$\cos^2(\alpha + \beta) - 2\cos(\alpha + \beta) + 1 + \sin^2(\alpha + \beta)$$
$$= \cos^2 \alpha - 2\cos \alpha \cos \beta + \cos^2 \beta + \sin^2 \alpha + 2\sin \alpha \sin \beta + \sin^2 \beta,$$

$$[\cos^2(\alpha + \beta) + \sin^2(\alpha + \beta)] - 2\cos(\alpha + \beta) + 1$$
$$= (\cos^2 \alpha + \sin^2 \alpha) + (\cos^2 \beta + \sin^2 \beta) - 2\cos \alpha \cos \beta + 2\sin \alpha \sin \beta.$$

Since for every $x \in \Re$, $\cos^2 x + \sin^2 x = 1$, you can replace the expressions with 1 to obtain

$$1 - 2\cos(\alpha + \beta) + 1 = 1 + 1 - 2\cos \alpha \cos \beta + 2\sin \alpha \sin \beta, \text{ or}$$

$$\mathbf{\cos(\alpha + \beta) = \cos \alpha \cos \beta - \sin \alpha \sin \beta.} \qquad (1)$$

This is known as the identity for the **cosine of the sum of two numbers** α and β (or of two angles with measures α and β).

EXAMPLE 1. Find (a) $\cos \dfrac{5\pi}{12}$, (b) $\cos 75°$.

Solution: **a.** $\dfrac{5\pi}{12} = \dfrac{\pi}{4} + \dfrac{\pi}{6} \cdot$ Using (1) with $\alpha = \dfrac{\pi}{4}$ and $\beta = \dfrac{\pi}{6}$, you

find: $\cos \left(\dfrac{\pi}{4} + \dfrac{\pi}{6} \right) = \cos \dfrac{\pi}{4} \cos \dfrac{\pi}{6} - \sin \dfrac{\pi}{4} \sin \dfrac{\pi}{6}$

$$= \dfrac{1}{\sqrt{2}} \cdot \dfrac{\sqrt{3}}{2} - \dfrac{1}{\sqrt{2}} \cdot \dfrac{1}{2} \cdot$$

$\therefore \cos \dfrac{5\pi}{12} = \dfrac{\sqrt{3} - 1}{2\sqrt{2}}$, or $\dfrac{\sqrt{6} - \sqrt{2}}{4}$, **Answer.**

b. Since $\cos \dfrac{5\pi}{12} = \cos \dfrac{5\pi^R}{12} = \cos 75°$,

$$\cos 75° = \dfrac{\sqrt{3} - 1}{2\sqrt{2}}, \text{ or } \dfrac{\sqrt{6} - \sqrt{2}}{4}, \textbf{ Answer.}$$

You use the sum formula (1), as well as the fact that cosine is an even function and sine an odd function (Exercises 33, 34, page 382), to derive the formula for the cosine of the difference of two numbers (or angles).

Thus, since $\sin(-x) = -\sin x$ and $\cos(-x) = \cos x$, you can replace β in (1) with $-\beta$ and find

$$\cos[\alpha + (-\beta)] = \cos \alpha \cos(-\beta) - \sin \alpha \sin(-\beta), \text{ or}$$

$$\mathbf{\cos(\alpha - \beta) = \cos \alpha \cos \beta + \sin \alpha \sin \beta.} \qquad (2)$$

EXAMPLE 2. Find cos 15°.

Solution: $15° = 45° - 30°$

$$\cos(45° - 30°) = \cos 45° \cos 30° + \sin 45° \sin 30°$$

$$= \frac{1}{\sqrt{2}} \cdot \frac{\sqrt{3}}{2} + \frac{1}{\sqrt{2}} \cdot \frac{1}{2}$$

$$\cos 15° = \frac{\sqrt{3} + 1}{2\sqrt{2}}, \quad \text{or} \quad \frac{\sqrt{6} + \sqrt{2}}{4}, \textbf{Answer.}$$

Using either (1) or (2) and replacing α with the appropriate value, you can prove all the following identities. These are called **reduction formulas** because they can be used to reduce the problem of finding a function value of a given number (or angle with given measure) in Quadrants II, III, and IV to one of finding a function value in Quadrant I.

For Real Numbers [or angles (radian measure)]	*For Angles* (degree measure)	
$\cos\left(\dfrac{\pi}{2} + x\right) = -\sin x$	$\cos(90° + \theta) = -\sin \theta$	(3)
$\cos\left(\dfrac{\pi}{2} - x\right) = \sin x$	$\cos(90° - \theta) = \sin \theta$	(4)
$\cos(\pi + x) = -\cos x$	$\cos(180° + \theta) = -\cos \theta$	(5)
$\cos(\pi - x) = -\cos x$	$\cos(180° - \theta) = -\cos \theta$	(6)
$\cos\left(\dfrac{3\pi}{2} + x\right) = \sin x$	$\cos(270° + \theta) = \sin \theta$	(7)
$\cos\left(\dfrac{3\pi}{2} - x\right) = -\sin x$	$\cos(270° - \theta) = -\sin \theta$	(8)

EXAMPLE 3. Prove that for all x in $\mathcal{R}$, $\cos(\pi - x) = -\cos x$.

Solution: Use (2) and set $\alpha = \pi, \beta = x$.

$$\cos(\pi - x) = \cos \pi \cos x + \sin \pi \sin x.$$

Since $\cos \pi = -1$ and $\sin \pi = 0$, you have

$$\cos(\pi - x) = (-1) \cos x + (0) \sin x.$$

$$\therefore \cos(\pi - x) = -\cos x.$$

EXAMPLE 4. Express $\cos 255°$ as a value of a function of an angle θ such that $0° < m°\angle\theta < 45°$.

Solution: You can do this directly by using the fact that $255° = 270° - 15°$, and Formula (8).
Thus $\cos(270 - 15)° = -\sin 15°$, **Answer.**

EXAMPLE 5. Prove: If $x \in \mathcal{R}$, $\sin\left(\dfrac{\pi}{2} - x\right) = \cos x$.

Solution: In formula (4), replace x by $\dfrac{\pi}{2} - x$.

$$\cos\left[\frac{\pi}{2} - \left(\frac{\pi}{2} - x\right)\right] = \sin\left(\frac{\pi}{2} - x\right)$$

$$\therefore \cos x = \sin\left(\frac{\pi}{2} - x\right)$$

$$\therefore \sin\left(\frac{\pi}{2} - x\right) = \cos x$$

Exercises

Using either the sum or difference formula, determine the value of each of the following numbers.

1. $\cos 105°$ **3.** $\cos\dfrac{11\pi}{12}$ **5.** $\cos 195°$ **7.** $\cos\left(-\dfrac{\pi}{12}\right)$

2. $\cos 165°$ **4.** $\cos\dfrac{13\pi}{12}$ **6.** $\cos 285°$ **8.** $\cos\left(-\dfrac{7\pi}{12}\right)$

Using an appropriate reduction formula, express each of the following as the value of a function at a number $0 < x < \dfrac{\pi}{4}$ or an angle θ such that $0° < m°\angle\theta < 45°$.

9. $\cos 65°$ **11.** $\cos(1.2\pi)$ **13.** $\cos(-85°)$ **15.** $\cos(-295°)$
10. $\cos 88°$ **12.** $\cos(1.9\pi)$ **14.** $\cos(-230°)$ **16.** $\cos(-142°)$

If $x \in \mathcal{R}$, prove the given identity.

17. $\cos\left(\dfrac{\pi}{2} + x\right) = -\sin x$ **20.** $\cos\left(\dfrac{3\pi}{2} + x\right) = \sin x$

18. $\cos\left(\dfrac{\pi}{2} - x\right) = \sin x$ **21.** $\cos\left(\dfrac{3\pi}{2} - x\right) = -\sin x$

19. $\cos(\pi + x) = -\cos x$ **22.** $\cos(180° - x) = -\cos x$

If α and β are two angles in standard position in Quadrant I, find $\cos(\alpha + \beta)$ under the given conditions.

B

23. $\sin \alpha = \frac{3}{5}; \cos \beta = \frac{12}{37}$

25. $\tan \alpha = \frac{3}{4}; \tan \beta = \frac{11}{60}$

24. $\cos \alpha = \frac{8}{17}; \sin \beta = \frac{12}{13}$

26. $\sec \alpha = \frac{5}{3}; \sec \beta = \frac{13}{5}$

27–30. Find $\cos(\alpha - \beta)$ given the conditions in Exercises 23–26.

31. Show that $\cos 5x \cos 4x + \sin 5x \sin 4x = \cos x$.

32. Show that $\cos 5x \cos 4x - \sin 5x \sin 4x = \cos 9x$.

C

33. Prove that for all α and β in $\Re$,
$$\cos(\alpha - \beta) + \cos(\alpha + \beta) = 2 \cos \alpha \cos \beta.$$

34. Prove that for all α and β in $\Re$,
$$\cos(\alpha - \beta) - \cos(\alpha + \beta) = 2 \sin \alpha \sin \beta.$$

35. Prove that for all α and β in $\Re$,
$$\cos\left(\frac{\pi}{2} + \alpha - \beta\right) = \cos \alpha \sin \beta - \sin \alpha \cos \beta.$$

36. Use the result in Exercise 35 to prove that for all α and β in $\Re$,
$$\sin(\alpha - \beta) = \sin \alpha \cos \beta - \cos \alpha \sin \beta.$$

11–2 Additional Sum, Difference, and Reduction Formulas

The identity
$$\cos(\alpha - \beta) = \cos \alpha \cos \beta + \sin \alpha \sin \beta$$

can be used to derive an identity for $\sin(\alpha + \beta)$. Replacing α with $\frac{\pi}{2}$ and β with $(\alpha + \beta)$, you have

$$\cos\left[\frac{\pi}{2} - (\alpha + \beta)\right] = \cos\left[\left(\frac{\pi}{2} - \alpha\right) - \beta\right]$$
$$= \cos\left(\frac{\pi}{2} - \alpha\right) \cos \beta + \sin\left(\frac{\pi}{2} - \alpha\right) \sin \beta.$$

Using reduction formula (4), page 417, and Example 5, page 418, you have

$$\sin(\alpha + \beta) = \sin \alpha \cos \beta + \cos \alpha \sin \beta. \tag{1}$$

By replacing β with $-\beta$ in this identity, you discover that

$$\sin(\alpha - \beta) = \sin \alpha \cos \beta - \cos \alpha \sin \beta. \tag{2}$$

Also, if $\cos(\alpha + \beta) \neq 0$,

$$\tan(\alpha + \beta) = \frac{\sin(\alpha + \beta)}{\cos(\alpha + \beta)} = \frac{\sin \alpha \cos \beta + \cos \alpha \sin \beta}{\cos \alpha \cos \beta - \sin \alpha \sin \beta}.$$

Therefore, for values of α and β for which $\cos \alpha \cos \beta \neq 0$,

$$\tan(\alpha + \beta) = \cfrac{\dfrac{\sin \alpha \cos \beta}{\cos \alpha \cos \beta} + \dfrac{\cos \alpha \sin \beta}{\cos \alpha \cos \beta}}{\dfrac{\cos \alpha \cos \beta}{\cos \alpha \cos \beta} - \dfrac{\sin \alpha \sin \beta}{\cos \alpha \cos \beta}}$$

$$\tan(\alpha + \beta) = \frac{\tan \alpha + \tan \beta}{1 - \tan \alpha \tan \beta}. \tag{3}$$

That is, for all values α and β for which $\cos \alpha$, $\cos \beta$, and $\cos(\alpha + \beta)$ are not zero, this identity is valid.

If you solved Exercise 27, page 395, you verified that $\tan(-x) = -\tan x$. Therefore, replacing β with $-\beta$ in (3), you find

$$\tan(\alpha - \beta) = \frac{\tan \alpha - \tan \beta}{1 + \tan \alpha \tan \beta}. \tag{4}$$

EXAMPLE. Find $\sin 15°$ and $\tan 15°$.

Solution: Since $15° = 45° - 30°$,

$$\sin 15° = \sin(45° - 30°) = \sin 45° \cos 30° - \cos 45° \sin 30°$$

$$= \frac{1}{\sqrt{2}} \cdot \frac{\sqrt{3}}{2} - \frac{1}{\sqrt{2}} \cdot \frac{1}{2} = \frac{\sqrt{3} - 1}{2\sqrt{2}}.$$

$$\tan 15° = \tan(45° - 30°) = \frac{\tan 45° - \tan 30°}{1 + \tan 45° \tan 30°}$$

$$= \frac{1 - \dfrac{1}{\sqrt{3}}}{1 + 1 \cdot \dfrac{1}{\sqrt{3}}} = \frac{\sqrt{3} - 1}{\sqrt{3} + 1}.$$

$$\therefore \sin 15° = \frac{\sqrt{3} - 1}{2\sqrt{2}} \quad \text{or} \quad \frac{\sqrt{6} - \sqrt{2}}{4};$$

$$\tan 15° = \frac{\sqrt{3} - 1}{\sqrt{3} + 1} \quad \text{or} \quad 2 - \sqrt{3}, \textbf{ Answer.}$$

The following additional reduction formulas, which are stated here only in terms of real numbers, can be derived using the foregoing sum and difference formulas. Analogous forms for angles are also valid.

For each x in $\mathcal{R}$,

$$\sin\left(\frac{\pi}{2} + x\right) = \cos x \qquad (5)$$

$$\sin(\pi + x) = -\sin x \qquad (6)$$

$$\sin(\pi - x) = \sin x \qquad (7)$$

$$\sin\left(\frac{3\pi}{2} + x\right) = -\cos x \qquad (8)$$

$$\sin\left(\frac{3\pi}{2} - x\right) = -\cos x \qquad (9)$$

Using the definition of the tangent function, together with the reduction formulas for sine ((5) — (9) above and Example 5, page 418) and the reduction formulas for cosine ((3) — (8), page 417), you can derive the following tangent reduction formulas.

For each x in $\mathcal{R}$ for which the indicated function values are defined,

$$\tan\left(\frac{\pi}{2} + x\right) = -\cot x \qquad (10)$$

$$\tan\left(\frac{\pi}{2} - x\right) = \cot x \qquad (11)$$

$$\tan(\pi + x) = \tan x \qquad (12)$$

$$\tan(\pi - x) = -\tan x \qquad (13)$$

$$\tan\left(\frac{3\pi}{2} + x\right) = -\cot x \qquad (14)$$

$$\tan\left(\frac{3\pi}{2} - x\right) = \cot x \qquad (15)$$

These and previous reduction formulas are evident from the symmetry of the unit circle, as shown in Figure 11–2, (a) — (d), on the following page. Stating these formulas in terms of degree measure is left to you.

Figure 11-2

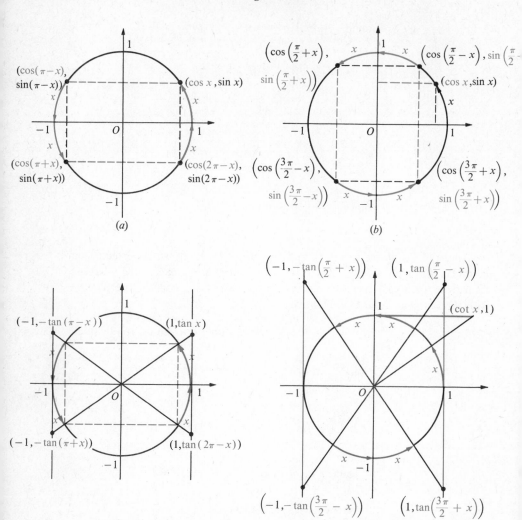

(a)

(b)

(c)

(d)

Exercises

Use an appropriate sum or difference formula to find the value of each of the following.

1. $\sin \dfrac{5\pi}{12}$ **3.** $\tan \dfrac{7\pi}{12}$ **5.** $\sin 195°$ **7.** $\cot 75°$

2. $\sin \dfrac{7\pi}{12}$ **4.** $\tan \dfrac{5\pi}{12}$ **6.** $\csc 75°$ **8.** $\tan 255°$

Given $\sin \alpha = \frac{3}{5}$, $\sin \beta = \frac{5}{13}$, $0 < \alpha < \frac{\pi}{2}$, $0 < \beta < \frac{\pi}{2}$, find the value of each of the following.

9. $\sin(\alpha + \beta)$ **12.** $\tan(\alpha - \beta)$

10. $\cos(\alpha + \beta)$ **13.** $\sin(\alpha - \beta)$

11. $\tan(\alpha + \beta)$ **14.** $\cos(\alpha - \beta)$

Prove each of the following reduction formulas.

15. $\sin\left(\frac{\pi}{2} + x\right) = \cos x$ **21.** $\tan(\pi - x) = -\tan x$

16. $\sin(\pi - x) = \sin x$ **22.** $\tan(\pi + x) = \tan x$

17. $\sin(180° + \theta) = -\sin \theta$ **23.** $\tan(90° - \theta) = \cot \theta$

18. $\sin\left(\frac{3\pi}{2} - x\right) = -\cos x$ **24.** $\tan(270° - \theta) = \cot \theta$

19. $\sin\left(\frac{3\pi}{2} + x\right) = -\cos x$ **25.** $\tan(270° + \theta) = -\cot \theta$

20. $\tan(90° + \theta) = -\cot \theta$ **26.** $\csc(90° - \theta) = \sec \theta$

Express each of the following as a value of a function at an angle θ, where $0° < m°\angle\theta < 45°$.

27. $\sin 137°$ **30.** $\sin 303°$

28. $\tan 145°$ **31.** $\sec 320°$

29. $\tan 232°$ **32.** $\csc 217°$

Verify that each of the following statements is true.

33. $2 \cos^2 330° - 1 = \cos 660°$

34. $1 - 2 \sin^2 225° = \cos 450°$

35. $\sec \frac{\pi^R}{3} = \tan \frac{\pi^R}{3} \tan \frac{\pi^R}{6} + 1$

36. $\sin \pi^R + \sin \frac{3\pi^R}{2} = 2 \sin \frac{5\pi^R}{4} \sin \frac{\pi^R}{4}$

37. $\cos 225° = -\sqrt{\dfrac{1 + \cos 450°}{2}}$

38. $2 \sin^2 \frac{4\pi}{3} = 1 - \cos \frac{2\pi}{3}$

Establish each of the following identities.

39. $\sin(\alpha + \beta) + \sin(\alpha - \beta) = 2 \sin \alpha \cos \beta$

40. $\sin(\alpha + \beta) - \sin(\alpha - \beta) = 2 \cos \alpha \sin \beta$

41. $\cot(180° - \theta) = -\cot \theta$

42. $\sec(90° + \theta) = -\csc \theta$

43. $\cot(\alpha + \beta) = \dfrac{\cot \alpha \cot \beta - 1}{\cot \alpha + \cot \beta}$

44. $\cot(\alpha - \beta) = \dfrac{\cot \alpha \cot \beta + 1}{\cot \beta - \cot \alpha}$

45. $\sin^2 \alpha - \sin^2 \beta = \sin(\alpha + \beta) \sin(\alpha - \beta)$

46. $\cos^2 \alpha - \sin^2 \beta = \cos(\alpha + \beta) \cos(\alpha - \beta)$

47. In Exercise 39, let $x_1 = \alpha + \beta$, $x_2 = \alpha - \beta$, and show that

$$\sin x_1 + \sin x_2 = 2 \sin \frac{x_1 + x_2}{2} \cos \frac{x_1 - x_2}{2}.$$

48. In Exercise 40, let $x_1 = \alpha + \beta$, $x_2 = \alpha - \beta$, and show that

$$\sin x_1 - \sin x_2 = 2 \cos \frac{x_1 + x_2}{2} \sin \frac{x_1 - x_2}{2}.$$

49. Let $a \in \mathfrak{R}$ and $b \in \mathfrak{R}$. If $x \in \mathfrak{R}$, prove that there exists a real number k such that $a \sin x + b \cos x = \sqrt{a^2 + b^2} \sin (x + k)$.

50. Show that $8 \sin x + 15 \cos x \leq 17$ for all $x \in \mathfrak{R}$.

11–3 Tables of Values for Circular and Trigonometric Functions

To find specific values of either the circular or the trigonometric functions, you use *trigonometric tables*. At the end of the book you will find tables for values of the circular and trigonometric functions. In terms of angle measure, Table 1 is graduated in intervals of .01 radians, while Table 2 is graduated in intervals of 10 minutes. Because the reduction formulas enable you to express a function value at any number (or any angle) in terms of a function value at a number (or an angle) in Quadrant I, the tables list values only for $m^R \angle \theta$ between 0 and $\dfrac{\pi}{2}$, or $m° \angle \theta$ between 0° and 90°.

You use trigonometric tables in a way similar to the way in which you use a table of logarithms, and you use linear interpolation as necessary. When you use linear interpolation, you should remember that as θ varies in measure from 0^R to $\dfrac{\pi^R}{2}$, or from 0° to 90°, $\sin \theta$, $\tan \theta$, and $\sec \theta$ increase, but $\cos \theta$, $\cot \theta$, and $\csc \theta$ decrease.

EXAMPLE 1. Find sin 0.234.

Solution: In Table 1, you locate .23 and .24 in the left-hand column, find the corresponding values for sin x in Column 3, and use linear interpolation to find the required value.

$$\begin{array}{cc} x & \sin x \end{array}$$

$$0.010\left[0.004\begin{bmatrix}0.230 & 0.2280\\0.234 & ?\\0.240 & 0.2377\end{bmatrix}e\right]0.0097$$

$$\frac{0.004}{0.010} = \frac{4}{10} = \frac{e}{0.0097}; e = 0.0039$$

$$\therefore \sin 0.234 \doteq 0.2280 + 0.0039 = 0.2319, \textbf{ Answer.}$$

Notice the use of the symbol $\doteq$ to indicate that the number 0.2319 is an approximation to the number $\sin 0.234$. In general, values of trigonometric functions given in Tables 1 and 2 are *four-significant-figure* rational approximations to irrational numbers. Despite this fact, we shall hereafter follow the customary practice of using the symbol $=$ instead of the (more precise) symbol $\doteq$.

EXAMPLE 2. Find $\cot 1.873$.

Solution:

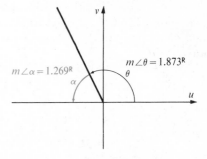

1. Define θ by $1.873 = m^R\angle\theta$. Since $\frac{\pi}{2} \doteq 1.571$ and $\pi \doteq 3.142$, the terminal side of θ lies in Quadrant II.

2. Make a sketch and note that angle α has approximate measure $\pi - 1.873$, or $3.142 - 1.873 = 1.269$.

3. Use Table 1 and linear interpolation to find $\cot\alpha$, that is, $\cot(\pi - \theta)$.

$$\begin{array}{cc} m\angle\alpha & \cot\alpha \end{array}$$

$$0.010\left[0.009\begin{bmatrix}1.260 & 0.3212\\1.269 & ?\\1.270 & 0.3102\end{bmatrix}e\right]-0.0110$$

$$\frac{0.009}{0.010} = \frac{9}{10} = \frac{e}{-0.0110}; e = -0.0099$$

Since $\cot\theta = -\cot\alpha$ (Why?),

$$\cot 1.873 = -(0.3212 - 0.0099) = -0.3113, \textbf{ Answer.}$$

When the sum of the measures of two angles is $90°$ $\left(\text{or } \frac{\pi^R}{2}\right)$ the angles are called **complementary angles**. The identities which follow suggest the relationships among the trigonometric functions of complementary angles. In fact, if you couple the trigonometric functions into the following pairs

$$\sin\left(\frac{\pi}{2} - \theta\right) = \cos\theta \qquad \cos\left(\frac{\pi}{2} - \theta\right) = \sin\theta \qquad \tan\left(\frac{\pi}{2} - \theta\right) = \cot\theta$$

$$\csc\left(\frac{\pi}{2} - \theta\right) = \sec\theta \qquad \sec\left(\frac{\pi}{2} - \theta\right) = \csc\theta \qquad \cot\left(\frac{\pi}{2} - \theta\right) = \tan\theta$$

of cofunctions — the *sine and cosine* functions, the *tangent and cotangent* functions, the *secant and cosecant* functions — you can state the preceding facts as a theorem.

THEOREM The value of any trigonometric function of an angle is equal to the value of the cofunction of the complementary angle.

Table 2 applies the preceding theorem. In this table angles whose measures are given in any one row are complementary angles, while the functions named at the top and bottom of a column are cofunctions.

In Table 2 to find an approximation of the value of a trigonometric function of an angle with measure between 0° and 90°, you use the following directions:

1. Reading in the first or last column, locate the row in which the measure of the angle is listed;

2. In this row find the entry in the column

   (a) at the *top* of which the function is named, if the angle measure is read at the *left;*

   (b) at the bottom of which the function is named, if the angle measure is read at the *right.*

For example: **a.** tan 35°20′ = 0.7089, **b.** sec 70°40′ = 3.021.

EXAMPLE 3. Find cos 232°42′.

Solution:

1. Make a sketch and observe that the reference angle α measures 232°42′ − 180° = 52°42′. Since cos α = cos(θ − 180°) = −cos θ, cos θ = −cos α.

2. Use Table 2 and linear interpolation to find cos 52°42′.

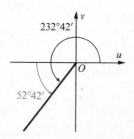

$$10' \left[2' \begin{bmatrix} 52°40' & 0.6065 \\ 52°42' & ? \\ 52°50' & 0.6041 \end{bmatrix} e \right] -0.0024$$

$$\frac{2}{10} = \frac{e}{-0.0024} \; ; e = -0.0005$$

$\therefore \cos 232°42' = -(0.6065 - 0.0005) = -0.6060,$ **Answer.**

If you know a function value for one of the circular or trigonometric functions, you can find the associated element in the domain of the function by using the tables.

EXAMPLE 4. If $\cos \theta = -0.8542$, and $0° < m°\angle\theta < 180°$, find $m°\angle\theta$.

Solution:

1. Since $\cos \theta < 0$ for $90° < m°\angle\theta < 180°$, make a sketch showing the terminal side of θ in Quadrant II.   Then $\cos \alpha = -\cos \theta = 0.8542$, and you can find $m°\angle\alpha$ from Table 2.

2. You locate 0.8542 in the eighth column from the left and read horizontally back to the first column to find 31°20'.

Since $m°\angle\theta = 180° - m°\angle\alpha$,
$m°\angle\theta = 180° - 31°20' = 148°40',$ **Answer.**

EXAMPLE 5. Find a real number t, $\pi < t < 2\pi$, such that $\sec t = 2.100$.

Solution:

1. Since $\sec t > 0$ in Quadrant IV, you expect to find a value for t, $4.712 < t < 6.283$. But the table extends only to $t = 1.570$; therefore, you find $\sec \alpha$, where $\alpha = 2\pi - t = 6.283 - t$.

2. In column 7 of Table 1 you find the values 2.083 and 2.122 on either side of 2.100. Hence, use linear interpolation.

$$\qquad\qquad \alpha \qquad \sec \alpha$$
$$0.010 \left[e \begin{bmatrix} 1.070 & 2.083 \\ ? & 2.100 \\ 1.080 & 2.122 \end{bmatrix} 0.017 \right] 0.039$$

$$\frac{0.017}{0.039} = \frac{17}{39} = \frac{e}{0.010} \; ; e = 0.004$$

$\therefore \alpha = 1.070 + 0.004 = 1.074$
$\therefore t = 6.283 - 1.074 = 5.209,$ **Answer.**

Exercises

Find the value of each function to four significant figures.

1. sin 72°43′
2. cos 21°36′
3. sec 54°14′
4. tan 50°25′
5. csc 0.716
6. sec 0.398

7. tan 0.115
8. csc 0.258
9. sec 0.991
10. cot 1.490
11. cos 102°20′
12. sin 131°48′

Find the least positive measure of each angle to the nearest minute.

13. tan θ = 3.106
14. cos θ = 0.3040
15. sec θ = 3.766

16. csc θ = 1.949
17. sin θ = 0.5415
18. cot θ = 0.3644

11–4 Double- and Half-Angle Identities

Is "cos 2α = 2 cos α" a true statement for every α in $\mathcal{R}$? Of course not, as the counterexample cos $\dfrac{\pi}{3} = \dfrac{1}{2}$, cos $\dfrac{\pi}{6} = \dfrac{\sqrt{3}}{2}$ clearly shows.

To express cos 2α in terms of circular (or trigonometric) functions of α alone, you replace β with α in the sum formula for cosine. (Formula (1), page 416.) You find that for every α in $\mathcal{R}$, you have the **double-angle** identity:

$$\cos(\alpha + \alpha) = \cos \alpha \cos \alpha - \sin \alpha \sin \alpha,$$

$$\cos 2\alpha = \cos^2 \alpha - \sin^2 \alpha. \tag{1}$$

Similarly, you can show that for every α in $\mathcal{R}$,

$$\sin 2\alpha = 2 \sin \alpha \cos \alpha; \tag{2}$$

and for every $\alpha \in \mathcal{R}$ for which tan α and tan 2α are defined,

$$\tan 2\alpha = \frac{2 \tan \alpha}{1 - \tan^2 \alpha}. \tag{3}$$

EXAMPLE 1. If $\sin \alpha = \dfrac{3}{\sqrt{10}}$, $0 < \alpha < \dfrac{\pi}{2}$, find **(a)** $\cos 2\alpha$, **(b)** $\sin 2\alpha$, and **(c)** $\tan 2\alpha$.

Solution: If $\sin \alpha = \dfrac{3}{\sqrt{10}}$, then from $\cos^2 \alpha + \sin^2 \alpha = 1$ you find

that $\cos \alpha = \sqrt{1 - \tfrac{9}{10}}$ or $\cos \alpha = -\sqrt{1 - \tfrac{9}{10}} = \dfrac{1}{\sqrt{10}}$

or $-\dfrac{1}{\sqrt{10}}$, and because α is in Quadrant I, $\cos \alpha = \dfrac{1}{\sqrt{10}}$.

Also, since $\tan \alpha = \dfrac{\sin \alpha}{\cos \alpha}$, $\tan \alpha = 3$.

$\therefore$ **(a)** $\cos 2\alpha = \cos^2 \alpha - \sin^2 \alpha = \tfrac{1}{10} - \tfrac{9}{10} = -\tfrac{4}{5}$,

(b) $\sin 2\alpha = 2 \sin \alpha \cos \alpha = 2 \left(\dfrac{3}{\sqrt{10}}\right)\left(\dfrac{1}{\sqrt{10}}\right) = \dfrac{3}{5}$,

(c) $\tan 2\alpha = \dfrac{2 \tan \alpha}{1 - \tan^2 \alpha} = \dfrac{2(3)}{1 - 9} = -\dfrac{3}{4}$, **Answer.**

You obtain alternative forms of the formula for $\cos 2\alpha$ when you use the identity $\sin^2 \alpha + \cos^2 \alpha = 1$ to transform the right-hand member of $\cos 2\alpha = \cos^2 \alpha - \sin^2 \alpha$.

$\cos 2\alpha = \cos^2 \alpha - \sin^2 \alpha$	$\cos 2\alpha = \cos^2 \alpha - \sin^2 \alpha$
$\quad = (1 - \sin^2 \alpha) - \sin^2 \alpha$	$\quad = \cos^2 \alpha - (1 - \cos^2 \alpha)$
$\therefore \cos 2\alpha = 1 - 2 \sin^2 \alpha$	$\therefore \cos 2\alpha = 2 \cos^2 \alpha - 1$

If you set $\alpha = \dfrac{x}{2}$ in each of the preceding formulas, you can discover the **half-angle** *identities:*

$\cos 2\left(\dfrac{x}{2}\right) = 1 - 2 \sin^2 \left(\dfrac{x}{2}\right)$	$\cos 2\left(\dfrac{x}{2}\right) = 2 \cos^2 \dfrac{x}{2} - 1$
$2 \sin^2 \left(\dfrac{x}{2}\right) = 1 - \cos x$	$2 \cos^2 \left(\dfrac{x}{2}\right) = 1 + \cos x$
(4) $\left\lvert \sin \dfrac{x}{2} \right\rvert = \sqrt{\dfrac{1 - \cos x}{2}}$	(5) $\left\lvert \cos \dfrac{x}{2} \right\rvert = \sqrt{\dfrac{1 + \cos x}{2}}$

To find $\sin \dfrac{x}{2}$ or $\cos \dfrac{x}{2}$, you must know the quadrant in which $\dfrac{x}{2}$ lies, and you must select the appropriate positive or negative value in each case.

Since $\tan \dfrac{x}{2} = \dfrac{\sin \dfrac{x}{2}}{\cos \dfrac{x}{2}}$ $\left(\cos \dfrac{x}{2} \neq 0\right)$, you have

$$\left|\tan \frac{x}{2}\right| = \sqrt{\frac{1 - \cos x}{1 + \cos x}} \quad (\cos x \neq -1), \tag{6}$$

where the quadrant in which $\dfrac{x}{2}$ lies determines whether you take $\left|\tan \dfrac{x}{2}\right|$ or $-\left|\tan \dfrac{x}{2}\right|$ for $\tan \dfrac{x}{2}$.

EXAMPLE 2. Find $\sin 105°$, $\cos 105°$, and $\tan 105°$.

Solution: Since $105° = \frac{1}{2}(210°)$, you find

$$\left|\sin 105°\right| = \left|\sin \frac{210°}{2}\right| = \sqrt{\frac{1 - \cos 210°}{2}}$$

$$= \sqrt{\frac{1 - \left(-\dfrac{\sqrt{3}}{2}\right)}{2}} = \frac{1}{2}\sqrt{2 + \sqrt{3}},$$

$$\left|\cos 105°\right| = \left|\cos \frac{210°}{2}\right| = \sqrt{\frac{1 + \cos 210°}{2}}$$

$$= \sqrt{\frac{1 + \left(-\dfrac{\sqrt{3}}{2}\right)}{2}} = \frac{1}{2}\sqrt{2 - \sqrt{3}},$$

$$\left|\tan 105°\right| = \left|\tan \frac{210°}{2}\right| = \sqrt{\frac{1 - \cos 210°}{1 + \cos 210°}}$$

$$= \sqrt{\frac{1 - \left(-\dfrac{\sqrt{3}}{2}\right)}{1 + \left(-\dfrac{\sqrt{3}}{2}\right)}} = \sqrt{\frac{2 + \sqrt{3}}{2 - \sqrt{3}}}.$$

Because $105°$ is in the second quadrant, $\sin 105° = \frac{1}{2}\sqrt{2 + \sqrt{3}}$ $\cos 105° = -\frac{1}{2}\sqrt{2 - \sqrt{3}}$, and $\tan 105° = -\sqrt{\dfrac{2 + \sqrt{3}}{2 - \sqrt{3}}} = -(2 + \sqrt{3})$,

Answer.

Of course, in the foregoing example, having found $|\sin 105°|$ and $|\cos 105°|$, you could find $\tan 105°$ without recourse to identity (6), by simply using

$$\tan 105° = \frac{\sin 105°}{-\cos 105°} .$$

Exercises

Use an appropriate identity from among (1) through (6) in this section to find the value of each of the following.

1. $\cos \dfrac{\pi}{8}$ **3.** $\sin \dfrac{3\pi}{8}$ **5.** $\cos \dfrac{11\pi}{12}$ **7.** $\tan \dfrac{5\pi}{24}$

2. $\sin \dfrac{\pi}{8}$ **4.** $\cos \dfrac{3\pi}{8}$ **6.** $\tan \dfrac{11\pi}{12}$ **8.** $\sin \dfrac{5\pi}{24}$

Angle θ in standard position has terminal side containing the direction vector $(3, 4)$, and $0° < m°\angle\theta < 90°$. Find each of the following.

9. $\sin 2\theta$ **11.** $\sin \tfrac{1}{2}\theta$ **13.** $\tan 2\theta$

10. $\cos 2\theta$ **12.** $\cos \tfrac{1}{2}\theta$ **14.** $\tan \tfrac{1}{2}\theta$

Angle θ in standard position has terminal side containing the direction vector $(-4, -3)$, and $180° < m°\angle\theta < 270°$. Find each of the following.

15. $\cos 2\theta$ **17.** $\cos \tfrac{1}{2}\theta$ **19.** $\tan \tfrac{1}{2}\theta$

16. $\sin 2\theta$ **18.** $\sin \tfrac{1}{2}\theta$ **20.** $\tan 2\theta$

Prove each of the following identities, and state any restrictions necessary on the variable involved.

B

21. $\sin 2\theta = 2 \sin \theta \cos \theta$ **26.** $\cot 2\theta = \dfrac{1 + \cos 4\theta}{\sin 4\theta}$

22. $\tan 2\theta = \dfrac{2 \tan \theta}{1 - \tan^2 \theta}$ **27.** $|\sec \tfrac{1}{2}\theta| = \dfrac{\sqrt{2 + 2\cos\theta}}{1 + \cos\theta}$

23. $\cot 2\theta = \dfrac{\cot^2 \theta - 1}{2 \cot \theta}$ **28.** $|\csc \tfrac{1}{2} \theta| = \dfrac{\sqrt{2 + 2\cos\theta}}{|\sin\theta|}$

24. $\csc 2\theta = \dfrac{\sec \theta \csc \theta}{2}$ **29.** $\tan \tfrac{1}{2}\theta = \dfrac{\sin\theta}{1 + \cos\theta}$

25. $\sec 2\theta = \dfrac{\sec^2 \theta}{2 - \sec^2 \theta}$ **30.** $\tan \tfrac{1}{2}\theta = \dfrac{1 - \cos\theta}{\sin\theta}$

C

31. $\sin 3x = 3 \sin x - 4 \sin^3 x$

32. $\cos 3x = 4 \cos^3 x - 3 \cos x$

33. $\sin 4x = 8 \cos^3 x \sin x - 4 \cos x \sin x$

34. $\cos 4x = 8 \cos^4 x - 8 \cos^2 x + 1$

INVERSES

11–5 Inverse Values

Can you find a real number x for which $\sin x = 5$? The answer, of course, is no, because $|\sin x| \leq 1$ for all x in $\Re$. Therefore, the solution set of the open sentence $\sin x = 5$ is $\emptyset$.

On the other hand, the solution set of $\sin x = \frac{1}{2}$ consists of the numbers $\frac{\pi}{6}, \frac{5\pi}{6}$, and all real numbers differing from either of these two numbers by an integral multiple of 2π. Therefore, the solution set is

$$\left\{ x\colon\ x = \frac{\pi}{6} + 2\pi k \quad \text{or} \quad x = \frac{5\pi}{6} + 2\pi k, k \in J \right\}.$$

This infinite set is denoted by $arcsin\,\frac{1}{2}$ or by $sin^{-1}\,\frac{1}{2}$. Each of the latter expressions can be read: "the set of numbers whose sine is $\frac{1}{2}$," or "arc sine $\frac{1}{2}$," or "inverse sine $\frac{1}{2}$."

Notice that $\sin^{-1}\frac{1}{2}$ and $(\sin\frac{1}{2})^{-1}$ do not mean the same thing. In the first expression, the symbol -1 is not an exponent; it is part of an abbreviation of, "the set of numbers whose sine is $\frac{1}{2}$." On the other hand, by $(\sin\frac{1}{2})^{-1}$ we mean $\dfrac{1}{\sin\frac{1}{2}}$.

In general, **arcsin b** is the set of real numbers for which the value of sine is b; that is, it is the solution set over $\Re$ of the equation $\sin x = b$. We define the sets $arccos\,b$, $arctan\,b$, $arccot\,b$, and so on, similarly.

EXAMPLE 1.   List the elements of arctan 1.

Solution:

arctan 1 $= \{x\colon\ \tan x = 1\}$

$$= \left\{ \frac{\pi}{4}, \frac{5\pi}{4}, \frac{9\pi}{4}, -\frac{3\pi}{4}, -\frac{7\pi}{4}, \cdots \right\}$$

$\therefore$ arctan 1 $= \left\{ x\colon\ x = \dfrac{\pi}{4} + \pi k \right\}$, **Answer.**

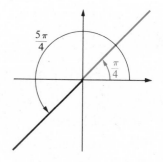

Notice that in the solution of Example 1 the symbols "$k \in J$" have been omitted. Here and throughout this chapter, however, k is understood to have the set of integers as domain.

Mathematics uses the notation sin(arctan 1), read "sine arc tangent one" or "sine of a number whose tangent is one," to denote the values of the sines of all numbers x for which it is true that $\tan x = 1$. Though there is an infinite set of such numbers x, there are nevertheless just two values of $\sin(\arctan 1)$. Using Example 1 above, we note that

$$\sin(\arctan 1) = \sin\left(\frac{\pi}{4} + \pi k\right) = \begin{cases} \dfrac{\sqrt{2}}{2}, \text{ when } k \text{ is an even integer,} \\ \\ -\dfrac{\sqrt{2}}{2}, \text{ when } k \text{ is an odd integer.} \end{cases}$$

Thus, $\sin(\arctan 1)$ equals $\dfrac{\sqrt{2}}{2}$ or $-\dfrac{\sqrt{2}}{2}$.

You can apply the reasoning in the preceding paragraph to give meaning to such expressions as $\sec(\text{arccot } 3)$ and $\csc(\text{arcsec } \frac{3}{2})$.

EXAMPLE 2.   Find $\tan(\arccos \frac{4}{5})$.

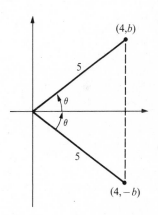

Solution:

The diagram shows θ such that $\cos \theta = \frac{4}{5}$.

Take $a = 4$, $\sqrt{a^2 + b^2} = 5$;

$b = 3$.

$\tan(\arccos \frac{4}{5}) = \tan \theta = \frac{3}{4}$ or $-\frac{3}{4}$, **Answer.**

Exercises

Find the elements of the set.

Ⓐ

1. $\arcsin 0$ **5.** $\arcsin(-\frac{1}{2})$ **9.** $\arccos 2$

2. $\arccos 0$ **6.** $\text{arccot}(-1)$ **10.** $\text{arccsc}(-\frac{1}{3})$

3. $\arctan \dfrac{1}{\sqrt{3}}$ **7.** $\text{arccsc } 2$ **11.** $\arcsin(-\frac{1}{2}) \cap \arccos \dfrac{\sqrt{3}}{2}$

4. $\text{arcsec}(-1)$ **8.** $\arcsin \dfrac{\sqrt{3}}{2}$ **12.** $\arctan 1 \cap \text{arccsc}(-\sqrt{2})$

Find all values of the following expressions.

Ⓑ

13. $\sin(\arctan \frac{5}{12})$ **16.** $\sin(\text{arcsec } 4)$ **19.** $\sin\left[\arctan\left(-\dfrac{\sqrt{3}}{\sqrt{2}}\right)\right]$

14. $\sec(\arcsin \frac{2}{3})$ **17.** $\tan(\text{arccot } \sqrt{5})$ **20.** $\cos\left(\arctan \dfrac{c}{d}\right)$

15. $\tan[\arccos(-\frac{1}{4})]$ **18.** $\cot\left(\arcsin \dfrac{1}{\sqrt{7}}\right)$

Find all values of the following expressions.

C **21.** $\sin(\arcsin \frac{3}{5} + \arctan \frac{5}{12})$ (Four values)

22. $\cos(\arctan 1 + \text{arcsec } 3)$ (Four values)

23. $\sin(2 \text{ arccot } \frac{1}{5})$

24. $\cot(2 \arcsin \frac{2}{7})$

25. $\tan(\frac{1}{2} \arccos \frac{1}{2})$

26. $\cos(\frac{1}{2} \arcsin \frac{2}{3})$

27. $\sin(4 \arcsin \frac{1}{3})$

28. $\cos(4 \arctan 6)$

11–6 Inverse Circular Functions

The graph of the equation $y = \sin x$ (Figure 11–3) reminds us that the sine function pairs each real number x with a unique real number y. Now, consider the inverse relation $\{(x, y): x = \sin y\}$, or $\{(x, y): y \in \arcsin x\}$.

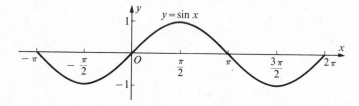

Figure 11–3

Clearly this inverse relation associates an infinite set of numbers y with each number x, $|x| \le 1$, and, therefore, is not a function. By restricting the range of the relation to the set $\left\{y: -\frac{\pi}{2} \le y \le \frac{\pi}{2}\right\}$, however, you can pair each number x, $|x| \le 1$, with a unique number y, and thereby specify a function (Figure 11–4). The unique number y such that

$$y \in \arcsin x \quad \textit{and} \quad -\frac{\pi}{2} \le y \le \frac{\pi}{2}$$

is called the **principal value of arcsin** x and is denoted by **Arcsin** x. The Arc sine function is

$$\{(x, y): y = \textbf{Arcsin } x\}.$$

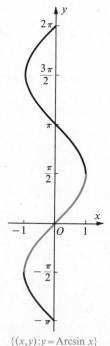

Figure 11–4

$\{(x,y): y = \text{Arcsin } x\}$

For each x, $|x| \leq 1$, the unique number y for which $y \in$ arccos x *and* $0 \leq y \leq \pi$, is called the **principal value** of arccos x, and is denoted by **Arccos x**. The Arc cosine function is

$$\{(x, y): \ y = \textbf{Arccos } x\}.$$

Its graph is shown in Figure 11–5 below.

The unique number y for which $y \in$ arctan x *and* $-\dfrac{\pi}{2} < y < \dfrac{\pi}{2}$ is called the **principal value** of arctan x, and is denoted by **Arctan x**. The Arc tangent function is

$$\{(x, y): \ y = \textbf{Arctan } x\}$$

and has the graph shown in Figure 11–6.

The principal values of arccot x, arcsec x and arccsc x are defined as follows:

$$\textbf{Arccot } x = \frac{\pi}{2} - \textbf{Arctan } x$$

$$\textbf{Arcsec } x = \textbf{Arccos } \frac{1}{x}, \ |x| \geq 1$$

$$\textbf{Arccsc } x = \textbf{Arcsin } \frac{1}{x}, \ |x| \geq 1$$

The Arc cotangent, Arc secant, and Arc cosecant functions are then defined in terms of these principal values.

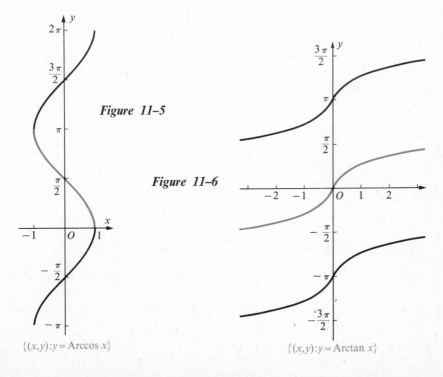

Figure 11–5

Figure 11–6

$\{(x,y):y = \text{Arccos } x\}$ $\{(x,y):y = \text{Arctan } x\}$

The six inverse functions, Arc sine, Arc cosine, and so on, are called the **inverse circular functions**.

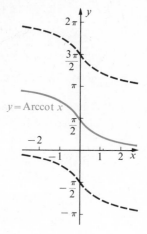

EXAMPLE 1. Graph the Arc cotangent function and extend the graph to show two more branches of the arc cotangent relation.

Solution: 1. The graph of Arc cotangent is shown in red.

2. Repeating the pattern as shown by the dash curves produces additional branches of the relation.

EXAMPLE 2. Evaluate $\cos [\text{Arctan}(-\frac{11}{60})]$.

Solution: Let $x = \text{Arctan}(-\frac{11}{60})$;

$\tan x = -\frac{11}{60}$ *and* $-\frac{\pi}{2} < x < 0.$

For $a = -11$ and $b = 60$, $c^2 = 11^2 + 60^2$.

$c = 61$

$\cos x = \dfrac{b}{c} = \dfrac{60}{61}$, **Answer.**

EXAMPLE 3. Using principal values, specify the set $\arccos(-\frac{3}{5})$.

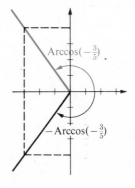

Solution: $\arccos(-\frac{3}{5})$

$= \{x\colon x = 2k\pi + \text{Arccos}(-\frac{3}{5})$
or $x = 2k\pi - \text{Arccos}(-\frac{3}{5})\}$,
Answer.

Can you explain why you can also specify $\arccos(-\frac{3}{5})$ as follows?

$$\arccos(-\tfrac{3}{5}) = \{x\colon x = (2k + 1)\pi \pm \text{Arccos}\,\tfrac{3}{5}\}.$$

EXAMPLE 4. Prove that $\text{Arcsin}\,\frac{3}{5} + \text{Arccos}\,\frac{12}{13} = \text{Arcsin}\,\frac{56}{65}$.

Solution: Each term of the left-hand member of the equation is a positive number less than $\dfrac{\pi}{4}$. (Why?) Each member of the equation is a positive number less than $\dfrac{\pi}{2}$. (Why?) There-

fore, the members must be equal if their sines are equal.

$$\text{Let } x = \text{Arcsin } \tfrac{3}{5}; \qquad y = \text{Arccos } \tfrac{12}{13}$$

$$\sin x = \tfrac{3}{5} \qquad \cos y = \tfrac{12}{13}$$

$$\cos x = \tfrac{4}{5} \qquad \sin y = \tfrac{5}{13}$$

$$\sin(x + y) = \sin x \cos y + \cos x \sin y$$

$$= \tfrac{3}{5} \cdot \tfrac{12}{13} + \tfrac{4}{5} \cdot \tfrac{5}{13}$$

$$= \tfrac{56}{65}$$

$$\therefore \sin(\text{Arcsin } \tfrac{3}{5} + \text{Arccos } \tfrac{12}{13}) = \tfrac{56}{65}$$

But $\sin(\text{Arcsin } \tfrac{56}{65}) = \tfrac{56}{65}$.

$$\therefore \text{Arcsin } \tfrac{3}{5} + \text{Arccos } \tfrac{12}{13} = \text{Arcsin } \tfrac{56}{65}.$$

Exercises

Give the value of each of the following numbers.

A

1. Arcsin $\tfrac{1}{2}$
2. Arcsin$(-\tfrac{1}{2})$
3. Arccos $\tfrac{1}{2}$
4. Arccos$(-\tfrac{1}{2})$

5. Arctan 1
6. Arctan(-1)
7. Arccot $\left(-\dfrac{1}{\sqrt{3}}\right)$
8. Arccot $(-\sqrt{3})$

9. Arcsec 1
10. Arcsec(-1)
11. Arccsc $\sqrt{2}$
12. Arccsc$(-\sqrt{2})$

Use principal values to specify each set.

13. arccos $\tfrac{2}{5}$
14. arctan $\tfrac{1}{3}$

15. arctan(-5)
16. arcsin$(-\tfrac{1}{2})$

17. arccsc(-3)
18. arcsec 7

19. Sketch the graph of $\{(x, y)\colon\ y \in \arcsin x\}$ for $-\pi \le y \le 2\pi$. Indicate the part of the graph that is the graph of $y = \text{Arcsin } x$.

20. Sketch the graph of $\{(x, y)\colon\ y \in \arctan x\}$ for $-2\pi \le y \le \pi$. Indicate the part of the graph that is the graph of $y = \text{Arctan } x$.

B

21. Sketch the graph of $y = \text{Arcsec } x$.
22. Sketch the graph of $y = \text{Arccsc } x$.

Evaluate each expression.

23. $\sin(\text{Arccos } \tfrac{3}{5})$
24. $\cos[\text{Arctan}(-\tfrac{5}{12})]$

25. $\csc(\text{Arcsin } \tfrac{3}{17})$
26. $\tan[\text{Arcsin}(-\tfrac{15}{17})]$

27. $\sin(\text{Arcsin } \tfrac{1}{2})$
28. $\tan[\text{Arccos}(-\tfrac{1}{2})]$

Evaluate each expression.

29. $\sin(\text{Arccot } b), b > 0$

32. $\text{Arctan}(\sec \pi)$

30. $\sec(\text{Arctan } j), j > 0$

33. $\text{Arccos}\left(\cos \dfrac{7\pi}{4}\right)$

31. $\text{Arcsin}\left(\cos \dfrac{\pi}{6}\right)$

34. $\text{Arccot}\left(\tan \dfrac{2\pi}{3}\right)$

C **35.** To define Arcsin x we restricted y in $y \in \arcsin x$ to $\left\{y: \ -\dfrac{\pi}{2} \le y \le \dfrac{\pi}{2}\right\}$.
How could the range of the arcsine relation be restricted to positive numbers so as to yield a function with the domain $\{x: \ -1 \le x \le 1\}$?

36. How could the range of the arccosine relation be restricted to negative numbers so as to yield a function with the domain $\{x: \ -1 \le x \le 1\}$?

Evaluate each expression.

37. $\sin\left[\text{Arccos}(\tfrac{3}{5}) + \dfrac{\pi}{2}\right]$

45. $\sin(\text{Arcsin } a + \text{Arcsin } b),$
$0 < a < 1, 0 < b < 1$

38. $\tan(\pi + \text{Arcsin } \tfrac{2}{3})$

46. $\cos(\text{Arctan } a - \text{Arcsec } b),$
$0 < a, 1 < b$

39. $\cos[\text{Arcsin}(-\tfrac{1}{2}) + \text{Arccos } \tfrac{5}{13}]$

47. $\tan[2 \text{ Arccos}(-\tfrac{7}{25})]$

40. $\sin[\text{Arctan}(-\tfrac{3}{4}) + \text{Arccot}(-\tfrac{4}{3})]$

48. $\tan(\tfrac{1}{2} \text{ Arcsin } \tfrac{15}{17})$

41 $\sin[2 \text{ Arccos}(-\tfrac{8}{17})]$

49. $\sin(\tfrac{1}{2} \text{ Arctan } \tfrac{3}{5})$

42. $\cos(\tfrac{1}{2} \text{ Arctan } \tfrac{3}{4})$

50. $\cos[2 \text{ Arccsc}(-\tfrac{7}{5})]$

43. $\cos(\text{Arcsin } \tfrac{1}{3} - \text{Arccos } \tfrac{1}{3})$

51. $\sin(2 \text{ Arccos } \tfrac{1}{2} + \text{Arccos } \tfrac{11}{61})$

44. $\tan(\text{Arccos } \tfrac{3}{5} - \text{Arcsin } \tfrac{5}{13})$

52. $\tan[\tfrac{1}{2} \text{ Arcsin}(-1) - \text{Arcsec } \tfrac{17}{8}]$

Prove the following assertions.

53. $\text{Arcsin } \tfrac{3}{5} + \text{Arcsin } \tfrac{12}{13} = \text{Arccos}(-\tfrac{16}{65})$

54. $\text{Arccos}(-\tfrac{2}{3}) - \text{Arccos } \tfrac{2}{3} = \text{Arccos } \tfrac{1}{9}$

55. $\text{Arctan } \tfrac{4}{3} - \text{Arcsin}(-\tfrac{8}{17}) = \text{Arctan } \tfrac{84}{13}$

56. $\text{Arcsec } \tfrac{5}{3} + \text{Arccsc } \tfrac{5}{4} = 2 \text{ Arctan } \tfrac{4}{3}$

57. $\text{Arctan } \dfrac{4}{7} + \text{Arctan } \dfrac{7}{4} = \dfrac{\pi}{2}$

58. $\text{Arctan}\left(-\dfrac{2}{3}\right) - \text{Arccot } \dfrac{2}{3} = -\dfrac{\pi}{2}$

11-7 Open Sentences and Circular Functions

To solve open sentences involving values of circular or trigonometric functions, you may employ a variety of techniques, some algebraic (factoring, for example) and some involving trigonometric identities.

EXAMPLE 1. Solve $\sin 2x = 3 \sin x$.

Solution: $2 \sin x \cos x = 3 \sin x$

$\sin x(2 \cos x - 3) = 0$

$\sin x = 0$ or $\cos x = \frac{3}{2}$

$x = 0 + 2\pi k$ or $\pi + 2\pi k$ | Impossible; $\cos x$ cannot exceed 1.

The solution set is $\{x:\ x = \pi k\}$, **Answer.**

EXAMPLE 2. **a.** Solve $4 \sec^2 t = 5$.

  b. To the nearest tenth, determine the least positive solution.

Solution: **a.** $\sec^2 t = \frac{5}{4}$

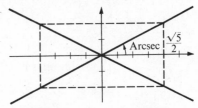

$\sec t = \dfrac{\sqrt{5}}{2}$ or

$\sec t = -\dfrac{\sqrt{5}}{2}$.

The solution set S is arcsec $\dfrac{\sqrt{5}}{2}$ or arcsec $\left(-\dfrac{\sqrt{5}}{2}\right)$

$$\therefore\ S = \left\{ t:\ t = k\pi + \text{Arcsec } \frac{\sqrt{5}}{2}\ or \right.$$

$$\left. t = k\pi - \text{Arcsec } \frac{\sqrt{5}}{2} \right\},\ \textbf{Answer.}$$

  b. The least positive value of t is Arcsec $\dfrac{\sqrt{5}}{2}$ or Arccos $\dfrac{2}{\sqrt{5}}$.

But Arccos $\dfrac{2}{\sqrt{5}}$ = Arccos $\dfrac{2\sqrt{5}}{5}$ = Arccos(0.8944).

Using Table 1, you find Arccos(0.8944) $\doteq$ 0.5, **Answer.**

EXAMPLE 3. Solve $\cos^4 2\theta - \sin^4 2\theta = 1$.

Solution:

$$\cos^4 2\theta - \sin^4 2\theta = 1$$
$$(\cos^2 2\theta + \sin^2 2\theta)(\cos^2 2\theta - \sin^2 2\theta) = 1.$$
$$1 \cdot \cos 2(2\theta) = 1$$
$$\cos 4\theta = 1$$
$$\therefore\ 4\theta = 2\pi k$$
$$\theta = \frac{\pi k}{2}.$$

The solution set is $\left\{\theta:\ \theta = \dfrac{\pi k}{2}\right\}$, **Answer.**

EXAMPLE 4. Solve: $2 \sin^2 x - 1 > 0$ *and* $0 \leq x \leq 2\pi$.

Solution: $\sin^2 x > \frac{1}{2}$

$$\sin x > \frac{1}{\sqrt{2}} \text{ or } \sin x < -\frac{1}{\sqrt{2}}.$$

(A sketch helps identify the solution set.)

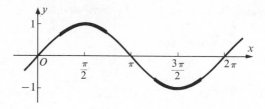

The solution set is $\left\{ x: \dfrac{\pi}{4} < x < \dfrac{3\pi}{4} \text{ or } \dfrac{5\pi}{4} < x < \dfrac{7\pi}{4} \right\}$,

Answer.

Exercises

Solve for x, using inverse notation when necessary.

A

1. $5 \cos x = 1$

2. $\sin^2 x - 7 \sin x = 0$

3. $2 \sec^2 x - 3 \sec x = 0$

4. $\tan^2 x - 5 = 0$

5. $\sqrt{3} \csc^2 x + 2 \csc x = 0$

6. $3 \csc^2 x + 4 \csc x = 0$

7. $\sin 2x = 3 \cos x$

8. $\sin 2x = 2 \sin x$

9. $\sin(\pi + x) = 2$

10. $\sin 2x = \dfrac{2 \sin x}{\sec x}$

11. $\sin \left(\dfrac{\pi}{4} + x \right) - \sin \left(\dfrac{\pi}{4} - x \right) = 1$

12. $\cos \left(\dfrac{\pi}{4} + x \right) + \cos \left(\dfrac{\pi}{4} - x \right) = 1$

B

13. $\cot x \tan 2x = 3$

14. $\sin^2 x + \cos 2x = \cos x$

15. $\left| \sin \frac{1}{2} x \right| = \left| \cos x \right|$

16. $\tan 2x \tan x = 1$

17. $\cos x = 2 - 2 \cos^2 \dfrac{x}{2}$

18. $3 \cos 2x + \cos x + 2 = 0$

19. $\cos 2x = \cos x$

20. $\cos 2x + \cos^2 x = \frac{7}{4}$

21. $\tan 2x - \cot x = 0$

22. $\left| \tan \frac{1}{2} x \right| = \left| \sin x \right|$

23. $\cos 2x \cos x + \sin 2x \sin x = 1$

24. $\sin 2x \cos x - \cos 2x \sin x = \frac{1}{2}$

25. $\tan \left(\dfrac{5\pi}{4} + x \right)$

$+ \tan \left(\dfrac{5\pi}{4} - x \right) = 4$

26. $\sin \left(\dfrac{\pi}{3} - x \right) - \sin \left(\dfrac{\pi}{3} + x \right) = \frac{1}{2}$

27. $\cos 2x + 3 \cos x = 1$ **30.** $4 \sin^2 \tfrac{1}{2}x + \tan^2 \tfrac{1}{2}x = 6$

28. $\cos 2x + \cos x + 1 = 0$ **31.** $\csc \tfrac{1}{2}x + \cot \tfrac{1}{2}x = 2 \sin \tfrac{1}{2}x$

29. $\tan^2 \tfrac{1}{2}x + 2 \cos x = \tfrac{4}{3}$ **32.** $\sec \tfrac{1}{2}x + \tan \tfrac{1}{2}x + 2 \cos \tfrac{1}{2}x = 0$

Solve for x, where $0 \le x \le 2\pi$.

C

33. $2 \cos^2 x - 1 > 0$ **37.** $\cot^2 x + \csc x + 1 \ge 0$

34. $\tan^2 x < 1$ **38.** $\cos x \le \sin x$

35. $2 \sin^2 x + 3 \sin x \ge 2$ **39.** $\sin 2x < \sin x$

36. $2 \sin^2 x + \cos x \ge 1$ **40.** $\sin x + \sin \dfrac{x}{2} < 0$

41. Sketch $y = \tan x$ and $y = x$ in the same coordinate system. The graph suggests a solution of the equation $\tan x = x$, with $\pi < x < \dfrac{3\pi}{2}$. Use Table 1 to find a decimal approximation of that solution.

42. Find a decimal approximation of the root of $x = 3 \sin x$, $x > 0$.

11-8 Converting Sums and Products

It is useful to know how to express certain trigonometric products as sums. Applying the equality property of addition to the identities

$$\sin \alpha \cos \beta + \cos \alpha \sin \beta = \sin(\alpha + \beta),$$
$$\sin \alpha \cos \beta - \cos \alpha \sin \beta = \sin(\alpha - \beta),$$

you obtain

$$2 \sin \alpha \cos \beta = \sin(\alpha + \beta) + \sin(\alpha - \beta), \tag{1}$$

EXAMPLE 1. Express as a sum: $2 \sin 5x \cos 2x$.

Solution: $2 \sin 5x \cos 2x = \sin(5x + 2x) + \sin(5x - 2x)$

$\therefore 2 \sin 5x \cos 2x = \sin 7x + \sin 3x$, **Answer.**

The use of identity (1) above to express a sum of sine values as a product is facilitated by the following change in notation.

Let $\alpha + \beta = x,$

and $\alpha - \beta = y.$

Transforming this pair of equations to express α and β in terms of x and y, you find:

$$\alpha = \frac{x + y}{2} \quad and \quad \beta = \frac{x - y}{2}.$$

Substituting in identity (1), you obtain

$$\sin x + \sin y = 2 \sin \frac{x+y}{2} \cos \frac{x-y}{2}. \tag{2}$$

Replacing y by $-y$ and using the identity $\sin(-y) = -\sin y$, you deduce from (2) the formula

$$\sin x - \sin y = 2 \cos \frac{x+y}{2} \sin \frac{x-y}{2}. \tag{3}$$

Beginning with the identities

$$\cos \alpha \cos \beta - \sin \alpha \sin \beta = \cos(\alpha + \beta)$$

$$\cos \alpha \cos \beta + \sin \alpha \sin \beta = \cos(\alpha - \beta),$$

you can similarly derive the following sequence of identities:

$$2 \cos \alpha \cos \beta = \cos(\alpha + \beta) + \cos(\alpha - \beta) \tag{4}$$

$$-2 \sin \alpha \sin \beta = \cos(\alpha + \beta) - \cos(\alpha - \beta) \tag{5}$$

$$\cos x + \cos y = 2 \cos \frac{x+y}{2} \cos \frac{x-y}{2} \tag{6}$$

$$\cos x - \cos y = -2 \sin \frac{x+y}{2} \sin \frac{x-y}{2} \tag{7}$$

EXAMPLE 2. Express $\sin \dfrac{5\pi}{14} + \sin \dfrac{\pi}{14}$ as a product.

Solution: Using formula (2) above, you find:

$$\sin \frac{5\pi}{14} + \sin \frac{\pi}{14} = 2 \sin \left(\frac{\frac{5\pi}{14} + \frac{\pi}{14}}{2} \right) \cos \left(\frac{\frac{5\pi}{14} - \frac{\pi}{14}}{2} \right).$$

$$\therefore \sin \frac{5\pi}{14} + \sin \frac{\pi}{4} = 2 \sin \frac{3\pi}{14} \cos \frac{\pi}{7}, \textbf{ Answer.}$$

EXAMPLE 3. Prove the identity

$$\frac{\cos 3t + \cos t}{\sin 3t - \sin t} = \frac{\csc t}{\sec t}.$$

Solution:

$$\text{L.M.} = \frac{2 \cos \left(\dfrac{3t + t}{2}\right) \cos \left(\dfrac{3t - t}{2}\right)}{2 \cos \left(\dfrac{3t + t}{2}\right) \sin \left(\dfrac{3t - t}{2}\right)} \qquad \text{R.M.} = \frac{\dfrac{1}{\sin t}}{\dfrac{1}{\cos t}}$$

$$= \frac{\cos t}{\sin t} \qquad\qquad\qquad = \frac{\cos t}{\sin t}$$

$$\therefore \frac{\cos 3t + \cos t}{\sin 3t - \sin t} = \frac{\csc t}{\sec t}.$$

You can often use the identities (1)–(7) to help you solve equations.

EXAMPLE 4. Solve the equation $\sin 5x + \sin 3x = \frac{3}{2} \cos x$.

Solution: $\sin 5x + \sin 3x = \frac{3}{2} \cos x$

$$2 \sin \left(\frac{5x + 3x}{2}\right) \cos \left(\frac{5x - 3x}{2}\right) = \frac{3}{2} \cos x$$

$$2 \sin 4x \cos x = \frac{3}{2} \cos x$$

$$4 \sin 4x \cos x - 3 \cos x = 0$$

$$\cos x(4 \sin 4x - 3) = 0$$

$$\cos x = 0 \quad or \quad 4 \sin 4x - 3 = 0$$

Arcsin $\frac{3}{4}$

$\pi -$ Arcsin $\frac{3}{4}$

(1) $\cos x = 0$ if and only if $x = \dfrac{\pi}{2}, \dfrac{3\pi}{2}, -\dfrac{\pi}{2}, \cdots$;

$$x = \frac{(2k + 1)\pi}{2}$$

(2) $4 \sin 4x - 3 = 0$ if and only if $\sin 4x = \frac{3}{4}$; $\therefore 4x \in \arcsin \frac{3}{4}$.

$\therefore 4x = $ Arcsin $\frac{3}{4} + 2\pi k \quad or \quad (\pi - $ Arcsin $\frac{3}{4}) + 2\pi k$

$\therefore$ the solution set is $\left\{x: \; x = \dfrac{(2k + 1)\pi}{2} \quad or \quad x = \dfrac{k\pi}{2} + \dfrac{1}{4} \text{ Arcsin } \frac{3}{4}\right.$

$\left. or \quad x = \dfrac{(2k + 1)\pi}{4} - \dfrac{1}{4} \text{ Arcsin } \frac{3}{4}, k \in J\right\}$, **Answer.**

Exercises

Write the product as a sum.

A

1. $2 \cos 5t \sin t$

5. $\sin\left(\dfrac{\pi}{2} - x\right) \sin\left(\dfrac{\pi}{2} + x\right)$

2. $-2 \sin 3x \sin 5x$

6. $\cos \dfrac{3\pi}{4} \cos \dfrac{\pi}{4}$

3. $\cos 2y \cos 8y$

7. $\sin(u + v) \cos(u - v)$

4. $\sin z \cos 7z$

8. $\cos\left(\dfrac{\pi}{6} + x\right) \sin\left(\dfrac{\pi}{3} - x\right)$

Write the sum as a product.

9. $\sin 3t + \sin t$

13. $\cos 6t - \cos 4t$

10. $\sin 8t - \sin 2t$

14. $\cos 4t - \cos 6t$

11. $\sin \frac{3}{4} + \sin \frac{1}{4}$

15. $5 \sin 7 - 5 \sin 3$

12. $\sin \dfrac{\pi}{3} - \sin \dfrac{\pi}{5}$

16. $\tan 2 \cos 3 - \cos 7 \tan 2$

Prove the identities.

B

17. $\sin \dfrac{2\pi}{9} + \sin \dfrac{\pi}{9} = \cos \dfrac{\pi}{18}$

20. $\dfrac{\sin x - \sin y}{\cos x + \cos y} = \tan\left(\dfrac{x - y}{2}\right)$

18. $\dfrac{\sin t + \sin q}{\cos t - \cos q} = -\cot\left(\dfrac{t - q}{2}\right)$

21. $\dfrac{\sin(2x - y) + \sin y}{\cos(2x - y) + \cos y} = \tan x$

19. $\dfrac{\cos 6x + \cos 4x}{\sin 6x - \sin 4x} = \cot x$

22. $\dfrac{\cos t - \cos(t + 2q)}{\sin t + \sin(t + 2q)} = \tan q$

23. $\dfrac{\sin x + \sin 3x + \sin 2x}{\cos x + \cos 3x + \cos 2x} = \dfrac{2 \tan x}{1 - \tan^2 x}$

24. $\dfrac{-\cos 4x + \cos 12x}{\cos 12x + \cos 4x} = \dfrac{2 \tan^2 (4x)}{-1 + \tan^2 (4x)}$

C

25. $4 \cos 3t \sin t \cos 2t = \sin 2t - \sin 4t + \sin 6t$

26. $4 \cos 3x \sin 2x \sin 5x = \cos 6x - \cos 4x - \cos 10x + 1$

27. $\sin t - \sin 3t = 2 \sin^3 t - 2 \sin t \cos^2 t$

28. $\dfrac{\cos t + \cos 3t}{2} = \dfrac{1 - 2 \sin^2 t}{\sec t}$

29. $\dfrac{\sin \theta + \sin 3\theta + \sin 5\theta}{\cos \theta + \cos 3\theta + \cos 5\theta} = \tan 3\theta$

30. $\sin \theta + \sin 3\theta + \sin 5\theta + \sin 7\theta = 4 \cos \theta \cos 2\theta \sin 4\theta$

Find the solution set.

31. $\sin x + \sin 2x + \sin 3x = 0$ 34. $\cos 2x = \cos 3x - \cos 4x$

32. $\cos 5t + \cos 3t = \cos t$ 35. $\sin x + \sin 3x \leq \cos x$

33. $\sin 4x - \sin x = \sin 2x$ 36. $\cos 3x - \sin 2x < \cos x$

CONTINUITY AND DERIVATIVES

C 11–9 Continuity of Sine and Cosine (*Optional*)

Look at Figure 11–7 which shows the unit circle $\mathcal{C}$, the point $\mathbf{S}(\cos x, \sin x)$ in Quadrant I, and the point $\mathbf{Q}[\cos(-x), \sin(-x)]$ in Quadrant IV. If you take for granted the fact that a chord of the circle is shorter than the arc it subtends, then you can deduce that

$$d(\mathbf{Q}, \mathbf{S}) < l(\widehat{\mathbf{QS}}),$$

so that $\quad 2|\sin x| < 2|x|, \quad 0 < |x| < \dfrac{\pi}{2}.$

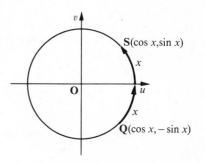

Figure 11–7

$\therefore$ (1) $|\sin x| \leq |x|, \quad 0 \leq |x| < \dfrac{\pi}{2},$

with equality holding for $x = 0$.

With inequality (1), you can prove that both sin and cos are continuous functions. We prove first that sin is continuous at the origin.

THEOREM	The function sin $= \{(x, y): y = \sin x\}$ is continuous at 0.

Proof: *Plan:* To demonstrate the continuity of sin at 0, you must prove that $\lim\limits_{x \to 0} \sin x = \sin 0 = 0$.

Let $x_1, x_2, \ldots, x_n, \ldots$ be an arbitrary sequence such that $\lim\limits_{n \to \infty} x_n = 0$. Then, for any real number h, $0 < h < 1$, you can choose a positive integer M so great that

$$|x_n| < h, \qquad\qquad n > M. \quad \text{(Why?)}$$

By inequality (1), $|\sin x_n| \leq |x_n|$, and, therefore,

$$|\sin x_n| < h, \qquad\qquad n > M.$$

Since for every sequence $x_1, x_2, \ldots x_n, \ldots$ of real numbers converging to 0 and every positive real number h, $h < 1$, you can find a positive integer M such that

$$|\sin x_n| < h, \qquad\qquad n > M,$$

it follows that

$$\lim_{x \to 0} \sin x = 0 = \sin 0,$$

and sin is continuous at 0.

COROLLARY 1. If $c \in \mathfrak{R}$, $\lim_{x \to 0} c \sin x = 0$.

The corollary follows from the theorem by invoking the corollary to the limit theorem stated on page 97. Thus,

$$\lim_{x \to 0} c \sin x = c \lim_{x \to 0} \sin x = c \cdot 0 = 0.$$

COROLLARY 2. cos is continuous at 0.

Proof of Corollary 2: Using the identity

$$\cos x = 1 - 2 \sin^2 \frac{x}{2},$$

and the theorem stated on page 97, you find

$$\lim_{x \to 0} \cos x = \lim_{x \to 0} \left(1 - 2 \sin^2 \frac{x}{2}\right)$$

$$= 1 - 2 \left(\lim_{x \to 0} \sin \frac{x}{2}\right)^2$$

$$= 1 - 2 \cdot 0.$$

$$\therefore \lim_{x \to 0} \cos x = 1.$$

Since $\cos 0 = 1$, $\lim_{x \to 0} \cos x = \cos 0$, and cos is continuous at 0.

THEOREM   The functions

$$\sin = \{(x, y): \ y = \sin x\}$$

$$\cos = \{(x, y): \ y = \cos x\}$$

are continuous at every real number c.

Proof: Let c denote any real number. Then $\lim_{x \to c} (x - c) = 0$. Hence, by the preceding theorem, and its second corollary,

$$\lim_{x \to c} \sin(x - c) = 0 \quad \text{and} \quad \lim_{x \to c} \cos(x - c) = 1.$$

Now, $x = [(x - c) + c]$, and $\sin x = \sin [(x - c) + c]$.

Therefore, by formula (1), page 419,

$$\sin x = \sin(x - c) \cos c + \cos(x - c) \sin c.$$

$$\therefore \ \lim_{x \to c} \sin x = \lim_{x \to c} [\sin(x - c) \cos c] + \lim_{x \to c} [\cos(x - c) \sin c]$$

$$= \cos c \lim_{x \to c} \sin(x - c) + \sin c \lim_{x \to c} \cos(x - c)$$

$$= \cos c \cdot 0 + \sin c \cdot 1 \quad \text{(Why?)}.$$

$$\therefore \ \lim_{x \to c} \sin x = \sin c.$$

Hence, sin is continuous at c.

An analogous argument proves that cos is continuous at c (Exercise 19, page 449).

You can use the continuity of sine and cosine to help you study the continuity of other circular functions.

EXAMPLE 1.   Find $\lim_{x \to 0} \sec x$.

Solution: Since $\sec x = \dfrac{1}{\cos x}$, and $\lim_{x \to 0} \cos x \neq 0$, you have

$$\lim_{x \to 0} \sec x = \lim_{x \to 0} \frac{1}{\cos x} = \frac{1}{\lim_{x \to 0} \cos x} = \frac{1}{1}.$$

$$\therefore \ \lim_{x \to 0} \sec x = 1, \textbf{ Answer.}$$

Another useful limit is given in the following theorem.

THEOREM $\lim\limits_{x\to 0} \dfrac{\sin x}{x} = 1.$

Proof: Observe that if $x \neq 0$, then

$$\frac{\sin(-x)}{-x} = \frac{-\sin x}{-x} = \frac{\sin x}{x}.$$

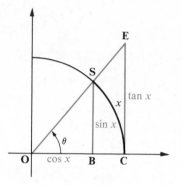

Figure 11–8

This fact means that in proving the theorem you may restrict consideration to the case in which $x > 0$.

In Figure 11–8 note that $\dfrac{\pi}{2} > x > 0$ and that the area of $\triangle\mathbf{OBS}$ is $\frac{1}{2}\cos x \sin x$, while the area of $\triangle\mathbf{OCE}$ is $\frac{1}{2}\tan x$. Moreover, since $m^R\angle\theta = x$, the area of the sector $\mathbf{OCS}$ is $\frac{1}{2}r^2 x$, or simply $\frac{1}{2}x$. Now

$$\underbrace{\text{area of }\triangle\mathbf{OBS}}_{\frac{1}{2}\cos x \sin x} < \underbrace{\text{area of sector }\mathbf{OCS}}_{\frac{1}{2}x} < \underbrace{\text{area of }\triangle\mathbf{OCE}}_{\frac{1}{2}\tan x};$$

Multiplying each member of this inequality by $\dfrac{2}{\sin x} > 0$, you obtain

$$\cos x < \frac{x}{\sin x} < \frac{1}{\cos x}.$$

$$\frac{1}{\cos x} > \frac{\sin x}{x} > \cos x, \text{ and}$$

$$\lim_{x\to 0}\frac{1}{\cos x} \geq \lim_{x\to 0}\frac{\sin x}{x} \geq \lim_{x\to 0}\cos x.$$

But $\lim\limits_{x\to 0}\cos x = 1$. Hence $\lim\limits_{x\to 0}\dfrac{\sin x}{x} = 1$ (Why?), and the theorem is proved.

EXAMPLE 2. Find $\lim\limits_{x\to 0} \dfrac{\sin\dfrac{x}{2}}{x}$.

Solution: Write $\dfrac{\sin\dfrac{x}{2}}{x} = \dfrac{1}{2}\left(\dfrac{\sin\dfrac{x}{2}}{\dfrac{x}{2}}\right).$ Then

$$\lim_{x \to 0} \frac{\sin \frac{x}{2}}{x} = \lim_{x \to 0} \frac{1}{2}\left(\frac{\sin \frac{x}{2}}{\frac{x}{2}}\right) = \frac{1}{2} \lim_{x \to 0} \frac{\sin \frac{x}{2}}{\frac{x}{2}}.$$

Now, as x approaches 0, $\frac{x}{2}$ approaches 0. (Why?) Therefore, using the preceding theorem, you have:

$$\lim_{x \to 0} \frac{\sin \frac{x}{2}}{x} = \frac{1}{2} \lim_{\frac{x}{2} \to 0} \frac{\sin \frac{x}{2}}{\frac{x}{2}} = \frac{1}{2} \cdot 1 = \frac{1}{2}, \textbf{ Answer.}$$

Exercises

Evaluate each of the following limits.

C 1. $\lim\limits_{x \to 0} \tan x$

4. $\lim\limits_{x \to 0} \tan \frac{x}{2}$

6. $\lim\limits_{x \to 0} \frac{\sin \frac{x}{3}}{x}$

9. $\lim\limits_{x \to 0} \frac{\sin 2x}{\sin x}$

2. $\lim\limits_{x \to 0} \sin x \cot x$

5. $\lim\limits_{x \to 0} \frac{\sin 2x}{x}$

7. $\lim\limits_{x \to \frac{\pi}{2}} \frac{x}{\sec x}$

10. $\lim\limits_{x \to 0} \frac{\cos 2x}{\sin x}$

3. $\lim\limits_{x \to 0} \cos \frac{x}{2}$

8. $\lim\limits_{x \to \frac{\pi}{2}} \frac{x}{\csc x}$

Prove each of the following.

11. The function tan is continuous for every $x \in \mathcal{R}$, $x \neq \frac{\pi}{2} + k\pi$, $k \in J$.

12. The function cot is continuous for every $x \in \mathcal{R}$, $x \neq k\pi$, $k \in J$.

13. $\lim\limits_{x \to 0} \left(\frac{x - \sin x}{x}\right) = 0$

16. $\lim\limits_{x \to \frac{\pi}{2}} \left(\frac{\cos x}{\frac{\pi}{2} - x}\right) = 1$

14. $\lim\limits_{x \to 0} \left(\frac{1 - \cos x}{\sin^2 x}\right) = \frac{1}{2}$

17. $\lim\limits_{x \to 0} \left(\frac{\sin ax}{x}\right) = a$

15. $\lim\limits_{x \to \pi} \left(\frac{\sin x}{\pi - x}\right) = 1$

18. $\lim\limits_{x \to c} \frac{\sin a(x - c)}{x - c} = a$.

(*Hint:* Use Exercise 17.)

19. Prove that cosine is continuous at every $x \in \mathcal{R}$.

20. Prove that $\lim\limits_{x \to 0} \frac{1 - \cos x}{x^2} = \frac{1}{2}$. $\left(Hint: 1 - \cos x = 2\sin^2 \frac{x}{2}.\right)$

C **11-10** **Tangents to the Graphs of Sin and Cos** (*Optional*)

On the basis of your experience with tangents to the graphs of polynomial, logarithmic, and exponential functions, you can probably guess how we define the tangent to the graph of $\sin = \{(x, y): y = \sin x\}$ at any point $\mathbf{S}(c, \sin c)$ of the graph. It is the line $\mathfrak{I}$ through $\mathbf{S}$ with slope equal to the limit (if it exists) of the sequence

$$\frac{\sin x_1 - \sin c}{x_1 - c}, \frac{\sin x_2 - \sin c}{x_2 - c}, \frac{\sin x_3 - \sin c}{x_3 - c}, \ldots$$

where $x_1, x_2, \ldots, x_n, \ldots$ is any convergent sequence of real numbers all different from c, such that $\lim\limits_{n \to \infty} x_n = c$. Figure 11-9 illustrates this definition.

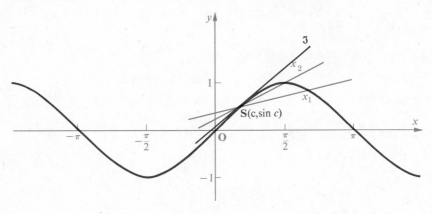

Figure 11-9

To determine $\lim\limits_{n \to \infty} \dfrac{\sin x_n - \sin c}{x_n - c}$, you use formula (3), page 442, to write

$$\sin x_n - \sin c = 2 \cos \tfrac{1}{2}(x_n + c) \sin \tfrac{1}{2}(x_n - c).$$

$$\therefore \frac{\sin x_n - \sin c}{x_n - c} = 2 \cos \frac{1}{2}(x_n + c) \frac{\sin \tfrac{1}{2}(x_n - c)}{x_n - c},$$

and

(1) $\quad \lim\limits_{n \to \infty} \dfrac{\sin x_n - \sin c}{x_n - c} = 2 \lim\limits_{n \to \infty} \cos \dfrac{1}{2}(x_n + c) \lim\limits_{n \to \infty} \dfrac{\sin \tfrac{1}{2}(x_n - c)}{x_n - c}.$

Now because cos is continuous at c,

(2) $\quad\quad\quad \lim\limits_{n \to \infty} \cos \tfrac{1}{2}(x_n + c) = \cos \tfrac{1}{2}(c + c) = \cos c.$

Also, using the fact that $\lim\limits_{x \to c} \dfrac{\sin a(x - c)}{x - c} = a$ (Exercise 18, page 449) with

$\frac{1}{2}$ in place of a, you find that

(3) $$\lim_{n\to\infty} \frac{\sin \frac{1}{2}(x_n - c)}{x_n - c} = \frac{1}{2}.$$

Thus, statements (1), (2), and (3) together imply that

(4) $$\lim_{n\to\infty} \frac{\sin x_n - \sin c}{x_n - c} = 2 (\cos c) \frac{1}{2} = \cos c.$$

Since statement (4) holds for every real number c and every sequence of real numbers x_n different from c such that $\lim_{n\to\infty} x_n = c$, we define the **slope of tangent to the graph of sin at $(c, \sin c)$ to be cos c.**

Thus, if $f = \{(x, y): y = \sin x\}$ and f', the derivative of f, is the function whose value at c is the slope of the tangent to the graph of f (or simply, the slope of the graph of f), then $f'(x) = \cos x$.

EXAMPLE 1. Find the slope of the graph of sin at the point **S** with abscissa $\frac{\pi}{4}$.

Solution: Let $f(x) = \sin x$. Then $f'(x) = \cos x$.

$$f'\left(\frac{\pi}{4}\right) = \cos \frac{\pi}{4} = \frac{1}{\sqrt{2}}.$$

$\therefore$ the slope of the graph of sin at **S** is $\frac{1}{\sqrt{2}}$, **Answer.**

By using the identity $\cos \alpha - \cos \beta = -2 \sin \frac{1}{2}(\alpha + \beta) \sin \frac{1}{2}(\alpha - \beta)$, you can show that if $\lim_{n\to\infty} x_n = c$ ($x_n \neq c$), then

$$\lim_{n\to\infty} \frac{\cos x_n - \cos c}{x_n - c} = -\sin c,$$

and hence prove that **the derivative of cos x is $-\sin x$.**

By considering $\lim_{x\to c} \frac{\sin ax - \sin ac}{x - c}$, and using Exercise 17, page 449, you can prove that

If $y = \sin ax$, then $y' = a \cos ax$,

and, in a similar manner, that

If $y = \cos ax$, then $y' = -a \sin ax$.

These, in turn, can be used to study the velocity and acceleration of a point moving along a straight line so that its position y at time t is given by an equation of the form $y = b \sin at$, or $y = b \cos at$ (*simple harmonic motion*).

EXAMPLE 2. A particle moves according to the relationship $y = \sin 3t$. Find **(a)** the displacement, **(b)** the velocity, and **(c)** the acceleration of the point when $t = \dfrac{\pi}{4}$.

Solution: **(a)** $y = \sin 3 \left(\dfrac{\pi}{4} \right) = \sin \dfrac{3\pi}{4} = \dfrac{1}{\sqrt{2}}$.

(b) y' is the velocity of the particle at any time t.

$$y' = 3 \cos 3 \left(\dfrac{\pi}{4} \right) = 3 \cos \dfrac{3\pi}{4} = 3 \left(-\dfrac{1}{\sqrt{2}} \right) = -\dfrac{3}{\sqrt{2}}.$$

The fact that y' is negative means that the particle is moving in a negative direction.

(c) The acceleration is the rate of change of the velocity, or y''. Since $y' = 3 \cos 3t$, and since you can show that the derivative of $y = a \cos x$ is $y' = -a \sin x$, you obtain $y'' = -9 \sin 3t$.

$$y'' = -9 \sin \dfrac{3\pi}{4} = -9 \left(\dfrac{1}{\sqrt{2}} \right) = -\dfrac{9}{\sqrt{2}}.$$

The fact that y'' is negative means that the particle is decelerating.

$$\text{displacement} = \dfrac{1}{\sqrt{2}}, \text{velocity} = -\dfrac{3}{\sqrt{2}},$$

$$\text{acceleration} = -\dfrac{9}{\sqrt{2}}, \textbf{Answer.}$$

Exercises

Assuming, for any circular functions $f(x)$ and $g(x)$, that if $y = cf(x)$, then $y' = cf'(x)$, and if $y = f(x) + g(x)$, then $y' = f'(x) + g'(x)$, find the derivative of each of the following and evaluate it at the given value of x.

C **1.** $y = \sin x + \cos x; \; x = \dfrac{\pi}{2}$

2. $y = \sin 3x + \cos 2x; \; x = \dfrac{3\pi}{4}$

3. $y = 2 \sin 3x - 3 \cos 2x; \; x = \dfrac{11\pi}{12}$

4. $y = \sin 2x - 2 \cos x; \; x = -\dfrac{2\pi}{3}$

5–8. In Exercises 1–4, find an equation of the tangent line to the graph of the given curve at the specified point.

9. Find the maximum and minimum points of the graph of the equation $y = 2 \sin x - 3 \cos x, \; 0 \le x \le 2\pi$.

10. Find the maximum and minimum points of the graph of the equation $y = 3 \sin x + \cos x, 0 \le x \le 2\pi$.

In Exercises 11–14, find (a) the displacement, (b) the velocity, and (c) the acceleration, of a particle moving according to the given relationship at the specified time.

11. $y = \cos 2t, t = \dfrac{\pi}{6}.$ **13.** $y = 2 \sin 3t, t = \dfrac{5\pi}{12}$

12. $y = \sin 4t, t = \dfrac{\pi}{12}$ **14.** $y = 3 \cos 3t, t = \dfrac{7\pi}{12}$

If f is the function with $f(x)$ as given, prove that f' is the function with $f'(x)$ as indicated. Assume that a and b denote constants, $a \ne 0$.

15. $f(x) = \cos x; f'(x) = -\sin x$ **18.** $f(x) = \cos ax; f'(x) = -a \sin ax$

16. $f(x) = -\sin x; f'(x) = -\cos x$ **19.** $f(x) = \sin(ax + b);$
$f'(x) = a \cos(ax + b)$

17. $f(x) = \sin ax; f'(x) = a \cos ax$ **20.** $f(x) = \cos(ax + b);$
$f'(x) = -a \sin(ax + b)$

Chapter Summary

1. You use the distance formula to derive the formula for the cosine of the sum of two numbers,

$$\cos(\alpha + \beta) = \cos \alpha \cos \beta - \sin \alpha \sin \beta.$$

This formula can then be used to derive the formula for the cosine of the difference of two numbers,

$$\cos(\alpha - \beta) = \cos \alpha \cos \beta + \sin \alpha \sin \beta.$$

2. The formula for the cosine of the sum of two numbers can also be used to derive formulas for the sine of the sum or difference of two numbers:

$$\sin(\alpha \pm \beta) = \sin \alpha \cos \beta \pm \cos \alpha \sin \beta.$$

Similarly, the formulas for the tangent of the sum or difference of two numbers are

$$\tan(\alpha \pm \beta) = \frac{\tan \alpha \pm \tan \beta}{1 \mp \tan \alpha \tan \beta}.$$

Reduction formulas derived from the preceding identities are used with trigonometric tables to determine approximations of function values.

3. The basic "cosine sum formula" also leads to the **double-angle formulas**:

$$\cos 2\alpha = \cos^2 \alpha - \sin^2 \alpha,$$

$$\sin 2\alpha = 2 \sin \alpha \cos \alpha, \qquad\qquad \tan 2\alpha = \frac{2 \tan \alpha}{1 - \tan^2 \alpha}.$$

In turn, the formula for $\cos 2\alpha$ implies the **half-angle formulas**:

$$\left| \sin \frac{\alpha}{2} \right| = \sqrt{\frac{1 - \cos \alpha}{2}}, \qquad\qquad \left| \cos \frac{\alpha}{2} \right| = \sqrt{\frac{1 + \cos \alpha}{2}},$$

$$\left| \tan \frac{\alpha}{2} \right| = \sqrt{\frac{1 - \cos \alpha}{1 + \cos \alpha}} \quad (\cos \alpha \neq -1).$$

4. You use **inverse notation** to designate an element in the domain of a circular or trigonometric function when given a specified element in the range. Thus:

$$\textbf{If } \sin x = y, \textbf{ then } x = \arcsin y.$$

$$\textbf{If } \cos x = y, \textbf{ then } x = \arccos y. \qquad\qquad \textbf{If } \tan x = y, \textbf{ then } x = \arctan y.$$

Similar notation is used for the cotangent, secant, and cosecant. Another representation for inverses such as **arcsin** and **arccos** is $\sin^{-1}$ and $\cos^{-1}$.

5. Each circular function has an inverse relation. By restricting the range as indicated, you define the **principal-valued inverse functions**:

$$\text{Arc sine} = \{(x, y)\colon \; y = \text{Arcsin } x\}, \; |x| \leq 1, \; |y| \leq \frac{\pi}{2}.$$

$$\text{Arc cosine} = \{(x, y)\colon \; y = \text{Arccos } x\}, \; |x| \leq 1, \; 0 \leq y \leq \pi.$$

$$\text{Arc tangent} = \{(x, y)\colon \; y = \text{Arctan } x\}, \; x \in \mathfrak{R}, \; |y| < \frac{\pi}{2}.$$

$$\text{Arc cotangent} = \left\{(x, y)\colon \; y = \frac{\pi}{2} - \text{Arctan } x\right\}, \; x \in \mathfrak{R}, \; 0 < y < \pi.$$

$$\text{Arc secant} = \left\{(x, y)\colon \; y = \text{Arccos } \frac{1}{x}\right\}, \; |x| \geq 1, \; 0 \leq y < \frac{\pi}{2} \text{ or } \frac{\pi}{2} < y \leq \pi.$$

$$\text{Arc cosecant} = \left\{(x, y)\colon \; y = \text{Arcsin } \frac{1}{x}\right\}, \; |x| \geq 1, \; 0 < |y| \leq \frac{\pi}{2}.$$

6. You can use inverse notation to designate the solution set of a trigonometric open sentence. To solve **trigonometric open sentences**, you employ algebraic techniques as well as trigonometric identities.
You convert products to sums by using the formulas

$$2 \sin \alpha \cos \beta = \sin(\alpha + \beta) + \sin(\alpha - \beta)$$

$$2 \cos \alpha \cos \beta = \cos(\alpha + \beta) + \cos(\alpha - \beta)$$

$$-2 \sin \alpha \sin \beta = \cos(\alpha + \beta) - \cos(\alpha - \beta)$$

7. You use the formulas

$$\sin x + \sin y = 2 \sin\left(\frac{x+y}{2}\right) \cos\left(\frac{x-y}{2}\right)$$

$$\sin x - \sin y = 2 \cos\left(\frac{x+y}{2}\right) \sin\left(\frac{x-y}{2}\right)$$

$$\cos x + \cos y = 2 \cos\left(\frac{x+y}{2}\right) \cos\left(\frac{x-y}{2}\right)$$

$$\cos x - \cos y = -2 \sin\left(\frac{x+y}{2}\right) \sin\left(\frac{x-y}{2}\right)$$

to convert sums to products.

8. Both sine and cosine are **continuous** over $\mathcal{R}$. An important limit is
$$\lim_{x \to 0} \frac{\sin x}{x} = 1.$$

9. The **derivative** of $\sin x$ is $\cos x$, and the derivative of $\cos x$ is $-\sin x$.

Chapter Test

11-1   1. The real numbers and the points of a unit circle, with center at the origin, are in correspondence in such a way that a number n corresponds with the terminal point of the arc with initial point $(1, 0)$ and length n. When points **A** and **B** correspond with the numbers $\frac{\pi}{3}$ and $\frac{2\pi}{3}$ respectively, show that $d(\mathbf{A}, \mathbf{B}) = 1$.

2. Use the formula for $\cos(\alpha - \beta)$ to prove that $\cos\left(\frac{\pi}{2} - t\right) = \sin t$.

3. By taking $\frac{\pi}{12}$ as $\frac{5\pi}{6} - \frac{3\pi}{4}$, find the exact value of $\cos \frac{\pi}{12}$.

11-2   4. Given: $\sin \alpha = \frac{12}{13}$, $\cos \beta = \frac{3}{5}$, $0 < \alpha < \frac{\pi}{2}$, $0 < \beta < \frac{\pi}{2}$. Find $\sin(\alpha + \beta)$

5. Using the information given in Exercise 4, find $\tan(\alpha - \beta)$.

6. Reduce sin 248° to a function of $n°$, where n is some number between 0 and 45.

11-3 **7.** Given: sin 38°20′ = 0.6202; sin 38°40′ = 0.6248. Find sin 38°23′.

8. Given: cot 0.8203 = 0.9325; cot 0.8261 = 0.9217; cot x = 0.9234; $0 < x < 1$. Find x.

11-4 **9.** Given, sin $t = \frac{4}{5}$ and $0 < t < \frac{\pi}{2}$, find sin $2t$.

10. Given, sin $t = -\frac{4}{5}$ and $\pi < t < \frac{3\pi}{2}$, find tan $\frac{1}{2}t$.

11-5 **11.** List any six elements of the set arcsin $\frac{1}{2}$.

12. Find the value of $\tan(\arccos(-\frac{3}{5}))$.

11-6 **13.** Give the exact value of $\text{Arccos}\left(-\frac{\sqrt{3}}{2}\right)$.

14. Evaluate $\sin(\text{Arctan}\,\frac{8}{15})$.

11-7 **15.** Solve $\cot^2 x - 7 = 0$, using inverse notation.

16. Solve sin $2x = 9$ sin x, using inverse notation when necessary.

11-8 **17.** Express the sum sin $7t +$ sin $3t$ as a product.

18. Prove the identity: $\dfrac{\cos t + \cos q}{\sin t - \sin q} = \cot\left(\dfrac{t - q}{2}\right)$.

11-9 (*Optional*)

19. Find $\lim\limits_{x\to 0} \dfrac{\sin \frac{x}{3}}{x}$.

11-10 (*Optional*)

20. Find an equation for the line tangent to $y = \cos 3x$ at $x = \dfrac{\pi}{4}$.

Reading List

COMMISSION ON MATHEMATICS. *Appendices* to the *Report of the Commission on Mathematics*. New York: College Entrance Examination Board, 1959.

HOUSEHOLDER, A. S. *The Addition Formulas in Trigonometry*. American Mathematical Monthly, vol. 49, pp. 326–327, 1942.

MCSHANE, E. J. *The Addition Formulas for the Sine and Cosine*. American Mathematical Monthly, vol. 48, pp. 688–689, 1941.

SCHAUMBER, NORMAN. *A Simple Proof of the Formula for sin(A + B)*. Mathematics Magazine, vol. 35, p. 229, 1962.

SCHOOL MATHEMATICS STUDY GROUP. *Elementary Functions, Part II*. New Haven, Conn.: Yale University Press, 1961.

E. H. Moore

In the early 1800's an Englishman once scoffed, "In the four quarters of the globe, who reads an American book, or goes to an American play, or looks at an American picture or statue?" He might well have added, "Who has heard of an American mathematician?", for until about 1890 there were very few research mathematicians in the United States, and the few that there were rarely met to discuss their ideas or ventured to have their works published. By the 1930's, however, this situation had changed. There had developed what might be called an "American school" of mathematics — a group of mathematicians who published works which were generally acknowledged to be original and valuable contributions to mathematics. In addition, the American Mathematical Society, which provided a means for mathematicians to meet and to have their work published, had become well organized. E. H. Moore (1862–1932) played an important and influential role in this development of mathematics in America.

Moore's mathematical ability became evident during his undergraduate years at Yale. His outstanding record convinced one of his professors to finance him for a year's study in Germany, where Klein, Weierstrass, and Kronecker were lecturing. After his return, he was made professor and head of the mathematics department at the newly opened University of Chicago —a position which he held for more than 30 years.

In his work Moore's interest centered on geometry, algebra, group theory, theory of functions, and analysis. He investigated the logical foundations of these areas and, in each case, tried to find a set of axioms from which the whole of the theory could be developed. The similarity which he found between the theories of several different branches of mathematics led him to believe in the existence of a general theory which would cover all of these branches. Much of his mathematical career was spent in trying to develop this general theory, and although he did not completely succeed, his work has been considered very important because it clarified the structure of the fields with which it was concerned, condensed the proofs of the theorems involved, and demonstrated the general nature of the underlying mathematical ideas.

457

2:1 ; 90°

1:1 + ε ; 90°

2:1 ; 0°

3:2 ; 45°

Lissajous figures are curves traced by a point whose motion is the resultant of two simple harmonic motions in perpendicular directions. These figures are used by radio engineers in frequency and phase measurement of wave motion. In the diagrams above, the ratio of the periods of the motions and their initial phase difference are given.

Vectors, Trigonometry, and Complex Numbers

The circular and trigonometric functions have applications cutting across many different branches of mathematics and extending to most of the sciences. Algebra, geometry, vector analysis, and the study of complex numbers all have aspects in which these functions help to clarify and simplify ideas. In this chapter, you will study several of these applications.

VECTORS AND ANGLES

12–1 Angle between Vectors

Figure 12–1 shows nonzero vectors **w** and **v** having θ_w and θ_v as direction angles. The angle $\phi = \theta_v - \theta_w$ whose initial ray has direction angle θ_w and whose terminal ray has direction angle θ_v is called the angle from **w** to **v**.

To discover a simple method of computing $\cos\phi$ and $\sin\phi$, consider the inner product **w** · **v**.

Since **w** = $\|\mathbf{w}\|$ ($\cos\theta_w$, $\sin\theta_w$) and **v** = $\|\mathbf{v}\|$ ($\cos\theta_v$, $\sin\theta_v$), you have

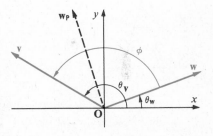

Figure 12–1

$$\mathbf{w} \cdot \mathbf{v} = \|\mathbf{w}\|\,\|\mathbf{v}\|\,(\cos\theta_v \cos\theta_w + \sin\theta_v \sin\theta_w);$$

$$\therefore \frac{\mathbf{w} \cdot \mathbf{v}}{\|\mathbf{w}\|\,\|\mathbf{v}\|} = \cos\theta_v \cos\theta_w + \sin\theta_v \sin\theta_w.$$

Using formula (2) on page 416, you find:

$$\cos\theta_v \cos\theta_w + \sin\theta_v \sin\theta_w = \cos(\theta_v - \theta_w) = \cos\phi.$$

459

Therefore:

(1)
$$\cos \phi = \frac{\mathbf{w} \cdot \mathbf{v}}{\|\mathbf{w}\| \, \|\mathbf{v}\|}.$$

Knowing that $\mathbf{w_P} = \|\mathbf{w}\| \, (-\sin \theta_w, \cos \theta_w)$, you can verify that:

(2)
$$\sin \phi = \frac{\mathbf{w_P} \cdot \mathbf{v}}{\|\mathbf{w}\| \, \|\mathbf{v}\|}$$

(See Exercise 25, page 464.) Results (1) and (2) are combined in the following theorem.

> **THEOREM** If $\mathbf{w}$ and $\mathbf{v}$ are nonzero vectors and ϕ is the angle from $\mathbf{w}$ to $\mathbf{v}$, then $\mathbf{w} \cdot \mathbf{v} = \|\mathbf{w}\| \, \|\mathbf{v}\| \cos \phi$ and $\mathbf{w_P} \cdot \mathbf{v} = \|\mathbf{w}\| \, \|\mathbf{v}\| \sin \phi.$

A particular case of this theorem occurs for $\mathbf{v}$ and $\mathbf{w}$ nonzero *perpendicular* vectors (Figure 12–2). In this case, $\mathbf{w} \cdot \mathbf{v} = 0$, so that $\cos \phi = 0$ and $\sin \phi = 1$ or -1. Thus, as you would expect, the angle from one of two nonzero perpendicular vectors to the other has a measure of $90°$ or $-90°$.

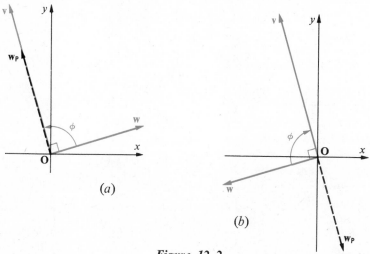

(a)

(b)

Figure 12–2

Using the quotient relationship $\tan \phi = \dfrac{\sin \phi}{\cos \phi}$, you can deduce the following corollary of the preceding theorem (Exercise 26, page 464).

COROLLARY. If ϕ is the angle from $\mathbf{w}$ to $\mathbf{v}$, and if $\mathbf{w}$ and $\mathbf{v}$ are not perpendicular vectors, then $\tan \phi = \dfrac{\mathbf{w_P} \cdot \mathbf{v}}{\mathbf{w} \cdot \mathbf{v}}.$

EXAMPLE 1. The points $A(4, -5)$, $B(-2, 2)$, and $C(6, 4)$ are the vertices of a triangle. If α is the angle from side $\overrightarrow{AC}$ to side $\overrightarrow{AB}$: **(a)** determine $\cos \alpha$ and $\sin \alpha$; **(b)** estimate $m°\angle\alpha$ to the nearest degree.

Solution: Sketch the triangle.

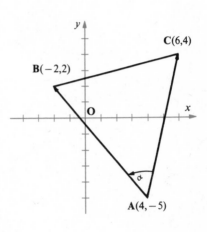

Let $\mathbf{w} = \overrightarrow{AC} = (6, 4) - (4, -5)$
$\mathbf{w} = (2, 9); \; \mathbf{w_P} = (-9, 2);$
$\mathbf{v} = \overrightarrow{AB} = (-2, 2) - (4, -5)$
$\mathbf{v} = (-6, 7).$
$\therefore \|\mathbf{w}\| = \sqrt{4 + 81} = \sqrt{85};$
$\|\mathbf{v}\| = \sqrt{36 + 49} = \sqrt{85}.$

(a) $\cos \alpha = \dfrac{(2, 9) \cdot (-6, 7)}{\sqrt{85}\sqrt{85}};$

$\sin \alpha = \dfrac{(-9, 2) \cdot (-6, 7)}{\sqrt{85}\sqrt{85}}.$

$\therefore \cos \alpha = \frac{51}{85} = \frac{3}{5};$

$\sin \alpha = \frac{68}{85} = \frac{4}{5},$ **Answer.**

(b) Using Table 2, you find $m°\angle\alpha \doteq 53°$, **Answer.**

EXAMPLE 2. Use a vector argument to prove that the angle inscribed in a semicircle is a right angle.

Proof: Given the semicircle shown in the figure, let $\mathbf{v}$ and $\mathbf{w}$ be the vectors with arrow representations $\overrightarrow{OA}$ and $\overrightarrow{CO}$. Then $\|\mathbf{v}\| = \|\mathbf{w}\| = $ radius of semicircle. Also, $\angle BCA$ is the angle from the vector $\mathbf{w} - \mathbf{v}$ to the vector $\mathbf{w} + \mathbf{v}$. (Why?) But

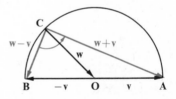

$$(\mathbf{w} - \mathbf{v}) \cdot (\mathbf{w} + \mathbf{v}) = \mathbf{w} \cdot \mathbf{w} - \mathbf{v} \cdot \mathbf{v}$$
$$= \|\mathbf{w}\|^2 - \|\mathbf{v}\|^2. \;\; \text{Why?}$$

$\therefore (\mathbf{w} - \mathbf{v}) \cdot (\mathbf{w} + \mathbf{v}) = 0.$

Hence, $\mathbf{w} - \mathbf{v}$ and $\mathbf{w} + \mathbf{v}$ are perpendicular vectors, and $m°\angle BCA = 90°.$

In Section 4–8 you learned how to resolve a vector **v** into components parallel and perpendicular to a nonzero vector **w**. In fact, if

$$\mathbf{v} = (\text{Comp}_\mathbf{w}\, \mathbf{v})\, \frac{\mathbf{w}}{\|\mathbf{w}\|} + (\text{Comp}_{\mathbf{w}_P}\, \mathbf{v})\, \frac{\mathbf{w}_P}{\|\mathbf{w}\|},$$

then

$$\text{Comp}_\mathbf{w}\, \mathbf{v} = \frac{\mathbf{w} \cdot \mathbf{v}}{\|\mathbf{w}\|} \quad \text{and} \quad \text{Comp}_{\mathbf{w}_P}\, \mathbf{v} = \frac{\mathbf{w}_P \cdot \mathbf{v}}{\|\mathbf{w}\|}.$$

Using the theorem stated on page 460, you therefore have:

$$\text{Comp}_\mathbf{w}\, \mathbf{v} = \|\mathbf{v}\| \cos \phi \quad \text{and} \quad \text{Comp}_{\mathbf{w}_P}\, \mathbf{v} = \|\mathbf{v}\| \sin \phi.$$

Figure 12–3 illustrates the preceding facts.

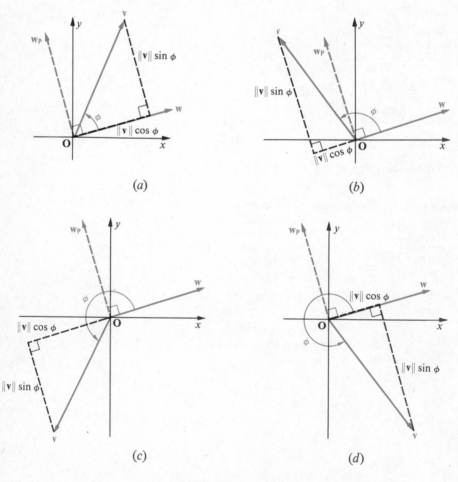

(a)

(b)

(c)

(d)

Figure 12–3

EXAMPLE 3.   If v is the vector with direction θ such that $\|v\| = 3$ and $m°\angle\theta = 70°$, resolve v into components parallel and perpendicular to the unit vector w with direction α, where $m°\angle\alpha = 20°$.

Solution:

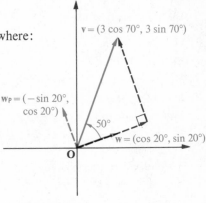

1. Draw a sketch showing v, w, and w_P, where:

   $v = (3 \cos 70°, 3 \sin 70°)$

   $w = (\cos 20°, \sin 20°)$

   $w_P = (-\sin 20°, \cos 20°)$

   $m°\angle\phi = 50°$

2. Use the following formulas:

   $\text{Comp}_w\, v = \|v\| \cos \phi;$

   $\text{Comp}_{w_P}\, v = \|v\| \sin \phi.$

   $\text{Comp}_w\, v = 3 \cos 50° = 3(0.6428);$

   $\text{Comp}_{w_P}\, v = 3 \sin 50° = 3(0.7660)$

   ∴ $\text{Comp}_w\, v = 1.9284;$

   $\text{Comp}_{w_P}\, v = 2.2980$

   ∴ $v = 1.9284w + 2.2980w_P,$ **Answer.**

(Note. Recall the convention regarding the use of $=$ in place of $\doteq$, page 425.)

Exercises

If ϕ is the angle from the first of the given vectors to the second vector: **(a)** determine $\sin \phi$, $\cos \phi$, and, if it exists, $\tan \phi$; **(b)** estimate to the nearest degree the least nonnegative measure of ϕ.

Ⓐ

1. $(1, 1); (-3, -3)$
2. $(-5, 10); (-2, -1)$
3. $(3, -2); (-6, -9)$
4. $(-1, 3); (2, -6)$

5. $(-\sqrt{2}, 3\sqrt{2}); (-2, 6)$
6. $(15, 3); (5\sqrt{3}, \sqrt{3})$
7. $(-2, -5); (-3, -7)$
8. $(3, 5); (2, -8)$

9. $2(\cos 80°, \sin 80°); (\cos 120°, \sin 120°)$
10. $(\cos 200°, \sin 200°); 3(\cos 100°, \sin 100°)$
11. $2(\cos 310°, \sin 310°); 5(\cos 10°, \sin 10°)$
12. $3(\cos 20°, \sin 20°); 6(\cos 350°, \sin 350°)$

Find, to the nearest 10′, the measure of the angles of triangle ABC.

13. $A(0, 0); B(3, 4); C(6, 0)$
14. $A(-1, -1); B(2, 1); C(0, 4)$
15. $A(5, -1); B(5, 3); C(-2, 2)$
16. $A(-2, 1); B(1, 0); C(5, 2)$

In Exercises 17–24, resolve the vector **v** with direction θ into a sum of perpendicular components, one of which has the given direction α. Use **w** for a unit vector with direction α.

17. $\|\mathbf{v}\| = 5, m° \angle \theta = 110°, m° \angle \alpha = 0°$

18. $\|\mathbf{v}\| = 16, m° \angle \theta = 190°, m° \angle \alpha = 0°$

B   **19.** $\|\mathbf{v}\| = 8, m° \angle \theta = 50°, m° \angle \alpha = 25°$

20. $\|\mathbf{v}\| = 10, m° \angle \theta = 120°, m° \angle \alpha = 80°$

21. $\|\mathbf{v}\| = 20, m° \angle \theta = 150°, m° \angle \alpha = 20°$

22. $\|\mathbf{v}\| = 12, m° \angle \theta = 245°, m° \angle \alpha = 110°$

23. $\|\mathbf{v}\| = k, m° \angle \theta = \theta°, m° \angle \alpha = \alpha°$

24. $\|\mathbf{v}\| = k, m^R \angle \theta = a^R, m^R \angle \alpha = b^R$

If **v** and **w** are nonzero vectors, and if ϕ is the angle from **w** to **v**, prove each of the following statements.

25. $\sin \phi = \dfrac{\mathbf{w_P} \cdot \mathbf{v}}{\|\mathbf{w}\| \; \|\mathbf{v}\|}$

26. $\tan \phi = \dfrac{\mathbf{w_P} \cdot \mathbf{v}}{\mathbf{w} \cdot \mathbf{v}}$, if **v** and **w** are not perpendicular vectors.

12–2 Angle between Lines

In Chapter 5 you learned that if **v** is a direction vector of a line $\mathcal{L}$, then any nonzero vector parallel to **v**, such as $2\mathbf{v}$, $-\mathbf{v}$, or $-\frac{1}{3}\mathbf{v}$, also is a direction vector of $\mathcal{L}$. To avoid ambiguity, we shall hereafter designate the **fundamental direction vector**, or simply *the* direction vector, of a nonvertical line in the plane to be the vector $(1, m)$, whose first coordinate is 1 and whose second coordinate is m, the slope of the line; *the* direction vector of a vertical line will be taken to be $(0, 1)$.

Now, suppose that $\mathcal{L}_1$ and $\mathcal{L}_2$ are lines with fundamental direction vectors **w** and **v**, respectively. We define the **angle from $\mathcal{L}_1$ to $\mathcal{L}_2$** to be the angle ϕ from **w** to **v**. (Figure 12–4).

In case $\mathcal{L}_1$ and $\mathcal{L}_2$ are both nonvertical lines with slopes m_1 and m_2, respectively, you can use the corollary stated on page 460 to derive a simple formula for $\tan \phi$. You have:

$$\mathbf{w} = (1, m_1), \; \mathbf{w_P} = (-m_1, 1); \; \mathbf{v} = (1, m_2)$$

Therefore, if $\mathbf{v} \cdot \mathbf{w} \neq 0$:

$$\tan \phi = \frac{(-m_1, 1) \cdot (1, m_2)}{(1, m_1) \cdot (1, m_2)}.$$

$$\tan \phi = \frac{m_2 - m_1}{1 + m_1 m_2}.$$

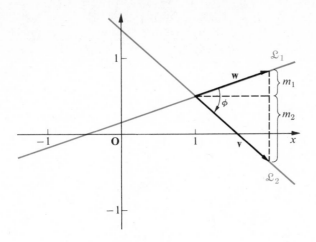

Figure 12–4

Of course, if $\mathbf{v} \cdot \mathbf{w} = 0$, then $1 + m_1 m_2 = 0$, so that $m_1 m_2 = -1$. But $m_1 m_2 = -1$ is the condition that $\mathcal{L}_1$ be perpendicular to $\mathcal{L}_2$, so that $m° \angle \phi = 90°$ or $m° \angle \phi = -90°$. We state these results formally as follows.

THEOREM In the plane, if ϕ is the angle from a line of slope m_1 to a line of slope m_2, then $\tan \phi = \dfrac{m_2 - m_1}{1 + m_1 m_2}$, provided the lines are not perpendicular.

Formulas for $\tan \phi$ in case $\mathcal{L}_1$ or $\mathcal{L}_2$ is a vertical line are left for you to derive. (See Exercises 33 and 34, page 468.)

EXAMPLE 1. Find the value of $\tan \phi$, if ϕ is the angle from a line with direction vector $(2, 3)$ to a line with direction vector $(4, 1)$.

Solution: 1. The fundamental direction vectors are $(1, \frac{3}{2})$ and $(1, \frac{1}{4})$.

2. Draw a sketch showing

$\mathcal{L}_1$ with $m_1 = \frac{3}{2}$ and

$\mathcal{L}_2$ with $m_2 = \frac{1}{4}$.

3. Use the thorem stated above.

$$\tan \phi = \frac{\frac{1}{4} - \frac{3}{2}}{1 + \frac{3}{2}(\frac{1}{4})} = -\frac{10}{11},$$

Answer.

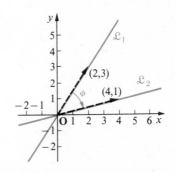

EXAMPLE 2. Estimate the least positive degree measure of the angle from the line $\mathcal{L}_1$ whose equation is $2x + 5y - 3 = 0$ to the line $\mathcal{L}_2$ with equation $x - 5y = 3$.

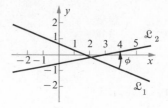

Solution: 1. Sketch the lines.

2. Write their equations in slope-intercept form (page 205).

$$2x + 5y - 3 = 0 \qquad\qquad x - 5y = 3$$
$$y = -\tfrac{2}{5}x + \tfrac{3}{5} \qquad\qquad y = \tfrac{1}{5}x - \tfrac{3}{5}$$
$$m_1 = -\tfrac{2}{5} \qquad\qquad m_2 = \tfrac{1}{5}$$

$$\therefore \tan \phi = \frac{\tfrac{1}{5} - (-\tfrac{2}{5})}{1 + (-\tfrac{2}{5})\tfrac{1}{5}} = \frac{15}{23} = 0.6522$$

$$\therefore m°\angle \phi = 33° \ 17', \textbf{ Answer.}$$

Can you explain why the least positive degree measure of the angle from $\mathcal{L}_2$ to $\mathcal{L}_1$ in Example 2 is approximately $360° - 33°17'$, or $326°43'$?*

The angle θ from the horizontal axis to a line in the plane is called the **angle of inclination** of the line. As Figure 12–5 suggests, for a line of positive slope you can assign $m°\angle\theta$ so that $0° < m°\angle\theta < 90°$; for a line of negative slope, $-90° < m°\angle\theta < 0°$.

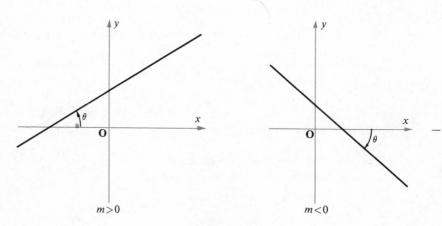

Figure 12–5

---

*Some authors define the angle from a line of slope m_1 to a line of slope m_2 to be the smaller of the angles from the vector $(1, m_1)$ to the vector $(1, m_2)$ and to the vector $-(1, m_2)$. Under this definition, the least positive measure of the angle from $\mathcal{L}_2$ to $\mathcal{L}_1$ in Example 2 would be $180° - 33°17'$, or $146°43'$.

Because the horizontal axis has slope 0, you can use the theorem stated on page 205 to derive the relationship between the slope m of a line and its angle of inclination θ. You have:

$$\tan \theta = \frac{m - 0}{1 + 0 \cdot m}$$

$$m = \tan \theta$$

Thus, *the slope of a line equals the tangent of its angle of inclination.*

EXAMPLE 3. What is the slope of a line whose angle of inclination measures $-45°$?

Solution: $m = \tan(-45°) = -1$, **Answer.**

Exercises

In Exercises 1–8 the first number listed is the slope of line $\mathcal{L}_1$ and the second is the slope of line $\mathcal{L}_2$. (a) Find to the nearest degree the measure of the angle ϕ from $\mathcal{L}_1$ to $\mathcal{L}_2$ such that $-90° \leq m°\angle\phi \leq 90°$. (b) To the nearest degree, state the angle of inclination of each line.

A

1. $3, 4$
2. $2, 0$
3. $\frac{1}{3}, -\frac{1}{2}$
4. $-\frac{2}{5}, 3$
5. $-\frac{1}{4}, -\frac{2}{3}$
6. $-5, \frac{1}{4}$
7. $\frac{1}{4}, \frac{1}{4}$
8. $\frac{2}{7}, -\frac{7}{2}$

Find the tangent of the positive acute angle between two lines whose direction vectors are given.

9. $(3, 1), (2, -4)$
10. $(-3, 1), (2, -4)$
11. $(3, 1), (-2, 4)$
12. $(3, 1), (2, 4)$
13. $(3, 1), (4, 2)$
14. $(4, 0), (1, 1)$
15. $(-4, 0), (1, -1)$
16. $(4, 0), (6, 0)$
17. $(\sqrt{3}, 1), (1, -\sqrt{3})$
18. $(5, -2), (-10, 4)$
19. $(2, 2), (3, -7)$
20. $(4, -3), (-12, -5)$

In Exercises 21–28 the first equation stated is the equation of line $\mathcal{L}_1$ and the second is the equation of line $\mathcal{L}_2$. Find the tangent of the angle from $\mathcal{L}_1$ to $\mathcal{L}_2$.

B

21. $y = 3x, y = -\frac{1}{2}x + 5$
22. $y = \frac{2}{3}x - 1, y = \frac{3}{2}x + 6$
23. $y - 2 = \frac{1}{2}(x + 4), y = 9x$
24. $y + 6 = -\frac{7}{3}x, y - 1 = \frac{4}{3}x + 5$
25. $2x + 3y = 7, 4x + 6y = 9$
26. $x + y = 0, 3x - 2y = 11$
27. $4x - y + 6 = 0, 3x + 7 = y$
28. $y = 5, y = x$

In Exercises 29–32 the first pair of parametric equations identifies line $\mathcal{L}_1$ and the second pair identifies line $\mathcal{L}_2$. Find the tangent of the angle from $\mathcal{L}_1$ to $\mathcal{L}_2$.

29. $x = 2 + q, y = 3 - 2q;$
$x = 2q, y = 4 - q$

31. $x = q, y = -5 + 2q;$
$x = 1 + q, y = 5 + q$

30. $x = -6 + q, y = -6 + 3q;$
$x = 2 + q, y = 3 - q$

32. $x = -1 - 3q, y = 6 + q;$
$x = -2 - 3q, y = 1 + q$

Let $\mathcal{L}_1$ be a vertical line and $\mathcal{L}_2$ a line of nonzero slope m. Prove each statement.

33. If ϕ is the angle from $\mathcal{L}_2$ to $\mathcal{L}_1$, $\tan \phi = \dfrac{1}{m}$ and $m^R \angle \phi = \dfrac{\pi}{2} - \text{Arctan } m$.

34. If ϕ is the angle from $\mathcal{L}_1$ to $\mathcal{L}_2$, $\tan \phi = -\dfrac{1}{m}$ and $m^R \angle \phi = \text{Arctan } m - \dfrac{\pi}{2}$.

In Exercises 35–38 find more than one solution when possible.

C

35. An angle of intersection of two lines measures 30°. A direction vector of one line is $(5, 3)$. Find the slope of the other line.

36. An angle of intersection of two lines measures 45°. One of the lines has direction vector $(2, -3)$. Find the slope of the other line.

37. An angle between the line $\mathcal{L}$ and the line $2x + 3y = 12$ measures 45°. The vertex of the angle is the point $(3, 2)$. Find an equation of $\mathcal{L}$.

38. An angle between the line $\mathcal{L}$ and the line $y - 3 = -\frac{1}{4}(x + 2)$ measures 60°. The line $\mathcal{L}$ contains the point $(1, 5)$. Find an equation of $\mathcal{L}$.

SOLVING TRIANGLES

12–3 The Right Triangle

In triangle **ABC** (Figure 12–6), the vectors $\mathbf{a} = \mathbf{C} - \mathbf{B}$, $\mathbf{b} = \mathbf{A} - \mathbf{C}$, and $\mathbf{c} = \mathbf{B} - \mathbf{A}$ are direction vectors of the sides $\overline{BC}$, $\overline{CA}$, and $\overline{AB}$. For simplicity of notation, we shall use the lightface letters $a, b,$ and c to denote the norms, $\|\mathbf{a}\|$, $\|\mathbf{b}\|$, and $\|\mathbf{c}\|$, of $\mathbf{a}$, $\mathbf{b}$, and $\mathbf{c}$. Thus, $a, b,$ and c are the lengths of sides $\overline{BC}$, $\overline{CA}$, and $\overline{AB}$. (Why?)

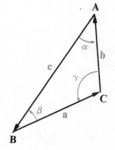

Figure 12–6

The angles of triangle **ABC** are angle α from $\mathbf{c}$ to $-\mathbf{b}$ ($\angle$**BAC**), angle β from $\mathbf{a}$ to $-\mathbf{c}$ ($\angle$**CBA**), and angle γ from $\mathbf{b}$ to $-\mathbf{a}$ ($\angle$**ACB**). We say that angles α, β, and γ are **opposite** sides $\overline{BC}$, $\overline{CA}$, and $\overline{AB}$, respectively. It is also customary to say that an angle is **adjacent** to each of its sides and is **included** by its sides. The measure of each angle of a triangle is usually given in degrees and is taken between 0° and 180°. An important fact about the angles of a triangle is stated in the following theorem that you learned in studying geometry.

| THEOREM | The sum of the measures of the angles of a triangle is 180°. |

For example, if α and β measure 40° and 30°, then γ measures $180° - (40° + 30°) = 110°$.

Solving a triangle consists in determining the lengths of its sides and the measures of its angles. Your knowledge of the trigonometric functions enables you to solve any right triangle (page 191). To begin, you know that the angle between the perpendicular sides of a right triangle (Figure 12–7) measures 90°. (Why?) Therefore, if $\gamma = 90°$, then $\alpha + \beta = 90°$. Secondly, the facts stated on page 462 and illustrated in Figure 12–3 imply that

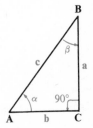

Figure 12–7

$$\cos \alpha = \frac{b}{c} = \frac{\text{length of side adjacent to } \alpha}{\text{length of hypotenuse}},$$

$$\sin \alpha = \frac{a}{c} = \frac{\text{length of side opposite } \alpha}{\text{length of hypotenuse}},$$

$$\tan \alpha = \frac{a}{b} = \frac{\text{length of side opposite } \alpha}{\text{length of side adjacent to } \alpha}.$$

Similarly, $\cos \beta = \dfrac{a}{c}$, $\sin \beta = \dfrac{b}{c}$, and $\tan \beta = \dfrac{b}{a}$. Thus, knowing the lengths of two sides, or the length of one side and the measure of either α or β, you can determine the measures of the other *parts* (angles and sides) of the right triangle.

EXAMPLE 1. In right triangle **ABC**, $\gamma = 90°$, $\beta = 20°$, and $c = 40$. Find α, a, and b.

Solution: 1. To find α: $90° - 20° = 70°$

2. To find a: $\cos \beta = \dfrac{a}{c}$, $\cos 20° = \dfrac{a}{40}$;

$$\therefore a = 40 \cos 20°$$

Using Table 2, you have

$$a = 40(0.9397), \text{ or } 37.59.$$

(*cont. on p. 470*)

3. To find b: $\sin \beta = \dfrac{b}{c}$; $\sin 20° = \dfrac{b}{40}$.

$$b = 40 \sin 20°$$
$$b = 40(0.3420), \text{ or } 13.68.$$

4. To check the computation, you can verify that the Pythagorean relationship holds within the range of accuracy of the computation.

$$a^2 + b^2 = c^2$$
$$(37.59)^2 + (13.68)^2 \doteq 1600 = (40)^2$$

Because the entries in Tables 1 and 2 are approximations, lengths computed using them should generally not be given to more than four significant figures, even when the given data are assumed to be exact.

In many applied problems, an angle is described as an *angle of elevation*, or an *angle of depression*. Since the point **B** shown in Figure 12-8 is elevated with respect to the observer at **A**, $\angle$**CAB**, the angle from the horizontal ray **AC** to the line of sight, is an **angle of elevation**. The point **Q** is depressed with respect to the observer at **R**; therefore, $\angle$**QRS**, the angle from the horizontal ray **RS** to the line of sight, is an **angle of depression**.

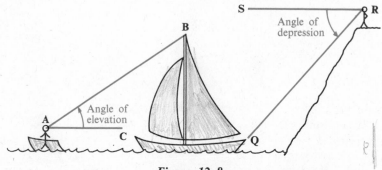

Figure 12-8

EXAMPLE 2. A television receiving antenna 10 feet high is mounted vertically on a vertical tower. To the nearest degree, the angle of elevation of the foot of the antenna from a point 20 feet from the base of the tower is 65°. How far above the ground is the top of the antenna?

Solution: Let x denote the distance above the ground of the foot of the antenna. Then:

$$\frac{x}{20} = \tan 65°,$$
$$x = 20 \tan 65°.$$

From Table 2, tan 65° = 2.145:

$$\therefore x = 20(2.145) = 43.$$

Since the antenna is 10 feet high, its top is approximately 43 + 10 feet, or 53 feet above the ground, **Answer.**

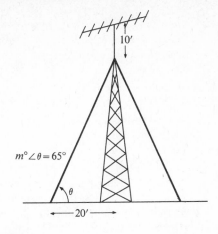

$m°\angle\theta = 65°$

Exercises

With the data given for right triangle **ABC** (in each case $\gamma = 90°$), find the measures of its other sides and angles. Assume the data are exact.

1. $\alpha = 25°, c = 50$ **5.** $a = 25, b = 7$

2. $\beta = 15°, c = 75$ **6.** $b = 61, c = 100$

3. $\beta = 43°, b = 20$ **7.** $a = 23, c = 30$

4. $\alpha = 71°, a = 40$ **8.** $a = 24, b = 18$

9. The angle of elevation of the summit from the base of a ski lift is 35°. If a skier rides 1000 feet on this lift to the summit, what is the vertical distance between the base of the lift and the summit?

10. The navigator of a jet airliner measures the angle of depression of an airport 10.0 miles away to be 9°20′. What is the altitude of the plane?

11. If a straight road falls 120 feet in 2000 feet along the road, find the angle at which the road is inclined from the horizontal.

12. A vein of ore makes an angle of 25° with the horizontal ground. If the width of the vein exposed at the surface is 18 feet, what is the actual width w of the vein?

13. A plane flies on course N28°E at 560 m.p.h. How many miles north and how many miles east of its starting point will it be at the end of two and a half hours?

14. The muzzle velocity of a bullet is 3000 feet per second. What are the horizontal and vertical components of this velocity if the gun is fired at an angle measuring 16° with the horizontal?

15. The angles of elevation to the top and bottom of a vertical flagpole on top of a building from a point 140 feet from the base of the building measure 59°0′ and 57°50′ respectively. How tall is the flagpole?

16. From two points 240 yards apart on a horizontal (straight) road running directly toward the launch pad, the angles of elevation to the nose cone of an accelerating rocket measure 44°0' and 28°10'. How high is the rocket at that instant?

17. At what bearing and speed should a pilot head if he wants to fly due south at 520 m.p.h. when a 40.0 m.p.h. east wind is blowing?

18. Phil can row at a rate of 3 m.p.h. He wants to row to a point directly across a river in which the current is 2 m.p.h. due south. **(a)** In what direction should he head in order to reach his destination? **(b)** How long will the trip take if the river is 1 mile wide?

19. A weight of 150.0 pounds is placed on a smooth plane inclined at an angle measuring 24°0' with the horizontal. What force pushing along the plane will just prevent the weight from slipping? (*Hint:* The weight exerts a vertical force **w** of 150.0 pounds downwards. The required force must be equal in magnitude but opposite in direction to the component of **w** parallel to the plane.)

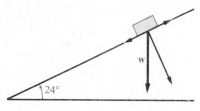

20. A right triangle whose shorter sides are 24.25 and 36.75 cm. long is inscribed in a circle. What is the length of the diameter of the circle and the measures of the angles of the triangle?

21. If s is the length of a side of a regular polygon of n sides and r is the radius of the circumscribed circle, prove that $s = 2r \sin \left(\dfrac{180}{n} \right)^{\circ}$.

22. A painting weighing 25 pounds is supported at the top corners by a taut wire which passes around a nail embedded in the wall. If the wire forms an angle of 120° at the nail, what is the total pull on the wire?

12–4 Law of Cosines

In Example 5 of Section 4–6, you found that

$$\|\mathbf{v} + \mathbf{t}\|^2 = \|\mathbf{v}\|^2 + \|\mathbf{t}\|^2 + 2\mathbf{v} \cdot \mathbf{t}.$$

You can use this fact to prove the following theorem, called the **Law of Cosines**.

THEOREM In any triangle with sides of length a, b, and c,

$$c^2 = a^2 + b^2 - 2ab \cos \gamma,$$

where γ is the angle opposite the side of length c.

Proof: Let **a, b, c** be the vectors **C** − **B**, **A** − **C**, and **B** − **A**, respectively. Then:

$$\mathbf{a} + \mathbf{b} + \mathbf{c} = \mathbf{0}.$$

Hence; −**c** = **a** + **b**

∴ $\|-\mathbf{c}\|^2 = \|\mathbf{a} + \mathbf{b}\|^2$, or

$\|-\mathbf{c}\|^2 = \|\mathbf{a}\|^2 + \|\mathbf{b}\|^2 + 2\mathbf{a} \cdot \mathbf{b}.$

But $2\mathbf{a} \cdot \mathbf{b} = -2(-\mathbf{a}) \cdot \mathbf{b}$; and by the theorem stated on page 460

$$(-\mathbf{a}) \cdot \mathbf{b} = \|-\mathbf{a}\| \cdot \|\mathbf{b}\| \cos \gamma.$$

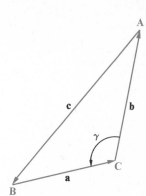

Figure 12–9

Therefore, since $\|-\mathbf{c}\| = \|\mathbf{c}\| = c$, $\|-\mathbf{a}\| = \|\mathbf{a}\| = a$, and $\|\mathbf{b}\| = b$, you find:

$$c^2 = a^2 + b^2 - 2ab \cos \gamma.$$

Of course, this theorem is valid for cyclic replacement of the variables. Thus, in triangle **ABC** the following statements are also true:

$$b^2 = a^2 + c^2 - 2ac \cos \beta,$$
$$a^2 = b^2 + c^2 - 2bc \cos \alpha.$$

Do you see that if $\gamma = 90°$, then the law of cosines reduces to the Pythagorean theorem?

EXAMPLE 1. Find the degree measure of each of the angles in the triangle with sides in the ratio 3:4:6.

Solution: 1. Let $a = 3r$, $b = 4r$, and $c = 6r$. Then, by the law of cosines,

$$c^2 = a^2 + b^2 - 2ab \cos \gamma,$$

$$(6r)^2 = (3r)^2 + (4r)^2 - 2(3r)(4r) \cos \gamma.$$

$$\therefore \cos \gamma = \frac{36 - 9 - 16}{-24} = -\frac{11}{24} \doteq -0.4583.$$

Since $\cos \gamma < 0$, $90° < \gamma < 180°$. From Table 2 and the relation $-\cos(180 - \gamma)° = \cos \gamma$, you find

$$\gamma = 180° - 62°43' = 117°17'.$$

(*cont. on p. 474*)

2. To find β, use $b^2 = a^2 + c^2 - 2ac \cos \beta$.

$$\cos \beta = \frac{16 - 9 - 36}{-36} = \frac{29}{36} = 0.8056,$$

$$\therefore \beta = 36°20'.$$

3. To find α, use $a^2 = b^2 + c^2 - 2bc \cos \alpha$

$$\cos \alpha = \frac{9 - 16 - 36}{-48} = \frac{43}{48} = 0.8958$$

$$\alpha = 26°23'.$$

4. To check the calculation, use the relationship

$$\alpha + \beta + \gamma = 180°.$$
$$26°23' + 36°20' + 117°17' = 180°.$$

$\therefore$ The angles of the triangle measure 26°23', 36°20', and 117°17', **Answer.**

EXAMPLE 2. A radar operator in an airport control tower observes two airplanes flying toward each other along a straight line. One plane, flying at 520 m.p.h., has a bearing (page 137) from the tower of 40° and is 20 miles from the tower. The other plane, flying at 460 m.p.h., has a bearing from the tower of 50° and is 25 miles away. How long do the pilots have in which to take evasive action, provided they are alerted at once by the control tower?

Solution: 1. Make a sketch illustrating the situation. The angle between the bearings of the airplanes measures 50° − 40°, or 10°.

2. To find the distance d between the airplanes, use the law of cosines:

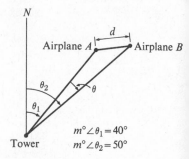

$m°\angle\theta_1 = 40°$
$m°\angle\theta_2 = 50°$

$d^2 = 20^2 + 25^2 - 2(20)(25) \cos 10°$

$d^2 = 400 + 625 - 1000(0.9848)$

$d^2 = 40.2;$

$\therefore d = \sqrt{40.2}$, or 6.34 miles.

3. The airplanes are approaching each other at $460 + 520 = 980$ m.p.h. Because time $= \dfrac{\text{distance}}{\text{rate}}$, the time remaining before collision is approximately

$$\frac{6.34}{980}, \text{ or } 0.00647 \text{ hours.}$$

Since 1 hour $= 60 \times 60$, or 3600 seconds, the airplanes have $0.00647 \times 3600 = 23.3$ seconds in which to avoid a collision, **Answer.**

Exercises

Use the law of cosines to solve each of the following triangles. Find the lengths of sides to the nearest tenth and the measures of angles to the nearest degree.

A

1. $a = 8, b = 6, \gamma = 60°$
2. $c = 5, a = 9, \beta = 120°$
3. $a = 3, b = 5, c = 7$
4. $a = 10, b = 12, c = 13$

5. $a = 10, b = 20, \gamma = 40°$
6. $b = 9, c = 11, \alpha = 123°$
7. $a = 29, b = 47, c = 32$
8. $a = 70, b = 42, c = 51$

9. Two airplanes take off from an airport at the same time. One travels on a heading of 45° at 420 miles per hour and the other on a heading of 150° at 400 miles per hour. After two hours, how far apart are the airplanes?

10. To measure the distance across a pond, a surveyor measures from a point **C** the distances to two points **A** and **B** at opposite ends of the pond. If these distances are 80 yards and 110 yards, respectively, and if the angle between the line segments joining **A** to **C** and **B** to **C** has measure 98°, how far is it across the pond?

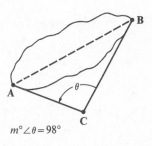

$m°\angle\theta = 98°$

11. A parallelogram had adjacent sides of length 8 inches and 10 inches, and the measure of one included angle is 35°. Find the length of each diagonal of the parallelogram.

12. An isosceles trapezoid with base angles measuring 80° has base of length 8 feet, and equal sides each of length 5 feet. Find the length of each diagonal of the trapezoid.

13. Find the measure of the angle between two forces of 30 lb. and 35 lb. if the magnitude of their resultant is 42 lb.

14. Two submarines, one cruising at 25 knots and the other at 20 knots, left a naval base at the same moment. Three hours later they were 100 nautical miles apart. What was the measure of the angle between their courses? (1 knot = 1 nautical mile per hour.)

In Exercises 15 and 16, **v** and **w** are vectors with norms and directions as given. Find $\|\mathbf{v} - \mathbf{w}\|$ and the direction of $\mathbf{v} - \mathbf{w}$.

15. $\|\mathbf{v}\| = 15, m° \angle \theta_\mathbf{v} = 10°, \|\mathbf{w}\| = 20, m° \angle \theta_\mathbf{w} = 240°$

16. $\|\mathbf{v}\| = 8, m° \angle \theta_\mathbf{v} = 110°, \|\mathbf{w}\| = 18, m° \angle \theta_\mathbf{w} = 310°$

17. Show algebraically that if $k = \dfrac{b^2 + c^2 - a^2}{2bc}$, then

$$1 + k = \frac{(b + c + a)(b + c - a)}{2bc}.$$

18. Show algebraically that if k is as given in Exercise 17, then

$$1 - k = \frac{(a + b - c)(a - b + c)}{2bc}.$$

In Exercises 19–21, show that in any triangle with sides measuring a, b, c, and with opposite angles α, β, and γ, respectively, the given relationship is true. Use the results in Exercises 17 and 18 as well as the law of cosines and any necessary identities.

19. $1 + \cos \alpha = \dfrac{(b + c + a)(b + c - a)}{2bc}$

20. $1 - \cos \alpha = \dfrac{(a + b - c)(a - b + c)}{2bc}$

21. $\tan \dfrac{\alpha}{2} = \sqrt{\dfrac{(a + b - c)(a - b + c)}{(b + c + a)(b + c - a)}}$ **(Half-angle Law)**

22. The **semiperimeter** s of a triangle with sides measuring a, b, and c is defined by $s = \dfrac{a + b + c}{2}$. Let $r = \sqrt{\dfrac{(s - a)(s - b)(s - c)}{s}}$, and use Exercise 21 to show that $\tan \dfrac{\alpha}{2} = \dfrac{r}{s - a}$.

23. Prove that the sum of the squares of the lengths of the diagonals of a parallelogram is equal to the sum of the squares of the lengths of the sides.

24. Prove that in any triangle, the sum of the squares of the lengths of any two sides equals twice the square of the length of the median to the third side plus half the square of the length of the third side.

12–5 Law of Sines

The law of cosines enables you to solve any triangle in which you are given the measures of

    1. Three sides, or

    2. Two sides and the angle determined by them.

When the given data consist of the measures of two angles and one side, you need another law to find the measures of the other parts of any triangle fitting the data.

As in Section 12–4, consider triangle **ABC** and the vectors **a**, **b**, and **c**. Since $\mathbf{a} + \mathbf{b} + \mathbf{c} = \mathbf{0}$, you find

$$(\mathbf{a} + \mathbf{b} + \mathbf{c}) \cdot \mathbf{c_P} = \mathbf{0} \cdot \mathbf{c_P}.$$

But

$$(\mathbf{a} + \mathbf{b} + \mathbf{c}) \cdot \mathbf{c_P} = \mathbf{a} \cdot \mathbf{c_P} + \mathbf{b} \cdot \mathbf{c_P} + \mathbf{c} \cdot \mathbf{c_P}.$$

Therefore, because $\mathbf{c} \cdot \mathbf{c_P} = 0$, $\mathbf{0} \cdot \mathbf{c_P} = 0$, and $-(\mathbf{b} \cdot \mathbf{c_P}) = (-\mathbf{b}) \cdot \mathbf{c_P}$, it follows that $\mathbf{a} \cdot \mathbf{c_P} + \mathbf{b} \cdot \mathbf{c_P} = 0$, and

(1) $$\mathbf{a} \cdot \mathbf{c_P} = (-\mathbf{b}) \cdot \mathbf{c_P}$$

(Figure 12–10 illustrates (1) by showing $\text{Comp}_{\mathbf{c_P}} \mathbf{a} = -\text{Comp}_{\mathbf{c_P}} \mathbf{b}$.)

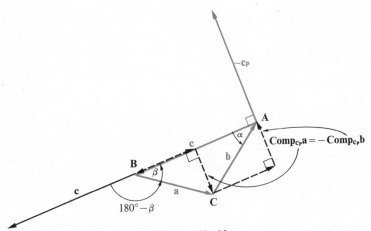

Figure 12–10

Now the theorem stated on page 460 implies that

$$(-\mathbf{b}) \cdot \mathbf{c_P} = \|-\mathbf{b}\| \, \|\mathbf{c}\| \text{ (sine of the angle from } \mathbf{c} \text{ to } -\mathbf{b}).$$

(2) $\therefore (-\mathbf{b}) \cdot \mathbf{c_P} = bc \sin \alpha.$

Similarly,

$$\mathbf{a} \cdot \mathbf{c_P} = \|\mathbf{a}\| \, \|\mathbf{c_P}\| \text{ (sine of the angle from } \mathbf{c} \text{ to } \mathbf{a}),$$
$$= ac \sin(180° - \beta).$$

(3) $\therefore \mathbf{a} \cdot \mathbf{c_P} = ac \sin \beta.$ (Why?)   Hence,

statements (1), (2), and (3) together imply that

$$ac \sin \beta = bc \sin \alpha.$$

Dividing each member of this equation by abc, you find:

$$\frac{\sin \beta}{b} = \frac{\sin \alpha}{a}.$$

By analogous arguments, you can show that

$$\frac{\sin \alpha}{a} = \frac{\sin \gamma}{c} \quad \text{and} \quad \frac{\sin \beta}{b} = \frac{\sin \gamma}{c},$$

and thus complete the proof of the following theorem, which is called the **Law of Sines**.

THEOREM In any triangle

$$\frac{\sin \alpha}{a} = \frac{\sin \beta}{b} = \frac{\sin \gamma}{c},$$

where α, β, and γ are the angles opposite the sides of length a, b, and c, respectively.

EXAMPLE 1. A ship traveling at a constant speed left a harbor on a heading of 30°, which it maintained for two hours. After two hours, the navigator of the ship observed that a lighthouse 35.0 nautical miles due north of the harbor bore 310° from the ship. What was the speed of the ship?

Solution: 1. Make a sketch illustrating the problem. By inspection, the angle β between the lines of sight from ship to lighthouse and from ship to harbor had as its measure 310° − 180° − 30°; thus, $\beta = 100°$. $\gamma = 180° − 100° − 30° = 50°$.

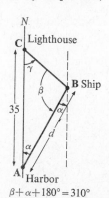

2. To find d, the distance from harbor to ship, use the law of sines:

$$\frac{\sin 100°}{35} = \frac{\sin 50°}{d}$$

$$d = 35 \cdot \frac{\sin 50°}{\sin 100°}$$

$$= 35 \cdot \frac{0.7660}{0.9848} = 27.2 \text{ nautical miles.}$$

The speed of the ship was $\dfrac{27.2}{2} = 13.6$ knots, **Answer.**

By using both the law of cosines and the law of sines, you can sometimes shorten the process of solving a triangle.

EXAMPLE 2. Solve triangle **ABC** if $a = 180$, $b = 150$, and $\gamma = 22°$.

Solution: *(Plan)*

1. Sketch the triangle and label the parts whose measures are given.

2. To find c use the law of cosines: $c^2 = a^2 + b^2 - 2ab \cos \gamma$.

3. The *smaller* of the remaining angles is β. (Why?) Also $\beta < 90°$. (Why?) Use the law of sines to write $\sin \beta = \dfrac{b \sin \gamma}{c}$, and thus determine β. (Using the law of cosines to find β is feasible, but requires more computation.)

4. To find α, use the relationship $\alpha + \beta + \gamma = 180°$.

5. Check the solution by comparing your results with the sketch and by substituting the results in an equation not employed in the solution, for example, in $\dfrac{\sin \alpha}{a} = \dfrac{\sin \beta}{b}$.

Carrying through the steps of the calculation is left to you.

Notice that the data specifying a triangle must include the measures of three parts, at least one of which is a side. Given the measures of three sides or of two sides and the angle included by them, or of two angles and one side, you can solve the triangle or show that there is no triangle fitting the data. Data consisting of the measures of two sides and the angle *opposite* one of them, however, are called **ambiguous**, because there may exist two, one, or no triangles fitting the given description. Suppose, for example, that α, a, and b are known. By sketching angle α and measuring the length

b on one of its sides, you find the possibilities suggested in Figure 12–11 ($\alpha < 90°$) and Figure 12–12 ($\alpha \geq 90°$).

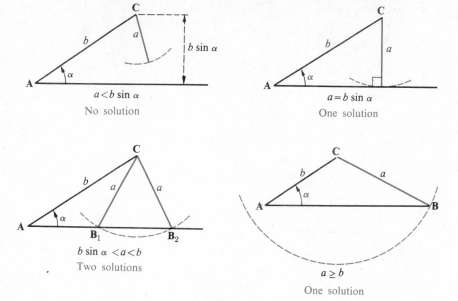

Figure 12–11

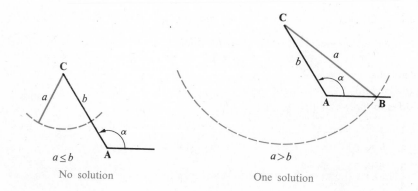

Figure 12–12

EXAMPLE 3. Solve the triangle with $b = 14$, $c = 18$, and $\beta = 35°$.

Solution: 1. The sketch of the triangle suggests two solutions.

2. To determine γ, use $\dfrac{\sin \gamma}{c} = \dfrac{\sin \beta}{b}$:

$$\frac{\sin \gamma}{18} = \frac{\sin 35°}{14}$$

$$\sin \gamma = \frac{18 \sin 35°}{14}$$

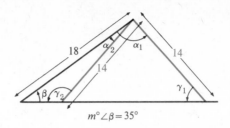

$$= \frac{9(0.5736)}{7} = 0.7375.$$

$m°\angle\beta = 35°$

$$\therefore \gamma = 47°31' \text{ or } \gamma = 180° - 47°31'$$
$$\gamma = 132°29'.$$

3. To determine α, use $\alpha = 180° - \beta - \gamma$.

$\alpha = 180° - 35° - 47°32'$ | $\alpha = 180° - 35° - 132°28'$
$\alpha = 97°29'$ or $\alpha = 12°31'$

4. To determine a, use $\dfrac{\sin \alpha}{a} = \dfrac{\sin \beta}{b}$.

Completing step 4 to find $a = 24.20$ or $a = 5.295$, and checking, are left to you.

$a = 24.20$, $\gamma = 47°31'$, $\alpha = 97°29'$; or

$a = 5.295$, $\gamma = 132°29'$, $\alpha = 12°31'$, **Answer.**

Exercises

Find the measures of the other parts of each triangle **ABC** (if any) fitting the given data. Assume that angles have been measured to the nearest 10′ and sides to three significant figures.

1. $a = 640$, $\alpha = 70°$, $\beta = 52°$ 7. $a = 4.00$, $b = 7.00$, $c = 2.00$
2. $b = 600$, $\beta = 11°$, $\gamma = 75°$ 8. $a = 2.00$, $b = 5.00$, $c = 3.00$
3. $b = 14.0$, $c = 17.0$, $\gamma = 28°20'$ 9. $a = 71.0$, $b = 23.0$, $\gamma = 45°$
4. $a = 400$, $b = 570$, $\beta = 107°10'$ 10. $a = \sqrt{3}$, $b = \sqrt{7}$, $c = 5$
5. $b = 20$, $c = 260$, $\beta = 148°$ 11. $c = 1.10$, $b = 1.20$, $\alpha = 60°$
6. $a = 2.40$, $b = 3.10$, $\alpha = 23°40'$ 12. $a = 4800$, $c = 2100$, $\alpha = 30°$

13. Two fire lookout towers are located 7 miles apart along a mountain ridge. If tower A is directly north of tower B, and a fire is spotted bearing 265° from tower B and 250° from tower A, how far is the fire from tower B?

14. From two points 400 yards apart on the bank of a straight river flowing due south, the bearings of a point on the opposite shore are 28°20′ and 148°20′, respectively. How wide is the river?

15. A diagonal of a parallelogram is 50 inches long and makes angles of 37°10′ and 49°20′ with the sides. How long are the sides?

16. One angle of a rhombus measures 102°, and the shorter diagonal is 4 inches long. How long is the side of the rhombus?

In each of the following exercises, refer to Figure 12–11 or Figure 12–12 to explain why the given statement is true for values of a, b, c, α, β, and γ satisfying the given open sentence.

B 17. There exists no triangle if $a < b \sin \alpha$, and $\alpha < 90°$.

18. There exists exactly one triangle if $a = b \sin \alpha$, and $\alpha < 90°$.

19. There exist two triangles if $b \sin \alpha < a < b$, and $\alpha < 90°$.

20. There exists no triangle if $a \le b$ and $\alpha \ge 90°$.

21. There exists exactly one triangle if $a \ge b$ and $\alpha < 90°$.

22. There exists exactly one triangle if $a > b$ and $\alpha \ge 90°$.

Prove that each of the following are true for any triangle **ABC**.

C 23. $\dfrac{a+b}{b} = \dfrac{\sin \alpha + \sin \beta}{\sin \beta}$ $\left(Hint: \text{ Add 1 to each member of } \dfrac{a}{b} = \dfrac{\sin \alpha}{\sin \beta}. \right)$

24. $\dfrac{a-b}{b} = \dfrac{\sin \alpha - \sin \beta}{\sin \beta}$

25. $\dfrac{a-b}{a+b} = \dfrac{\sin \alpha - \sin \beta}{\sin \alpha + \sin \beta}$ (Hint: Use Exercises 23 and 24.)

26. $\dfrac{a-b}{a+b} = \dfrac{\cos \frac{1}{2}(\alpha + \beta) \sin \frac{1}{2}(\alpha - \beta)}{\sin \frac{1}{2}(\alpha + \beta) \cos \frac{1}{2}(\alpha - \beta)} = \dfrac{\tan \frac{1}{2}(\alpha - \beta)}{\tan \frac{1}{2}(\alpha + \beta)}$

(Hint: Use Exercise 25 and the appropriate formulas on page 442.)

(This relationship is called the **Law of Tangents**.)

27. $c = a \cos \beta + b \cos \alpha$ (Hint: $(\mathbf{a} + \mathbf{b} + \mathbf{c}) \cdot \mathbf{c} = 0 \cdot \mathbf{c}$.)

28. If $\dfrac{\cos \alpha}{b} = \dfrac{\cos \beta}{a}$, then triangle **ABC** is either an isosceles or a right triangle.

12–6 Areas of Triangles

The familiar formula $K = \frac{1}{2}bh$ for the area K of a triangle with base b and height h can be used to derive other area formulas. For example, taking $\overline{AB}$ to be the base of triangle ABC (Figure 12–13), you can find the corresponding height h as follows:

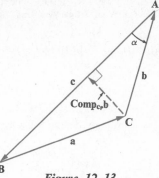

Figure 12–13

$$h = |\mathrm{Comp}_{\mathbf{c_P}}\, \mathbf{b}| = \left|\frac{\mathbf{b} \cdot \mathbf{c_P}}{\|\mathbf{c}\|}\right| = \frac{|\mathbf{b} \cdot \mathbf{c_P}|}{\|\mathbf{c}\|}.$$

$$\therefore\ K = \tfrac{1}{2}\|\mathbf{c}\| \frac{|\mathbf{b} \cdot \mathbf{c_P}|}{\|\mathbf{c}\|} = \tfrac{1}{2}|\mathbf{b} \cdot \mathbf{c_P}|.$$

Because $|\mathbf{b} \cdot \mathbf{c_P}| = |bc \sin \alpha| = bc \sin \alpha$ (Why?), you have

$$K = \tfrac{1}{2}bc \sin \alpha.$$

Similar reasoning enables you to prove that $K = \tfrac{1}{2}\,|\mathbf{a} \cdot \mathbf{c_P}|$ and $K = \tfrac{1}{2}\,|\mathbf{b} \cdot \mathbf{a_P}|$, and thus to obtain the companion formulas

$$K = \tfrac{1}{2}ac \sin \beta \quad \text{and} \quad K = \tfrac{1}{2}ab \sin \gamma.$$

With the preceding formulas you can find the area of a triangle if you know

1. The measures of two sides and the angle included by them, or

2. The coordinates of the vertices of the triangle.

EXAMPLE 1. Find the area of triangle **ABC**, if $b = 28$, $c = 5$, and $\alpha = 30°$.

Solution: $K = \tfrac{1}{2}bc \sin \alpha = \tfrac{1}{2} \cdot 28 \cdot 5 \sin 30° = 14 \cdot 5 \cdot \tfrac{1}{2} = 35$,
Answer.

EXAMPLE 2. Find the area of the triangle whose vertices are the points $A(6, 5)$, $B(-2, 7)$, and $C(0, 4)$.

Solution: Let $\mathbf{a} = \mathbf{C} - \mathbf{B} = (0, 4) - (-2, 7) = (2, -3)$;
$\mathbf{b} = \mathbf{A} - \mathbf{C} = (6, 5) - (0, 4) = (6, 1)$.

$$K = \tfrac{1}{2}|\mathbf{b} \cdot \mathbf{a_P}| = \tfrac{1}{2}|(6, 1) \cdot (3, 2)| = \tfrac{1}{2}(18 + 2) = 10,\ \textbf{Answer.}$$

You can also derive formulas for the area of a triangle in terms of its angles and one of its sides. You know that

$$K = \tfrac{1}{2}ab \sin \gamma.$$

From the law of sines you have $b = \dfrac{a \sin \beta}{\sin \alpha}$.

Substituting for b in the area formula, you discover that

$$K = \tfrac{1}{2}a^2 \frac{\sin \beta \sin \gamma}{\sin \alpha}.$$

You can similarly derive the formulas

$$K = \tfrac{1}{2}b^2 \frac{\sin \alpha \sin \gamma}{\sin \beta} \quad \text{and} \quad K = \tfrac{1}{2}c^2 \frac{\sin \alpha \sin \beta}{\sin \gamma}.$$

Given the lengths of three sides of a triangle, you find the area by using the following relationship, known as **Heron's Formula**, whose proof is indicated in Exercises 25, 26 on page 485.

$$K = \sqrt{s(s - a)(s - b)(s - c)}$$

where s is $\dfrac{a + b + c}{2}$, the *semiperimeter* of the triangle.

EXAMPLE 3. Find the area of triangle **ABC**, if

(**a**) $a = 4$, $\beta = 30°$, and $\gamma = 120°$;

(**b**) $a = 5$, $b = 6$, $c = 7$.

Solution:

(**a**) $\alpha = 180° - (\beta + \gamma) = 180° - 150° = 30°$.

$$K = \frac{a^2}{2} \frac{\sin \beta \sin \gamma}{\sin \alpha} = \frac{16}{2} \frac{\sin 30° \sin 120°}{\sin 30°} = 8 \cdot \frac{\sqrt{3}}{2} = 4\sqrt{3}, \textbf{ Answer.}$$

(**b**) $s = \dfrac{a + b + c}{2} = \dfrac{5 + 6 + 7}{2} = 9$

$$K = \sqrt{s(s - a)(s - b)(s - c)} = \sqrt{9(4)(3)(2)} = 6\sqrt{6}, \textbf{ Answer.}$$

Exercises

(A) **1–12.** Find the area of the triangle or triangles (if any) fitting the data in Exercises 1–12, page 481.

Find the area of the triangle whose vertices are the given points.

13. $A(0, 0)$, $B(5, 3)$, $C(-1, 4)$ 15. $A(1, -1)$, $B(-3, -5)$, $C(3, 0)$

14. $A(-2, 7)$, $B(0, 0)$, $C(6, 1)$ 16. $A(0, -4)$, $B(-1, -1)$, $C(3, 7)$

Find the measure of the indicated part of the triangle **ABC** determined by the given data.

B **17.** $K = 52, \beta = 27°, \gamma = 64°; a = $?

18. $K = 3.1 \times 10^9, a = 8.3 \times 10^4, b = 9.2 \times 10^4; \beta > 90°; \gamma = $?

19. The adjacent sides of a parallelogram are 16 cm. and 24 cm. long, and one angle measures 60°. Find its area.

20. The diagonals of a parallelogram are 60 and 70 in. long and they intersect at an angle measuring 45°. Find the area.

21. The diagonals of the quadrilateral have lengths a and b and meet at angle ϕ. Prove the area of the figure to be $\frac{1}{2}ab \sin \phi$.

22. Derive a formula for the area of an isosceles triangle whose base has length b and whose base angles each have measure α.

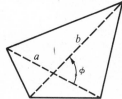

Prove that each formula holds in triangle **ABC**.

C **23.** $K = \frac{1}{2}a^2 \dfrac{\sin \beta \sin \gamma}{\sin(\beta + \gamma)}$ **24.** $K = bc \sin \frac{1}{2}\alpha \cos \frac{1}{2}\alpha$

25. $K^2 = \dfrac{(a + b + c)(b + c - a)(a + b - c)(a - b + c)}{16}$

   (*Hint:* Use Exercise 24, the half-angle formulas, page 454, and Exercises 19 and 20, page 476.)

26. $K = \sqrt{s(s - a)(s - b)(s - c)}$, where $s = \dfrac{a + b + c}{2}$.

   (*Hint:* Use Exercise 25.)

27. Determine an equation of the line through the points **A**(2, 3) and **B**(−4, 5) by using the fact that **C**(x, y) belongs to the line if and only if the area of triangle **ABC** is zero.

POLAR COORDINATES AND GRAPHS

12–7 Polar Coordinates

   You can locate any point **T** on ray q in Figure 12–14 if you know the distance r of **T** from **O**. In fact, to locate **T**, it is sufficient to know r and a measure of the direction angle θ of ray q. We call the ordered pair of numbers $(r, m\angle\theta)$ or simply (r, θ), *polar coordinates* of **T**.

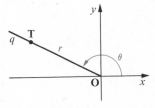

Figure 12–14

EXAMPLE 1. Locate the point **R** having (4, 265°) as polar coordinates.

Solution: 1. Draw θ in standard position such that $m°\angle\theta = 265°$.

2. On the terminal side of θ measure 4 units from **O** to the point **R**.

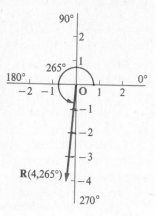

Do you see that for *every* integer k, the ordered pair $(4, [265 + 360k]°)$ specifies the point **R**, described in Example 1? Thus, as shown in Figure 12–15, **R** is determined not only by the polar coordinates (4, 265°), but also by such pairs as (4, 625°) and (4, −95°).

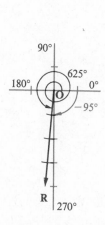

Figure 12–15

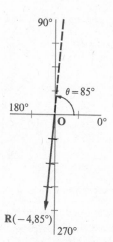

Figure 12–16

Figure 12–16 indicates still another pair of polar coordinates that specifies **R**. In this case, the value of r is a negative number, −4, and is measured from **O** along the ray obtained by extending through the origin the terminal side of the associated angle θ. (Note that the terminal side of θ is shown as a dash ray in Figure 12–16.)

In general, if $r \in \mathfrak{R}$ and θ is an angle in standard position, then (r, θ) are **polar coordinates** of the point which is $|r|$ units from the origin and which lies on the terminal side of:

(i) θ, if $r \geq 0$;

(ii) $\theta + 180°$ (or $\theta + \pi^R$), if $r < 0$.

Figure 12–17 illustrates the general situation.

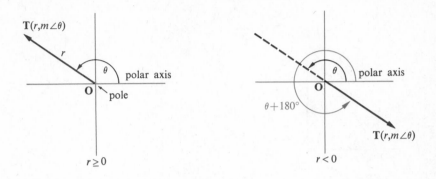

Figure 12–17

EXAMPLE 2. $\left(2, -\frac{4\pi^R}{3}\right)$ are polar coordinates of point **M**. State three other pairs of polar coordinates of **M**, in each of which $-2\pi^R < m^R \angle \theta < 2\pi^R$.

Solution:

By inspection you can determine that

$$\left(2, \frac{2\pi^R}{3}\right), \left(2, -\frac{4\pi^R}{3}\right),$$

$$\left(-2, \frac{5\pi^R}{3}\right), \left(-2, -\frac{\pi^R}{3}\right)$$

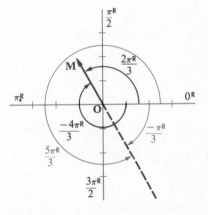

all designate **M**, **Answer**.

In a system of polar coordinates, the ray in the plane corresponding to the initial side of θ is called the **polar axis**, and the origin is called the **pole**. When the polar axis coincides with the positive x-axis in a Cartesian coordinate system, the trigonometric functions provide the link between the Cartesian coordinates (x, y) and the polar coordinates (r, θ) of any point **T**. As indicated in Figure 12–18, page 488,

(1) $(x, y) = (r \cos \theta, r \sin \theta)$, if $r \geq 0$;

(2) $(x, y) = (|r| \cos[\pi + \theta], |r| \sin[\pi + \theta])$, if $r < 0$.

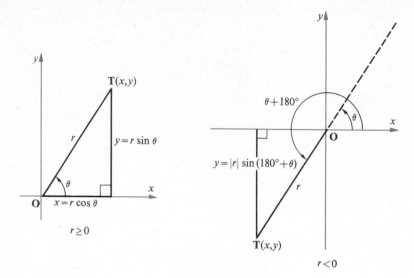

Figure 12–18

Because you can verify that if $r < 0$, $|r| \cos[\pi + \theta] = r \cos \theta$ and $|r| \sin[\pi + \theta] = r \sin \theta$, equations (1) and (2) both imply that

(3) $\qquad x = r \cos \theta \quad \text{and} \quad y = r \sin \theta.$

The equations in statement (3) enable you to convert from polar coordinates (r, θ) to Cartesian coordinates (x, y). Similarly, the statements

(4) $\qquad |r| = \sqrt{x^2 + y^2},$

(5) $\qquad \text{If } x > 0, \theta = \text{Arctan} \dfrac{y}{x},$

(6) $\qquad \text{If } x < 0, \theta = \pi + \text{Arctan} \dfrac{y}{x},$

permit you to find polar coordinates for any point other than $\mathbf{O}$ whose Cartesian coordinates are known. Note that, for any angle θ, $(0, \theta)$ are polar coordinates of $\mathbf{O}$.

EXAMPLE 3. **(a)** Find Cartesian coordinates of $(3, 50°)$.

(b) Using degree measure, find polar coordinates of $(1, -1)$.

Solution: (a) Using (3), you have:

$$x = 3 \cos 50° \doteq 3(0.6428), \text{ or } 1.9284;$$
$$y = 3 \sin 50° \doteq 3(0.7660), \text{ or } 2.2980.$$

The Cartesian coordinates of (3, 50°) are (1.9284, 2.2980), **Answer.**

(b) 1. Plot the point in the plane.

2. Using (4), you have:

$$r = \sqrt{1^2 + (-1)^2} = \sqrt{2}.$$

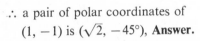

Applying (5), you obtain

$$\theta = \text{Arctan } \frac{-1}{1} = \text{Arctan } (-1).$$

$$m°\angle\theta = -45°.$$

∴ a pair of polar coordinates of (1, −1) is ($\sqrt{2}$, −45°), **Answer.**

Exercises

Find two sets of polar coordinates for each point with the given Cartesian coordinates.

1. (0, 0)   3. $(-2, 2\sqrt{3})$ 5. (3, −4)
2. (2, 2)   4. $(-\sqrt{3}, -1)$ 6. $(-3, \frac{3}{2})$

Plot the point whose polar coordinates are given and find its Cartesian coordinates.

7. (−1, 180°)   9. $\left(2, \frac{3\pi}{4}^R\right)$ 11. $(-1, 2.1^R)$

8. (3, −30°)   10. $\left(-4, -\frac{\pi}{2}^R\right)$ 12. (−3, 15°)

By using statement (3) on page 488, convert the given equation into an equation in polar coordinates.

13. $x = 2$ 15. $x^2 + y^2 = 4$ 17. $x^2 + y^2 + 2y = 0$
14. $y = 3$ 16. $x^2 + y^2 + 2x = 0$ 18. $x^2 + y^2 = 0$

By using statements (4), (5), and (6) on page 488, convert the given equation into an equation in Cartesian coordinates.

19. $r = 2$ 21. $\theta = 30°$ 23. $r = 2 \sec \theta$

20. $-r = 2$ 22. $\theta = -\frac{\pi}{6}$ 24. $r = 2 \csc \theta$

Prove that the following pairs of polar coordinates denote the same point in the plane.

B   **25.** (r, θ); $(-r, \theta - 180°)$ **27.** (r, θ); $(-r, \theta + 180°)$

     26. (r, θ); $(r, \theta - 360°)$ **28.** (r, θ); $(r, \theta + k \cdot 360°)$, $k \in J$

29. Prove that if a point (x_1, y_1) has polar coordinates (r, θ), and (x_2, y_2) has polar coordinates $(-r, \theta)$, then $x_1 = -x_2$ and $y_1 = -y_2$.

30. Prove that if a point (x_1, y_1) has polar coordinates (r, θ), and (x_2, y_2) has polar coordinates $(r, -\theta)$, then $x_1 = x_2$ and $y_1 = -y_2$.

C   **31.** Show that the distance between the points (r_1, θ_1) and (r_2, θ_2) is given by

$$d = \sqrt{r_1^2 + r_2^2 - 2r_1r_2 \cos(\theta_1 - \theta_2)}.$$

32. Use the result in Exercise 31 to show that a polar equation for the circle of radius a and with center at (r_1, θ_1) is

$$r^2 - 2rr_1 \cos(\theta - \theta_1) + r_1^2 - a^2 = 0.$$

12–8 Polar Graphs

In the plane, the set of points having at least one pair of polar coordinates (r, θ) which satisfy an equation such as $r = 3$, $\theta = 150°$, or $r = 2 \sin \theta$ is called the **polar graph** of the equation.

EXAMPLE 1. Sketch the polar graph of:

       (a) $r = 3$; **(b)** $\theta = 150°$; **(c)** $r = 2 \sin \theta$; **(d)** $r = \cos 2\theta$.

Solution:

(a) The points for which $r = 3$ constitute the circle with center at **O** and radius 3.

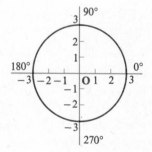

(b) The points for which $\theta = 150°$ belong to the line passing through the origin and containing the ray whose direction angle measures 150°. Note that on this line the points for which $r > 0$ lie in Quadrant II, while the points with $r < 0$ are in Quadrant IV.

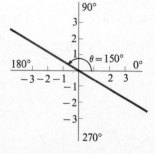

(c) Plotting the points whose polar coordinates are listed in the following table suggests that the graph of $r = 2 \sin \theta$ is the circle of diameter 2 tangent to the polar axis at the pole. (This observation will be confirmed in Section 13–1.)

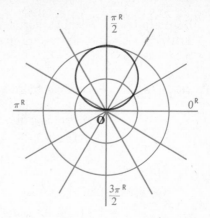

Notice that as the measure of θ runs from π^R to $2\pi^R$, the corresponding points merely retrace the graph obtained for $0^R \le m^R \angle \theta \le \pi^R$.

θ	0^R	$\dfrac{\pi^R}{6}$	$\dfrac{\pi^R}{3}$	$\dfrac{\pi^R}{2}$	$\dfrac{2\pi^R}{3}$	$\dfrac{5\pi^R}{6}$	π^R	$\dfrac{7\pi^R}{6}$	$\dfrac{4\pi^R}{3}$	$\dfrac{3\pi^R}{2}$	$\dfrac{5\pi^R}{3}$	$\dfrac{11\pi^R}{6}$	$2\pi^R$
$r = 2 \sin \theta$	0	1	$\sqrt{3}$	2	$\sqrt{3}$	1	0	-1	$-\sqrt{3}$	-2	$-\sqrt{3}$	-1	0

(d) Plotting the points with tabulated coordinates, you obtain a curve called a *four-leaved rose*. In the figure, the arrowheads and numerals indicate the path of a point that starts at **P** and moves along the curve, with θ increasing from $0°$ to $360°$.

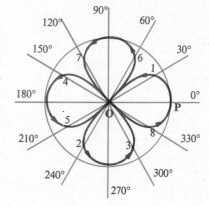

		①			②			③			④
θ	$0°$	$30°$	$45°$	$60°$	$90°$	$120°$	$135°$	$150°$	$180°$
2θ	$0°$	$60°$	$90°$	$120°$	$180°$	$240°$	$270°$	$300°$	$360°$
$r = \cos 2\theta$	1	$\dfrac{1}{2}$	0	$-\dfrac{1}{2}$	-1	$-\dfrac{1}{2}$	0	$\dfrac{1}{2}$	1

		⑤			⑥			⑦			⑧
θ	$180°$	$210°$	$225°$	$240°$	$270°$	$300°$	$315°$	$330°$
2θ	$360°$	$420°$	$450°$	$480°$	$540°$	$600°$	$630°$	$660°$
$r = \cos 2\theta$	1	$\dfrac{1}{2}$	0	$-\dfrac{1}{2}$	-1	$-\dfrac{1}{2}$	0	$\dfrac{1}{2}$

The following example illustrates an interesting consequence of the fact that the polar coordinates are not unique. (See also Exercises 29 and 30, page 493.)

EXAMPLE 2. Determine coordinates of the point(s) of intersection of the polar graphs of the equations $r = 2 + 4 \sin \theta$ and $r = 2$, (a) by solving the equations simultaneously; (b) by inspecting sketches of their graphs in the same coordinate system.

Solution:

(a) *Plan:* Eliminate r between the two equations and solve for θ.

If $r = 2 + 4 \sin \theta$ and $r = 2$, then

$$2 = 2 + 4 \sin \theta$$
$$0 = \sin \theta$$
$$\therefore \theta = 0^R \text{ or } \pi^R$$

The pairs $(2, 0^R)$ and $(2, \pi^R)$ satisfy both equations, because $\sin 0^R = \sin \pi^R = 0$ and:

$r = 2 + 4 \sin \theta$	$r = 2$
$2 \overset{?}{=} 2 + 4 \cdot 0$	$2 = 2$
$2 = 2$	

$\therefore$ $\mathbf{P}(2, 0^R)$ and $\mathbf{T}(2, \pi^R)$ are points of intersection of the graphs.

(b)   The figure indicates that the graphs intersect not only at $\mathbf{P}$ and $\mathbf{T}$, but also at $\mathbf{S}$. To satisfy the equation $r = 2 + 4 \sin \theta$, you can assign to $\mathbf{S}$ the coordinates $\left(-2, \dfrac{3\pi^R}{2} \right)$; to satisfy

$r = 2$, assign $\mathbf{S}$ the coordinates $(2, \frac{1}{2}\pi^R)$. Although $\mathbf{S}$ has no pair of coordinates which satisfies *both* equations, $\mathbf{S}$ is still said to be a point of intersection of the graphs of the equations.

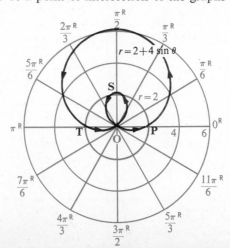

Exercises

Sketch the polar graphs of the following equations. In Exercises 21–24 use radian measure for θ.

A

1. $-r = 2$

2. $r = 1$

3. $\theta = -\dfrac{\pi}{6}$

4. $\theta = 30°$

5. $r = \cos \theta$

6. $r = 2 \cos \theta$

7. $r \cos \theta = 4$

8. $r \sin \theta = 3$

9. $r = \sin 2\theta$ (four-leaved rose)

10. $r = \sin 3\theta$ (three-leaved rose)

11. $r = \cos 5\theta$ (five-leaved rose)

12. $r = \cos 4\theta$ (eight-leaved rose)

13. $r = 1 + \cos \theta$ (cardioid)

14. $r = 1 - \sin \theta$ (cardioid)

15. $r = 2 - \sin \theta$ (limaçon)

16. $r = 2 + \cos \theta$ (limaçon)

17. $r = 1 + 2 \cos \theta$ (limaçon)

18. $r = 1 - 2 \sin \theta$ (limaçon)

B

19. $r^2 = 4 \sin 2\theta$ (lemniscate)

20. $r^2 = 4 \cos 2\theta$ (lemniscate)

21. $r = 2\theta$ (spiral of Archimedes)

22. $r\theta = 2$ (hyperbolic spiral)

23. $r = e^\theta$ (logarithmic spiral)

24. $r^2\theta = 1$ (lituus)

In the same coordinate system sketch the polar graphs of each pair of equations and determine the points of intersection of the graphs.

25. $r = 1 + \sin \theta$
$r = 2 \sin \theta$

26. $r^2 = r \cos \theta$
$r = 1 + \cos \theta$

27. $r = 1 - \sin \theta$
$r = \cos 2\theta$

28. $r^2 = \sin 2\theta$
$r^2 = \cos 2\theta$

C

29. Prove that the polar graphs of $r = 1 - \sin \theta$ and $r = -1 - \sin \theta$ are identical.

30. Let **T** be a point of intersection of the polar graph of $r = f(\theta)$ and $r = g(\theta)$. Show that either **T** is the origin, or **T** has coordinates (r^*, θ^*) such that $r^* = f(\theta^*)$ and for some integer n, either $r^* = g(\theta^* + 2n\pi)$, or $-r^* = g(\theta^* + \pi + 2n\pi)$.

12-9 Polar Form for Complex Numbers

The relationships between the Cartesian coordinates (a, b) and polar coordinates (r, θ) of a point (Figure 12–19)

(1)
$$a = r \cos \theta$$
$$b = r \sin \theta$$
$$\frac{b}{a} = \tan \theta \quad (a \neq 0)$$
$$r = \sqrt{a^2 + b^2} = |a + bi|$$

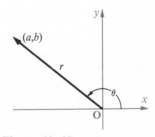

Figure 12–19

enable you to express any complex number $a + bi$ in terms of r and θ. Using equations (1), you have

$$a + bi = (r \cos \theta) + (r \sin \theta)i;$$

$$\therefore a + bi = r(\cos \theta + i \sin \theta).$$

We call $r(\cos \theta + i \sin \theta)$ the **polar** or **trigonometric form** of $a + bi$, and refer to θ as an **amplitude** of the complex number. Note that θ can be replaced by $\theta + 2k\pi$, where $k \in J$. Thus, two nonzero complex numbers are equal if and only if their absolute values are equal and their amplitudes differ by an integral multiple of 2π.

EXAMPLE 1. Express $2 - \sqrt{3}\, i$ in polar form.

Solution:

1. Sketch a figure and note that θ is in the fourth quadrant.

2. Use equations (1) and Table 2 to find:

$$r = \sqrt{2^2 + (-\sqrt{3})^2} = \sqrt{7},$$

$$\theta = \text{Arctan}\left(-\frac{\sqrt{3}}{2}\right) \doteq \text{Arctan}\,(-0.8660),$$

$$\theta \doteq -40°54'.$$

$$\therefore 2 - \sqrt{3}i = \sqrt{7}\,[\cos(-40°54') + i \sin(-40°54')], \textbf{Answer.}$$

Note: Using the least positive measure for θ, you would find

$$2 - \sqrt{3}i = \sqrt{7}\,(\cos 319°6' + i \sin 319°6'). \quad \text{(Why?)}$$

When complex numbers are written in polar form, their product can be computed very easily, as the following theorem asserts.

THEOREM If $z_1 = r_1(\cos \theta_1 + i \sin \theta_1)$ and

$$z_2 = r_2(\cos \theta_2 + i \sin \theta_2),$$

then $z_1 z_2 = r_1 r_2[\cos(\theta_1 + \theta_2) + i \sin(\theta_1 + \theta_2)]$.

Proof: $z_1 z_2 = [r_1(\cos \theta_1 + i \sin \theta_1)][r_2(\cos \theta_2 + i \sin \theta_2)]$

$$z_1 z_2 = r_1 r_2(\cos \theta_1 + i \sin \theta_1)(\cos \theta_2 + i \sin \theta_2)$$

$$= r_1 r_2(\cos \theta_1 \cos \theta_2 + i \sin \theta_2 \cos \theta_1$$

$$+ i \sin \theta_1 \cos \theta_2 + i^2 \sin \theta_1 \sin \theta_2)$$

$$z_1 z_2 = r_1 r_2 [(\cos \theta_1 \cos \theta_2 - \sin \theta_1 \sin \theta_2)$$
$$+ i(\sin \theta_1 \cos \theta_2 + \sin \theta_2 \cos \theta_1)]$$

Using formula (1), page 416, and formula (1), page 419,

$$z_1 z_2 = r_1 r_2 [\cos (\theta_1 + \theta_2) + i \sin(\theta_1 + \theta_2)].$$

EXAMPLE 2. If $z_1 = 2 + 2i\sqrt{2}$ and $z_2 = -4 + 4i$, use the polar form of z_1 and z_2 to find $z_1 z_2$, and then express the result in the form $a + bi$.

Solution:

Since $z_1 = 2 + 2i\sqrt{2}$,

$$r_1 = |z_1| = \sqrt{4 + 8} = 2\sqrt{3},$$

$$\theta_1 = \text{Arctan } \sqrt{2} \doteq 54° \ 44'.$$

$$\therefore z_1 = 2\sqrt{3} \ (\cos 54° \ 44' + i \sin 54° \ 44').$$

Also, for $z_2 = -4 + 4i$,

$$r_2 = |z_2| = \sqrt{16 + 16} = 4\sqrt{2},$$

$$\theta_2 = 180° + \text{Arctan } \frac{1}{-1} = 135°.$$

$$\therefore z_2 = 4\sqrt{2} \ (\cos 135° + i \sin 135°).$$

Applying the preceding theorem, you obtain

$$z_1 z_2 = (2\sqrt{3})(4\sqrt{2})[\cos (54° \ 44' + 135°) + i \sin (54° \ 44' + 135°)]$$
$$= 8\sqrt{6} \ (\cos 189° \ 44' + i \sin 189° \ 44').$$

From reduction formulas, pages 417 and 421,

$$z_1 z_2 = 8\sqrt{6} \ [-\cos 9° \ 44' + i(-\sin 9° \ 44')].$$

From Tables 2 and 3,

$$z_1 z_2 = 8(2.449)[-(0.9856) + (-0.1691)i].$$

$$\therefore z_1 z_2 = -19.31 - 3.31i, \textbf{ Answer.}$$

The quotient of two complex numbers also has a simple representation in polar form, as shown in the following theorem.

THEOREM If $z_1 = r_1(\cos \theta_1 + i \sin \theta_1)$, $z_2 = r_2(\cos \theta_2 + i \sin \theta_2)$, and $z_2 \neq 0 + 0i$, then

$$\frac{z_1}{z_2} = \frac{r_1}{r_2} [\cos(\theta_1 - \theta_2) + i \sin(\theta_1 - \theta_2)].$$

Proof: Observe that the conjugate $\bar{z}$ of $z = (r \cos \theta) + (r \sin \theta)i$ is

$$\bar{z} = (r \cos \theta) - (r \sin \theta)i, \text{ and}$$

$$r \cos \theta - (r \sin \theta)i = r \cos (-\theta) + [r \sin(-\theta)]i.$$

Therefore, the conjugate of $r(\cos \theta + i \sin \theta)$ is

$$r[\cos (-\theta) + i \sin (-\theta)].$$

Now $\dfrac{z_1}{z_2} = \dfrac{z_1}{z_2} \dfrac{\bar{z}_2}{\bar{z}_2}$

$$= \frac{r_1(\cos \theta_1 + i \sin \theta_1)}{r_2(\cos \theta_2 + i \sin \theta_2)} \frac{r_2[\cos(-\theta_2) + i \sin(-\theta_2)]}{r_2[\cos(-\theta_2) + i \sin(-\theta_2)]}$$

$$= \frac{r_1 r_2[\cos(\theta_1 - \theta_2) + i \sin(\theta_1 - \theta_2)]}{r_2 r_2[\cos(\theta_2 - \theta_2) + i \sin(\theta_2 - \theta_2)]}$$

$$= \frac{r_1[\cos(\theta_1 - \theta_2) + i \sin(\theta_1 - \theta_2]}{r_2(\cos 0 + i \sin 0)}.$$

$$\therefore \frac{z_1}{z_2} = \frac{r_1}{r_2} [\cos(\theta_1 - \theta_2) + i \sin(\theta_1 - \theta_2)].$$

EXAMPLE 3. If $z_1 = 6\left(\cos \dfrac{5\pi}{12} + i \sin \dfrac{5\pi}{12}\right)$ and

$z_2 = 2\left(\cos \dfrac{\pi}{12} + i \sin \dfrac{\pi}{12}\right)$, express $\dfrac{z_1}{z_2}$ in the form $a + bi$.

Solution: According to the theorem just proved,

$$\frac{z_1}{z_2} = \frac{6\left(\cos \dfrac{5\pi}{12} + i \sin \dfrac{5\pi}{12}\right)}{2\left(\cos \dfrac{\pi}{12} + i \sin \dfrac{\pi}{12}\right)} = 3\left(\cos \frac{\pi}{3} + i \sin \frac{\pi}{3}\right).$$

$$\therefore \frac{z_1}{z_2} = 3\left(\cos \frac{\pi}{3} + i \sin \frac{\pi}{3}\right) = 3\left(\frac{1}{2} + \frac{\sqrt{3}}{2} i\right)$$

$$= \frac{3}{2} + \frac{3\sqrt{3}}{2} i, \text{ **Answer.**}$$

Exercises

Write each of the given complex numbers in polar form. Use Table 2 as needed.

A

1. $4 + 0i$ **3.** $1 + i$ **5.** $3 - 2\sqrt{3}\,i$ **7.** $-2 + 3i$

2. $0 - 3i$ **4.** $-2 - 2i$ **6.** $-2\sqrt{3} + 3i$ **8.** $2 - 5i$

In Exercises 9–16, write in the form $a + bi$ the complex number whose absolute value and amplitude are given.

9. $4;\ 30°$ **11.** $2;\ \dfrac{5\pi}{4}$ **13.** $6;\ -\dfrac{\pi}{3}$ **15.** $2;\ 15°3'$

10. $3;\ 60°$ **12.** $3;\ \dfrac{5\pi}{6}$ **14.** $5;\ -\dfrac{3\pi}{4}$ **16.** $2;\ 231°10'$

If z_1 and z_2 are the given complex numbers, find an expression in the form $a + bi$ for (a) $z_1 z_2$; (b) $\dfrac{z_1}{z_2}$.

17. $z_1 = \cos \dfrac{\pi}{2} + i \sin \dfrac{\pi}{2},\ z_2 = 2\left(\cos \dfrac{\pi}{6} + i \sin \dfrac{\pi}{6}\right)$

18. $z_1 = 8\left(\cos \dfrac{5\pi}{4} + i \sin \dfrac{5\pi}{4}\right),\ z_2 = 4\left(\cos \dfrac{11\pi}{6} + i \sin \dfrac{11\pi}{6}\right)$

19. $z_1 = 3(\cos 50° + i \sin 50°),\ z_2 = 6(\cos 5° + i \sin 5°)$

20. $z_1 = 2(\cos 80° + i \sin 80°),\ z_2 = (\cos 270° + i \sin 270°)$

21. $z_1 = -1 + \sqrt{3}\,i,\ z_2 = 1 - i$ **23.** $z_1 = 4 + 4i,\ z_2 = -2i$

22. $z_1 = -2 + 2i,\ z_2 = -1 + i$ **24.** $z_1 = 5i,\ z_2 = 2 - 3i$

B

25. Use the polar form for z to prove that, if $z \neq 0 + 0i$, then $\dfrac{z}{z} = 1$.

26. Prove that if $z \neq 0 + 0i$, then

$$\frac{1}{z} = \frac{1}{r}[\cos(-\theta) + i \sin(-\theta)].$$

27. Prove that if $\bar{z}$ denotes the conjugate of z, and if $z \neq 0 + 0i$, then

$$\frac{\bar{z}}{z} = \cos(-2\theta) + i \sin(-2\theta).$$

28. Prove that $[r(\cos \theta + i \sin \theta)]^2 = r^2(\cos 2\theta + i \sin 2\theta)$.

C

29. State the conditions under which the conjugate and the reciprocal of a complex number are equal.

30. Prove: If $\theta \neq (2k + 1)\pi,\ k \in J$, then

$$\frac{1 + \cos \theta + i \sin \theta}{1 + \cos \theta - i \sin \theta} = \cos \theta + i \sin \theta.$$

12-10 Powers and Roots of Complex Numbers

The theorem stated on page 494 enables you to compute the square of any complex number very quickly. In fact, if $z = r(\cos\theta + i\sin\theta)$, then

$$z^2 = [r(\cos\theta + i\sin\theta)][r(\cos\theta + i\sin\theta)].$$

$$\therefore z^2 = r^2(\cos 2\theta + i\sin 2\theta). \quad (\text{Why?})$$

On the basis of this example, you probably suspect the truth of the following proposition, known as **De Moivre's Theorem** (for Abraham De Moivre, 1667–1754).

THEOREM If $z = r(\cos\theta + i\sin\theta)$ and n denotes a positive integer, then

$$z^n = r^n(\cos n\theta + i\sin n\theta).$$

Proof: Let S be the set of natural numbers for which the assertion is true.

1. $1 \in S$ because $z^1 = r(\cos\theta + i\sin\theta)$
$$= r^1[\cos(1\cdot\theta) + i\sin(1\cdot\theta)].$$

2. Now, assume the theorem to be true for $k \in N$; that is, assume that

$$z^k = r^k[\cos(k\cdot\theta) + i\sin(k\cdot\theta)]$$

Then

$$z^{k+1} = z^k \cdot z^1 = r^k[\cos(k\cdot\theta) + i\sin(k\cdot\theta)] \cdot [r(\cos\theta + i\sin\theta)]$$

Hence, by the theorem stated on page 494,

$$z^{k+1} = r^{k+1}[\cos(k\theta + \theta) + i\sin(k\theta + \theta)].$$

$$\therefore z^{k+1} = r^{k+1}[\cos(k+1)\theta + i\sin(k+1)\theta].$$

Therefore, if $k \in S$, $(k+1) \in S$.

Accordingly, by the principle of mathematical induction, $S = N$. (Why?)

EXAMPLE 1. Express $\left(\dfrac{3\sqrt{3}}{2} + \dfrac{3}{2}i\right)^3$ in the form $a + bi$.

Solution: Write $\dfrac{3\sqrt{3}}{2} + \dfrac{3}{2}i$ in polar form:

$$r = \sqrt{\tfrac{27}{4} + \tfrac{9}{4}} = \sqrt{\tfrac{36}{4}} = 3,$$

$$\theta = \text{Arctan } \frac{1}{\sqrt{3}} = 30°.$$

$$\therefore \frac{3\sqrt{3}}{2} + \frac{3}{2}i = 3(\cos 30° + i \sin 30°)$$

By De Moivre's Theorem,

$$[3(\cos 30° + i \sin 30°)]^3 = 3^3[\cos(3 \cdot 30°) + i \sin(3 \cdot 30°)]$$
$$= 27(\cos 90° + i \sin 90°) = 0 + 27i.$$

$$\therefore \left(\frac{3\sqrt{3}}{2} + \frac{3}{2}i\right)^3 = 0 + 27i, \textbf{ Answer.}$$

Suppose $z \neq 0 + 0i$. By defining $z^0 = 1 + 0i$ and $z^{-n} = \dfrac{1}{z^n}$ for every $n \in N$, you can extend De Moivre's Theorem to include all integral exponents.

THEOREM   If $z = r(\cos \theta + i \sin \theta)$, $z \neq 0 + 0i$, and $n \in J$, then
$$z^n = r^n[\cos(n\theta) + i \sin(n\theta)].$$

The proof will be left for you (Exercise 22, page 502).

EXAMPLE 2.   Express $(-1 + i)^{-4}$ in the form $a + bi$.

Solution: 1. Express $-1 + i$ in polar form:

$$-1 + i = \sqrt{2}\,(\cos 135° + i \sin 135°).$$

2. Apply the extended De Moivre's Theorem to obtain

$$(-1 + i)^{-4} = (\sqrt{2})^{-4}[\cos(-4 \cdot 135°) + i \sin(-4 \cdot 135°)]$$
$$= \tfrac{1}{4}[\cos(-540°) + i \sin(-540°)]$$
$$= \tfrac{1}{4}(\cos 180° + i \sin 180°) = -\tfrac{1}{4} + 0i.$$

$$\therefore (-1 + i)^{-4} = -\tfrac{1}{4} + 0i, \textbf{ Answer.}$$

De Moivre's Theorem can also be used to find roots of complex numbers, as illustrated in the following Example.

EXAMPLE 3. Find all the cube roots of $2i$.

Solution: The cube roots of $2i = 2\left(\cos\dfrac{\pi}{2} + i\sin\dfrac{\pi}{2}\right)$ are the solutions over the field C of complex numbers of the equation

(1) $$z^3 = 2\left(\cos\frac{\pi}{2} + i\sin\frac{\pi}{2}\right).$$

Writing z in polar form $r(\cos\theta + i\sin\theta)$, you can apply De Moivre's Theorem to express equation (1) as follows:

$$[r(\cos\theta + i\sin\theta)]^3 = 2\left(\cos\frac{\pi}{2} + i\sin\frac{\pi}{2}\right);$$

(2) $$r^3(\cos 3\theta + i\sin 3\theta) = 2\left(\cos\frac{\pi}{2} + i\sin\frac{\pi}{2}\right).$$

Since complex numbers are equal if and only if their absolute values are equal and their amplitudes differ in radian measure by integral multiples of 2π, equation (2) is equivalent to

$$r^3 = 2 \quad and \quad 3\theta = \frac{\pi}{2} + 2k\pi, \quad k \in J;$$

$$\therefore r = \sqrt[3]{2} \quad and \quad \theta = \frac{\pi}{6} + \frac{2k\pi}{3}, \quad k \in J.$$

$\therefore$ if k is any integer,

$$\sqrt[3]{2}\left[\cos\left(\frac{\pi}{6} + \frac{2k\pi}{3}\right) + i\sin\left(\frac{\pi}{6} + \frac{2k\pi}{3}\right)\right]$$

is a root of $2i$.

Replacing k in turn by $0, 1, 2, 3, \ldots$, you find the roots to be:

$$\sqrt[3]{2}\left(\cos\frac{\pi}{6} + i\sin\frac{\pi}{6}\right)$$

$$\sqrt[3]{2}\left(\cos\frac{5\pi}{6} + i\sin\frac{5\pi}{6}\right)$$

$$\sqrt[3]{2}\left(\cos\frac{3\pi}{2} + i\sin\frac{3\pi}{2}\right)$$

$$\sqrt[3]{2}\left(\cos\frac{13\pi}{6} + i\sin\frac{13\pi}{6}\right) = \sqrt[3]{2}\left(\cos\frac{\pi}{6} + i\sin\frac{\pi}{6}\right)$$

When you substitute 3 for k, you obtain again the first root stated. You know, of course, that the values must repeat because equation (1) has exactly 3 roots in C. (Why?)

∴ the three cube roots of $2i$ are

$$\sqrt[3]{2}\left(\cos\frac{\pi}{6} + i\sin\frac{\pi}{6}\right),$$

$$\sqrt[3]{2}\left(\cos\frac{5\pi}{6} + i\sin\frac{5\pi}{6}\right),$$

$$\sqrt[3]{2}\left(\cos\frac{3\pi}{2} + i\sin\frac{3\pi}{2}\right), \text{ Answer.}$$

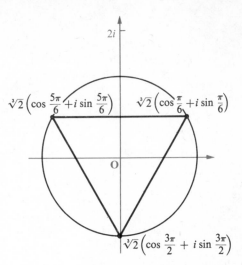

Figure 12–20 pictures the three cube roots of $2i$ as points in the plane, and indicates that these points are the vertices of an equilateral triangle inscribed in the circle whose radius is $\sqrt[3]{2}$ and whose center is **O**.

The reasoning in the solution of Example 3 can be generalized to yield the formula stated in the following theorem for the nth-roots of any nonzero complex number.

Figure 12–20

THEOREM If $n \in N$, $r \in \Re^+$, and $\alpha \in \Re$, then the n roots of the equation

$$z^n = r(\cos\alpha + i\sin\alpha)$$

are given by

$$\sqrt[n]{r}\left[\cos\left(\frac{\alpha}{n} + \frac{2k\pi}{n}\right) + i\sin\left(\frac{\alpha}{n} + \frac{2k\pi}{n}\right)\right],$$

$$k = 0, 1, 2, \ldots, n - 1.$$

It is customary to assign the following meaning to the exponential $e^{i\theta}$ where θ denotes any real number:

$$e^{i\theta} = \cos\theta + i\sin\theta.$$

You can verify that under this definition, called *Euler's equation*, the laws of exponents (page 338) continue to hold. (Exercises 23–26, page 502.)

Notice that Euler's equation links exponential and circular functions. Using it, you can express the cube roots of $2i$ (see Example 3) in exponential form:

$$\sqrt[3]{2}\left(\cos\frac{\pi}{6} + i\sin\frac{\pi}{6}\right) = \sqrt[3]{2}\,e^{i\frac{\pi}{6}}$$

$$\sqrt[3]{2}\left(\cos\frac{5\pi}{6} + i\sin\frac{5\pi}{6}\right) = \sqrt[3]{2}\,e^{i\frac{5\pi}{6}}; \quad \sqrt[3]{2}\left(\cos\frac{3\pi}{2} + i\sin\frac{3\pi}{2}\right) = \sqrt[3]{2}\,e^{i\frac{3\pi}{2}}$$

Exercises

Use De Moivre's Theorem or its extension to find each of the following powers.
State each result in exponential form.

1. $(1 + i)^3$ **3.** $(2 - 2i)^{-2}$ **5.** $(\sqrt{3} + i)^{12}$

2. $(2 - 2i\sqrt{3})^4$ **4.** $\left(\dfrac{3}{2} - \dfrac{i}{2}\right)^{-5}$ **6.** $(3 - 3i)^6$

Express the given number in the form $a + bi$.

7. $e^{i \cdot 0}$ **9.** $e^{-\pi i}$ **11.** $(1 + i)^3(\sqrt{3} + i)^{-4}$

8. $e^{2\pi i}$ **10.** $e^{\frac{\pi}{2}i}$ **12.** $(\sqrt{3}\,i + 1)^4(1 - i)^3$

In Exercises 13–18, **(a)** express the required roots in polar form; **(b)** represent
the roots as points in the complex plane.

13. The three cube roots of 1.   **16.** The five fifth roots of $1 + i$.

14. The three cube roots of i.   **17.** The two square roots of $-1 - \sqrt{3}\,i$.

15. The six sixth roots of -1.   **18.** The four fourth roots of 1.

Solve each equation over C.

19. $z^4 = (1 + i)^3$ **20.** $z^2 - 16 - 16\sqrt{3}\,i = 0$

21. Apply the binomial theorem and De Moivre's Theorem to $(\cos\theta + i\sin\theta)^3$
to prove that $\cos 3\theta = 4\cos^3\theta - 3\cos\theta$, and $\sin 3\theta = 3\sin\theta - 4\sin^3\theta$.

22. By recalling (page 494) that if $z = r(\cos\theta + i\sin\theta)$, $r \neq 0$, then $\bar{z}$, the
conjugate of z, is $r[\cos(-\theta) + i\sin(-\theta)]$, prove that De Moivre's Theorem
is true for every negative integer.

Let $\theta_1 \in \Re$, $\theta_2 \in \Re$, and $n \in J$. Prove each statement.

23. $e^{i\theta_1} \cdot e^{i\theta_2} = e^{i(\theta_1 + \theta_2)}$ **25.** $\dfrac{e^{i\theta_1}}{e^{i\theta_2}} = e^{i(\theta_1 - \theta_2)} = \dfrac{1}{e^{i(\theta_2 - \theta_1)}}$

24. $(e^{i\theta_1})^n = e^{in\theta_1}$ **26.** $e^{i\theta_1} = e^{i\theta_2}$ if and only if $\theta_1 = \theta_2 + 2n\pi$
for some integer n.

27. Show that the three cube roots of 1 are 1, ω, and ω^2, where $\omega = e^{\frac{2\pi i}{3}}$.

28. Show that the four fourth roots of 1 are 1, ω, ω^2, and ω^3, where $\omega = e^{\frac{\pi i}{2}}$.

29. Prove that the n nth-roots of 1 (the nth roots of unity) are 1, ω, ω^2, ..., ω^{n-1},
where $\omega = e^{\frac{2\pi i}{n}}$. Then show that these roots form a commutative group
under multiplication.

30. **(a)** Prove that if n is any positive integer, and $\omega = e^{\frac{2\pi i}{n}}$, then

$$1 + \omega + \omega^2 + \cdots + \omega^{n-1} = 0. \qquad (\textit{Hint:} \text{ Use Exercise 29.})$$

(b) From part **(a)** deduce the following assertions:

(1) $1 + \cos \dfrac{2\pi}{n} + \cos \dfrac{4\pi}{n} + \cdots + \dfrac{\cos 2(n-1)\pi}{n} = 0;$

(2) $\sin \dfrac{2\pi}{n} + \sin \dfrac{4\pi}{n} + \cdots + \sin \dfrac{2(n-1)\pi}{n} = 0.$

If $\theta \in \mathcal{R}$, **prove each statement.**

31. $\cos \theta = \dfrac{e^{i\theta} + e^{-i\theta}}{2}$ **32.** $\sin \theta = \dfrac{e^{i\theta} - e^{-i\theta}}{2i}$

Chapter Summary

1. If ϕ is the angle from a vector $\mathbf{w}$ to a vector $\mathbf{v}$, then

$$\cos \phi = \frac{\mathbf{w} \cdot \mathbf{v}}{\|\mathbf{w}\| \, \|\mathbf{v}\|} \quad \text{and} \quad \sin \phi = \frac{\mathbf{w_p} \cdot \mathbf{v}}{\|\mathbf{w}\| \, \|\mathbf{v}\|}.$$

2. The angle ϕ from a line of slope m_1 to a line of slope m_2 satisfies the equation $\tan \phi = \dfrac{m_2 - m_1}{1 + m_1 m_2}.$ The slope of a nonvertical line equals the tangent of its **angle of inclination**.

3. When the measures of three parts, including one side, of a triangle are known, the measures of the remaining parts can be found by the **Law of Cosines** or by the **Law of Sines**.

4. If the **polar coordinates** of a point are (r, θ) then its Cartesian coordinates are (x, y) where

$$x = r \cos \theta \quad \text{and} \quad y = r \sin \theta.$$

5. A complex number $a + bi$ can be expressed in **polar form** $r(\cos \theta + i \sin \theta)$ and in **exponential form** $re^{i\theta}$, where $r = |a + bi| = \sqrt{a^2 + b^2}.$ If $r \neq 0$, then you may choose

$$\theta = \text{Arctan } \frac{b}{a} \text{ for } a > 0, \text{ and } \theta = \pi + \text{Arctan } \frac{b}{a} \text{ for } a < 0.$$

6. If $z_1 = r_1(\cos \theta_1 + i \sin \theta_1)$ and $z_2 = r_2(\cos \theta_2 + i \sin \theta_2)$, then

$$z_1 z_2 = r_1 r_2 [\cos(\theta_1 + \theta_2) + i \sin(\theta_1 + \theta_2)] = r_1 r_2 e^{i(\theta_1 + \theta_2)};$$

$$\frac{z_1}{z_2} = \frac{r_1}{r_2} [\cos(\theta_1 - \theta_2) + i \sin(\theta_1 - \theta_2)] = \frac{r_1}{r_2} e^{i(\theta_1 - \theta_2)}, \qquad z_2 \neq 0.$$

Also, by **De Moivre's Theorem**, $z_1^n = r_1^n (\cos n\theta_1 + i \sin n\theta_1)$ for every integer n. Each n-th root of z_1 $(n \in N)$ is of the form

$$\sqrt[n]{r_1} \left(\cos \frac{\theta_1 + 2k\pi}{n} + i \sin \frac{\theta_1 + 2k\pi}{n} \right), k \in J.$$

Chapter Test

handwritten: $cos = \frac{-7170}{170}, \sin = \frac{-1371}{170}$

12-1   **1.** If ϕ is the angle from $(-2, 1)$ to $(3, 5)$, determine $\cos \phi$ and $\sin \phi$. *(handwritten: $\cos^{-1}$)*

12-2   **2.** If ϕ is the angle from a line of slope -2 to a line of slope 1, find $\tan \phi$. *(handwritten: $\tan = -3$)*

       3. If θ is the angle of inclination of the line with equation $2x - 3y = 6$, which of the following statements is true?

         (a) $0° < m°\angle\theta < 45°$;   **(c)** $45° < m°\angle\theta < 90°$;

         (b) $-45° < m°\angle\theta < 0°$;   **(d)** $-90° < m°\angle\theta < -45°$.

12-3   **4.** The length in inches of the shortest side of a right triangle, one angle of which measures $50°$ and the hypotenuse of which measures 10 in., is

         (a) $10 \sin 50°$;   **(b)** $10 \cos 50°$;   **(c)** $10 \tan 40°$;   **(d)** $10 \cos 40°$.

12-4   **5.** If two sides of a triangle have lengths 4 inches and 5 inches, and the angle between these sides measures $60°$, find the length of the third side. *(handwritten: 4.6 inches)*

12-5   **6.** If angles α and β in a triangle measure $30°$ and $45°$, respectively, and the side a is 4 feet long, find the length of side b. *(handwritten: 4√2 ft.)*

       7. For given values of a, b, and α, how many triangles can there be if $a < b \sin \alpha$, and $m°\angle\alpha < 90°$? *(handwritten: none)*

12-6   **8.** To the nearest square centimeter, find the area of the triangle whose sides measure 5 cm., 7 cm., and 10 cm. *(handwritten: 16 sq. cm)*

12-7   **9.** State three sets of polar coordinates for the point whose Cartesian coordinates are $(-1, \sqrt{3})$. *(handwritten: $(2, \frac{2\pi}{3})(2, \frac{-4\pi}{3})(-2, \frac{-\pi}{3})$)*

12-8   **10.** Sketch the polar graph of $r = -1 + \cos \theta$.

12-9   **11.** Express $\sqrt{3} - i$ in polar form.

      12. If $z_1 = i$ and $z_2 = 1 - i$, write an expression in polar form for $z_1 z_2$. *(handwritten: $\sqrt{2}\cos 45° + i \sin 45°$)*

12-10   **13.** If $z = 2 \cos 15° + 2i \sin 15°$, express z^4 in the form $a + bi$, where $a \in \mathcal{R}$ and $b \in \mathcal{R}$. *(handwritten: $8 + 8\sqrt{3}\, i$)*

      14. Express the three cube roots of $-16 - 16\sqrt{3}\, i$ in exponential form.

(handwritten: $2\sqrt[3]{4}\, e^{i \frac{4\pi}{9}} \quad 2\sqrt[3]{4}\, e^{i \frac{10\pi}{9}} \quad 2\sqrt[3]{4}\, e^{i \frac{16\pi}{9}}$)

Reading List

LITTLEWOOD, D. E. *Skeleton Key of Mathematics.* New York: Harper Torchbooks, 1960.

RICHMOND, DONALD E. *Calculus with Analytic Geometry.* Reading, Mass.: Addison-Wesley, 1959.

WEISNER, LOUIS. *Introduction to the Theory of Equations.* New York: Macmillan Co., 1938.

L. E. Dickson

In 1770 an English mathematician named Edward Waring made the following conjecture: Every positive integer I can be represented as the sum of N or fewer kth powers of integers, where N and k are integers and $k \geq 2$. In 1909 Hilbert proved this conjecture; that is, he proved that for any given value of k, the integer N exists. His proof, however, did not indicate what the value of N would be in each case. A few particular values of N were known. It had been demonstrated that for $k = 2$, $N \leq 4$, and for $k = 3$, $N \leq 9$. In other words, any integer I can be expressed as the sum of four or fewer squares of integers or as the sum of nine or fewer cubes of integers. For example, suppose $I = 12$ and $k = 2$. Since $12 = 3^2 + 1^2 + 1^2 + 1^2$ or $2^2 + 2^2 + 2^2$, the conjecture holds with $N \leq 4$. The problem of finding the value of N for arbitrary values of k has occupied many mathematicians during this century, among them Leonard Dickson (1874–1954). By using the analytic methods of the Russian mathematician Vinogradov, Dickson was able to solve this problem except for a few special cases.

Dickson did undergraduate work at the University of Texas and graduate work at the University of Chicago, where he was awarded the University's first Ph.D. degree in mathematics. His dissertation was written under the supervision of E. H. Moore. His research work falls roughly into five areas: groups, finite fields, algebraic invariants, linear algebra, and theory of numbers. He was particularly interested in the theory of numbers and wrote a three-volume history of this field.

One of the many problems which he investigated was that of determining whether the equation $x^n + y^n = z^n$, where x, y, z are nonzero integers and $n \geq 3$, has a solution. Dickson showed that if x, y, z are not divisible by an odd prime, there is no solution for $n < 7000$. Subsequent research using high-speed computers has indicated that any integers x, y, and z satisfying the equation would have to be so large that it would take a person more than 200 years to write them down!

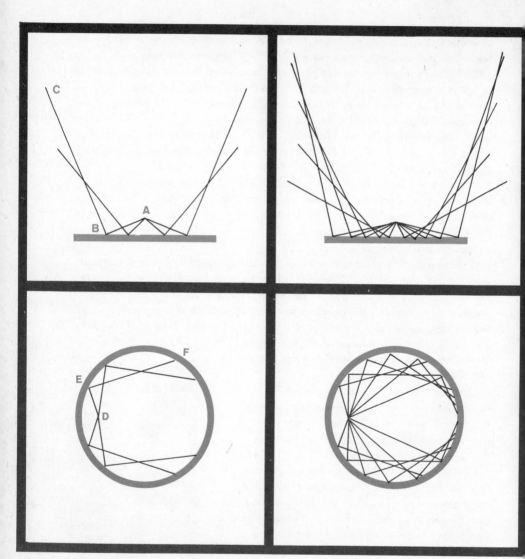

13

A curve tangent at each of its points to some member of a family of curves is called an envelope. The envelope of the family of broken-line curves *ABC*, where *A* is a fixed point, *B* lies on a given line, and ∠*ABC* is a right angle, is a parabola. The envelope of *DEF*, where *D* is a fixed point inside a circle, *E* lies on the circle, and ∠*DEF* is a right angle, is an ellipse.

Analytic Geometry

and Matrices

In earlier chapters of this book, you have studied the graphs of many different equations. Some of the equations defined functions, and others simply relations. One class of relations having particular significance in many different areas of science and technology is the class defined by second-degree polynomial equations in two variables. In this chapter, you will study these relations. The concept of a matrix will develop from this study.

SECOND-DEGREE LOCI

13–1 Circles

The concepts of point, line, and distance in $\mathcal{R} \times \mathcal{R}$ that you studied in Chapter 5 are fundamental notions in describing other geometrical figures. For example, you define a circle by saying it is the set of all points in $\mathcal{R} \times \mathcal{R}$ at a given distance (the *radius*) from a given point (the *center*). Thus, if the radius of a circle $\mathcal{S}$ is 5 and its center is the point $C(1, 3)$, (see Figure 13–1), then a point $P(x, y)$ in $\mathcal{R} \times \mathcal{R}$ belongs to $\mathcal{S}$ if and only if

(1) $\|P - C\| = 5$.

But $\|P - C\| = \|(x, y) - (1, 3)\|$

$= \|(x - 1, y - 3)\|$

$= \sqrt{(x - 1)^2 + (y - 3)^2}$.

Thus, $P \in \mathcal{S}$ if and only if

$\sqrt{(x - 1)^2 + (y - 3)^2} = 5$.

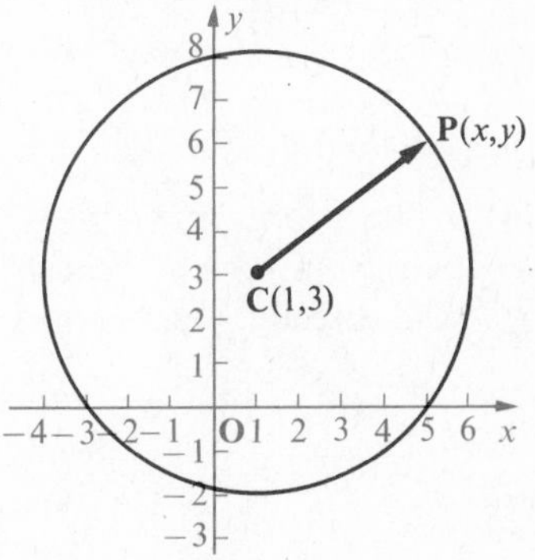

Since both members of the preceding equation denote nonnegative numbers, you can square both members to obtain the equivalent equation $(x - 1)^2 + (y - 3)^2 = 25$.

Figure 13–1

$\therefore \mathcal{S} = \{(x, y): (x - 1)^2 + (y - 3)^2 = 25\}$.

We call $(x - 1)^2 + (y - 3)^2 = 25$ an *equation* of $\mathcal{S}$, and say that $\mathcal{S}$ is the graph or the **locus** in $\mathcal{R} \times \mathcal{R}$ of the equation.

You can generalize the preceding discussion to prove the following theorem (Exercise 31, page 511).

THEOREM   If $C(h, k)$ is the center and $r\ (r > 0)$ is the radius of a circle $\mathcal{S}$ in $\mathcal{R} \times \mathcal{R}$, then

$$\mathcal{S} = \{(x, y): (x - h)^2 + (y - k)^2 = r^2\}.$$

Using the binomial theorem, you can express the equation

$$(x - 1)^2 + (y - 3)^2 = 25$$

in the equivalent form $x^2 + y^2 - 2x - 6y - 15 = 0$.   (Why?)   This observation suggests the following corollary of the foregoing theorem (Exercise 32, page 511).

COROLLARY.   Every circle in $\mathcal{R} \times \mathcal{R}$ has an equation of the form

$$x^2 + y^2 + Dx + Ey + F = 0,$$

where D, E, and F are constants in $\mathcal{R}$.

To discover whether the converse of this corollary is true, study the following example.

EXAMPLE 1.   In $\mathcal{R} \times \mathcal{R}$ determine the locus of the given equation.

(a) $x^2 + y^2 - 10x + 8y - 4 = 0$

(b) $x^2 + y^2 - 10x + 8y + 41 = 0$

(c) $x^2 + y^2 - 10x + 8y + 50 = 0$

Solution:

(a) To transform $x^2 + y^2 - 10x + 8y - 4 = 0$ into an equivalent equation from which the center and radius of the circle (if any) can be read directly, you "complete the square" in x and in y:

$$x^2 - 10x + (-5)^2 + y^2 + 8y + 4^2 = 4 + (-5)^2 + 4^2$$
$$= 4 + 25 + 16$$
$$(x - 5)^2 + (y + 4)^2 = 45, \text{ or}$$
$$(x - 5)^2 + [y - (-4)]^2 = (3\sqrt{5})^2$$

∴ the locus is a circle with center at $(5, -4)$ and radius $3\sqrt{5}$, **Answer.**

(b) Completing the square as in part **(a)**, you obtain the equation

$$(x - 5)^2 + (y + 4)^2 = -41 + 41 = 0.$$

Only one point has coordinates satisfying this equation, namely, the point $(5, -4)$. (Why?)

$\therefore$ the locus is the point $(5, -4)$, **Answer.**

(c) Completing squares yields the equation

$$(x - 5)^2 + (y + 4)^2 = -9,$$

which is satisfied by *no* point of $\mathcal{R} \times \mathcal{R}$.

$\therefore$ the locus is $\emptyset$, **Answer.**

EXAMPLE 2. Find an equation of the circle containing the points $(-5, 2), (-3, 4), (1, 2)$.

Solution: The coordinates of each point must satisfy

$$x^2 + y^2 + Dx + Ey + F = 0.$$

Therefore,

$$25 + 4 - 5D + 2E + F = 0,$$
$$9 + 16 - 3D + 4E + F = 0,$$
$$1 + 4 + D + 2E + F = 0,$$

or

$$-5D + 2E + F = -29,$$
$$-3D + 4E + F = -25,$$
$$D + 2E + F = -5.$$

Solving this system, you find that $D = 4$, $E = -2$, and $F = -5$.

$\therefore x^2 + y^2 + 4x - 2y - 5 = 0$, **Answer.**

Because the tangent $\mathfrak{I}$ to a circle is perpendicular to the diameter containing the point of contact **P** (Figure 13–2), you know that

(1) If $\mathfrak{I}$ is not a vertical or horizontal line, its slope is the negative reciprocal of the slope of the diameter.

(2) The distance from the center to $\mathfrak{I}$ is the radius.

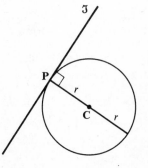

Figure 13–2

EXAMPLE 3. Find an equation of the circle with center at $(-4, 2)$ and tangent to the graph of $3x + y = -5$.

Solution: Using fact (2), page 509, and the distance formula given on page 196, you find

$$r = \frac{|3(-4) + 1 \cdot 2 + 5|}{\sqrt{9 + 1}} = \frac{5}{\sqrt{10}} = \frac{\sqrt{10}}{2}.$$

∴ an equation of the circle is

$$(x + 4)^2 + (y - 2)^2 = \tfrac{5}{2}, \textbf{ Answer.}$$

EXAMPLE 4. Prove that the polar graph of the equation $r = 2 \sin \theta$ is a circle.

Solution: *Plan:* Use statements (3) and (4), sec. 12–7, to convert the given equation into an equation in Cartesian coordinates:

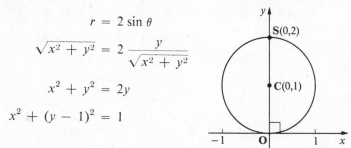

$$r = 2 \sin \theta$$

$$\sqrt{x^2 + y^2} = 2 \frac{y}{\sqrt{x^2 + y^2}}$$

$$x^2 + y^2 = 2y$$

$$x^2 + (y - 1)^2 = 1$$

∴ the graph is a circle with center at $C(0, 1)$ and radius 1, **Answer.**

Note that O and $S(0, 2)$ are the endpoints of a diameter of the circle. (Why?) Hence, the x-axis is tangent to the circle at O. (Why?)

Exercises

In Exercises 1–10, sketch the circle and write its equation in the form $x^2 + y^2 + Dx + Ey + F = 0$.

A
1. Center $(2, 3)$, radius 3.
2. Center $(4, -1)$, radius 5.

3. Center $(-3, -2)$, radius $\sqrt{7}$.
4. Center $(-2, 6)$, radius $\sqrt{13}$.

5. Center $(4, 3)$ and tangent to the x-axis.
6. Center $(-3, 6)$ and tangent to the y-axis.
7. Center $(3, 0)$ and containing the origin.

8. Diameter $\overline{PQ}$, where $\mathbf{P} = (1, 0)$ and $\mathbf{Q} = (5, 0)$.

9. Center on the graph of $y = 2x$, and tangent to the x-axis at $(3, 0)$.

10. Center on the graph of $y = -2x$, and tangent to the y-axis at $(0, 3)$.

In Exercises 11–16, write the given equation in the form $(x - h)^2 + (y - k)^2 = r^2$, and sketch its graph.

11. $x^2 + y^2 - 8x + 12y + 2 = 0$ **14.** $x^2 + y^2 + \frac{2}{3}x - \frac{4}{3}y = 0$

12. $x^2 + y^2 - 8x + 12y + 52 = 0$ **15.** $3x^2 + 3y^2 - 6x + 4y - 1 = 0$

13. $x^2 + y^2 - 2x - 8y = 0$ **16.** $2x^2 + 2y^2 - 3x - 5y + 3 = 0$

In Exercises 17–20, find an equation of the circle passing through the given points.

17. $(-1, 2), (3, 4), (2, 3)$ **19.** $(-2, -2), (10, -8), (7, 1)$

18. $(3, -2), (-1, -4), (2, -5)$ **20.** $(5, 3), (-1, 9), (3, -3)$

The polar graph of each of the following equations is a circle. In each case determine the center and radius of the circle.

21. $r = -3 \sin \theta$ **23.** $r = 8(\cos \theta + \sin \theta)$

22. $r = 6 \cos \theta$ **24.** $r = 8 \cos\left(\theta - \dfrac{\pi}{6}\right)$

(B) **25.** Find an equation of the circle with center at $(-1, 4)$ and tangent to the graph of $5x + 12y + 9 = 0$.

26. Find a Cartesian equation of the circle with center on the graph of $x = 4$, tangent to the x-axis, and with radius 5.

27. Find a Cartesian equation of the circle having for diameter the segment of the graph of $4x - 5y = 4$ cut off by the coordinate axes.

28. Find the equations of the circles tangent to the graph of $x + y = 4$ at $(1, 3)$ and having radius equal to $\sqrt{2}$.

29. Find equations of the two tangents from $(6, -5)$ to the circle

$$x^2 + y^2 - 2x = 4.$$

(*Hint:* Use fact (2), page 509.)

30. Find an equation of the circle tangent to the line $3x + 4y + 5 = 0$ at $(1, -2)$ and having its center on the line $x + y = 6$.

31. Prove the theorem on page 508.

32. Prove the corollary to the theorem on page 508.

(C) **33.** Prove that if the equation $x^2 + y^2 + Dx + Ey + F = 0$ has a single point for a locus, then $D^2 + E^2 - 4F = 0$.

34. Prove that if $D^2 + E^2 - 4F < 0$, then $x^2 + y^2 + Dx + Ey + F = 0$ has no locus in $\mathcal{R} \times \mathcal{R}$.

35. Use the distance formula to show that the distance along a tangent to a circle with equation $(x - h)^2 + (y - k)^2 = r^2$ from a point $\mathbf{P}(x_1, y_1)$ on the tangent to the point of tangency is

$$d = \sqrt{(x_1 - h)^2 + (y_1 - k)^2 - r^2}.$$

(*Hint:* Make a sketch and consider a right triangle that is involved.)

36. In triangle **POC**, use the law of cosines (page 472) to show that an equation in polar coordinates of the circle with center at $\mathbf{C}(a, \alpha)$ and radius b is

$$b^2 = a^2 + r^2 - 2ar \cos(\theta - \alpha).$$

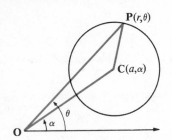

37. Find the locus of a point that moves so that the square of its distance from $(2, 0)$ is always one-half its distance from the line $x = -4$.

38. Show that if two distinct circles intersect, and if they have equations

$$x^2 + y^2 + Dx + Ey + F = 0 \quad \text{and} \quad x^2 + y^2 + D'x + E'y + F' = 0,$$

then the line $(D - D')x + (E - E')y + (F - F') = 0$ passes through the points of intersection. (Note: This line is called the **radical axis** of the two circles.)

13–2 Parabolas

In $\Re \times \Re$ let $\mathfrak{I}$ be the set of every point $\mathbf{P}(x, y)$ whose distance from the point $\mathbf{F}(0, 3)$ equals its distance from the line $\mathfrak{D}$ whose equation is $y = -3$ (Figure 13–3). Since

$$\|\mathbf{P} - \mathbf{F}\| = d(\mathbf{P}, \mathfrak{D}),$$

$$\|(x - 0, y - 3)\| = |y + 3|. \quad \text{(Why?)}$$

$$\therefore \sqrt{x^2 + (y - 3)^2} = |y + 3|. \quad \text{(Why?)}$$

Squaring each member of the equation, you obtain the equivalent (Why?) equation

$$x^2 + (y - 3)^2 = (y + 3)^2.$$

Simplifying this equation, you find

$$x^2 = 12y.$$

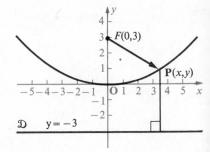

Figure 13–3

Hence, $\mathfrak{I} = \{(x, y): x^2 = 12y\}$.

$\mathfrak{I}$ is called a *parabola*, having the point $(0, 3)$ as *focus* and the line $y = -3$ as *directrix*. We say that $x^2 = 12y$ is an equation of $\mathfrak{I}$, and that $\mathfrak{I}$ is the graph or *locus* of $x^2 = 12y$ in $\mathcal{R} \times \mathcal{R}$. In the plane, the set of points equidistant from a fixed line and a fixed point not on the line is a **parabola**. The fixed line is called the **directrix**, and the fixed point, the **focus** of the parabola. Figure 13–4 identifies two other features of the parabola:

axis (or **axis of symmetry**), the line through the focus perpendicular to the directrix;

vertex, the point in which the parabola intersects its axis.

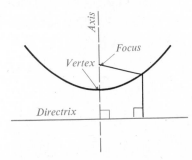

Figure 13–4

Can you explain why the vertex is the midpoint of the segment of the axis between the focus and the directrix? Thus, the parabola $\mathfrak{I}$, shown in Figure 13–3, has the origin as its vertex.

The reasoning which produced $x^2 = 12y$ as an equation of $\mathfrak{I}$ can be restated in general terms to derive an equation of the parabola having the point $(0, p)$ as focus ($p \neq 0$) and the line $y = -p$ as directrix. The fact is stated in the following theorem, whose proof is left as Exercise 19, page 515.

THEOREM   If p is a nonzero real number such that $(0, p)$ is the focus and $y = -p$ is an equation of the directrix of a parabola $\mathfrak{I}$ in $\mathcal{R} \times \mathcal{R}$, then

$$\mathfrak{I} = \{(x, y): x^2 = 4py\}.$$

In case $p > 0$, the parabola $x^2 = 4py$ opens in the direction of the positive ray of the y-axis (Figure 13–3). If $p < 0$, then, as the following example indicates, the parabola opens in the direction of the negative ray of the y-axis.

EXAMPLE 1.   Find an equation of the parabola with vertex at the origin and focus at $(0, -1)$. Sketch the parabola.

Solution:

Since the vertex is midway between the focus and the point in which the directrix intersects the axis, the directrix is the line $y = 1$. $\therefore p = -1$ (Why?), and an equation of the parabola is

$$\sqrt{x^2 + (y + 1)^2} = |y - 1|,$$

or $x^2 = -4y$, **Answer.**

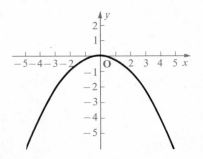

The graph of the relation $\{(x, y): y^2 = 4px\}$ obtained by interchanging the coordinates of each ordered pair in the relation $\{(x, y): x^2 = 4py\}$ is also a parabola having the origin as vertex. Its focus, however, is the point $(p, 0)$ and its directrix is the line $x = -p$. This fact is stated in the following theorem and illustrated in Figure 13–5.

THEOREM   If p is a nonzero real number such that $(p, 0)$ is the focus and $x = -p$ is an equation of the directrix of a parabola $\mathfrak{I}$ in $\mathfrak{R} \times \mathfrak{R}$, then

$$\mathfrak{I} = \{(x, y): y^2 = 4px\}.$$

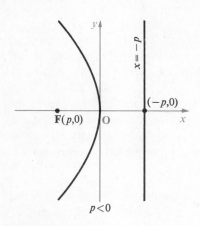 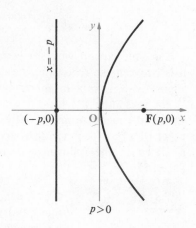

Figure 13–5

Exercises

In Exercises 1–8, write an equation of the parabola specified, and sketch the locus.

1. Directrix $x = -4$, focus $(4, 0)$
2. Directrix $y = -7$, focus $(0, 7)$
3. Directrix $y = \frac{7}{4}$, focus $(0, -\frac{7}{4})$
4. Directrix $x = \frac{3}{2}$, focus $(-\frac{3}{2}, 0)$

5. Vertex $(0, 0)$, focus $(0, -6)$
6. Vertex $(0, 0)$, focus $(-3, 0)$
7. Vertex $(0, 0)$, directrix $y = -8$
8. Vertex $(0, 0)$, directrix $x = 6$

In Exercises 9–16, find (a) the focus and (b) the directrix of the parabola whose equation is given, and show them on a sketch of the locus.

9. $y^2 = 4x$
10. $y^2 = -12x$
11. $x^2 = -8y$
12. $x^2 = 6y$

13. $y^2 + x = 0$
14. $y - 2x^2 = 0$
15. $\|(x, y - 6)\| = |y + 6|$
16. $\|(x, y + 10)\| = |y - 10|$

B **17.** Find an equation of the circle having its center at the origin and passing through a point of intersection of the graphs of $y^2 = 4x$ and $x^2 = 4y$.

18. Find a Cartesian equation of the line through the foci of the parabolas with equations $y^2 = 4x$ and $x^2 = -8y$.

Use the definition of a parabola to prove the indicated theorem.

19. Theorem stated on page 513.   **20.** Theorem stated on page 514.

21. The distance from a point (x_1, y_1) on a parabola to the focus is called the *focal radius* of the point. Show that the length of the focal radius to the point (x_1, y_1) on the parabola with equation $y^2 = 4px$ is $|x_1 + p|$.

22. The line segment through the focus of a parabola, perpendicular to the axis of the parabola, and with endpoints on the parabola, is called the **latus rectum** of the parabola $x^2 = 4py$. Show that the length of the latus rectum is $|4p|$.

23. Show that the circle with the latus rectum of the parabola $x^2 = 2py$ as a diameter is tangent to the directrix of the parabola.

24. Prove that the lines from the endpoints of the latus rectum of a parabola to the point of intersection of the axis and directrix of the parabola are perpendicular to each other.

In Exercises 25–28, use the definition of a parabola to find an equation of the parabola specified.

25. Directrix $x = -2$, focus $(2, 2)$

26. Directrix $y = 3$, focus $(-3, -3)$

27. Vertex $(4, 2)$, directrix $y = 0$

28. Vertex $(0, -2)$, focus $(0, 6)$

13-3 Ellipses

An **ellipse** is a set of points in the plane such that the sum of the distance from each point in the set to two fixed points, called the **foci** of the ellipse, is a constant (Figure 13–6).

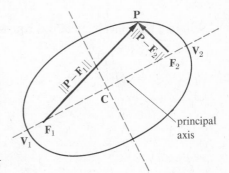

Figure 13–6

The line containing the foci F_1 and F_2 is called the **principal axis**, and the midpoint C of the segment $\overline{F_1 F_2}$ is called the **center** of the ellipse. The points V_1 and V_2 where the ellipse intersects the principal axis are called the **vertices**. For each point P of the ellipse the distances $\|P - F_1\|$ and $\|P - F_2\|$ are called the **focal radii** of P.

To discover a vector equation for an ellipse ε with foci $\mathbf{F}_1$ $(c, 0)$ and $\mathbf{F}_2$ $(-c, 0)$, look at Figure 13–7. The definition of an ellipse implies that $\mathbf{P}(x, y) \in \varepsilon$ if and only if

(1) $\|\mathbf{P} - \mathbf{F}_1\| + \|\mathbf{P} - \mathbf{F}_2\| = 2a$

where $2a > 0$ denotes the constant sum of the focal radii. Other forms of equation (1) are those below.

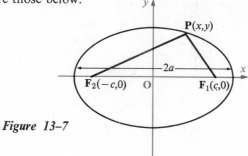

Figure 13–7

$$\|(x, y) - (c, 0)\| + \|(x, y) - (-c, 0)\| = 2a,$$

$$\|(x - c, y)\| + \|(x + c, y)\| = 2a,$$

and

(2) $\sqrt{(x - c)^2 + y^2} + \sqrt{(x + c)^2 + y^2} = 2a.$

Adding $-\sqrt{(x + c)^2 + y^2}$ to each member of equation (2) and squaring, you obtain the equation

$$a\sqrt{(x + c)^2 + y^2} = a^2 + cx.$$

Squaring both members of this equation,

$$(a^2 - c^2)x^2 + a^2y^2 = a^2(a^2 - c^2).$$

Since $a > c$ (Why?), $a^2 - c^2 > 0$, so that $a^2 - c^2$ can be denoted by b^2, and you have

$$b^2x^2 + a^2y^2 = a^2b^2.$$

Because $a^2b^2 > 0$, you can divide each member of this equation by a^2b^2 to obtain

(3) $\dfrac{x^2}{a^2} + \dfrac{y^2}{b^2} = 1.$

The preceding derivation proves that if $\mathbf{P} \in \varepsilon$, then its coordinates satisfy equation (3). On the other hand, you can show that any point whose coordinates satisfy equation (3) must be a point of ε. (Exercise 29, page 520.) Consequently, the following theorem is true.

THEOREM   If $c \in \mathcal{R}^+$, $a \in \mathcal{R}^+$, and $a > c$, and if in $\mathcal{R} \times \mathcal{R}$ the points $(-c, 0)$ and $(c, 0)$ are the foci of an ellipse $\mathcal{E}$ in which the sum of the focal radii of each point is $2a$, then

$$\mathcal{E} = \left\{ (x, y): \frac{x^2}{a^2} + \frac{y^2}{b^2} = 1 \right\}$$

where $b^2 = a^2 - c^2$.

Replacing, in turn, y by 0 and x by 0 in the equation of $\mathcal{E}$, you can see that the vertices of the ellipse are $(-a, 0)$ and $(a, 0)$, and that the y-intercepts are $-b$ and b.

EXAMPLE 1. Find an equation of the ellipse with foci at $(4, 0)$ and $(-4, 0)$, and vertices at $(6, 0)$ and $(-6, 0)$.

Solution: You have $c = 4$ and $a = 6$.
Since $b^2 = a^2 - c^2$, you know that $b^2 = 6^2 - 4^2 = 20$.

$$\frac{x^2}{36} + \frac{y^2}{20} = 1, \textbf{ Answer.}$$

You can sketch the graph of

$$\frac{x^2}{a^2} + \frac{y^2}{b^2} = 1$$

very quickly by observing that the curve is an ellipse symmetric with respect to both coordinate axes and with center at the origin, x-intercepts a and $-a$, and y-intercepts b and $-b$ (Figure 13–8). Do you see that the distance from the point $(0, b)$ or $(0, -b)$ to a focus is always a?

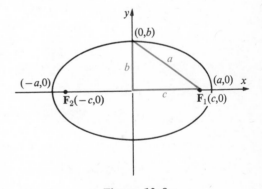

Figure 13–8

If the foci of an ellipse are the points $(0, c)$ and $(0, -c)$, then the y-axis is the principal axis, and you can show (Exercise 30, page 520) that equations of the curve are

$$\|(x, y - c)\| + \|(x, y + c)\| = 2a \quad \text{and} \quad \frac{x^2}{b^2} + \frac{y^2}{a^2} = 1$$

where, again, $b^2 = a^2 - c^2$, and $2a$ is the sum of the focal radii of each point of the ellipse.

The line segment joining the vertices of an ellipse is called the **major axis** of the ellipse, and the line segment cut off by the ellipse on the perpendicular bisector of the major axis is called the **minor axis**.

EXAMPLE 2.   Find an equation of and sketch the ellipse whose major axis has length 20 and whose foci are $(0, -5\sqrt{3})$ and $(0, 5\sqrt{3})$.

Solution: You have $2a = 20$, $c = 5\sqrt{3}$, and the y-axis is the principal axis. (Why?)

$$\therefore a = 10$$

Since $b^2 = a^2 - c^2 = 100 - 75$,
$$b^2 = 25.$$

$$\therefore \frac{x^2}{25} + \frac{y^2}{100} = 1, \textbf{ Answer.}$$

On the basis of the following table of *first-quadrant* points, the curve is sketched as shown.

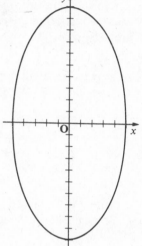

x	0	3	4	5
y	10	8	6	0

The number $\dfrac{c}{a}$, called the **eccentricity** e of the ellipse, indicates the shape of the curve. Since
$$\frac{c^2}{a^2} = \frac{a^2 - b^2}{a^2} = 1 - \left(\frac{b}{a}\right)^2,$$
$\dfrac{c}{a}$, or e, is close to 1 when b is considerably smaller than a. (Why?) In this case, the ellipse tends to be elongated (Figure 13–9). On the other hand, when b is close to a, $\dfrac{c}{a}$ is close to 0, and the ellipse tends to resemble a circle (Figure 13–10). Do you see why a circle is sometimes described as an ellipse with eccentricity 0?

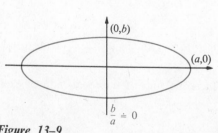

Figure 13–9

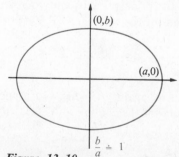

Figure 13–10

Exercises

Sketch the graph of the given sentence.

A

1. $\dfrac{x^2}{4} + y^2 = 1$ 4. $\dfrac{x^2}{9} + \dfrac{y^2}{36} = 1$ 7. $x^2 + 36y^2 \geq 144$

2. $\dfrac{x^2}{9} + \dfrac{y^2}{4} = 1$ 5. $x^2 + 6y^2 = 6$ 8. $4x^2 + y^2 \leq 16$

3. $\dfrac{x^2}{49} + \dfrac{y^2}{81} = 1$ 6. $10x^2 + 2y^2 = 20$

Find a Cartesian equation of the ellipse with the given characteristics and sketch the ellipse.

9. Major axis of length 10, foci $(4, 0)$ and $(-4, 0)$.

10. Major axis of length 8, foci $(2, 0)$ and $(-2, 0)$.

11. Minor axis of length 6, foci $(3, 0)$ and $(-3, 0)$.

12. Minor axis of length 8, foci $(2\sqrt{6}, 0)$ and $(-2\sqrt{6}, 0)$.

13. Vertices $(5, 0)$ and $(-5, 0)$, minor axis of length 6.

14. One vertex $(6, 0)$, center $(0, 0)$, and one focus $(-4, 0)$.

15. Eccentricity $\frac{1}{2}$, distance between foci 1, center $(0, 0)$.

16. Eccentricity $\frac{2}{5}$, vertices $(10, 0)$ and $(-10, 0)$.

17. Vertices $(4, 0)$ and $(-4, 0)$ and containing $(2\sqrt{2}, -1)$.

18. Vertices $(0, -3)$ and $(0, 3)$ and containing $(-2, -1)$.

B

19. Distance between foci $\frac{4}{3}\sqrt{33}$, center $(0, 0)$, containing $(2, 1)$, and having a coordinate axis as its principal axis.

20. Minor axis of length 4, center at $(0, 0)$, containing $\left(1, \dfrac{4\sqrt{2}}{3}\right)$, and having a coordinate axis as its principal axis.

21. Center at origin, passing through $(2, 2)$ and $(3, -1)$, and having a coordinate axis as its principal axis.

22. Center at origin, passing through $(4, 1)$ and $(1, 2)$, and having a coordinate axis as its principal axis.

23. Use the definition of an ellipse to find an equation of the form $Ax^2 + Cy^2 + Dx + Ey + F = 0$ for the ellipse with major axis of length 10 and foci at $(8, 2)$ and $(0, 2)$.

24. Use the definition of an ellipse to find an equation of the form $Ax^2 + Cy^2 + Dx + Ey + F = 0$ for the ellipse with minor axis of length 6, and foci at $(2, 8)$ and $(2, -4)$.

25. Show that the length of the chord of an ellipse perpendicular to the principal axis at a focus is $\dfrac{2b^2}{a}$. [*Note:* This line segment is called a *latus rectum* of the ellipse. Thus, an ellipse has two latera recta (plural of latus rectum)].

26. Prove that the length of the minor axis of an ellipse is a mean proportional between the lengths of the major axis and the latus rectum. (*Hint:* Use Exercise 25.)

C 27. Find a Cartesian equation for the locus of a point that moves so that its distance from the line $x = 6$ is always twice its distance from the point $(2, 0)$.

28. Find a Cartesian equation for the locus of a point that moves so that its distance from the point $(0, 4)$ is always half of its distance to the line $y = 10$.

29. Prove that the graph of $\dfrac{x^2}{a^2} + \dfrac{y^2}{b^2} = 1$, $a > b > 0$, is the ellipse whose foci are $(-c, 0)$ and $(c, 0)$, where $c^2 = a^2 - b^2$ and in which the sum of focal radii of each point is $2a$.

30. Use the definition of an ellipse to show that the ellipse with foci at $(0, c)$ and $(0, -c)$, and vertices $(0, a)$ and $(0, -a)$, is the graph of $\dfrac{x^2}{b^2} + \dfrac{y^2}{a^2} = 1$, where $b^2 = a^2 - c^2$.

31. Find a Cartesian equation of the locus of a point that moves so that its distance from the point $(ae, 0)$ is e times its distance from the line with equation $x = \dfrac{a}{e}$.

By assuming $0 < e < 1$ and letting $e = \dfrac{c}{a}$, and $b^2 = a^2(1 - e^2)$, show that the locus is an ellipse with foci $(c, 0)$, $(-c, 0)$, vertices $(a, 0)$ and $(-a, 0)$, and eccentricity e.

32. Prove that the graph of $\dfrac{x^2}{a^2 - c^2} + \dfrac{y^2}{a^2} = 1$ $(0 < c < a)$ is the locus of the point that moves so that its distance from the point $(0, c)$ is $\dfrac{c}{a}$ times its distance from the line $y = \dfrac{a^2}{c}$.

13–4 Hyperbolas

Figure 13–11 pictures a curve that consists of two separate *branches* and is called a *hyperbola*. A **hyperbola** is a set of points in the plane such that the *absolute value* of the difference of the distances from each point of the set to two given points, called **foci**, is a constant. The terms **principal axis, center,** and **vertices** refer, as in the case of the ellipse, to the line containing the foci $\mathbf{F}_1$ and $\mathbf{F}_2$, the midpoint $\mathbf{C}$ of the segment $\overline{\mathbf{F}_1\mathbf{F}_2}$, and the points of intersection $\mathbf{V}_1$ and $\mathbf{V}_2$ of the hyperbola and its principal axis.

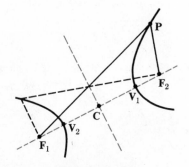

Figure 13–11

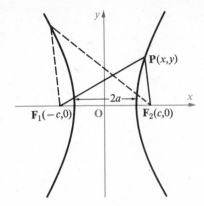

Figure 13–12

If $P(x, y)$ is any point of a hyperbola $\mathcal{K}$ whose foci are $F_1(-c, 0)$ and $F_2(c, 0)$, (Figure 13–12), and if $\|P - F_1\|$ and $\|P - F_2\|$, the **focal radii** of P, differ by $2a$, then the definition of $\mathcal{K}$ requires that

$$\|P - F_1\| - \|P - F_2\| = 2a$$

or

$$\|P - F_1\| - \|P - F_2\| = -2a.$$

Thus, $P(x, y) \in \mathcal{K}$ if and only if

$$\sqrt{(x + c)^2 + y^2} - \sqrt{(x - c)^2 + y^2} = \pm 2a.$$

Using the squaring process to obtain an equation free of radicals, you can show that this compound sentence is equivalent to

$$\frac{x^2}{a^2} - \frac{y^2}{b^2} = 1$$

where $b^2 = c^2 - a^2$. (Note that for an ellipse $b^2 = a^2 - c^2$.) Thus, you can prove (Exercise 35, page 525) the following theorem.

THEOREM If $c \in \mathcal{R}^+$, $a \in \mathcal{R}^+$, and $c > a$, and if in $\mathcal{R} \times \mathcal{R}$ the points $(-c, 0)$ and $(c, 0)$ are the foci of a hyperbola $\mathcal{K}$ in which the absolute value of the difference of the focal radii of each point is $2a$, then

$$\mathcal{K} = \left\{ (x, y) \colon \frac{x^2}{a^2} - \frac{y^2}{b^2} = 1 \right\}$$

where $b^2 = c^2 - a^2$.

The equation $\dfrac{x^2}{a^2} - \dfrac{y^2}{b^2} = 1$ reveals at once several properties of the hyperbola $\mathcal{H}$.

Property	*Reason*
1. $\mathcal{H}$ is symmetric with respect to both coordinate axes.	1. Whenever (r, t) satisfies the equation, so also do $(r, -t)$, and $(-r, t)$.
2. Its x-intercepts are a and $-a$. [That is, its vertices are $(a, 0)$ and $(-a, 0)$.]	2. Replace y by 0: $\dfrac{x^2}{a^2} - \dfrac{0^2}{b^2} = 1,$ $\therefore\ x = a\ \ or\ \ x = -a.$
3. It has no y-intercept; in fact, it contains no point for which $|x| < a$.	3. Solve for y: $\dfrac{y^2}{b^2} = \dfrac{x^2}{a^2} - 1,$ $\therefore\ y = \dfrac{b}{a}\sqrt{x^2 - a^2}\ or$ $y = -\dfrac{b}{a}\sqrt{x^2 - a^2}$ $\therefore\ y$ denotes a real number if and only if $x^2 - a^2 \geq 0$; that is, $x^2 \geq a^2$, or $|x| \geq a$.

Figure 13–13 suggests another property of $\mathcal{H}$. Notice that the hyperbola lies entirely within two of the sectors of the plane bounded by the diagonals of the rectangle formed by the lines $x = a$, $x = -a$, $y = b$, $y = -b$. The equations of these diagonals, called the **asymptotes** of the hyperbola, are

$$bx - ay = 0 \quad \text{and} \quad bx + ay = 0.$$

It can be proved (Exercise 37, page 525) that the distance between a branch of the hyperbola and the corresponding asymptote approaches 0 as $|r|$ increases without bound. This means that as $|x|$ increases, the hyperbola gets closer and closer to its asymptotes, so that you can use these lines as guides in sketching the curve.

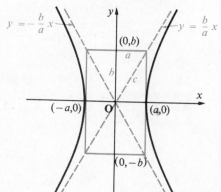

Figure 13–13

EXAMPLE 1. Find an equation of the hyperbola with foci at $(4, 0)$ and $(-4, 0)$ and a vertex at $(-2, 0)$. Sketch the graph, showing the asymptotes, and state equations of the asymptotes.

Solution: You have $c = 4$ and $a = 2$, so that $b^2 = 4^2 - 2^2 = 12$.

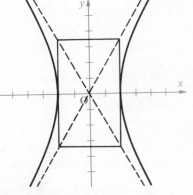

$$\therefore \frac{x^2}{4} - \frac{y^2}{12} = 1, \textbf{ Answer.}$$

The asymptotes are $y = \pm \dfrac{b}{a} x$, or

$y = \sqrt{3} x$ and $y = -\sqrt{3} x$, **Answer.**

The graph appears at the right.

The relation $\left\{ (x, y) \colon \dfrac{y^2}{a^2} - \dfrac{x^2}{b^2} = 1 \right\}$

whose ordered pairs are obtained by·

interchanging the ordered pairs in the relation $\left\{ (x, y) \colon \dfrac{x^2}{a^2} - \dfrac{y^2}{b^2} = 1 \right\}$ is the

hyperbola with foci $(0, -c)$ and $(0, c)$ and with vertices $(0, -a)$ and $(0, a)$ where $b^2 = c^2 - a^2$ (Exercise 36, page 525).

The line segment whose endpoints are the vertices of a hyperbola is called the **transverse axis** of the curve. The transverse axis is perpendicular to and bisects the **conjugate axis**, which is a segment of length $2b$. As for an ellipse, the eccentricity of a hyperbola is defined to be $\dfrac{c}{a}$.

EXAMPLE 2. Find an equation of and sketch the hyperbola whose transverse axis is contained in the y-axis and has length 6, whose center is the origin, and whose eccentricity is $\frac{4}{3}$.

Solution:

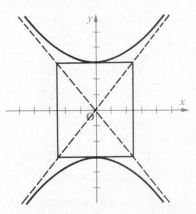

You have $2a = 6$, $e = \frac{4}{3}$, the y-axis as the principal axis. (Why?)

$$\therefore a = 3 \text{ and } \frac{c}{a} = \frac{4}{3},$$

so that $c = 4$.

$$b^2 = c^2 - a^2 = 16 - 9 = 7$$

$$\therefore \frac{y^2}{9} - \frac{x^2}{7} = 1, \textbf{ Answer.}$$

Exercises

Sketch the locus of the given equation. Include the asymptotes in your sketch.

1. $\dfrac{x^2}{16} - \dfrac{y^2}{9} = 1$ **3.** $\dfrac{y^2}{16} - \dfrac{x^2}{9} = 1$ **5.** $y^2 - 3x^2 = 27$

2. $\dfrac{x^2}{9} - \dfrac{y^2}{4} = 1$ **4.** $\dfrac{y^2}{9} - \dfrac{x^2}{4} = 1$ **6.** $2x^2 - 3y^2 = 120$

7. $16x^2 = 144 + 9y^2$ **8.** $40y^2 = 9x^2 + 360$

9–16. In Exercises 1–8, state (**a**) the coordinates of the vertices, (**b**) the coordinates of the foci, (**c**) the equations of the asymptotes, and (**d**) the eccentricity of the hyperbola.

In Exercises 17–24, find an equation of the hyperbola with center at the origin and with the given characteristics.

17. Eccentricity $\sqrt{2}$, vertex $(6, 0)$.   **18.** Eccentricity $\frac{3}{2}$, focus $(-6, 0)$.

19. Transverse axis of length 4, focus $(-2\sqrt{5}, 0)$.

20. Conjugate axis of length 12, vertex $(4, 0)$.

21. One end of conjugate axis at $(0, 3)$, eccentricity 2.

22. One end of transverse axis at $(0, 1)$, eccentricity $\sqrt{2}$.

23. Containing $(7, 4)$ and $(-2, -1)$, with principal axis the x-axis.

24. Containing $(7, 10)$ and $(-1, 2)$, with principal axis the y-axis.

25. A chord of a hyperbola perpendicular to the principal axis at a focus is called a **latus rectum** of the hyperbola. Show that the length of a latus rectum of the hyperbola with equation $\dfrac{x^2}{a^2} - \dfrac{y^2}{b^2} = 1$ is $\dfrac{2b^2}{a}$.

26. Find an equation of the hyperbola with latus rectum (Exercise 25) of length 6, eccentricity 2, center at the origin, and principal axis the y-axis.

27. Find an equation of the hyperbola with foci $(4, 0)$ and $(-4, 0)$ and with asymptotes having slopes of 3 and -3.

28. Find an equation of the hyperbola with vertices $(8, 0)$ and $(-8, 0)$ and with asymptotes having slopes $\frac{3}{4}$ and $-\frac{3}{4}$.

29. Prove that $3x^2 - y^2 = 12$ and $9x^2 + 25y^2 = 225$ have the same foci.

30. If V_1 and V_2 are the vertices and B_1 and B_2 are the endpoints of the conjugate axis of the hyperbola whose equation is $b^2x^2 - a^2y^2 = a^2b^2$, then $\angle V_1 B_1 V_2$ and $\angle V_1 B_2 V_2$ are right angles if and only if $a = b$. (Such a hyperbola is called **equilateral** or **rectangular**.)

31. Show that the hyperbolas with equations $\dfrac{x^2}{a^2} - \dfrac{y^2}{b^2} = 1$ and $\dfrac{y^2}{b^2} - \dfrac{x^2}{a^2} = 1$ have the same asymptotes. These loci are called **conjugate hyperbolas**.

32. Find an equation of the equilateral hyperbola (Exercise 30) whose foci are $(7, 0)$ and $(-7, 0)$.

C 33. Find an equation of the locus of a point that moves so that its distance from the point $(4, 0)$ is always twice its distance from the line whose equation is $x = 1$.

34. Find an equation of the locus of a point that moves so that its distance from the point $(0, 3)$ is always 1.5 times its distance from the line whose equation is $y = \frac{4}{3}$.

In Exercises 35 and 36, let $c \in \mathcal{R}^+$, $a \in \mathcal{R}^+$, $c > a > 0$, $b^2 = c^2 - a^2$, and let $2a$ be the absolute value of the difference of the focal radii of each point of the indicated hyperbola. Prove each statement.

35. A point belongs to the hyperbola with foci $(-c, 0)$ and $(c, 0)$ if and only if its coordinates satisfy the equation $\dfrac{x^2}{a^2} - \dfrac{y^2}{b^2} = 1$.

36. A point belongs to the hyperbola with foci $(0, -c)$ and $(0, c)$ if and only if its coordinates satisfy the equation $\dfrac{y^2}{a^2} - \dfrac{x^2}{b^2} = 1$.

37. In the figure, $\mathbf{T}(r, t)$, a point in the first quadrant, belongs to

$$\left\{(x, y): \frac{x^2}{a^2} - \frac{y^2}{b^2} = 1\right\},$$

and $\mathcal{L}$ is the asymptote

$$\left\{(x, y): \frac{x}{a} - \frac{y}{b} = 0\right\}.$$

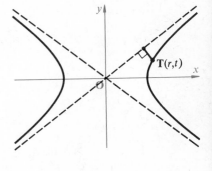

a. Prove that $d(\mathbf{T}, \mathcal{L}) = \dfrac{ab}{\sqrt{a^2 + b^2}}\left(\dfrac{r}{a} - \dfrac{t}{b}\right)$

$$= \dfrac{ab}{\sqrt{a^2 + b^2}} \dfrac{1}{\dfrac{r}{a} + \dfrac{t}{b}} \quad \text{and}$$

use this result to show that $\lim\limits_{r \to \infty} d(\mathbf{T}, \mathcal{L}) = 0$.

b. Explain why symmetry implies corresponding results in the other quadrants.

38. Let $a \in \mathcal{R}^+$, $e \in \mathcal{R}^+$, and $\mathcal{C}$ be the locus of a point that moves in the plane so that its distance from a fixed point $\mathbf{F}(ae, 0)$ is always e times its distance from the line $x = \dfrac{a}{e}$. Prove that an equation of $\mathcal{C}$ is

$$(1 - e^2)x^2 + y^2 = a^2(1 - e^2).$$

Then show that if $e > 1$, the locus is a hyperbola while, if $0 < e < 1$, the locus is an ellipse, and that in each case $\mathbf{O}$ is the center and $\mathbf{F}$ is a focus of the locus.

TRANSFORMATIONS IN THE PLANE

13–5 Translations

In studying functions, you have been principally concerned with mappings from one subset of $\Re$ to another subset of $\Re$. For example, the function f with $f(x) = 2x$ maps each real number into its double, and, therefore, maps $\Re$ onto $\Re$. On the other hand, the exponential function $\exp_2$ maps $\Re$ onto $\Re^+$. (Why?)

Using arrows to represent the vector $(1, 4)$, Figure 13–14 suggests a function τ whose domain is $\Re \times \Re$. In fact, τ maps each point (x, y) of $\Re \times \Re$ into the point $(x + 1, y + 4)$. Thus, τ maps $(3, 2)$ into the point $(3 + 1, 2 + 4) = (4, 6)$, and it maps $(-4, -5)$ into $(-3, -1)$. The origin is mapped into $(1, 4)$ by τ, while $(-1, -4)$ is mapped into **O**. We call τ a *translation*.

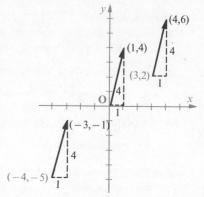

In $\Re \times \Re$ a **translation** is a function which maps each point (x, y) into the point $(x + r, y + s)$ where (r, s) is a given vector. If you write (x', y') as the *image* of (x, y) under the translation, you have

Figure 13–14

$$(x', y') = (x + r, y + s), \text{ or}$$

$$\begin{array}{lll}
& x' = x + r & x = x' - r \\
(1) & \qquad \text{and} \quad (2) & \\
& y' = y + s & y = y' - s
\end{array}$$

Thus, knowing (r, s), you can determine the image (x', y') of (x, y); conversely, given (x', y'), you can determine its *pre-image* (x, y). Can you suggest why the translation determined by the vector $(-r, -s)$ is called the inverse, τ^{-1}, of the translation τ determined by (r, s)?

EXAMPLE 1. Let τ be the translation determined by the vector $(-2, 5)$. For τ determine **(a)** the image of $(1, -3)$; **(b)** the pre-image of $(-4, -2)$.

Solution: $(r, s) = (-2, 5)$.

a. Using the formulas labeled (1), above, with $(x, y) = (1, -3)$, you have $x' = x - 2$ *and* $y' = y + 5$,

$$\therefore x' = 1 - 2 \quad and \quad y' = -3 + 5,$$

$$x' = -1 \quad and \quad y' = 2.$$

$\therefore$ the image of $(1, -3)$ is $(-1, 2)$, **Answer.**

b. Using the formulas labeled (2) on page 526 with (x', y') $= (-4, -2)$, you have

$$x = x' - (-2) = x' + 2 \quad and \quad y = y' - 5$$
$$x = -4 + 2 \quad and \quad y = -2 - 5,$$
$$x = -2 \quad and \quad y = -7.$$

∴ the pre-image of $(-4, -2)$ is $(-2, -7)$, **Answer.**

The following example implies that a translation "preserves" distances.

EXAMPLE 2. Let τ be the translation determined by the vector (r, s), and let the points $\mathbf{P}(x_1, y_1)$ and $\mathbf{S}(x_2, y_2)$ be mapped into $\mathbf{P}'(x_1', y_1')$ and $\mathbf{S}'(x_2', y_2')$ by τ.

Prove: $\|\mathbf{P} - \mathbf{S}\| = \|\mathbf{P}' - \mathbf{S}'\|$.

Solution: By the definition of τ,

$$(x_1', y_1') = (x_1, y_1) + (r, s) \quad and$$
$$(x_2', y_2') = (x_2, y_2) + (r, s).$$
$$\|\mathbf{P}' - \mathbf{S}'\| = \|(x_1, y_1) - (x_2, y_2)\| = \|\mathbf{P} - \mathbf{S}\|.$$

You can also show that a translation preserves angles (Exercise 36, page 532).

Since a translation preserves distances and angles, the image under a translation of the locus of any equation has the same geometric character as the given locus. This fact enables you to identify the graphs of certain equations. For example, under the translation determined by the equations

$$x' = x - 4 \quad and \quad y' = y - 2$$

the image of the graph of $\qquad (x - 4)^2 = 8(y - 2)$

is the graph of $\qquad x'^2 = 8y'$.

Since $x'^2 = 8y'$ has for its locus the parabola with vertex $(0, 0)$, focus $(0, 2)$, axis the y-axis, and directrix $y = -2$ (Why?), the locus of $(x - 4)^2$ $= 8(y - 2)$ is the parabola with

vertex $(0, 0) + (4, 2) = (4, 2)$

focus $(0, 2) + (4, 2) = (4, 4)$

axis. $x = 0 + 4$, or $x = 4$

directrix $y = -2 + 2$, or $y = 0$.

Figure 13–15 pictures both parabolas.

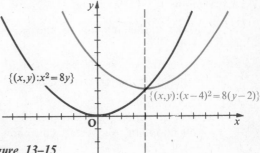

Figure 13–15

By generalizing the preceding argument, you can verify that the graph of

(3)
$$(x - h)^2 = 4p(y - k)$$

is mapped by the translation $x' = x - h$, $y' = y - k$ into the graph of $x'^2 = 4py'$. Hence, (3) is an equation of the parabola with vertex (h, k), and axis parallel to the y-axis.

Similarly, you can show that

(4)
$$(y - k)^2 = 4p(x - h)$$

is an equation of the parabola with vertex (h, k) and axis parallel to the x-axis.

In a manner similar to that used for the parabola, you can argue that the equation for an ellipse with center at (h, k) can be written either in the form

(5)
$$\frac{(x - h)^2}{a^2} + \frac{(y - k)^2}{b^2} = 1$$

or in the form

(6)
$$\frac{(y - k)^2}{a^2} + \frac{(x - h)^2}{b^2} = 1,$$

depending on whether the principal axis of the ellipse is parallel to the x- or y-axis, respectively. Also, the equation for a hyperbola with center at (h, k) can be written

(7)
$$\frac{(x - h)^2}{a^2} - \frac{(y - k)^2}{b^2} = 1$$

or

(8)
$$\frac{(y - k)^2}{a^2} - \frac{(x - h)^2}{b^2} = 1,$$

according as its principal axis is parallel to the x-axis or to the y-axis.

EXAMPLE 3. Find an equation of the ellipse with vertices $(-4, 3)$ and $(6, 3)$ and eccentricity $\frac{3}{5}$. Sketch the curve, and in the diagram label the center, foci, and endpoints of the minor axis.

Solution:

1. Make a sketch showing the given data.

2. The center of the ellipse is the midpoint of the major axis and is therefore $C(1, 3)$.

3. Since a denotes the distance from this midpoint to a vertex, you know

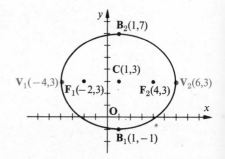

that $a = 5$.   Also, $e = \dfrac{c}{a}$, and you can find c by solving $\dfrac{3}{5} = \dfrac{c}{5}$, from which $c = 3$.

∴ the foci are $(1 \pm 3, 3)$, or $\mathbf{F}_1(-2, 3)$ and $\mathbf{F}_2(4, 3)$.

4. In an ellipse, $b^2 = a^2 - c^2$, so $b^2 = (5)^2 - (3)^2 = 16$.

∴ the endpoints of the minor axis are $(1, 3 \pm 4)$, or $\mathbf{B}_1(1, -1)$ and $\mathbf{B}_2(1, 7)$.

$$\frac{(x - 1)^2}{25} + \frac{(y - 3)^2}{16} = 1, \textbf{ Answer.}$$

Given an equation of the form

$$Ax^2 + Cy^2 + Dx + Ey + F = 0,$$

where not both A and C are zero, you can always write it in one of the forms (3)–(8) and analyze its graph.

EXAMPLE 4.   Identify the locus of

$$x^2 - 4y^2 - 6x - 16y + 29 = 0$$

and determine its principal characteristics.

Solution: Complete the square in x and y:

$$(x^2 - 6x \qquad) - 4(y^2 + 4y \qquad) = -29$$
$$(x^2 - 6x + 9) - 4(y^2 + 4y + 4) = -29 + 9 - 16$$
$$(x - 3)^2 - 4(y + 2)^2 = -36$$
$$\therefore \frac{(y + 2)^2}{9} - \frac{(x - 3)^2}{36} = 1.$$

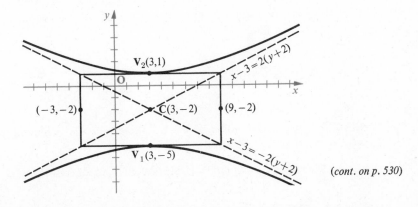

(*cont. on p. 530*)

The preceding equation is that of a hyperbola with center at $(3, -2)$, with $a = 3$ and $b = 6$, and having its major axis parallel to the y-axis. The vertices, then, can be obtained by adding ± 3 to the y-coordinate of the center, -2. Thus, $(3, -5)$ and $(3, 1)$ are the vertices. From $c^2 = a^2 + b^2$, you find that $c = 3\sqrt{5}$. Therefore, the foci are $(3, -2 + 3\sqrt{5})$ and $(3, -2 - 3\sqrt{5})$. The endpoints of the conjugate axis are $(-3, -2)$ and $(9, -2)$ (Why?), and the eccentricity is $\dfrac{c}{a}$ or $\sqrt{5}$. The asymptotes have equations $x - 3 = 2(y + 2)$ and $x - 3 = -2(y + 2)$. (Why?) The graph appears as shown on page 529.

It is useful to observe that you can classify the graph of $Ax^2 + Cy^2 + Dx + Ey + F = 0$ according to the value of AC (Exercises 31–34, page 531). The following chart indicates the classification:

Nature of AC	Nature of graph of $Ax^2 + Cy^2 + Dx + Ey + F = 0$
$AC = 0$	parabola (or 2 parallel lines, a line, or $\emptyset$)
$AC > 0$	ellipse or circle (or a point or $\emptyset$)
$AC < 0$	hyperbola (or a pair of intersecting lines)

Exercises

In Exercises 1 and 2, determine the images of the given points under the translation determined by the vector **v**.

A

1. $(0, 0)$, $(3, -2)$, $(5, 1)$; $\mathbf{v} = (-5, -1)$.

2. $(0, 0)$, $(-6, -1)$, $(7, -2)$; $\mathbf{v} = (-7, 2)$.

In Exercises 3–6, let τ be the translation determined by the vector **v**. Determine the equation of the image under τ of the graph of the given equation.

3. $y = x^2 + 4x$, $\mathbf{v} = (2, 4)$

4. $x = 4y^2 - 16y + 7$, $\mathbf{v} = (-3, 4)$

5. $16x^2 + 25y^2 - 64x + 50y - 311 = 0$, $\mathbf{v} = (-2, 1)$

6. $9x^2 - 16y^2 - 36x + 96y + 36 = 0$, $\mathbf{v} = (-3, -2)$

In Exercises 7–12, find an equation of the parabola with the given characteristics, and sketch the curve.

7. Vertex $(2, 0)$, directrix $x = 0$.

8. Vertex $(4, 2)$, directrix $x = 1$.

9. Focus $(1, 0)$, vertex $(1, -3)$.

10. Focus $(0, 1)$, vertex $(-\frac{5}{2}, 1)$.

11. Focus $(-2, 6)$, directrix $y = -4$.

12. Focus $(3, -2)$, directrix $x = -1$.

In Exercises 13–18, find an equation of the ellipse with the given characteristics and sketch the curve.

13. Length of major axis 10, foci $(0, 2)$ and $(8, 2)$.

14. Length of major axis 10, foci $(-1, -2)$ and $(3, -2)$.

15. Center $(2, 2)$, one focus $(-1, 2)$, length of major axis 10.

16. Vertices $(-4, 3)$ and $(6, 3)$, length of minor axis 8.

17. Vertices $(8, 3)$ and $(-3, 3)$, eccentricity $\frac{2}{3}$.

18. Foci $(-2, 2)$ and $(-2, -6)$, eccentricity $\frac{4}{5}$.

In Exercises 19–24 find an equation of the hyperbola with the given characteristics and sketch the curve.

19. Foci $(0, 2)$ and $(10, 2)$, length of transverse axis 8.

20. Vertices $(6, 6)$ and $(0, 6)$, length of conjugate axis 8.

21. Center $(2, 1)$, one focus $(0, 1)$, length of transverse axis 6.

22. Foci $(-2, 4)$ and $(6, 4)$, slope of one asymptote $\frac{3}{4}$.

23. Vertices $(-3, -1)$ and $(5, -1)$, eccentricity $\frac{4}{3}$.

24. One vertex $(3, -2)$, foci $(-6, -2)$ and $(4, -2)$.

In Exercises 25–30, the given equation has a locus that is either a circle, a
parabola, an ellipse, or a hyperbola. Find (if they exist) (a) the center, (b) the
vertices, (c) the foci, (d) the asymptotes; and sketch the curve.

25. $x^2 - y^2 + 3x - y + 8 = 0$

26. $x^2 + 3y^2 + 6x + 6 = 0$

27. $y^2 + 8x - 6y + 1 = 0$

28. $9x^2 - 16y^2 - 18x + 96y - 279 = 0$

29. $3x^2 + 3y^2 - 7x + y = 0$

30. $4x^2 + 8y^2 + 4x - 24y + 1 = 0$

Exercises 31–34 refer to the locus $\mathcal{K}$ of the equation $Ax^2 + Cy^2 + Dx +
Ey + F = 0$, where not all coefficients are 0. Prove each statement.

B 31. If $AC = 0$, then $\mathcal{K}$ is a parabola, a pair of parallel lines, a line, or $\emptyset$.

32. If $A = C \neq 0$, then $\mathcal{K}$ is a circle, a point, or $\emptyset$.

33. If $A \neq C$ and $AC > 0$, then $\mathcal{K}$ is an ellipse, a point, or $\emptyset$.

34. If $AC < 0$, then $\mathcal{K}$ is a hyperbola or a pair of intersecting lines.

532

Let τ be the translation determined by the vector $\mathbf{v} = (r, s)$, and let $\mathbf{P'}$, $\mathbf{R'}$, and $\mathbf{S'}$ be the images under τ of any three points $\mathbf{P}$, $\mathbf{R}$, and $\mathbf{S}$.

C **35.** Prove that $(\mathbf{P} - \mathbf{S}) \cdot (\mathbf{R} - \mathbf{S}) = (\mathbf{P'} - \mathbf{S'}) \cdot (\mathbf{R'} - \mathbf{S'})$

36. Prove that $\angle \mathbf{RSP} = \angle \mathbf{R'S'P'}$. (*Hint:* $\angle \mathbf{R'S'P'}$ is the angle from $\mathbf{R'} - \mathbf{S'}$ to $\mathbf{P'} - \mathbf{S'}$.)

37. The transformation equations $x' = x$ and $y' = ky$ "expand" or "contract" a locus in a direction parallel to the y-axis. Prove that any ellipse can be mapped into a circle by making a suitable choice for k.

38. The transformation equations $x' = kx$ and $y' = ky$ expand or contract every line segment by the same factor, and hence map figures into "similar" figures. Use these equations to prove that any two parabolas are "similar."

13–6 Rotations

Figure 13–16 suggests a mapping ρ of $\mathcal{R} \times \mathcal{R}$, obtained by rotating the plane counterclockwise about the origin through an angle of radian measure ϕ. Thus, ρ maps $(1, 0)$ into $(\cos \phi, \sin \phi)$ and $(0, 1)$ into $(-\sin \phi, \cos \phi)$. The origin is mapped into itself by ρ. (Why?)

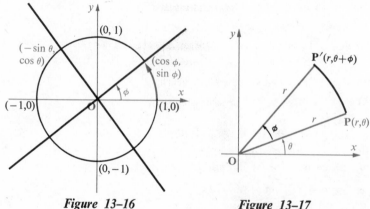

| *Figure 13–16* | *Figure 13–17* |

By using polar coordinates, you can easily discover the relationship between the Cartesian coordinates of any point $\mathbf{P}(x, y)$ and its image $\mathbf{P'}(x', y')$ under ρ. For, as Figure 13–17 indicates, if (r, θ) are polar coordinates of $\mathbf{P}$, then $(r, \theta + \phi)$ are polar coordinates of $\mathbf{P'}$. Hence,

$$x' = r \cos (\theta + \phi) = r \cos \theta \cos \phi - r \sin \theta \sin \phi$$
$$y' = r \sin (\theta + \phi) = r \sin \theta \cos \phi + r \cos \theta \sin \phi.$$

Since $x = r \cos \theta$ and $y = r \sin \theta$ (Why?), you find

$$\text{(1)} \qquad \begin{aligned} x' &= x \cos \phi - y \sin \phi \\ y' &= x \sin \phi + y \cos \phi. \end{aligned}$$

Thus, in $\Re \times \Re$ a **rotation about the origin**, or simply a **rotation**, is a function which maps each point (x, y) into the point

$$(x \cos \phi - y \sin \phi, \ x \sin \phi + y \cos \phi)$$

where ϕ denotes a real constant (or the radian or degree measure of an angle). We call the pair of equations (1) the **equations of the rotation**. If you solve these equations for x and y in terms of x' and y', you obtain

(2)
$$x = x' \cos \phi + y' \sin \phi$$
$$y = -x' \sin \phi + y' \cos \phi.$$

Do you see that the second pair of equations specify a rotation about **O** through the angle $-\phi$? [Recall that $\cos(-\phi) = \cos \phi$ and $\sin(-\phi) = -\sin \phi$.] We call the rotations specified by the equations of sets (1) and (2) **inverse rotations**.

EXAMPLE 1. Let ρ be the rotation about **O** such that $\phi = $ Arcsin $\frac{3}{5}$, and let **P'** and **Q'** be the images of **P** and **Q** under ρ.

    a. If **P** has coordinates $(1, -2)$, determine **P'**.

    b. If **Q'** has coordinates $(-3, 0)$, determine **Q**.

Solution: Since $\phi = $ Arcsin $\frac{3}{5}$, $\sin \phi = \frac{3}{5}$ and $\cos \phi = \frac{4}{5}$. (Why?)

    a. Using the equations labeled (1) on page 532 with $(x, y) = (1, -2)$, you have

$$x' = \frac{4x - 3y}{5} = \frac{4 \cdot 1 - 3(-2)}{5} = 2,$$

$$y' = \frac{3x + 4y}{5} = \frac{3 \cdot 1 + 4(-2)}{5} = -1.$$

    P' is the point with coordinates $(2, -1)$, **Answer.**

    b. Using the pair of equations labeled (2), above, with $(x', y') = (-3, 0)$, you have

$$x = \frac{4x' + 3y'}{5} = \frac{4(-3) + 3 \cdot 0}{5} = -\frac{12}{5}$$

$$y = \frac{-3x' + 4y'}{5} = \frac{-3(-3) + 4 \cdot 0}{5} = \frac{9}{5}.$$

The following example suggests that a rotation preserves distances (Exercise 25, page 536).

EXAMPLE 2. For the points **P**, **Q**, **P′**, and **Q′** in Example 1, verify that

$$\|\mathbf{P} - \mathbf{Q}\| = \|\mathbf{P'} - \mathbf{Q'}\|.$$

Solution: From Example 1, you have:

$$\mathbf{P} = (1, -2) \qquad\qquad \mathbf{P'} = (2, -1)$$

$$\mathbf{Q} = (-\tfrac{12}{5}, \tfrac{9}{5}) \qquad\qquad \mathbf{Q'} = (-3, 0)$$

$$\mathbf{P} - \mathbf{Q} = (\tfrac{17}{5}, -\tfrac{19}{5}) \qquad\qquad \mathbf{P'} - \mathbf{Q'} = (5, -1)$$

$$\therefore \|\mathbf{P} - \mathbf{Q}\| = \sqrt{(\tfrac{17}{5})^2 + (-\tfrac{19}{5})^2} \qquad \therefore \|\mathbf{P'} - \mathbf{Q'}\| = \sqrt{5^2 + (-1)^2}$$

$$= \sqrt{26} \qquad\qquad\qquad\qquad = \sqrt{26}$$

$$\therefore \|\mathbf{P} - \mathbf{Q}\| = \|\mathbf{P'} - \mathbf{Q'}\|.$$

Since it can be proved that a rotation preserves angles as well as distances (Exercise 26, page 536), it follows that a rotation maps lines into lines, parabolas into parabolas, ellipses into ellipses, and so on.

EXAMPLE 3. Determine the image under the rotation about **O** with $\phi = -\dfrac{\pi}{4}$ of the graph of the equation $x^2 + xy + y^2 = 6$ and use the result to identify the graph.

Solution: Using equations (2), page 533, you have:

$$x = \frac{x' - y'}{\sqrt{2}} \quad and \quad y = \frac{x' + y'}{\sqrt{2}}.$$

Substituting these expressions for x and y in the equation

$$x^2 + xy + y^2 = 6$$

you obtain

$$\left(\frac{x' - y'}{\sqrt{2}}\right)^2 + \left(\frac{x' - y'}{\sqrt{2}}\right)\left(\frac{x' + y'}{\sqrt{2}}\right) + \left(\frac{x' + y'}{\sqrt{2}}\right)^2 = 6,$$

or $\quad 3x'^2 + y'^2 = 12 \quad$ or $\quad \dfrac{x'^2}{4} + \dfrac{y'^2}{12} = 1.$

$\therefore$ the image of the graph of the given equation is an ellipse with center at the origin, and having the y-axis as principal axis. Hence, the graph of the given equation is an ellipse with principal axis making an angle of $-\dfrac{\pi^R}{4}$ with the *x*-axis. (See figure.)

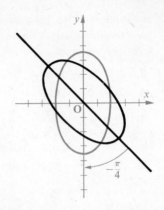

EXAMPLE 4. Determine a rotation ρ about **O** that maps the *x*-axis into the line $\mathscr{L}$ through **O** with slope $\tfrac{8}{15}$.

Solution: As the figure shows, there are two such rotations, ρ_1 and ρ_2.

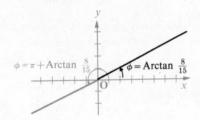

For ρ_1:

$$\phi = \text{Arctan } \tfrac{8}{15}$$

$$\cos\phi = \tfrac{15}{17}, \ \sin\theta = \tfrac{8}{17}$$

$$x' = \frac{15x - 8y}{17}$$

$$y' = \frac{8x + 15y}{17}$$

For ρ_2:

$$\phi = \pi + \text{Arctan } \tfrac{8}{15}$$

$$\cos\phi = -\tfrac{15}{17}, \ \sin\theta = -\tfrac{8}{17}$$

$$x' = \frac{-15x + 8y}{17}$$

$$y' = \frac{-8x - 15y}{17}$$

Exercises

Determine the images of the given points under the rotation about **O** with ϕ as indicated.

1. $(1, 3), (-2, 4), (-6, -3), (5, -3); \phi = -\dfrac{\pi}{6}$

2. $(2, 3), (-3, 7), (-1, -1), (0, -4); \phi = -\dfrac{3\pi}{4}$

In Exercises 3–10, (a) determine an equation of the image of the locus of the given equation under the rotation about **O** with ϕ as indicated; (b) sketch the locus and its image.

3. $x - 2y = 3; \phi = \text{Arcsin } \frac{5}{13}$

4. $2x + 3y = 1; \phi = \text{Arcsin } (-\frac{5}{13})$

5. $x + y = 1; \phi = -\dfrac{\pi}{4}$

6. $x - y = 7; \phi = \text{Arctan } (-\frac{1}{3})$

7. $x^2 + y^2 = 4; \phi = \text{Arccos } (\frac{1}{3})$

8. $x^2 + y^2 = 9; \phi = \dfrac{\pi}{5}$

9. $(x - 1)^2 + (y + 2)^2 = 16; \phi = -\dfrac{\pi}{4}$

10. $(x + 1)^2 + y^2 = 25; \phi = -\dfrac{\pi}{6}$

Identify the graph of the given equation by determining an equation of its image under the rotation about **O** with ϕ as indicated.

11. $2x^2 + 3xy + 2y^2 = 7; \phi = \dfrac{\pi}{4}$

12. $8x^2 - 4xy + 5y^2 = 36; \phi = \text{Sin}^{-1}\left(-\dfrac{2}{\sqrt{5}}\right)$

13. $2x^2 - 4xy - y^2 = 10; \phi = \text{Sin}^{-1}\left(-\dfrac{2}{\sqrt{5}}\right)$

14. $x^2 + xy + y^2 = 3; \phi = \text{Sin}^{-1}\left(-\dfrac{1}{\sqrt{2}}\right)$

Determine (a) the equations of a rotation about **O** that maps the given line into a line $\mathfrak{M}$ with slope m; (b) an equation of $\mathfrak{M}$.

(B)

15. $2x - y = 3; m = 0$ **17.** $x + y = 4; m = \frac{1}{2}$

16. $x - y = 5; m = 0$ **18.** $3x + y = 5; m = -1$

Determine the equations of a rotation about **O** that maps **P** into **P'**.

19. $P(2, 1); P'(-1, 2)$ **21.** $P(3, 5), P'(-4, -3\sqrt{2})$

20. $P(-4, 7); P'(7, -4)$ **22.** $P(5, -5), P'(1, 7)$

(C)

23. Show that every line through **O** is its own image (**is invariant**) under the rotation about **O** with $\theta = \pi$.

24. Show that every circle with center at **O** is invariant under a rotation about **O**.

25. Let points **P'** and **Q'** be the images of points **P** and **Q** under a rotation about **O**. Prove that $\|P - Q\| = \|P' - Q'\|$.

26. Let points **P'**, **Q'**, and **S'** be the images of points **P**, **Q**, and **S** under a rotation about **O**. Prove that $\angle PQS = \angle P'Q'S'$.

13-7 Applications of Rotations

Can you identify the graph of an equation such as

$$8x^2 - 12xy - 8y^2 + 6\sqrt{10}x - 2\sqrt{10}y - 30 = 0?$$

Example 3 (page 534) suggests that you may be able to recognize the graph of an equation of the form

(1) $$Ax^2 + Bxy + Cy^2 + Dx + Ey + F = 0$$

where $B \neq 0$ by finding a rotation under which the image of this graph is a locus whose equation is familiar. Now you can identify loci with equations of form (1) *provided* $B = 0$, that is, provided the equation does not contain an "xy-term." Thus, the problem of recognizing the graph of an equation of form (1) can be solved by determining a rotation which will yield a locus in which the mixed-product term is missing.

Assuming that $B \neq 0$, let us substitute

$$x = x' \cos \phi + y' \sin \phi$$
$$y = -x' \sin \phi + y' \cos \phi$$

in equation (1). You obtain the equation

$$A'x'^2 + B'x'y' + C'y'^2 + D'x' + E'y' + F = 0$$

where

(2) $$A' = A \cos^2 \phi - B \cos \phi \sin \phi + C \sin^2 \phi$$

(3) $$B' = 2(A - C) \sin \phi \cos \phi + B(\cos^2 \phi - \sin^2 \phi)$$

(4) $$C' = A \sin^2 \phi + B \cos \phi \sin \phi + C \cos^2 \phi$$

(5) $$D' = D \cos \phi - E \sin \phi$$

(6) $$E' = D \sin \phi + E \cos \phi$$

To eliminate the $x'y'$ term, you must choose ϕ so that $B' = 0$. Since $2 \sin \phi \cos \phi = \sin 2\phi$ and $\cos^2 \phi - \sin^2 \phi = \cos 2\phi$, formula (3) can be written

$$B' = (A - C) \sin 2\phi + B \cos 2\phi.$$

Therefore, $B' = 0$ if and only if

(7) $$(A - C) \sin 2\phi + B \cos 2\phi = 0.$$

(i) Suppose $A = C$. In this case, equation (7) simplifies to

$$B \cos 2\phi = 0.$$

This equation is satisfied if $\cos 2\phi = 0$, and $2\phi \in \arccos 0$. Thus, you may choose $2\phi = -\dfrac{\pi}{2}$ and $\phi = -\dfrac{\pi}{4}$. (Of course, you may assign to 2ϕ the value $\dfrac{\pi}{2}, \dfrac{3\pi}{2}$, or any other element of arccos 0.)

(ii) Suppose $A \neq C$. In this case, equation (7) is equivalent to

$$\tan 2\phi = \frac{B}{C - A}.$$

Hence, $2\phi \in \arctan \dfrac{B}{C - A}$. In particular, you may choose 2ϕ so that $-\pi < 2\phi < 0$. Then, $2\phi = \text{Arctan} \dfrac{B}{C - A}$ or $-\pi + \text{Arctan} \dfrac{B}{C - A}$, according as $\dfrac{B}{C - A} < 0$ or $\dfrac{B}{C - A} > 0$. Hence, $-\dfrac{\pi}{2} < \phi < 0$ and $\phi = \tfrac{1}{2} \text{Arctan} \dfrac{B}{C - A}$ or $-\dfrac{\pi}{2} + \tfrac{1}{2} \text{Arctan} \dfrac{B}{C - A}$.

The following theorem summarizes the discussion.

THEOREM   Let $A, B, C, D, E,$ and F denote real numbers, $B \neq 0$.

If $A = C$, let $\phi = -\dfrac{\pi}{4}$; if $A \neq C$, let

$$\tan 2\phi = \frac{B}{C - A} \text{ and } -\pi < 2\phi < 0.$$

Then, under the rotation

$$x = x' \cos \phi + y' \sin \phi$$
$$y = -x' \sin \phi + y' \cos \phi$$

the graph of

$$Ax^2 + Bxy + Cy^2 + Dx + Ey + F = 0$$

is mapped into the locus of

$$A'x'^2 + C'y'^2 + D'x' + E'y' + F = 0$$

where A', C', D', and E' are given by formulas (2), (4), (5), and (6), page 537.

EXAMPLE. Use a rotation to identify the graph of

$$8x^2 - 12xy - 8y^2 + 6\sqrt{10}\,x - 2\sqrt{10}\,y - 30 = 0.$$

Solution: $A = 8, B = -12, C = -8.$

$$\tan 2\phi = \frac{B}{C - A} = \frac{-12}{-8 - (8)} = \frac{3}{4}.$$

Choosing 2ϕ so that $-\pi < 2\phi < -\dfrac{\pi}{2}$ (Why?), you find

$\cos 2\phi = -\frac{4}{5}.$ Hence, $-\dfrac{\pi}{2} < \phi < -\dfrac{\pi}{4}$ and

$$\cos\phi = \sqrt{\frac{1 + \cos 2\phi}{2}} = \frac{1}{\sqrt{10}}$$

$$\sin\phi = -\sqrt{\frac{1 - \cos 2\phi}{2}} = -\frac{3}{\sqrt{10}}.$$

∴ the rotation equations are

$$x = \frac{x' - 3y'}{\sqrt{10}} \quad \text{and} \quad y = \frac{3x' + y'}{\sqrt{10}}.$$

Substituting these expressions for x and y in the equation

$$8x^2 - 12xy - 8y^2 + 6\sqrt{10}\,x - 2\sqrt{10}\,y - 30 = 0,$$

you obtain an equation equivalent to

$$-x'^2 + y'^2 - 2y' = 3.$$

Completing the square in y produces the equation

$$(y' - 1)^2 - x'^2 = 4.$$

Thus, the graph of the given equation is the hyperbola which by a rotation with $\phi = \text{Arctan}\,(-3)$ is mapped into the hyperbola with center at $(0, 1)$ and principal axis, the y-axis. Drawing the image (shown in red), you can sketch the given hyperbola (shown in black) by using the fact that the rotation maps its principal axis into the y-axis.

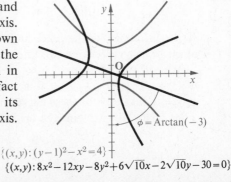

$\phi = \text{Arctan}(-3)$

$\{(x,y): (y-1)^2 - x^2 = 4\}$
$\{(x,y): 8x^2 - 12xy - 8y^2 + 6\sqrt{10}x - 2\sqrt{10}y - 30 = 0\}$

Considerable information about the graph of equation (1) can be obtained from formulas (2)–(4), page 537.   In the first place, notice that by adding equations (2) and (4), you obtain for every value of ϕ

$$A' + C' = A(\cos^2 \phi + \sin^2 \phi) + C(\cos^2 \phi + \sin^2 \phi);$$

(8) $A' + C' = A + C.$ (Why?)

Secondly, as an exercise in algebraic procedures and the use of trigonometric identities (Exercise 19, page 541), you can verify that for every value of ϕ

(9) $B'^2 - 4A'C' = B^2 - 4AC.$

Because statements (8) and (9) are valid for all ϕ, we say that the expressions $A + C$ and $B^2 - 4AC$ (called the **characteristic**) are **invariant under a rotation**.   In particular, under the rotation that reduces B' to 0, you find that the characteristic

$$B^2 - 4AC = -4A'C'.$$

Thus, using the information in the chart on page 530 you can prove the following theorem (Exercises 21–23, page 541).

THEOREM   Let A, B, C, D, E, F denote real numbers with at least one of the numbers A, B, and C different from zero, and let

$$\mathcal{K} = \{(x, y): Ax^2 + Bxy + Cy^2 + Dx + Ey + F = 0\}.$$

  (i) If $B^2 - 4AC = 0$, then $\mathcal{K}$ is a parabola, two parallel lines, a line, or $\emptyset$.

  (ii) If $B^2 - 4AC < 0$, then $\mathcal{K}$ is a circle, an ellipse, a point, or $\emptyset$.

  (iii) If $B^2 - 4AC > 0$, then $\mathcal{K}$ is a hyperbola, or a pair of intersecting lines.

Observe that for the equation in the Example, page 539,

$$B^2 - 4AC = 12^2 - 4(8)(-8) > 0.$$

Thus, using merely the preceding theorem, you would know that the graph must be a hyperbola or two intersecting lines.

We call the graph in $\mathfrak{R} \times \mathfrak{R}$ of an equation of the form $Ax^2 + Bxy + Cy^2 + Dx + Ey + F = 0$ a **conic section**, or a **conic**.   Figure 13–18 suggests that each of these curves occurs as the intersection of a plane with a cone.   This fact explains the origin of the term "conic section."

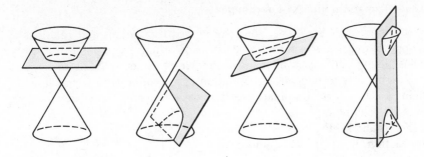

Figure 13–18

Exercises

Without using a rotation, state the nature of the locus of each of the given equations.

A

1. $xy - y = 2$

2. $x^2 + xy - y^2 = 4$

3. $2x^2 + 4xy - y^2 - 2x + 3y = 6$

4. $7x^2 + 6xy + 15y^2 = 144$

5. $8y^2 + 6xy - 26y - 12x + 11 = 0$

6. $x^2 + xy + y^2 = 8$

7. $x^2 - 2x - 2y + y^2 + 4 = 0$

8. $y^2 - 2xy + x^2 - 5x = 0$

9–16. In Exercises 1–8, use a rotation to identify and sketch the locus of each of the given equations.

B

17. Show that the locus of $3x^2 + 2xy - y^2 + 4y - 3 = 0$ is a **degenerate conic**; that is, a point, a line, two intersecting lines, two parallel lines, or the empty set.

18. Show that the locus of $3x^2 + 10xy + 3y^2 - 2x - 14y - 5 = 0$ is a degenerate conic. (See Exercise 17.)

Let $\mathcal{K} = \{(x, y) \colon Ax^2 + Bxy + Cy^2 + Dx + Ey + F = 0\}$. Prove each of the following statements. In Exercises 21–24, you may use the results stated in the chart on page 530.

19. $B^2 - 4AC$ is invariant under a rotation about **O**.

20. $B^2 - 4AC$ is invariant under a translation.

21. If $B^2 - 4AC = 0$, then $\mathcal{K}$ is a parabola, two parallel lines, a line, or $\emptyset$.

22. If $B^2 - 4AC < 0$, then the locus is a circle, an ellipse, a point, or $\emptyset$.

23. If $B^2 - 4AC > 0$, then the locus is a hyperbola or two intersecting lines.

24. If $B \neq 0$, the locus is not a circle.

13-8 **Transformation of Coordinates**

In the preceding sections, you have viewed translations and rotations as mappings that transform each point of $\Re \times \Re$ into some point of $\Re \times \Re$. Thus, you visualize each mapping as "moving" points of the plane.

Another way to interpret a translation or a rotation is to regard it as defining a new pair of coordinate axes and, thus, assigning a new set of coordinates to each point.

For example, Figure 13–19 shows a translation by which the original coordinate axes, labeled x and y, are replaced by the new coordinate axes, labeled x' and y', where $\mathbf{O}'$ is the new origin. Thus, if (h, k) denote the coordinates of $\mathbf{O}'$ in the xy-coordinate system, then

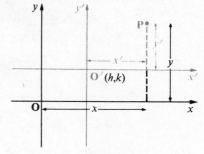

$$x' = x - h \quad and \quad y' = y - k$$

are the **translation equations** giving the coordinates in the $x'y'$-system of any point with coordinates (x, y) in the xy-system.

Figure 13–19

EXAMPLE 1.   If the origin is translated to the point $(2, -5)$, determine the new coordinates of $(1, -3)$.

   Solution: The translation equations are

$$x' = x - 2 \quad and \quad y' = y - (-5).$$
$$\therefore x' = 1 - 2 \qquad y' = -3 + 5$$
$$= -1 \qquad\qquad = 2$$

   $\therefore$ the new coordinates of $(1, -3)$ are $(-1, 2)$, **Answer.**

Figure 13–20 shows the x'- and y'-axes resulting when the x- and y-axes are rotated through the angle ϕ. If (r, θ) are polar coordinates of a point $\mathbf{P}$ in the xy-system, then $(r, \theta - \phi)$ are its coordinates in the $x'y'$-system.

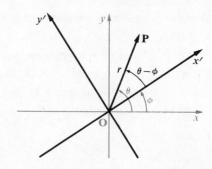

Figure 13–20

Thus, $\quad x' = r\cos(\theta - \phi) = r\cos\theta\cos\phi + r\sin\theta\sin\phi$

$\qquad\quad y' = r\sin(\theta - \phi) = -r\cos\theta\sin\phi + r\sin\theta\cos\phi.$

Therefore, the transformation equations are:

(1)
$$x' = x\cos\phi + y\sin\phi$$
$$y' = -x\sin\phi + y\cos\phi.$$

Correspondingly, you find

(2)
$$x = x'\cos\phi - y'\sin\phi$$
$$y = x'\sin\phi + y'\cos\phi$$

If you compare the preceding sets of rotation equations with those stated on pages 532 and 533, you will see that *rotating the coordinate axes* through an angle ϕ assigns to **P** new coordinates which are the coordinates of the point into which **P** would have been mapped had you *rotated the plane* through the angle $-\phi$. This observation enables you to restate in terms of rotation of axes the theorem given on page 540.

THEOREM Let A, B, C, D, E, and F denote real numbers, $B \neq 0$. If $A = C$, let $\phi = \dfrac{\pi}{4}$; if $A \neq C$, let $\tan 2\phi = \dfrac{B}{A - C}$ and $0 < 2\phi < \pi$. If the coordinate axes are rotated about the origin through the angle ϕ, then the equation

$$Ax^2 + Bxy + Cy^2 + Dx + Ey + F = 0$$

is transformed into

$$A'x'^2 + C'y'^2 + D'x' + E'y' + F = 0.$$

Note that the theorem implies that you can always eliminate the mixed-product term in a quadratic equation in x and y by rotating the coordinate axes through a *positive acute* angle.

EXAMPLE 2. **(a)** Determine equations of rotation of axes that will transform the equation

$$8x^2 - 12xy - 8y^2 + 6\sqrt{10}\,x - 2\sqrt{10}\,y - 30 = 0$$

into one without a mixed-product term.

(b) Sketch the curve showing both sets of axes.

(Solution follows)

Solution: Choose ϕ so that $\tan 2\phi = \dfrac{B}{A - C}$, $0 < 2\phi < \pi$.

$$\therefore \tan 2\phi = \frac{-12}{8 - (-8)} = -\frac{3}{4}, \text{ and } \frac{\pi}{2} < 2\phi < \pi. \quad (\text{Why?})$$

Hence, $\cos 2\phi = -\frac{4}{5}$, and

$$\cos \phi = \sqrt{\frac{1 + \cos 2\phi}{2}} = \frac{1}{\sqrt{10}}$$

$$\sin \phi = \sqrt{\frac{1 - \cos 2\phi}{2}} = \frac{3}{\sqrt{10}}$$

Using equations (2), page 533, you obtain

$$x = \frac{x' - 3y'}{\sqrt{10}} \quad \text{and} \quad y = \frac{3x' + y'}{\sqrt{10}}$$

Substituting in the given equation and simplifying the result, you obtain the equation

$$\frac{(y' - 1)^2}{4} - \frac{x'^2}{4} = 1$$

You should compare the adjoining figure with the figure shown on page 539.

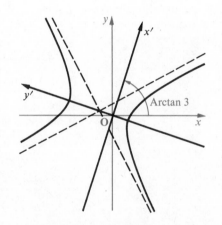

Since the characteristics of conics are unchanged by a translation or rotation of axes, you can demonstrate general properties of these curves by arguments in terms of the simplest forms of their equations.

EXAMPLE 3.   Prove that in every parabola the chord $\overline{AB}$ through the focus perpendicular to the axis (the latus rectum) subtends a right angle at the intersection **D** of the directrix and axis.

Solution: As shown in the figure, choose coordinate axes so that the focus is **F**$(0, p)$ and the directrix is the line $y = -p$. Then, the equation of the parabola is $x^2 = 4py$ and **D** is the point $(0, -p)$.

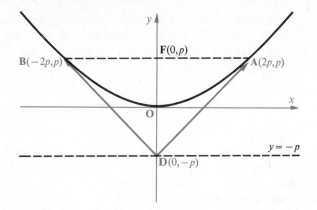

Also, **A** and **B** have coordinates $(2p, p)$ and $(-2p, p)$. (Why?)

$$\therefore \cos \angle ADB = \frac{(A - D) \cdot (B - D)}{\|A - D\| \, \|B - D\|} = \frac{(2p, 2p) \cdot (-2p, 2p)}{8p^2} = 0$$

$\therefore \angle ADB$ is a right angle (Why?), **Answer.**

Exercises

In Exercises 1–6, transform the given equation by a translation of axes so that the new equation has as few linear terms as possible. Sketch the graph of the resulting equation; show both sets of axes.

A

1. $x^2 - 2y + 8x + 10 = 0$
2. $y^2 + 2x - 4y - 3 = 0$
3. $4x^2 + 5y^2 + 16x - 20y + 31 = 0$
4. $4x^2 + 9y^2 - 48x + 72y + 144 = 0$
5. $3x^2 - y^2 - 12x - 6y = 0$
6. $4x^2 - 4y^2 + 4x - 8y = 0$

In Exercises 7–10, find $\sin \theta$ and $\cos \theta$ so that a rotation of axes through an angle θ will result in an equation without a mixed-product term.

7. $x^2 + 10xy + y^2 + 6 = 0$ 9. $7x^2 - 4xy + 4y^2 = 240$
8. $3x^2 + 4\sqrt{3}xy - y^2 - 7 = 0$ 10. $x^2 - 2xy = 10$

11–14. In Exercises 7–10, find the transformed equation; sketch the locus and show both sets of axes.

In Exercises 15–18, apply suitable translations and rotations to produce an equation in x'' and y'' free of linear and mixed-product terms insofar as this is possible. Sketch the locus and show both sets of coordinate axes.

15. $4x^2 + 4xy + y^2 - 24x + 38y - 139 = 0$

16. $20x^2 - 24xy + 27y^2 + 20x - 12y - 325 = 0$

17. $3x^2 + 2\sqrt{3}xy + y^2 - 8x + 8\sqrt{3}\,y + 4 = 0$

18. $9x^2 - 24xy + 16y^2 - 20x - 15y = 0$

B 19. Find the value (or values) of c for which the graph of $2xy - 4x + 7y + c = 0$ is two intersecting straight lines.

20. Find the value or values of c for which the graph of $xy - 2x + 3y + c = 0$ is two intersecting straight lines.

21. Prove that the angle subtended by the latus rectum at the vertex is the same for all parabolas.

22. Prove that if $\mathbf{P}$ is a point of a hyperbola whose transverse and conjugate axes have the same length, the product of the focal radii of $\mathbf{P}$ is equal to the square of the distance of $\mathbf{P}$ from the center.

C 23. A line is tangent to a parabola at a point $\mathbf{T}$ and intersects the axis of the parabola at $\mathbf{Q}$. Prove that the tangent to the parabola at its vertex bisects the line segment $\overline{\mathbf{TQ}}$. (*Hint:* Take the parabola to be the locus of $x^2 = 4py$, and use the methods of Chapter 8 to determine the slope of the tangent at any point (x_0, y_0) of the curve.)

24. A line $\mathcal{L}$ is tangent to a parabola at a point $\mathbf{T}$. Prove that $\mathcal{L}$ makes equal angles with the line joining $\mathbf{T}$ to the focus and the line through $\mathbf{T}$ parallel to the axis of the parabola. (*Hint:* See the suggestion for Exercise 23.)

25. A line $\mathcal{L}$ is tangent to an ellipse at a point $\mathbf{T}$. Prove that $\mathcal{L}$ makes equal angles with the lines joining $\mathbf{T}$ to the foci of the ellipse. (*Hint:* Use the fact that the slope of the tangent to the ellipse $\dfrac{x^2}{a^2} + \dfrac{y^2}{b^2} = 1$ at $\mathbf{T}(x_0, y_0)$ is $-\dfrac{b^2 x_0}{a^2 y_0}$.)

26. Determine whether the hyperbola has a tangent property analogous to the property described in Exercise 25 for the ellipse. (*Hint:* Use the fact that the slope of the tangent to the hyperbola $\dfrac{x^2}{a^2} - \dfrac{y^2}{b^2} = 1$ at (x_0, y_0) is $\dfrac{b^2 x_0}{a^2 y_0}$.)

27. Let $\mathcal{E}$ be an ellipse having the same foci as a hyperbola $\mathcal{H}$. Prove that at a point of intersection of $\mathcal{E}$ and $\mathcal{H}$ the tangents to the curves are perpendicular to each other. (*Hint:* See the suggestions for Exercises 25 and 26.)

28. Prove that the foci of a hyperbola and those of its conjugate hyperbola lie on a circle. (*Hint:* See Exercise 31, page 524.)

For the given values of p and e, show that the polar graphs of the equations

$$r = \frac{pe}{1 - e\cos\theta} \quad \text{and} \quad r = \frac{pe}{1 - e\sin\theta}$$ are conic sections. Identify the conics.

29. $p = 3, e = \frac{1}{2}$

30. $p = \frac{3}{2}, e = 2$

31. $p > 0, e = 1$

32. $p > 0, 0 < e < 1$

TRANSFORMATIONS AND MATRICES

13-9 Matrices and Vectors

Rotations form a subset of a general class of mappings of $\Re \times \Re$ called *linear transformations*. A **linear transformation** is a mapping specified by transformation equations of the form

(1)
$$x' = a_1 x + a_2 y$$
$$y' = b_1 x + b_2 y.$$

Thus, the rotation

(2)
$$x' = x \cos \frac{\pi}{4} + y \sin \frac{\pi}{4}$$
$$y' = -x \sin \frac{\pi}{4} + y \cos \frac{\pi}{4}$$

is a linear transformation.

Notice that the pair of equations labeled (1) above can be specified by stating simply the coefficient array

$$\begin{bmatrix} a_1 & a_2 \\ b_1 & b_2 \end{bmatrix}.$$

We call any rectangular array of numbers a **matrix**. Examples of matrices are

$$\begin{bmatrix} \cos \frac{\pi}{4} & \sin \frac{\pi}{4} \\ -\sin \frac{\pi}{4} & \cos \frac{\pi}{4} \end{bmatrix}, \quad \begin{bmatrix} 2 \\ 1 \end{bmatrix}, \quad \begin{bmatrix} 3 & 2 \\ 1 & 4 \\ 5 & 0 \end{bmatrix}, \quad [0 \;\; 5].$$

To state the **dimensions** of a matrix, you give the number of rows, and then, the number of columns it contains. Thus, the foregoing matrices are 2×2 (read "two by two"), 2×1, 3×2, and 1×2 matrices. A matrix having n rows and n columns is called a **square matrix of order n**. Hence, a 2×2 matrix is a square matrix of order 2.

It is sometimes convenient to call the rows of a matrix **row vectors** and to call its columns, **column vectors**. A matrix that contains only one row is called a **row matrix** or **row vector**. A matrix containing a single column is called a **column matrix** or **column vector**. You ordinarily denote matrices by using capital letters, A, B, C, D, or, to indicate dimensions, $A_{2 \times 2}$, $B_{2 \times 1}$, $C_{3 \times 2}$, $D_{1 \times 2}$.

The numbers that make up a matrix are called its **entries**. If all the entries of a matrix are zeros, the matrix is a **zero matrix**.

You say that two matrices A and B are **equal**, and write

$$A = B$$

if and only if they have the same dimensions and their corresponding entries are equal.

If the rows of a matrix A are the same as the columns of a matrix B, then each is called the **transpose** of the other; you then write

$$A = B^{\mathsf{T}} \text{ (read ``}A\text{ is equal to } B \text{ transpose'')}$$

and

$$B = A^{\mathsf{T}}.$$

EXAMPLE 1. If $A = \begin{bmatrix} x & 3 \\ 2 & y \end{bmatrix}$ and $B = \begin{bmatrix} 4 & 2 \\ 3 & 1 \end{bmatrix}$, find values of x and y so that $A^{\mathsf{T}} = B$.

Solution: $A^{\mathsf{T}} = \begin{bmatrix} x & 2 \\ 3 & y \end{bmatrix}$; $B = \begin{bmatrix} 4 & 2 \\ 3 & 1 \end{bmatrix}$.

Because equal matrices must have equal corresponding entries, $A^{\mathsf{T}} = B$ if and only if $x = 4$ and $y = 1$.

$\therefore$ the value of x is 4; the value of y is 1, **Answer.**

The **sum** of two matrices A and B *of the same dimensions* is the matrix $A + B$, each entry of which is the sum of the corresponding entries in A and B.

Thus, if

$$A = \begin{bmatrix} 3 & 1 \\ -2 & 0 \end{bmatrix} \text{ and } B = \begin{bmatrix} -1 & 7 \\ 6 & 1 \end{bmatrix},$$

then

$$A + B = \begin{bmatrix} 3 & 1 \\ -2 & 0 \end{bmatrix} + \begin{bmatrix} -1 & 7 \\ 6 & 1 \end{bmatrix} = \begin{bmatrix} 3 + (-1) & 1 + 7 \\ -2 + 6 & 0 + 1 \end{bmatrix} = \begin{bmatrix} 2 & 8 \\ 4 & 1 \end{bmatrix}.$$

You define the **negative** or **additive inverse** of a matrix A to be the matrix $-A$ each entry of which is the negative of the corresponding entry in A. If

$$A = \begin{bmatrix} 1 & 7 \\ 6 & -2 \end{bmatrix}, \text{ then } -A = \begin{bmatrix} -1 & -7 \\ -6 & 2 \end{bmatrix}.$$

With this agreement, you can define the **difference** $A - B$ of two matrices by

$$A - B = A + (-B).$$

The sum or difference of two matrices of different dimensions is not defined.

In matrix algebra, as in vector algebra, a real number is called a **scalar**.

The product of a scalar r and a matrix A is the matrix rA or Ar, each entry of which is r times the corresponding entry of A.

For example,

$$2\begin{bmatrix} 3 & -1 \\ 5 & 4 \end{bmatrix} = \begin{bmatrix} 2\cdot 3 & 2(-1) \\ 2\cdot 5 & 2\cdot 4 \end{bmatrix} = \begin{bmatrix} 6 & -2 \\ 10 & 8 \end{bmatrix}, \quad \text{and} \quad r\begin{bmatrix} x \\ y \end{bmatrix} = \begin{bmatrix} rx \\ ry \end{bmatrix}.$$

The transformation equations (2), page 547, are sometimes said to map the vector $\begin{bmatrix} x \\ y \end{bmatrix}$ into the vector $\begin{bmatrix} x' \\ y' \end{bmatrix}$; the coefficient array

$$\begin{bmatrix} \cos\dfrac{\pi}{4} & \sin\dfrac{\pi}{4} \\ -\sin\dfrac{\pi}{4} & \cos\dfrac{\pi}{4} \end{bmatrix}$$

is then called the matrix of the transformation.

This suggests that you write the *matrix equation*

$$\begin{bmatrix} x' \\ y' \end{bmatrix} = \begin{bmatrix} \cos\dfrac{\pi}{4} & \sin\dfrac{\pi}{4} \\ -\sin\dfrac{\pi}{4} & \cos\dfrac{\pi}{4} \end{bmatrix}\begin{bmatrix} x \\ y \end{bmatrix}.$$

If you have noticed that

$$x' = \left(\cos\frac{\pi}{4},\ \sin\frac{\pi}{4}\right)\cdot(x, y) \quad \text{and} \quad y' = \left(-\sin\frac{\pi}{4},\ \cos\frac{\pi}{4}\right)\cdot(x, y),$$

that is,

$$\begin{bmatrix} x' \\ y' \end{bmatrix} = \begin{bmatrix} \left(\cos\dfrac{\pi}{4},\ \sin\dfrac{\pi}{4}\right)\cdot(x, y) \\ \left(-\sin\dfrac{\pi}{4},\ \cos\dfrac{\pi}{4}\right)\cdot(x, y) \end{bmatrix}$$

then you have discovered the motivation for the following definition of the product of a matrix and a column vector.

Let A be an $m \times n$ matrix and let V be an n-rowed column vector. Then AV is the m-rowed column vector whose kth entry is the sum of the products of the entries in the kth row of A and the corresponding entries in V.

EXAMPLE 2. If $A = \begin{bmatrix} 3 & 7 & 1 \\ 9 & 5 & -1 \\ 4 & 1 & 0 \end{bmatrix}$, $B = \begin{bmatrix} -1 & 0 & 1 \\ 0 & 2 & 5 \end{bmatrix}$, and $V = \begin{bmatrix} 1 \\ 2 \\ 3 \end{bmatrix}$,

determine AV and BV.

Solution:

$$AV = \begin{bmatrix} 3 & 7 & 1 \\ 9 & 5 & -1 \\ 4 & 1 & 0 \end{bmatrix} \begin{bmatrix} 1 \\ 2 \\ 3 \end{bmatrix} = \begin{bmatrix} 3 \cdot 1 + 7 \cdot 2 + 1 \cdot 3 \\ 9 \cdot 1 + 5 \cdot 2 + (-1)3 \\ 4 \cdot 1 + 1 \cdot 2 + 0 \cdot 3 \end{bmatrix} = \begin{bmatrix} 20 \\ 16 \\ 6 \end{bmatrix}$$

$$BV = \begin{bmatrix} -1 & 0 & 1 \\ 0 & 2 & 5 \end{bmatrix} \begin{bmatrix} 1 \\ 2 \\ 3 \end{bmatrix} = \begin{bmatrix} -1 \cdot 1 + 0 \cdot 2 + 1 \cdot 3 \\ 0 \cdot 1 + 2 \cdot 2 + 5 \cdot 3 \end{bmatrix} = \begin{bmatrix} 2 \\ 19 \end{bmatrix}.$$

Observe that the product AV is defined only when the number of columns of A equals the number of rows of V.

EXAMPLE 3. Determine the images of $\begin{bmatrix} 5 \\ 1 \end{bmatrix}$ and $\begin{bmatrix} 0 \\ 2 \end{bmatrix}$ under the mapping whose matrix is **(a)** $\begin{bmatrix} 1 & 3 \\ 2 & -2 \end{bmatrix}$; **(b)** $\begin{bmatrix} 1 & 0 \\ 0 & 1 \end{bmatrix}$.

Solution:

(a) $\begin{bmatrix} 1 & 3 \\ 2 & -2 \end{bmatrix} \begin{bmatrix} 5 \\ 1 \end{bmatrix} = \begin{bmatrix} 8 \\ 8 \end{bmatrix}$; $\begin{bmatrix} 1 & 3 \\ 2 & -2 \end{bmatrix} \begin{bmatrix} 0 \\ 2 \end{bmatrix} = \begin{bmatrix} 6 \\ -4 \end{bmatrix}$.

(b) $\begin{bmatrix} 1 & 0 \\ 0 & 1 \end{bmatrix} \begin{bmatrix} 5 \\ 1 \end{bmatrix} = \begin{bmatrix} 5 \\ 1 \end{bmatrix}$; $\begin{bmatrix} 1 & 0 \\ 0 & 1 \end{bmatrix} \begin{bmatrix} 0 \\ 2 \end{bmatrix} = \begin{bmatrix} 0 \\ 2 \end{bmatrix}$.

(a) $\begin{bmatrix} 8 \\ 8 \end{bmatrix}, \begin{bmatrix} 6 \\ -4 \end{bmatrix}$;   **(b)** $\begin{bmatrix} 5 \\ 1 \end{bmatrix}, \begin{bmatrix} 0 \\ 2 \end{bmatrix}$, **Answer.**

Do you see that $\begin{bmatrix} 1 & 0 \\ 0 & 1 \end{bmatrix}$ is the matrix of the identity mapping in $\mathcal{R} \times \mathcal{R}$, that is, the transformation that maps $\begin{bmatrix} x \\ y \end{bmatrix}$ into itself? We call $\begin{bmatrix} 1 & 0 \\ 0 & 1 \end{bmatrix}$ the *identity matrix of order 2*. In general, the square matrix of order n whose main diagonal from upper left to lower right consists of entries of 1, while all other entries are 0, is called the **identity matrix of order n** and is denoted by I.

Exercises

Find a single matrix equal to each of the following.

A 1. $\begin{bmatrix} 3 \\ 1 \end{bmatrix}^T$

2. $\begin{bmatrix} 4 & -1 & 2 \\ 3 & 1 & 7 \end{bmatrix}^T$

3. $\begin{bmatrix} 2 & 1 \\ -1 & 2 \end{bmatrix} + \begin{bmatrix} 1 & -1 \\ 2 & 1 \end{bmatrix}$

4. $\begin{bmatrix} 0 \\ 1 \end{bmatrix} + \begin{bmatrix} -1 \\ 0 \end{bmatrix}$

5. $3\begin{bmatrix} 7 & -1 \\ 2 & 0 \end{bmatrix}^T$

6. $-3\begin{bmatrix} 6 & 1 \\ 2 & -1 \end{bmatrix}^T$

7. $2\begin{bmatrix} 5 \\ -1 \end{bmatrix} - 3\begin{bmatrix} 1 \\ 2 \end{bmatrix}$

12. $\left(3\begin{bmatrix} 1 & 0 \\ 0 & 1 \end{bmatrix} - 6\begin{bmatrix} 1 & 0 \\ 0 & 1 \end{bmatrix} \right)^T$

8. $3\begin{bmatrix} 10 & 15 \\ -1 & -2 \end{bmatrix} + 6\begin{bmatrix} 1 & 8 \\ 9 & 15 \end{bmatrix}$

13. $\begin{bmatrix} 3 & 2 & 0 \\ 4 & -1 & 5 \end{bmatrix} \begin{bmatrix} 1 \\ 2 \\ -3 \end{bmatrix}$

9. $2\left(\begin{bmatrix} 3 \\ 1 \end{bmatrix} - \begin{bmatrix} -1 \\ 4 \end{bmatrix} \right) + \begin{bmatrix} -8 \\ 6 \end{bmatrix}$

14. $\begin{bmatrix} -7 & 6 & 3 & 9 \end{bmatrix} \begin{bmatrix} 1 \\ 2 \\ -1 \\ 3 \end{bmatrix}$

10. $-3\begin{bmatrix} 1 \\ 6 \end{bmatrix} + \left(\begin{bmatrix} 1 \\ 6 \end{bmatrix} - 2\begin{bmatrix} 1 \\ 7 \end{bmatrix} \right)$

15. $\begin{bmatrix} 2 & -7 \\ 11 & 4 \end{bmatrix} \begin{bmatrix} 0 \\ 0 \end{bmatrix}$

11. $3\begin{bmatrix} 1 & 0 \\ 0 & 1 \end{bmatrix} - 6\begin{bmatrix} 1 & 0 \\ 0 & 1 \end{bmatrix}^T$

16. $\begin{bmatrix} 1 & 0 \\ -1 & 3 \\ -3 & 5 \\ 0 & 2 \end{bmatrix} \begin{bmatrix} 5 \\ -6 \end{bmatrix}$

In Exercises 17 and 18, verify that $(AV)^T = V^T A^T$.

17. $A = \begin{bmatrix} 0 & 1 & -6 \end{bmatrix}; V = \begin{bmatrix} 1 \\ 2 \\ -9 \end{bmatrix}$

18. $A = \begin{bmatrix} 2 & 1 & 4 \end{bmatrix} ; V = \begin{bmatrix} 4 \\ -2 \\ 3 \end{bmatrix}$

Solve the matrix equation.

19. $\begin{bmatrix} u \\ v \end{bmatrix} + \begin{bmatrix} 3 \\ 6 \end{bmatrix} = -2\begin{bmatrix} 1 \\ 6 \end{bmatrix}$

20. $\begin{bmatrix} x \\ y \end{bmatrix} - 3\begin{bmatrix} -1 \\ 2 \end{bmatrix} = 2\begin{bmatrix} 1 \\ 0 \end{bmatrix}$

21. $3\begin{bmatrix} u_1 & v_1 \\ u_2 & v_2 \end{bmatrix}^T - \begin{bmatrix} 1 & 6 \\ 4 & 2 \end{bmatrix} = \begin{bmatrix} -1 & 3 \\ 6 & 0 \end{bmatrix}$

22. $\begin{bmatrix} u_1 & v_1 \\ u_2 & v_2 \end{bmatrix} + \begin{bmatrix} 3 & 2 \\ -7 & 5 \end{bmatrix} = \begin{bmatrix} 3 & 2 \\ -7 & 5 \end{bmatrix}^T$

23. $\begin{bmatrix} 1 & 2 \\ 3 & 2 \end{bmatrix} \begin{bmatrix} x \\ y \end{bmatrix} = \begin{bmatrix} -1 \\ 1 \end{bmatrix}$

24. $\begin{bmatrix} 3 & 2 \\ 1 & 2 \end{bmatrix} \begin{bmatrix} x \\ y \end{bmatrix} = \begin{bmatrix} -12 \\ -4 \end{bmatrix}$

Determine the images P' and Q' of given points P and Q under the linear transformation whose matrix A is given and show that in each case the lines PP' and QQ' intersect at the origin.

B   **25.** $P(1, -1), Q(7, 9); A = \begin{bmatrix} 3 & 7 \\ 9 & 5 \end{bmatrix}$

26. $P(5, 2), Q(-1, 1); A = \begin{bmatrix} 2 & 5 \\ 2 & -1 \end{bmatrix}$

Let $r, s \in \Re$, and let $A = \begin{bmatrix} a_1 & b_1 \\ c_1 & d_1 \end{bmatrix}$, $B = \begin{bmatrix} a_2 & b_2 \\ c_2 & d_2 \end{bmatrix}$, $C = \begin{bmatrix} a_3 & b_3 \\ c_3 & d_3 \end{bmatrix}$, $V = \begin{bmatrix} x \\ y \end{bmatrix}$ and $W = \begin{bmatrix} u \\ v \end{bmatrix}$ be matrices with real entries.   Prove each of the following assertions.

27. $A + B = B + A$ **32.** $r(sA) = (rs)A$
28. $(A + B) + C = A + (B + C)$ **33.** $(r + s)A = rA + sA$
29. $(A + B)^\mathsf{T} = A^\mathsf{T} + B^\mathsf{T}$ **34.** $-1 \cdot A = -A$
30. $(AV)^\mathsf{T} = V^\mathsf{T}A^\mathsf{T}$ **35.** $A(rV) = r(AV)$
31. $rA + rB = r(A + B)$ **36.** $A(V + W) = AV + AW$

C   **37.** Prove that the set of all 2×1 matrices is a group with respect to addition.
38. Prove that the set of all 2×2 matrices is a group with respect to addition.

13–10 Products of Matrices

In $\Re \times \Re$ let α and σ be the linear transformations with the respective matrices $A = \begin{bmatrix} a_1 & a_2 \\ b_1 & b_2 \end{bmatrix}$ and $S = \begin{bmatrix} r_1 & s_1 \\ r_2 & s_2 \end{bmatrix}$. Can you describe the mapping $\alpha \circ \sigma$. If you recall the meaning of composition of functions discussed in Chapter 9, you know that you obtain the image of $X = \begin{bmatrix} x \\ y \end{bmatrix}$ under $\alpha \circ \sigma$ by first finding its image X' under σ, and then finding the image X'' of X' under α. Now

$$X' = SX = \begin{bmatrix} r_1 & s_1 \\ r_2 & s_2 \end{bmatrix}\begin{bmatrix} x \\ y \end{bmatrix} = \begin{bmatrix} r_1x + s_1y \\ r_2x + s_2y \end{bmatrix}.$$

Hence, the image of X' under α is

$$X'' = A(SX) = \begin{bmatrix} a_1 & a_2 \\ b_1 & b_2 \end{bmatrix}\begin{bmatrix} r_1x + s_1y \\ r_2x + s_2y \end{bmatrix}$$

$$= \begin{bmatrix} a_1(r_1x + s_1y) + a_2(r_2x + s_2y) \\ b_1(r_1x + s_1y) + b_2(r_2x + s_2y) \end{bmatrix}$$

$$= \begin{bmatrix} (a_1r_1 + a_2r_2)x + (a_1s_1 + a_2s_2)y \\ (b_1r_1 + b_2r_2)x + (b_1s_1 + b_2s_2)y \end{bmatrix}$$

$$= \begin{bmatrix} a_1r_1 + a_2r_2 & a_1s_1 + a_2s_2 \\ b_1r_1 + b_2r_2 & b_1s_1 + b_2s_2 \end{bmatrix} \begin{bmatrix} x \\ y \end{bmatrix}.$$

Thus, if you define the product of the matrices A and S so that

$$AS = \begin{bmatrix} a_1 & a_2 \\ b_1 & b_2 \end{bmatrix} \begin{bmatrix} r_1 & s_1 \\ r_2 & s_2 \end{bmatrix} = \begin{bmatrix} a_1r_1 + a_2r_2 & a_1s_1 + a_2s_2 \\ b_1r_1 + b_2r_2 & b_1s_1 + b_2s_2 \end{bmatrix},$$

then you can say that $\alpha \circ \sigma$ is a linear transformation whose matrix is AS. (Why?)

When you observe that the first-column vector of AS is the product of A and the first-column vector of S, and that the second-column vector of AS is the product of A and the second-column vector of S, you can understand the motivation for the following definition of the product of matrices.

The product of an $m \times n$ matrix A and an $n \times p$ matrix S is the $m \times p$ matrix whose entry in the ith row and jth column is the sum of the products of the corresponding entries in the ith row of A and the jth column of S.

The following example shows, in three stages, the multiplication of a pair of matrices.

$$\begin{bmatrix} 1 & 0 & -1 \\ 2 & 1 & 3 \end{bmatrix} \begin{bmatrix} -1 & 0 & 2 \\ 3 & 1 & -4 \\ 1 & 0 & 0 \end{bmatrix} = \begin{bmatrix} -2 & & \\ 4 & & \end{bmatrix}$$

$$\begin{bmatrix} 1 & 0 & -1 \\ 2 & 1 & 3 \end{bmatrix} \begin{bmatrix} -1 & 0 & 2 \\ 3 & 1 & -4 \\ 1 & 0 & 0 \end{bmatrix} = \begin{bmatrix} -2 & 0 & \\ 4 & 1 & \end{bmatrix}$$

$$\begin{bmatrix} 1 & 0 & -1 \\ 2 & 1 & 3 \end{bmatrix} \begin{bmatrix} -1 & 0 & 2 \\ 3 & 1 & -4 \\ 1 & 0 & 0 \end{bmatrix} = \begin{bmatrix} -2 & 0 & 2 \\ 4 & 1 & 0 \end{bmatrix}$$

Notice that the two matrices to be multiplied must be such that each row in the first matrix has the same number of entries as each column of the second matrix. Thus, when the factors in the preceding example are reversed, the product is not defined. Hence, multiplication of matrices is not a commutative operation. Indeed, even when the products in both orders exist, the products may not be equal. For example,

$$\begin{bmatrix} 1 & 3 \\ -1 & 2 \end{bmatrix}\begin{bmatrix} 1 & 0 \\ 2 & 1 \end{bmatrix} = \begin{bmatrix} 7 & 3 \\ 3 & 2 \end{bmatrix} \quad \text{and} \quad \begin{bmatrix} 1 & 0 \\ 2 & 1 \end{bmatrix}\begin{bmatrix} 1 & 3 \\ -1 & 2 \end{bmatrix} = \begin{bmatrix} 1 & 3 \\ 1 & 8 \end{bmatrix},$$

so that $\begin{bmatrix} 1 & 3 \\ -1 & 2 \end{bmatrix}\begin{bmatrix} 1 & 0 \\ 2 & 1 \end{bmatrix} \neq \begin{bmatrix} 1 & 0 \\ 2 & 1 \end{bmatrix}\begin{bmatrix} 1 & 3 \\ -1 & 2 \end{bmatrix}.$

Although the multiplication of matrices is not commutative, it does satisfy the associative and distributive laws. (Exercises 15–16, page 555.)

EXAMPLE 1. If $X = \begin{bmatrix} x \\ y \end{bmatrix}$ and $Q = \begin{bmatrix} 5 & 3 \\ 3 & -4 \end{bmatrix},$

verify that $(X^TQ)X = X^T(QX).$

Solution:
$$X^T = [x \quad y].$$

$$\therefore (X^TQ)X = [x \quad y]\begin{bmatrix} 5 & 3 \\ 3 & -4 \end{bmatrix}\begin{bmatrix} x \\ y \end{bmatrix}$$

$$= [5x + 3y \quad 3x - 4y]\begin{bmatrix} x \\ y \end{bmatrix}.$$

$$\therefore (X^TQ)X = [5x^2 + 6xy - 4y^2].$$

Similarly,

$$X^T(QX) = [x \quad y]\begin{bmatrix} 5x + 3y \\ 3x - 4y \end{bmatrix}.$$

$$\therefore X^T(QX) = [5x^2 + 6xy - 4y^2]$$

$$\therefore (X^TQ)X = X^T(QX).$$

The preceding example suggests that you can write the equation $5x^2 - 6xy - 4y^2 = 7$ in the matrix form $[x \quad y]\begin{bmatrix} 5 & -3 \\ -3 & -4 \end{bmatrix}\begin{bmatrix} x \\ y \end{bmatrix} = [7].$ We will call $\begin{bmatrix} 5 & -3 \\ -3 & -4 \end{bmatrix}$ the matrix of the *quadratic form* $5x^2 - 6xy - 4y^2.$

In general, the matrix of the quadratic form $ax^2 + 2bxy + cy^2$ is $\begin{bmatrix} a & b \\ b & c \end{bmatrix}.$

Exercises

In Exercises 1–6, determine AB and, if they exist, BA, A^2, and B^2.

A

1. $A = \begin{bmatrix} 1 & 2 \\ -1 & 3 \end{bmatrix}$; $B = \begin{bmatrix} 3 & -1 \\ 2 & 1 \end{bmatrix}$ **2.** $A = \begin{bmatrix} 7 & 6 \end{bmatrix}$; $B = \begin{bmatrix} 3 \\ 4 \end{bmatrix}$

3. $A = \begin{bmatrix} 1 & 3 & 1 \\ 4 & 2 & -1 \\ 0 & 0 & 1 \end{bmatrix}$; $B = \begin{bmatrix} 1 & 2 \\ 0 & -2 \\ 3 & 5 \end{bmatrix}$

4. $A = \begin{bmatrix} -3 & 7 & 1 \\ 4 & 6 & -2 \end{bmatrix}$; $B = \begin{bmatrix} 4 & 0 \\ -2 & 6 \\ 5 & 8 \end{bmatrix}$

Let α and β be the linear transformations with matrices A and B. Determine the matrices of the transformations $\alpha \circ \beta$ and $\beta \circ \alpha$.

5. $A = \begin{bmatrix} 7 & -1 \\ 1 & 0 \end{bmatrix}$; $B = \begin{bmatrix} 0 & 1 \\ 1 & 0 \end{bmatrix}$

6. $A = \begin{bmatrix} 2 & -1 \\ 1 & 5 \end{bmatrix}$; $B = \begin{bmatrix} 0 & -1 \\ -1 & 0 \end{bmatrix}$

Let $M = \begin{bmatrix} 3 & 2 \\ 2 & 5 \end{bmatrix}$, $N = \begin{bmatrix} 4 & -1 \\ -1 & 1 \end{bmatrix}$, $P = \begin{bmatrix} 0 & 1 \\ 1 & 5 \end{bmatrix}$, and $X = \begin{bmatrix} x \\ y \end{bmatrix}$. Find the quadratic form represented by each of the following matrix expressions.

B

7. $X^T(M + N)X$ **9.** $X^TNX + X^TMX - X^TPX$

8. $X^T(M - N)X$ **10.** $X^T(M + N)X + X^TPX$

Let $A = \begin{bmatrix} a_1 & b_1 \\ c_1 & d_1 \end{bmatrix}$, $B = \begin{bmatrix} a_2 & b_2 \\ c_2 & d_2 \end{bmatrix}$, $C = \begin{bmatrix} a_3 & b_3 \\ c_3 & d_3 \end{bmatrix}$ be matrices with real entries. Prove each of the following assertions.

C

11. $(AB)C = A(BC)$

12. $A(B + C) = AB + AC$

13. $(A + B)C = AC + BC$

14. $(AB)^T = B^TA^T$

15. If A is an $m \times n$ matrix, and B is a matrix, then *both* products AB and BA exist if and only if B is an $n \times m$ matrix.

16. Determine whether the equation $(A - B)^2 = A^2 - 2AB + B^2$ is satisfied by all 2×2 matrices A and B.

13-11 Inverses of Matrices

If you restrict your consideration to the set of square matrices of a given order, you can see that in that set the identity matrix acts as the identity element for multiplication. For example,

$$\begin{bmatrix} 1 & 0 \\ 0 & 1 \end{bmatrix}\begin{bmatrix} a & b \\ c & d \end{bmatrix} = \begin{bmatrix} a & b \\ c & d \end{bmatrix} = \begin{bmatrix} a & b \\ c & d \end{bmatrix}\begin{bmatrix} 1 & 0 \\ 0 & 1 \end{bmatrix}.$$

Because the products

$$\begin{bmatrix} -1 & 3 \\ 1 & -2 \end{bmatrix}\begin{bmatrix} 2 & 3 \\ 1 & 1 \end{bmatrix} = \begin{bmatrix} 1 & 0 \\ 0 & 1 \end{bmatrix} \quad \text{and} \quad \begin{bmatrix} 2 & 3 \\ 1 & 1 \end{bmatrix}\begin{bmatrix} -1 & 3 \\ 1 & -2 \end{bmatrix} = \begin{bmatrix} 1 & 0 \\ 0 & 1 \end{bmatrix}$$

are equal to the identity matrix, we call the factors *inverses of each other*. Any two matrices A and B such that $AB = BA = I$ are called **inverses** and we write $A = B^{-1}$ and $B = A^{-1}$.

It is easy to see that only square matrices can have inverses. (Why?) But determining whether a given square matrix of high order has an inverse, and then finding the inverse when it exists, can involve considerable computational effort. The case of 2×2 matrices, however, is easy to discuss.

Suppose $A = \begin{bmatrix} a_1 & b_1 \\ a_2 & b_2 \end{bmatrix}$. To see whether A^{-1} exists, you seek a matrix

$$A^{-1} = \begin{bmatrix} u_1 & v_1 \\ u_2 & v_2 \end{bmatrix} \text{ such that } AA^{-1} = \begin{bmatrix} a_1 & b_1 \\ a_2 & b_2 \end{bmatrix}\begin{bmatrix} u_1 & v_1 \\ u_2 & v_2 \end{bmatrix} = \begin{bmatrix} 1 & 0 \\ 0 & 1 \end{bmatrix}, \text{ or}$$

$$\begin{bmatrix} a_1u_1 + b_1u_2 & a_1v_1 + b_1v_2 \\ a_2u_1 + b_2u_2 & a_2v_1 + b_2v_2 \end{bmatrix} = \begin{bmatrix} 1 & 0 \\ 0 & 1 \end{bmatrix}$$

The last equation is equivalent to the two systems of equations

(1) $\quad \begin{aligned} a_1u_1 + b_1u_2 &= 1 \\ a_2u_1 + b_2u_2 &= 0 \end{aligned}$ (2) $\quad \begin{aligned} a_1v_1 + b_1v_2 &= 0 \\ a_2v_1 + b_2v_2 &= 1. \end{aligned}$

Using the theorem stated on page 201, you can state the solutions of these pairs of equations as follows:

$$u_1 = \frac{b_2}{a_1b_2 - a_2b_1} \qquad v_1 = \frac{-b_1}{a_1b_2 - a_2b_1}$$

$$u_2 = \frac{-a_2}{a_1b_2 - a_2b_1} \qquad v_2 = \frac{a_1}{a_1b_2 - a_2b_1}$$

provided $a_1b_2 - a_2b_1 \neq 0$. Writing $\delta(A) = a_1b_2 - a_2b_1$ (read, "the

determinant of A equals $a_1b_2 - a_2b_1$"), you have:

$$A^{-1} = \frac{1}{\delta(A)}\begin{bmatrix} b_2 & -b_1 \\ -a_2 & a_1 \end{bmatrix}, \text{ provided } \delta(A) \neq 0.$$

It is a simple exercise to verify that $AA^{-1} = A^{-1}A = I$ (Exercise 13, page 558). Thus, if $\delta(A) \neq 0$, you obtain the inverse of A by interchanging a_1 and b_2, replacing b_1 and a_2 by their negatives, and multiplying the resulting matrix by $\dfrac{1}{\delta(A)}$. On the other hand, if $\delta(A) = 0$, it can be proved that equations (1) and (2) above have no solution so that A has no inverse.

EXAMPLE 1. If $A = \begin{bmatrix} 6 & 1 \\ -1 & 2 \end{bmatrix}$, find A^{-1}.

Solution: $\delta(A) = 12 - (1)(-1) = 13.$

$$\therefore A^{-1} = \tfrac{1}{13}\begin{bmatrix} 2 & -1 \\ 1 & 6 \end{bmatrix} = \begin{bmatrix} \frac{2}{13} & -\frac{1}{13} \\ \frac{1}{13} & \frac{6}{13} \end{bmatrix}, \textbf{ Answer.}$$

Note: You should compute AA^{-1} and $A^{-1}A$ to verify that each product equals I.

Given the matrix of a linear transformation in $\Re \times \Re$, you can now determine the inverse of the transformation. For, if α is the mapping whose matrix is A, then α maps $X = \begin{bmatrix} x \\ y \end{bmatrix}$ into $X' = \begin{bmatrix} x' \\ y' \end{bmatrix}$ where $AX = X'$.

Hence, if $\delta(A) \neq 0$, then A^{-1} exists, and $X = A^{-1}X'$.   (Why?)

Therefore, α^{-1} is the mapping whose matrix is A^{-1}.

EXAMPLE 2. Let α be the mapping whose transformation equations are

$$x' = x + y$$
$$y' = x.$$

Determine the transformation equation of α^{-1}.

Solution: The matrix of α is $A = \begin{bmatrix} 1 & 1 \\ 1 & 0 \end{bmatrix}$. Since $\delta(A) = -1$,

$$A^{-1} = \begin{bmatrix} 0 & 1 \\ 1 & -1 \end{bmatrix} \text{ and the transformation equations of } \alpha^{-1}$$

are $x = y'$

$$y = x' - y', \textbf{ Answer.}$$

Exercises

State whether the given matrix has an inverse. If the inverse exists, find it.

A **1.** $\begin{bmatrix} 1 & 3 \\ 2 & -1 \end{bmatrix}$ **3.** $\begin{bmatrix} 2 & 6 \\ -1 & 3 \end{bmatrix}$ **5.** $\begin{bmatrix} 4 & -1 \\ -8 & 2 \end{bmatrix}$

2. $\begin{bmatrix} 1 & 0 \\ 0 & 1 \end{bmatrix}$ **4.** $\begin{bmatrix} 2 & 6 \\ 1 & 3 \end{bmatrix}$ **6.** $\begin{bmatrix} 3 & -1 \\ -1 & 2 \end{bmatrix}$

Use the fact that if $AX = B$, then $X = A^{-1}B$, to solve each equation.

7. $\begin{bmatrix} 2 & 1 \\ 1 & 1 \end{bmatrix}\begin{bmatrix} x \\ y \end{bmatrix} = \begin{bmatrix} 3 \\ 2 \end{bmatrix}$ **9.** $\begin{bmatrix} 1 & 3 \\ 2 & 3 \end{bmatrix}\begin{bmatrix} x \\ y \end{bmatrix} = \begin{bmatrix} 2 \\ 7 \end{bmatrix}$

8. $\begin{bmatrix} 1 & 2 \\ 3 & 2 \end{bmatrix}\begin{bmatrix} x \\ y \end{bmatrix} = \begin{bmatrix} -1 \\ 1 \end{bmatrix}$ **10.** $\begin{bmatrix} 3 & 2 \\ 1 & 2 \end{bmatrix}\begin{bmatrix} x \\ y \end{bmatrix} = \begin{bmatrix} -12 \\ -4 \end{bmatrix}$

Solve for the matrix A.

11. $\begin{bmatrix} 5 & 3 \\ 3 & 2 \end{bmatrix} A - \begin{bmatrix} 2 & 4 \\ 3 & 2 \end{bmatrix} = \begin{bmatrix} 0 & 1 \\ -2 & 2 \end{bmatrix}$

12. $\begin{bmatrix} 3 & 4 \\ 2 & 3 \end{bmatrix} A + \begin{bmatrix} 4 & 0 \\ 2 & 3 \end{bmatrix} = \begin{bmatrix} -1 & 1 \\ -2 & 0 \end{bmatrix}$

B **13.** Show that if

$$A = \begin{bmatrix} a_1 & b_1 \\ a_2 & b_2 \end{bmatrix}, \; \delta(A) = a_1 b_2 - a_2 b_1,$$

and

$$A^{-1} = \frac{1}{\delta(A)}\begin{bmatrix} b_2 & -b_1 \\ -a_2 & a_1 \end{bmatrix}, \text{ then } AA^{-1} = A^{-1}A = I.$$

14. Show that for every 2×2 matrix A such that $\delta(A) \neq 0$, $(A^{\mathsf{T}})^{-1} = (A^{-1})^{\mathsf{T}}$.

15. Show that $\delta(AB) = \delta(A) \cdot \delta(B)$ for all 2×2 matrices A and B.

16. Show that for every 2×2 matrix A such that $\delta(A) \neq 0$, $\delta(A^{-1}) = \dfrac{1}{\delta(A)}$.

17. Show that each matrix of the form $\begin{bmatrix} \cos\theta & \sin\theta \\ -\sin\theta & \cos\theta \end{bmatrix}$ has an inverse.

18. Show that the product of two matrices of the form $\begin{bmatrix} \cos\theta & \sin\theta \\ -\sin\theta & \cos\theta \end{bmatrix}$ is a matrix of the same form.

19. Find x and y in terms of x' and y'. $\begin{bmatrix} \cos\theta & \sin\theta \\ -\sin\theta & \cos\theta \end{bmatrix}\begin{bmatrix} x \\ y \end{bmatrix} = \begin{bmatrix} x' \\ y' \end{bmatrix}$

20. Find x' and y' in terms of x and y. $\begin{bmatrix} \cos\theta & \sin\theta \\ -\sin\theta & \cos\theta \end{bmatrix}\begin{bmatrix} x \\ y \end{bmatrix} = \begin{bmatrix} x' \\ y' \end{bmatrix}$

C

21. Show that $(AB)^{-1} = B^{-1}A^{-1}$ for all 2 $\times$ 2 matrices A and B with nonzero determinants.

22. Show that $(ABA^{-1})^{-1} = AB^{-1}A^{-1}$ for all 2$\times$2 matrices A and B with nonzero determinants.

Chapter Summary

1. The set of points in $\mathcal{R} \times \mathcal{R}$ satisfying an equation is called the **locus** or graph of the equation. The loci of equations of second-degree are called conic sections.

2. Conic sections whose equations do not contain a mixed-product term have an axis of symmetry parallel to one of the coordinate axes and can be quickly identified and sketched. The following list identifies the main features of the graph of any equation equivalent to an equation of the given form.

Circle $\qquad (x - h)^2 + (y - k)^2 = r^2 \qquad$ Center (h, k), radius r

Parabola $\qquad (y - k)^2 = 4p(x - h) \qquad (x - h)^2 = 4p(y - k)$

Vertex		(h, k)
Axis	$y = k$	$x = h$
Focus	$(h + p, k)$	$(h, k + p)$
Directrix	$x = h - p$	$y = k - p$

Ellipse $\qquad \dfrac{(x - h)^2}{a^2} + \dfrac{(y - k)^2}{b^2} = 1 \qquad \dfrac{(y - k)^2}{a^2} + \dfrac{(x - h)^2}{b^2} = 1$

$$c^2 = a^2 - b^2$$

Center		(h, k)
Principal Axis	$y = k$	$x = h$
Vertices	$(h \pm a, k)$	$(h, k \pm a)$
Foci	$(h \pm c, k)$	$(h, k \pm c)$
Ends of Minor Axis	$(h, k \pm b)$	$(h \pm b, k)$

Hyperbola $\qquad \dfrac{(x - h)^2}{a^2} - \dfrac{(y - k)^2}{b^2} = 1 \qquad \dfrac{(y - k)^2}{a^2} - \dfrac{(x - h)^2}{b^2} = 1$

$$c^2 = a^2 + b^2$$

Asymptotes $\qquad y - k = \pm \dfrac{b}{a}(x - h) \qquad y - k = \pm \dfrac{a}{b}(x - h)$

Center, principal axis, vertices, foci, and ends of conjugate axis are obtained as indicated above for the ellipse.

3. In $\mathcal{R} \times \mathcal{R}$ translations and rotations are mappings that preserve distance and angles. Hence, under these mappings the images of lines are lines, of ellipses are ellipses, and so on. A conic section $\mathcal{K}$ whose equation contains a mixed-product term can be identified by determining a rotation under which the image of $\mathcal{K}$ does not have a mixed-product term in its equation.

4. The translation equations

$$x' = x - h \quad \text{and} \quad y' = y - k$$

define *a translation of the plane* determined by the vector $(-h, -k)$, or a *translation of the coordinate axes* with (h, k) as the new origin.

5. The rotation equations

$$x = x' \cos \phi - y' \sin \phi$$
$$y = x' \sin \phi + y' \cos \phi$$

define a *rotation of the plane* about **O** through the angle $-\phi$, or *a rotation of the coordinate axes* about **O** through the angle ϕ. To eliminate the mixed-product term in the equation

$$Ax^2 + Bxy + Cy^2 + Dx + Ey + F = 0,$$

rotate the axes about **O** through the angle ϕ where (1) $\phi = \dfrac{\pi}{4}$, if $A = C$, and (2) $\tan 2\phi = \dfrac{B}{A - C}, 0 < 2\phi < \pi$, if $A \neq C$. The nature of the graph of the equation can be determined from the value of the **characteristic** $B^2 - 4AC$.

6. The matrix $\begin{bmatrix} a & b \\ c & d \end{bmatrix}$ defines a linear transformation $x' = ax + by$, $y' = cx + dy$.

7. The **sum of two matrices** of the *same dimensions* is the matrix whose entries are the sums of the corresponding entries of the matrices to be added.

8. In the set of $m \times n$ matrices, the **additive identity** element is the zero matrix, $O_{m \times n}$; the **additive inverse** of $A_{m \times n}$ is $-A_{m \times n}$. The **product** of a **scalar** r and a matrix A is the matrix each of whose entries is r times the corresponding entry of A.
Matrix addition and scalar multiplication are both **associative** and **commutative**.

9. The **product of matrices** $A_{m \times n}$ and $B_{n \times p}$ is a matrix $C_{m \times p}$ whose entry in row i and column j is the sum of the products of the corresponding entries in row i of A and column j of B. Matrix multiplication is **associative** but not **commutative**; a product is found in the order in which it is

written. Multiplication is **distributive with respect to addition.**

In the set of square matrices, the **multiplicative identity** is I, such that $AI = IA = A$. Provided $\delta(A) \neq 0$, A has a **multiplicative inverse** A^{-1}, such that $AA^{-1} = A^{-1}A = I$.

Chapter Test

13-1   **1.** Find an equation for the circle which has as a diameter the line segment with endpoints $(2, 0)$ and $(6, 0)$.

13-2   **2.** Find an equation of the parabola with vertex at the origin and directrix $\{(x, y): y = -2\}$.

13-3   **3.** Find (**a**) the foci, (**b**) the vertices, (**c**) the eccentricity, and (**d**) the length of the minor axis, of the locus of $4x^2 + 9y^2 = 36$.

13-4   **4.** Find an equation of the hyperbola with center at the origin, eccentricity 2, and conjugate axis of length 4.

13-5   **5.** Determine the image of the locus of $xy + y + x = 3$ under the translation determined by the vector $(1, 1)$.

6. Find an equation of the parabola with focus $(4, 4)$ and the line with equation $x = -6$ as directrix.

13-6   **7.** Determine the image of the locus of $xy + y + x = 3$ under a rotation about $\mathbf{O}$ with $\theta = \dfrac{\pi}{4}$ and use the result to identify the given locus.

13-7   **8.** Without applying a rotation, identify the locus of
$$2x^2 - 3xy + 5y^2 - 2x \doteq 0.$$

13-8   **9.** Determine the rotation equations that will transform the equation $4x^2 - 3xy + y^2 = 1$ into an equation without a mixed-product term.

13-9   **10.** Solve for x: $2 \begin{bmatrix} 4 & 1 \\ -1 & 2 \end{bmatrix} = \begin{bmatrix} 3 & 2 \\ x & -1 \end{bmatrix}^{\mathsf{T}} + \begin{bmatrix} 4 & -1 \\ 0 & -5 \end{bmatrix}$.

13-10   **11.** If α and β are linear transformations with matrices
$$\begin{bmatrix} 3 & 5 \\ -2 & 7 \end{bmatrix} \text{ and } \begin{bmatrix} 0 & 1 \\ 1 & 1 \end{bmatrix},$$
determine the matrices of the mappings $\alpha \circ \beta$ and $\beta \circ \alpha$.

13-11   **12.** Find the inverse of $\begin{bmatrix} 1 & 3 \\ 2 & 7 \end{bmatrix}$, and then solve the equation
$$\begin{bmatrix} 1 & 3 \\ 2 & 7 \end{bmatrix} A = \begin{bmatrix} 0 & 2 \\ -1 & 3 \end{bmatrix}$$
for the matrix A.

Reading List

AMIR-MOÉZ, A. R. *Use of Matrices in Teaching Conic Sections.* Mathematics Magazine, vol. 33, pp. 145–156, 1960.

COFFMAN, R. T. *The "Reflection Property" of the Conics.* Mathematics Magazine, vol. 36, pp. 11–12, 1963.

COFFMAN, R. T. *A Study of Conic Section Orbits by Elementary Mathematics.* Mathematics Magazine, vol. 36, pp. 271–280, 1963.

HAGIS, PETER, JR. *A Note on the Rotation of Axes.* Mathematics Magazine, vol. 36, pp. 127–128, 1963.

JENNRICH, ROBERT I., and RAYMOND B. KILLGROVE. *A Use of Inequalities for Loci in Analytic Geometry.* Mathematics Magazine, vol. 35, pp. 105–106, 1962.

KELLEY, JOHN L. *Introduction to Modern Algebra.* Princeton, N. J.: D. Van Nostrand, 1960.

SAWYER, W. W. *Prelude to Mathematics.* Baltimore, Md.: Penguin Books, 1955.

SCHOOL MATHEMATICS STUDY GROUP. Mathematics for High School: *Introduction to Matrix Algebra.* New Haven, Conn.: Yale University Press, 1961.

WEXLER, CHARLES. *Analytic Geometry: A Vector Approach.* Reading, Mass.: Addison-Wesley, 1962.

G. H. Hardy

"What we do may be small, but it has a certain character of permanence; and to have produced anything of the slightest permanent interest, whether it be a copy of verses or a geometrical theorem, is to have done something utterly beyond the power of the vast majority of men." In these words the English mathematician G. H. Hardy describes the significance of mathematicians and of the mathematical works which they create. He thought of mathematicians as makers of serious and beautiful patterns — serious in their depth and generality, and beautiful in their unexpectedness, inevitability, and conciseness. He believed in the enduring quality of mathematics. As he explains in *A Mathematician's Apology*, mathematics is a study which "did not begin with Pythagoras, and will not end with Einstein, but is the oldest and the youngest of all."

Hardy (1877–1947) showed an early interest in numbers, and it is said that when he was a small child he amused himself in church by factoring the hymn numbers. He studied mathematics at Cambridge University and was made an instructor there after he completed his studies. A long career as a teacher and as a research mathematician followed. In 1908 his textbook, *A Course of Pure Mathematics*, was published. This book appreciably changed the nature of mathematics instruction in Great Britain, since this was the first time that a rigorous presentation of elementary analysis was available.

In his research investigations, Hardy explored many areas of analysis and number theory. Among these were series, integral equations, inequalities, and continued fractions. Hardy was able to combine the ideas of number theory, which is concerned with the integers, with those of analysis, which deals with the real and complex numbers. Although Hardy's work covered a wide range, he was, above all, a pure mathematician. He once remarked that the results of another mathematician who worked in abstract mathematics would, because they were pure mathematics, be of interest long after the physical theories under discussion had become outdated.

563

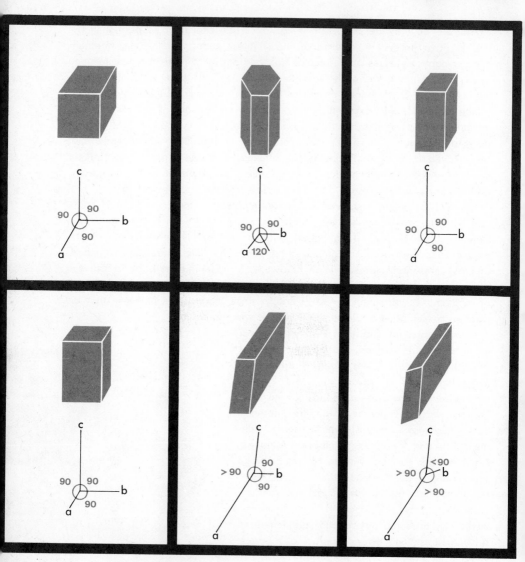

14

Every crystal belongs to one of the six crystal systems. In each of the diagrams above, a basic building block for the given system and the crystallographic axes for a building block of that system are shown. From left to right, the systems are (top row) the cubic, hexagonal, and tetragonal, and (bottom row) the orthorhombic, monoclinic, and triclinic.

Space Geometry

When you establish a number line by designating an origin and a scale, and then assign numbers to points on a geometric line, you create a one-dimensional coordinate system. The assignment of ordered pairs of numbers to the points in a geometric plane estabishes a two-dimensional coordinate system. In this chapter, you will learn to assign ordered triples to points in space by means of a three-dimensional coordinate system and will see how the properties of such a system can be studied using vectors and the algebra of real numbers.

VECTORS IN THREE-SPACE

14–1 Ordered Number Triples and Vectors

In Section 4–1 you learned that the Cartesian product of two sets K and M is the set

$$K \times M = \{(x, y): \ x \in K, y \in M\}.$$

A similar definition applies to three sets. Thus,

$$K \times L \times M = \{(x, y, z): \ x \in K, y \in L, \text{ and } z \in M\}.$$

EXAMPLE 1. Give a roster of $K \times L \times M$ if $K = \{1, 2\}$, $L = \{2, 4\}$, and $M = \{1, 2, 3\}$.

Solution: $K \times L \times M$ consists of the triples in the following array:

(1,2,1)	(1,4,1)	(2,2,1)	(2,4,1)
(1,2,2)	(1,4,2)	(2,2,2)	(2,4,2)
(1,2,3)	(1,4,3)	(2,2,3)	(2,4,3)

In this chapter, the Cartesian product in which we are most interested is $\mathcal{R} \times \mathcal{R} \times \mathcal{R} = \mathcal{R}_3$. In analogy with the terminology used in Chapter 4, we shall call an ordered triple a **vector** with three entries, and we shall extend to these vectors the algebraic concepts defined originally for vectors that are

565

ordered pairs of real numbers. (Instead of simply reading the extended definitions, you should first try to devise them on your own, and then compare your definitions with the generalizations listed below.)

Let $\mathbf{v} = (v_1, v_2, v_3)$ and $\mathbf{w} = (w_1, w_2, w_3)$ denote elements of $\mathfrak{R}_3$ and let r denote a real number.

EQUALITY	$\mathbf{v} = \mathbf{w}$ if and only if $v_1 = w_1$, $v_2 = w_2$, and $v_3 = w_3$.
ADDITION	$\mathbf{v} + \mathbf{w} = (v_1 + w_1, v_2 + w_2, v_3 + w_3)$.
ADDITIVE INVERSE	$-\mathbf{v} = (-v_1, -v_2, -v_3)$ and $\mathbf{v} + (-\mathbf{v}) = (0, 0, 0) = \mathbf{0}$.
SUBTRACTION	$\mathbf{v} - \mathbf{w} = \mathbf{v} + (-\mathbf{w})$ $= (v_1 - w_1, v_2 - w_2, v_3 - w_3)$.
NORM	$\|\mathbf{v}\| = \sqrt{v_1^2 + v_2^2 + v_3^2}$.
UNIT VECTOR	$\mathbf{v}$ is a unit vector if and only if $\|\mathbf{v}\| = 1$.
MULTIPLICATION BY A SCALAR	$r\mathbf{v} = \mathbf{v}r = (rv_1, rv_2, rv_3)$.
INNER PRODUCT	$\mathbf{v} \cdot \mathbf{w} = v_1 w_1 + v_2 w_2 + v_3 w_3$.
PERPENDICULAR VECTORS	$\mathbf{v}$ is perpendicular to $\mathbf{w}$ if and only if $\mathbf{v} \cdot \mathbf{w} = 0$.
PARALLEL VECTORS	$\mathbf{v}$ is parallel to $\mathbf{w}$ if and only if 1. $\mathbf{w} = \mathbf{0}$; or 2. $\mathbf{w} \neq \mathbf{0}$ and $\mathbf{v} = r\mathbf{w}$.

You can verify that these extended definitions preserve the properties of vector addition (page 134), of multiplication of a vector by a scalar (page 143), and of the inner product of vectors (page 151). Indeed, the proofs that these properties are still valid are entirely analogous to the corresponding proofs for vectors with two entries. With somewhat greater effort you can also prove that the statements

$$-\|\mathbf{v}\| \, \|\mathbf{w}\| \le \mathbf{v} \cdot \mathbf{w} \le \|\mathbf{v}\| \, \|\mathbf{w}\| \quad \text{and} \quad \|\mathbf{v} + \mathbf{w}\| \le \|\mathbf{v}\| + \|\mathbf{w}\|$$

remain valid. (Exercises 47 and 48, page 568.)

EXAMPLE 2. If $\mathbf{v} = (4, -1, 3)$ and $\mathbf{w} = (1, -2, -2)$, find **(a)** $\mathbf{v} + \mathbf{w}$; **(b)** $\mathbf{v} \cdot \mathbf{w}$; **(c)** whether or not $\mathbf{v}$ and $\mathbf{w}$ are orthogonal (that is, perpendicular) or parallel.

Solution: **(a)** $\mathbf{v} + \mathbf{w} = (4 + 1, -1 + (-2), 3 + (-2)) = (5, -3, 1)$.

(b) $\mathbf{v} \cdot \mathbf{w} = 4 \cdot 1 + (-1)(-2) + 3(-2) = 0$.

(c) Since $\mathbf{v} \cdot \mathbf{w} = 0$, the vectors are perpendicular. The vectors are not parallel, because $(4, -1, 3) = r(1, -2, -2)$ is true for no real number r. (Why?)

Guided by the theorem stated on page 460 for vectors with two entries, we define the angle ϕ between two nonzero vectors **v** and **w** by

$$\cos \phi = \frac{\mathbf{v} \cdot \mathbf{w}}{\|\mathbf{v}\| \cdot \|\mathbf{w}\|}, \quad 0 \leq \phi \leq \pi.$$

Under this definition the angle between two orthogonal vectors has radian measure $\frac{\pi}{2}$ (Why?), while the angle between nonzero parallel vectors measures 0^R or π^R. (Why?)

EXAMPLE 3. Determine the cosine of the angle between $\mathbf{v} = (1, -1, 0)$ and $\mathbf{w} = (3, -5, 4)$.

Solution: $\mathbf{v} = (1, -1, 0); \|\mathbf{v}\| = \sqrt{1^2 + (-1)^2 + 0^2} = \sqrt{2}$

$\mathbf{w} = (3, -5, 4); \|\mathbf{w}\| = \sqrt{3^2 + (-5)^2 + 4^2} = \sqrt{50}$

$\mathbf{v} \cdot \mathbf{w} = 3 \cdot 1 + -5(-1) + 4 \cdot 0 = 8$

$\therefore \cos \phi = \dfrac{8}{\sqrt{2}\sqrt{50}} = \dfrac{8}{10} = 0.8$ **Answer.**

Exercises

In Exercises 1–4, find values of p, q, and r so that the given equality holds.

1. $(p, 2q, r - 1) = (5, q, 2r)$
2. $(p - 1, 2q + 3, 2r + 1) = (3, q + 1, r - 2)$
3. $(p + q, 2p - q, r + 1) = (3, 3, 3)$
4. $(3p - r, p + 2r, 3q) = (1, 5, q)$

In Exercises 5–6, specify by roster $K \times L \times M$ for K, L, and M as given.

5. $K = \{0, 1, 2\}, L = \{-1, 3\}, M = \{5, 7\}$
6. $K = \{5, 4\}, \quad L = \{3, 4\}, \quad M = \{-2, 0, 1\}$

In Exercises 7–18, let $\mathbf{v} = (3, 1, 5)$, $\mathbf{u} = (-2, 6, -3)$, $r = 2$, and $s = -3$. Find a vector or scalar equal to the given expressions.

7. $\mathbf{v} + \mathbf{u}$ **11.** $(r - 2s)\mathbf{u}$ **15.** $\mathbf{v} \cdot (\mathbf{u} - 2\mathbf{v})$

8. $\mathbf{v} - \mathbf{u}$ **12.** $r\mathbf{u} + s(\mathbf{u} - \mathbf{v})$ **16.** $(\mathbf{u} - \mathbf{v}) \cdot (\mathbf{u} + \mathbf{v})$

9. $r\mathbf{v} + s\mathbf{u}$ **13.** $r\mathbf{v} \cdot \mathbf{u}$ **17.** $\|-(\mathbf{v} + \mathbf{u})\|$

10. $r(\mathbf{v} - s\mathbf{u})$ **14.** $\mathbf{v} \cdot s\mathbf{u}$ **18.** $\|\mathbf{u} - \mathbf{v}\|$

In Exercises 19–24, find the cosine of the angle between the given vectors.

19. $(1, 2, -2), (-2, 1, 2)$ **22.** $(1, 2, 3), (-1, 2, 0)$

20. $(1, -1, 1), (-1, 1, 1)$ **23.** $(2, 0, 5), (3, -2, 1)$

21. $(1, 3, 0), (2, 1, 0)$ **24.** $(4, 1, -3), (1, 2, 2)$

Let s, t, u, and v be respectively the vectors (s_1, s_2, s_3), (t_1, t_2, t_3), (u_1, u_2, u_3), and (v_1, v_2, v_3) in $\Re_3$. Let r and s be elements of $\Re$. Prove each of the following statements.

B **25.** $s + t$ belongs to $\Re_3$.

26. If $s = u$ and $t = v$, $s + t = u + v$.

27. $s + t = t + s$

28. $(s + t) + u = s + (t + u)$

29. $v + 0 = 0 + v = v$

30. $v + (-v) = (-v) + v = 0$

31. rv belongs to $\Re_3$.

32. If $r = s$ and $v = t$, $rv = st$.

33. If $rv = vs$, and $v \neq 0$, then $r = s$.

34. $(rs)v = r(sv)$

35. $1v = v$

36. $rv = 0$ if and only if $r = 0$ or $v = 0$.

37. $(-1)v = -v$ **42.** $r(v \cdot t) = (rv) \cdot t$

38. $r(v + t) = rv + rt$ **43.** $v \cdot (t + s) = v \cdot t + v \cdot s$

39. $(r + s)v = rv + sv$ **44.** $v \cdot v = \|v\|^2$

40. $\|rv\| = |r| \cdot \|v\|$ **45.** $\|v + t\|^2 = \|v\|^2 + 2v \cdot t + \|t\|^2$

41. $v \cdot t = t \cdot v$ **46.** $\|v - t\|^2 = \|v\|^2 - 2v \cdot t + \|t\|^2$

C **47.** $-\|v\| \|t\| \leq v \cdot t \leq \|v\| \|t\|$ **48.** $\|v + t\| \leq \|v\| + \|t\|$

A nonempty set $\mathcal{V}$ is called a **vector space** over the field of real numbers, if there is defined in $\mathcal{V}$ a binary operation called addition $(+)$ of elements of $\mathcal{V}$ and an operation of scalar multiplication of the elements of $\mathcal{V}$ by real numbers satisfying the properties listed in Exercises 25–39. Show that with suitable operations for addition and scalar multiplication, each of the following sets is a vector space over $\Re$.

49. $\Re \times \Re$ **50.** $\Re_3$

51. The subset of $\Re \times \Re$ consisting of the vectors whose first entry is 0.

52. The subset of $\Re_3$ consisting of the vectors whose third entry is 0.

53. The field of complex numbers.

54. The set of all 2×2 matrices with elements in $\Re$.

55. The set of polynomials in x of degree 5 or less.

56. The set of all ordered "5-tuples" of real numbers: $(r_1, r_2, r_3, r_4, r_5)$.

14-2 Points and Distances

Just as you used vectors with two entries to discuss analytic geometry in the plane, you can now use vectors with three entries to study analytic geometry in space. For this purpose, you first select three mutually perpendicular axes intersecting at an origin **O**. Next, choose a scale to make each axis a number line whose zero-point is **O**, and indicate the scale on each axis. (Ordinarily, the same scale is used on the three axes).

Although you may label the axes and choose the positive directions on them as you wish, the choice shown in Figure 14-1 is a common one. Taken in pairs, the three coordinate axes determine three **coordinate planes**, called the *xy*-plane, the *yz*-plane, and the *xz*-plane.

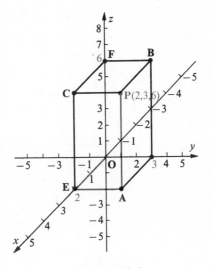

To associate an ordered triple in $\Re_3$ with a point **P** in space, think of three planes through **P**, one perpendicular to the *x*-axis, another perpendicular to the *y*-axis, and the third perpendicular to the *z*-axis. The numbers paired with the points in which these planes intersect the respective axes are, in order, the **x-coordinate**, the **y-coordinate**, and the **z-coordinate** of **P**. For example, **P** in Figure 14-1 has coordinates (2, 3, 6). We call **P** the **graph** of the ordered triple (2, 3, 6).

Figure 14-1

Notice that together with the coordinate planes the three planes drawn through **P** form a *rectangular parallelepiped*. Starting at the origin, you can arrive at **P** by moving along edges parallel to each axis in succession. One such path is shown in red in Figure 14-1: **O** to **E**, **E** to **A**, **A** to **P**. This suggests a procedure for locating a point whose coordinates are given. For example, Figure 14-2 shows the plotting of the point **T**(4, −2, 5):

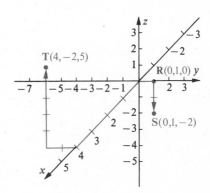

1. From the origin proceed 4 units along the *x*-axis;

2. Then move −2 units (2 units in the negative direction) parallel to the *y*-axis;

Figure 14-2

3. Then proceed 5 units parallel to the *z*-axis.

Notice that the coordinate planes separate space into 2^3, or 8, **octants**. The octant in which x, y, and z are each positive numbers is called the *first octant*, or the $(+, +, +)$ octant. The remaining octants are sometimes assigned numbers, but are more often designated by signs, such as $(+, -, -)$.

The procedure described above enables you to establish a one-to-one correspondence between the elements of $\mathcal{R}_3$ and the points of space. This correspondence enables you to develop geometry in space by using vector concepts. In fact, you can identify points with elements of $\mathcal{R}_3$ and refer to the totality of these points as **space** or, more precisely, as **three-space**. In analogy with plane analytic geometry as discussed in Chapter 5, we define the **distance** between two points $\mathbf{P}(x_1, y_1, z_1)$ and $\mathbf{T}(x_2, y_2, z_2)$ to be the norm of the vector $\|\mathbf{P} - \mathbf{T}\|$. Thus,

$$d(\mathbf{P}, \mathbf{T}) = \sqrt{(x_2 - x_1)^2 + (y_2 - y_1)^2 + (z_2 - z_1)^2}.$$

Can you describe the set of points at a given distance from a fixed point $\mathbf{C}$? In the plane, such a locus is a circle.

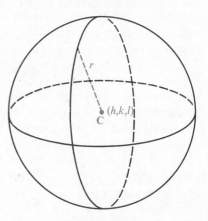

In space, the locus is a **sphere**. If the fixed point $\mathbf{C}$ has coordinates $(1, 3, 5)$ and the given distance is 6 (the **radius** of the sphere), an equation of the sphere is

$$\sqrt{(x - 1)^2 + (y - 3)^2 + (z - 5)^2} = 6$$

or

$$(x - 1)^2 + (y - 3)^2 + (z - 5)^2 = 36.$$

In general, in space the locus of an equation of the form

$$(x - h)^2 + (y - k)^2 + (z - l)^2 = r^2$$

Figure 14–3

is a sphere with **center** (h, k, l) and radius r. (Figure 14–3.)

Exercises

In Exercises 1–8, sketch a graph of the given points in space, using line segments to illustrate coordinates in a coordinate system.

1. $(3, 2, 3)$ **3.** $(3, 2, 1)$ **5.** $(1, 2, -1)$ **7.** $(-1, 2, 1)$

2. $(2, 5, 0)$ **4.** $(1, 2, 3)$ **6.** $(1, -2, 1)$ **8.** $(-1, 2, -1)$

In Exercises 9–14, find the distance between the given points.

9. $(3, 1, 2), (0, 0, 0)$ **10.** $(0, 0, 0), (3, -2, 6)$

11. $(3, -1, 2), (5, -2, -3)$ **13.** $(-3, 4, 5), (7, 4, 5)$

12. $(-2, 2, 1), (4, 5, -1)$ **14.** $(1, -1, 3), (3, 2, 1)$

State the condition that must be satisfied by the coordinates of every point lying in the indicated coordinate plane(s).

15. xy-plane   **17.** xz-plane

16. yz-plane   **18.** xy- and yz-planes

Determine the equation of the sphere whose center **C** and radius r are given.

19. $\mathbf{C}(1, 3, 0); r = 4$ **21.** $\mathbf{C}(0, 0, 0); r = 5$

20. $\mathbf{C}(-1, 2, 5); r = 1$ **22.** $\mathbf{C}(0, 0, 1); r = \sqrt{2}$

Determine the radius and the coordinates of the center of the sphere (if any) whose equation is given.

B

23. $x^2 + y^2 + z^2 - 4x + 2y - 11 = 0$

24. $x^2 + y^2 + z^2 - 2z + 8y - 8 = 0$

25. $x^2 + y^2 + z^2 - 18x - 24y + 6z + 200 = 0$

26. $x^2 + y^2 + z^2 - 2x + 4y - 6z + 14 = 0$

Find an equation of the locus of all points in space equidistant from:

27. $\mathbf{O}(0, 0, 0), \mathbf{P}(6, 10, 2)$ **28.** $\mathbf{P}(1, 3, 4), \mathbf{R}(-3, 5, 0)$

14–3 Parallel and Perpendicular Vectors

In Section 4–7, you learned several theorems concerning parallel and perpendicular vectors in $\Re \times \Re$. In particular, you found that (t_1, t_2) is parallel to (v_1, v_2) if and only if $(t_1, t_2) \cdot (-v_2, v_1) = 0$, that is, if and only if $-t_1 v_2 + t_2 v_1 = 0$. An attempt to discover in $\Re_3$ an analogue of this result leads to the following theorem.

THEOREM   Two vectors $\mathbf{t} = (t_1, t_2, t_3)$ and $\mathbf{v} = (v_1, v_2, v_3)$ in $\Re_3$ are parallel if and only if the vector

$$\mathbf{c} = (t_2 v_3 - t_3 v_2, t_3 v_1 - t_1 v_3, t_1 v_2 - t_2 v_1)$$

is the zero vector.

Proof: 1. To prove the "only if" part of the theorem, suppose that $\mathbf{t}$ and $\mathbf{v}$ are parallel vectors. If $\mathbf{v} = \mathbf{0}$, then $\mathbf{c} = \mathbf{0}$ (Why?), and the desired result is true. If $\mathbf{v} \neq \mathbf{0}$, there exists a real number r such that $\mathbf{t} = r\mathbf{v}$. Then $t_1 = rv_1, t_2 = rv_2$, and $t_3 = rv_3$. Replacing t_1, t_2, t_3 by these values, you have

$$\mathbf{c} = (v_2 \cdot rv_3 - v_3 \cdot rv_2, v_3 \cdot rv_1 - v_1 \cdot rv_3, v_1 \cdot rv_2 - v_2 \cdot rv_1).$$

$$\therefore \mathbf{c} = (0, 0, 0) = \mathbf{0}.$$

2. To prove the "if" part of the theorem, suppose that $c = 0$. There are two cases to consider.

Case i.　$v = 0$.　In this case, t and v are parallel by definition.

Case ii.　$v \neq 0$.　In this event, at least one of the numbers v_1, v_2, v_3 is not equal to 0, say $v_3 \neq 0$. Then, because $c = (0, 0, 0)$, you have

$$t_2 v_3 - t_3 v_2 = 0; \quad \text{or} \quad t_2 = \frac{t_3}{v_3} v_2;$$

$$t_3 v_1 - t_1 v_3 = 0, \quad \text{or} \quad t_1 = \frac{t_3}{v_3} v_1.$$

Hence, $(t_1, t_2, t_3) = \dfrac{t_3}{v_3} (v_1, v_2, v_3)$.　(Why?)

Thus, t is a scalar multiple of v, so that t and v are parallel vectors.

The vector c used in the preceding theorem occurs often enough in the algebra of vectors in $\mathcal{R}_3$ to be given a name.

If $t = (t_1, t_2, t_3)$ and $v = (v_1, v_2, v_3)$, then the **cross product** $c = t \times v$ is defined by

$$t \times v = (t_2 v_3 - t_3 v_2, t_3 v_1 - t_1 v_3, t_1 v_2 - t_2 v_1).$$

Using this terminology, you restate the preceding theorem as follows: Two vectors t and v in $\mathcal{R}_3$ are parallel if and only if $t \times v = 0$.

Notice that the cross product of two vectors is a vector, not a scalar. You can remember the entries in $t \times v$ by noticing that they are the determinants associated with the arrays obtained from the matrix $\begin{bmatrix} t_1 & t_2 & t_3 \\ v_1 & v_2 & v_3 \end{bmatrix}$ by suppressing the first column, then suppressing the second column and changing the sign of the resulting determinant, and, finally, deleting the third column. Thus

$$t \times v = \left(\begin{vmatrix} t_2 & t_3 \\ v_2 & v_3 \end{vmatrix}, \ - \begin{vmatrix} t_1 & t_3 \\ v_1 & v_3 \end{vmatrix}, \begin{vmatrix} t_1 & t_2 \\ v_1 & v_2 \end{vmatrix} \right).$$

EXAMPLE 1.　Determine whether the vectors $t = (1, 5, 8)$ and $v = (3, 2, 4)$ are parallel.

Solution:　$t \times v = \left(\begin{vmatrix} 5 & 8 \\ 2 & 4 \end{vmatrix}, \ - \begin{vmatrix} 1 & 8 \\ 3 & 4 \end{vmatrix}, \begin{vmatrix} 1 & 5 \\ 3 & 2 \end{vmatrix} \right)$

$\therefore t \times v = (4, 20, -13) \neq 0.$

$\therefore$ the vectors are not parallel, **Answer.**

EXAMPLE 2. Let $t = (1, 5, 8)$, $v = (3, 2, 4)$, and $s = (-1, 2, 6)$. Verify each of the following statements.

(a) $t \times v = -(v \times t)$;

(b) $t \times (v + s) = (t \times v) + (t \times s)$;

(c) $t \times (2v) = (2t) \times v = 2(t \times v)$.

Solution: (a) $v \times t = \left(\begin{vmatrix} 2 & 4 \\ 5 & 8 \end{vmatrix}, -\begin{vmatrix} 3 & 4 \\ 1 & 8 \end{vmatrix}, \begin{vmatrix} 3 & 2 \\ 1 & 5 \end{vmatrix} \right)$.

$\therefore$ $v \times t = (-4, -20, 13)$.

$\therefore$ Using the result of Example 1, $t \times v = -(v \times t)$.

(b) and (c) are left for you to complete.

Example 2 illustrates general properties of $t \times v$. (See Exercises 23, 24, and 25, page 576.)

Properties of the Cross Product of Vectors

Let t, v, and s denote any elements of $\mathcal{R}_3$, and let r denote any real number.

ANTICOMMUTATIVE PROPERTY $\quad t \times v = -(v \times t)$

DISTRIBUTIVE PROPERTY $\quad t \times (v + s) = (t \times v) + (t \times s)$

ASSOCIATIVE PROPERTY $\quad t \times (rv) = (rt) \times v = r(t \times v)$

ZERO PRODUCT PROPERTY $\quad t \times t = 0$

VECTOR TRIPLE PRODUCT $\quad t \times (v \times s) = (t \cdot s)v - (t \cdot v)s$

$\qquad\qquad\qquad\qquad\qquad\quad (t \times v) \times s = (s \cdot t)v - (s \cdot v)t$

Note that the product $(t \times v) \times s$ is generally not equal to $t \times (v \times s)$. (Exercises 27, 28, page 576.)

It is easy to prove the following property of $t \times v$.

THEOREM If t and v are vectors in $\mathcal{R}_3$, then $t \times v$ is perpendicular to each of the vectors t and v.

Proof: For the inner product $(t \times v) \cdot t$ you find:

$$(t \times v) \cdot t = t_1 \begin{vmatrix} t_2 & t_3 \\ v_2 & v_3 \end{vmatrix} - t_2 \begin{vmatrix} t_1 & t_3 \\ v_1 & v_3 \end{vmatrix} + t_3 \begin{vmatrix} t_1 & t_2 \\ v_1 & v_2 \end{vmatrix} = 0. \quad \text{(Why?)}$$

Similarly, you can verify that $(t \times v) \cdot v = 0$. Hence, by the definition of perpendicular vectors (page 566), $t \times v$ is perpendicular to t and to v.

EXAMPLE 3. Find a unit vector orthogonal to each of $(3, -1, 2)$ and $(4, -1, 3)$.

Solution: *Plan:* Find a unit vector parallel to the cross product of the given vectors.

$$(3, -1, 2) \times (4, -1, 3) = (-1, -1, 1).$$

∴ a unit vector in the direction of $(-1, -1, 1)$ is

$$\frac{(-1, -1, 1)}{\sqrt{1 + 1 + 1}} = \frac{1}{\sqrt{3}}(-1, -1, 1)$$

$$= \left(-\frac{1}{\sqrt{3}}, -\frac{1}{\sqrt{3}}, \frac{1}{\sqrt{3}}\right), \textbf{Answer.}$$

Notice that the solution of Example 3 made use of the following analogue of the theorem stated on page 155. The new theorem can be proved by an argument exactly similar to the one for that theorem.

THEOREM In $\mathcal{R}_3$ a vector perpendicular to one of two nonzero parallel vectors is perpendicular to the other.

EXAMPLE 4. Prove that $(\mathbf{t} \cdot \mathbf{v})^2 + \|\mathbf{t} \times \mathbf{v}\|^2 = \|\mathbf{t}\|^2 \|\mathbf{v}\|^2$.

Solution: Let $\mathbf{t} = (t_1, t_2, t_3)$ and $\mathbf{v} = (v_1, v_2, v_3)$. Then

$$(\mathbf{t} \cdot \mathbf{v})^2 + \|\mathbf{t} \times \mathbf{v}\|^2 = (t_1v_1 + t_2v_2 + t_3v_3)^2$$
$$+ (t_2v_3 - t_3v_2)^2 + (t_3v_1 - t_1v_3)^2 + (t_1v_2 - t_2v_1)^2.$$

Expanding the squares in the right member of the preceding equation and combining similar terms, you obtain

$$(\mathbf{t} \cdot \mathbf{v})^2 + \|\mathbf{t} \times \mathbf{v}\|^2 = (t_1v_1)^2 + (t_2v_2)^2 + (t_3v_3)^2 + (t_2v_3)^2 + (t_3v_2)^2$$
$$+ (t_3v_1)^2 + (t_1v_3)^2 + (t_1v_2)^2 + (t_2v_1)^2$$
$$= (t_1^2 + t_2^2 + t_3^2)(v_1^2 + v_2^2 + v_3^2).$$

∴ $(\mathbf{t} \cdot \mathbf{v})^2 + \|\mathbf{t} \times \mathbf{v}\|^2 = \|\mathbf{t}\|^2 \|\mathbf{v}\|^2$.

The result proved in Example 4 leads to a useful expression for $\mathbf{t} \times \mathbf{v}$ in terms of the angle ϕ between $\mathbf{t}$ and $\mathbf{v}$. Since $(\mathbf{t} \cdot \mathbf{v})^2 = \|\mathbf{t}\|^2 \|\mathbf{v}\|^2 \cos^2 \phi$ (Why?), you find

$$\|\mathbf{t}\|^2 \|\mathbf{v}\|^2 \cos^2 \phi + \|\mathbf{t} \times \mathbf{v}\|^2 = \|\mathbf{t}\|^2 \|\mathbf{v}\|^2.$$

Hence, $\|\mathbf{t} \times \mathbf{v}\|^2 = \|\mathbf{t}\|^2 \|\mathbf{v}\|^2 (1 - \cos^2 \phi);$

∴ (1) $\|\mathbf{t} \times \mathbf{v}\|^2 = \|\mathbf{t}\|^2 \|\mathbf{v}\|^2 \sin^2 \phi.$

Because $\|t \times v\|$, $\|t\|$, $\|v\|$, and $\sin \phi$ all denote nonnegative numbers (Why?), statement (1) is equivalent to

(2) $\|t \times v\| = \|t\|\|v\| \sin \phi$.

Figure 14–4 illustrates statement (2) for $v \neq 0$.

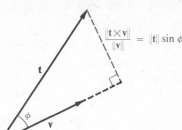

Figure 14–4

Exercises

In Exercises 1–8, determine whether the given vectors are parallel to each other, orthogonal to each other, or neither.

A

1. $(6, -3, -9), (-2, 1, 3)$ **5.** $(2, -3, -4), (-6, -8, 3)$

2. $(6, 5, -3), (5, -3, 5)$ **6.** $(9, 6, -15), (14, -6, 6)$

3. $(-1, 0, 2), (2, 1, -1)$ **7.** $(1, 0, 2), (0, 3, 0)$

4. $(3, 1, 2), (-6, 4, 7)$ **8.** $(2, 3, 0), (0, 0, 5)$

In Exercises 9–12, find a unit vector orthogonal to each of the given vectors.

9. $(1, 1, 1), (2, 3, -1)$ **11.** $(3, 2, 1), (0, -2, 5)$

10. $(4, 3, -2), (6, 1, -1)$ **12.** $(3, 2, 0), (0, 1, 5)$

In Exercises 13–18, let $i = (1, 0, 0)$, $j = (0, 1, 0)$, and $k = (0, 0, 1)$, and show that the given equation is true.

B

13. $i \times j = k$ **15.** $k \times i = j$ **17.** $k \times j = -i$

14. $j \times k = i$ **16.** $j \times i = -k$ **18.** $i \times k = -j$

C

19. Show that every vector $v \in \mathcal{R}_3$ can be expressed as a sum of the form $v = xi + yj + zk$, where i, j, and k are unit vectors in the direction of the positive coordinate axes. (*Note:* The vectors i, j, and k are said to be a set of orthogonal basis vectors for the vector space $\mathcal{R}_3$.)

20. Show that every vector v in $\mathcal{R}_3$ can be expressed as a sum of the form $v = xa + yb + zc$ where a, b, and c are unit vectors that are mutually orthogonal. (*Hint:* Consider $v \cdot a$, $v \cdot b$, and $v \cdot c$.)

Note: x, y, and z are called **scalar components** of v in the directions of the **basis vectors** a, b, and c.

21. Find three vectors t, v, and s such that

$$(t \times v) \times s \neq t \times (v \times s).$$

22. Explain why the expression $(t \cdot v) \times s$ is meaningless.

Let t, v, and s denote elements of $\mathcal{R}_3$ and let r denote any real number. Prove each statement in Exercises 23–30.

23. $t \times v = -(v \times t)$

24. $t \times (v + s) = (t \times v) + (t \times s)$

25. $t \times (rv) = (rt) \times v = r(t \times v)$

26. $t \times t = 0$

27. $t \times (v \times s) = (t \cdot s)v - (t \cdot v)s$

28. $(t \times v) \times s = (s \cdot t)v - (s \cdot v)t$

29. $t \cdot (v \times s) = (t \times v) \cdot s$

30. $t \cdot (v \times s) = s \cdot (t \times v) = v \cdot (s \times t)$

31. Prove that the area of the triangle **PQR** is given by $\frac{1}{2}\|(P - Q) \times (R - Q)\|$.

32. Prove that the area of the parallelogram having **P**, **Q**, **R** as three consecutive vertices has area given by $\|(P - Q) \times (R - Q)\|$.

LINES AND PLANES IN SPACE

14–4 Lines in Space

Diagrams such as Figure 14–1 (page 569), which pictures (2, 3, 6), or the point **P**, as a dot in a Cartesian coordinate system, are useful aids to understanding abstract concepts. Sometimes, however, it is helpful to think of a vector as a displacement represented by an arrow from one point to another as in Figure 14–3 (page 570). Figure 14–5 below pictures (2, 3, 6) by the arrow $\overrightarrow{OP}$ with initial point **O** and terminal point **P**; it also represents (2, 3, 6) by the arrow $\overrightarrow{RS}$ from **R**(2, −3, 6) to **S**(4, 0, 12). Indeed, you can visualize (2, 3, 6) as a displacement from any point **T**(a, b, c) to the point **Q**$(a + 2, b + 3, c + 6)$. Thus, in $\mathcal{R}_3$, just as in $\mathcal{R} \times \mathcal{R}$, you can think of a nonzero vector as specifying a direction.

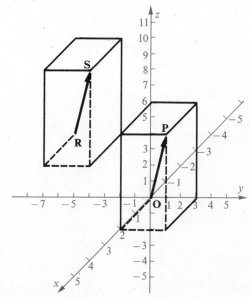

Figure 14–5

With these ideas in mind, you can extend to $\Re_3$ the concept of line that you learned for $\Re \times \Re$ (page 170). Thus, a set $\mathcal{L}$ of points $X(x, y, z)$ in $\Re_3$ is called a **line** if there exists in $\Re_3$ a point **P** and a nonzero vector **v** such that $\mathcal{L} = \{X \colon X = P + tv, t \in \Re\}$.

$\mathcal{L}$ is called the **line through P with direction vector v**, and $X = P + tv$ is called a **vector equation** of $\mathcal{L}$. Another notation for $\mathcal{L}$ is $\{P + tv\}$.

EXAMPLE 1. Find a vector equation of the line $\mathcal{L}$ through $P(3, 2, 1)$ with direction vector $v = (-1, 3, 2)$.

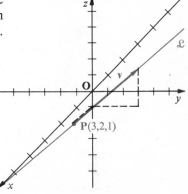

Solution:

$$\mathcal{L} = \{P + tv\} = \{(3, 2, 1) + t(-1, 3, 2)\}$$
$$= \{(3 - t, 2 + 3t, 1 + 2t)\}$$

$\therefore$ a vector equation of $\mathcal{L}$ is $(x, y, z) =$
$(3 - t, 2 + 3t, 1 + 2t)$, **Answer.**

The figure pictures $\mathcal{L}$.

The following theorems which are analogues of results proved in Chapter 5 for lines in $\Re \times \Re$ are valid for lines in $\Re_3$. They can be proved by using essentially the same arguments as in Chapter 5.

THEOREM 1 Let **P** be a point and **v** a nonzero vector in space. If $\mathcal{L}$ is a line through **P** with direction vector **v**, then a point **X** lies on $\mathcal{L}$ if and only if $X - P$ is parallel to **v**.

COROLLARY. A point **X** lies on the line through **P** with direction vector **v** if and only if $(X - P) \times v = 0$.

THEOREM 2 If **P** and **T** denote points in space and **v** denotes a nonzero vector, and if $T \in \{P + tv\}$, then

$$\{P + tv\} = \{T + sv\}.$$

THEOREM 3 If **P** denotes a point and **v** and **w** denote nonzero vectors in space, then $\{P + tv\} = \{P + sw\}$ if and only if **v** and **w** are parallel vectors.

THEOREM 4 In space, lines having a point in common coincide if and only if they are **parallel**, that is, have parallel direction vectors.

THEOREM 5 If **P** and **S** are distinct points in space, then one and only one line in space contains both **P** and **S**.

THEOREM 6 If **P** is any point and $\mathfrak{M}$ any line in space, one and only one line in space passes through **P** parallel to $\mathfrak{M}$.

THEOREM 7 The points **P**, **T**, and **S** in space are **collinear** (lie on the same line) if and only if $\mathbf{T} - \mathbf{P}$ and $\mathbf{S} - \mathbf{P}$ are parallel vectors.

EXAMPLE 2. Find a vector equation of the line $\mathfrak{L}$ that passes through $P(2, -3, 1)$ and is parallel to the line

$$\mathfrak{M} = \{X: \ X = (3 + 2t, 1 + 4t, 2 - 2t)\}.$$

Solution: $\mathfrak{M} = \{X: \ X = (3, 1, 2) + t(2, 4, -2)\}.$

A direction vector for $\mathfrak{L}$ is $(1, 2, -1)$. (Why?)

$$\therefore \ (x, y, z) = (2, -3, 1) + t(1, 2, -1), \textbf{ Answer.}$$

The vector equation $X = (x, y, z) = (2 + t, -3 + 2t, 1 - t)$ is equivalent to the *three equations*

$$x = 2 + t, \quad y = -3 + 2t, \quad \text{and} \quad z = 1 - t.$$

We call these three equations **parametric equations** of $\mathfrak{L}$, and refer to t as a parameter. If you solve each of these equations for t, you obtain

$$t = \frac{x - 2}{1}, \quad t = \frac{y + 3}{2}, \quad \text{and} \quad t = \frac{z - 1}{-1}.$$

Writing these equations in the combined form

$$\frac{x - 2}{1} = \frac{y + 3}{2} = \frac{z - 1}{-1},$$

you obtain a relationship called a **symmetric equation** of line $\mathfrak{L}$. The numbers $1, 2, -1$ are called *direction numbers* of $\mathfrak{L}$.

In general, the entries in the direction vector $\mathbf{v} = (v_1, v_2, v_3)$ of a line $\mathfrak{L}$ are often called **direction numbers** of the vector and of the line. Can you explain why a line has infinitely many sets of direction numbers?

The definition of the angle between vectors stated on page 567 implies that if α is the angle between $\mathbf{v}$ and $(1, 0, 0)$, β is the angle between $\mathbf{v}$ and $(0, 1, 0)$, and γ is the angle between $\mathbf{v}$ and $(0, 0, 1)$, (Figure 14–6), then

$$\cos \alpha = \frac{\mathbf{v} \cdot (1, 0, 0)}{\|\mathbf{v}\|} = \frac{v_1}{\|\mathbf{v}\|},$$

$$\cos \beta = \frac{\mathbf{v} \cdot (0, 1, 0)}{\|\mathbf{v}\|} = \frac{v_2}{\|\mathbf{v}\|},$$

$$\cos \gamma = \mathbf{v} \cdot (0, 0, 1) = \frac{v_3}{\|\mathbf{v}\|}.$$

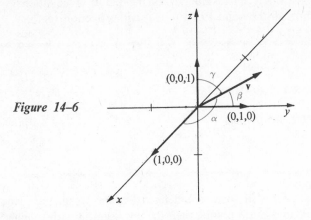

Figure 14-6

Hence, we call $\cos \alpha$, $\cos \beta$, and $\cos \gamma$ the **direction cosines** of **v** and of $\mathcal{L}$, and we say that α, β, and γ are the **direction angles** of **v** and $\mathcal{L}$. Notice that

$$\cos^2 \alpha + \cos^2 \beta + \cos^2 \gamma = \frac{v_1^2 + v_2^2 + v_3^2}{\|\mathbf{v}\|^2}.$$

This fact leads to the following important relationship for direction cosines:

$$\cos^2 \alpha + \cos^2 \beta + \cos^2 \gamma = 1.$$

EXAMPLE 3. **(a)** Find direction cosines for the line $\mathcal{L}$ containing $P(9, 2, -1)$ and $S = (-3, 5, -5)$; **(b)** state a symmetric equation of the line.

Solution: **(a)** A direction vector of $\mathcal{L}$ is $\mathbf{P} - \mathbf{S} = [9 - (-3), 2 - 5, -1 - (-5)]$, or $(12, -3, 4)$.

$$\therefore \cos \alpha = \frac{12}{\sqrt{12^2 + (-3)^2 + (4)^2}} = \frac{12}{\sqrt{169}} = \frac{12}{13},$$

$$\cos \beta = \frac{-3}{13}, \cos \gamma = \frac{4}{13}.$$

$$\therefore \cos \alpha = \frac{12}{13}, \cos \beta = -\frac{3}{13}, \cos \gamma = \frac{4}{13}, \textbf{Answer.}$$

(b) $P(9, 2, -1) \in \mathcal{L}$ and $(12, -3, 4)$ is a direction vector of $\mathcal{L}$. (Why?)

$\therefore$ a symmetric equation of $\mathcal{L}$ is

$$\frac{x - 9}{12} = \frac{y - 2}{-3} = \frac{z + 1}{4}, \textbf{Answer.}$$

The following chart summarizes the kinds of equations specifying the line $\mathcal{L}$ through the point $P(x_1, y_1, z_1)$ with direction vector $\mathbf{v} = (v_1, v_2, v_3)$.

VECTOR EQUATION $X = P + t\mathbf{v}$, or $(x, y, z) = (x_1, y_1, z_1) + t(v_1, v_2, v_3)$.

PARAMETRIC EQUATIONS $x = x_1 + tv_1, y = y_1 + tv_2, z = z_1 + tv_3$.

SYMMETRIC EQUATION $\dfrac{x - x_1}{v_1} = \dfrac{y - y_1}{v_2} = \dfrac{z - z_1}{v_3}$, provided $v_1 \neq 0$,

$v_2 \neq 0, v_3 \neq 0$.

Line segments in space are defined as they are in the plane (page 182). Thus, if P and S are points, then the **line segment** with **endpoints** P and S is

$$\overline{PS} = \{X: X = (1 - t)P + tS, \ 0 \leq t \leq 1\},$$

and the length of $\overline{PS}$ is $\|S - P\|$. (See Exercise 37, page 581.)

Figure 14–4 (page 575) and Figure 14–7 suggest how to define the distance between a line $\mathcal{L}$ and a point S in space (in symbols, $d(S, \mathcal{L})$).

$$d(S, \mathcal{L}) = \frac{\|(S - T) \times \mathbf{v}\|}{\|\mathbf{v}\|}$$

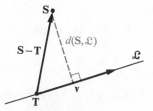

where T is any point of $\mathcal{L}$, and $\mathbf{v}$ any direction vector of $\mathcal{L}$.

Figure 14–7

EXAMPLE 4.   Find the distance from $S(3, 1, -2)$ to

$$\mathcal{L} = \{X: X = (1 + t, 2 - t, 1 + 2t)\}.$$

Solution: $T(1, 2, 1) \in \mathcal{L}$ and $\mathbf{v} = (1, -1, 2)$ is a direction vector of $\mathcal{L}$.
$S - T = (2, -1, -3)$

$$(S - T) \times \mathbf{v} = \left(\begin{vmatrix} -1 & -3 \\ -1 & 2 \end{vmatrix}, -\begin{vmatrix} 2 & -3 \\ 1 & 2 \end{vmatrix}, \begin{vmatrix} 2 & -1 \\ 1 & -1 \end{vmatrix} \right)$$

$$= (-5, -7, -1).$$

$$\therefore \|(S - T) \times \mathbf{v}\| = \sqrt{(-5)^2 + (-7)^2 + (-1)^2} = \sqrt{75}$$

$$\|\mathbf{v}\| = \sqrt{1^2 + (-1)^2 + 2^2} = \sqrt{6}$$

$$\therefore d(S, \mathcal{L}) = \frac{\|(S - T) \times \mathbf{v}\|}{\|\mathbf{v}\|} = \frac{\sqrt{75}}{\sqrt{6}} = \sqrt{\frac{25}{2}}$$

$$d(S, \mathcal{L}) = \tfrac{5}{2}\sqrt{2}, \textbf{ Answer.}$$

Exercises

In Exercises 1–6, find **(a)** a vector equation and **(b)** a set of parametric equations of the line containing the given points. How far is the line from $(1, 1, 1)$?

A

1. $(2, 4, 1), (-4, 7, 2)$ **4.** $(3, -1, 4), (4, -2, -3)$

2. $(2, 2, 4), (0, 3, 6)$ **5.** $(2, 3, 1), (-2, 4, 1)$

3. $(0, -3, 8), (7, 2, 9)$ **6.** $(2, 5, 2), (-1, 5, 2)$

7–12. Find the distance from the origin to each line in Exercises 1–6.

13–18. Find a set of direction cosines for each line in Exercises 1–6.

19. Find a vector equation of a line that contains $(0, -1, 3)$ and is parallel to the line $\{X: X = (2 - t, 3 + t, 2 - 3t)\}$.

20. Find a vector equation of the line that contains $(-1, -1, -1)$ and is parallel to the line $\{X: X = (t, 5 - 3t, 1 + 3t)\}$.

21. Find a symmetric equation of the line that passes through $(4, 2, -5)$ and has direction angles $\alpha = 60°, \beta = 60°$, and γ, with $0° < \gamma < 90°$.

22. Find a symmetric equation of the line that passes through $(4, 2, -5)$ and has direction angles $\alpha = 90°, \beta = \text{Arccos } \frac{2}{3}$, and γ, such that $\cos \gamma > 0$.

B

23. Find the coordinates of the midpoint of the line segment joining $(3, -1, 4)$ and $(2, 1, 1)$.

24. Find the coordinates of the points of trisection of the line segment joining $(-1, 3, 5)$ and $(4, 1, 2)$.

25. Show that the points $(3, -2, 4), (8, 0, 7), (6, 1, -3)$, and $(11, 3, 0)$ are the vertices of a parallelogram, and find the area.

26. Show that the points $(4, -4, 7), (9, -2, 10), (7, -1, 0)$, and $(12, 1, 3)$ are the vertices of a parallelogram, and find the area.

27. Show that $(0, 2, 1), (2, 1, 3), (1, 6, 2)$, and $(3, 5, 4)$ are the vertices of a rectangle, and find its area.

28. Show that $(1, 2, 2), (3, 1, 4), (2, 6, 3)$, and $(4, 5, 5)$ are the vertices of a rectangle, and find its area.

Prove each of the following theorems, stated on pages 577 and 578.

29. Theorem 1, page 577   **33.** Theorem 4, page 577

30. Corollary, page 577   **34.** Theorem 5, page 577

31. Theorem 2, page 577   **35.** Theorem 6, page 578

32. Theorem 3, page 577   **36.** Theorem 7, page 578

37. If P, S, and T are distinct points in $\Re_3$, then T is on the line segment $\overline{PS}$ if and only if $d(P, T) + d(T, S) = d(P, S)$.

38. If v_1 and v_2 are perpendicular vectors with direction angles $\alpha_1, \beta_1, \gamma_1$, and $\alpha_2, \beta_2, \gamma_2$, then $\cos \alpha_1 \cos \alpha_2 + \cos \beta_1 \cos \beta_2 + \cos \gamma_1 \cos \gamma_2 = 0$.

14–5 Planes in Space

If **n** is a nonzero vector in the plane, then a vector perpendicular to **n** can have but one of two directions (Figure 14–8a). If, however, **n** is a vector in $\Re_3$, then vectors perpendicular to **n** can have an unlimited number of directions (Figure 14–8b). The figure suggests how we define a plane in $\Re_3$.

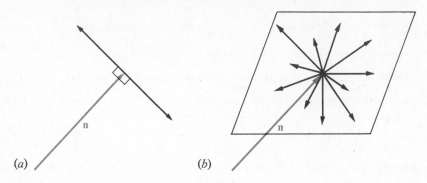

(a)   (b)

Figure 14–8

A set $\mathcal{P}$ of points $X(x, y, z)$ in $\Re_3$ is called a **plane** if there exists a point **T** and a nonzero vector **n** such that $(X - T) \cdot n = 0$. We call $\mathcal{P}$ the **plane through T** with **normal vector n** and say that $\mathcal{P}$ is perpendicular to **n** and that **n** is perpendicular or normal to $\mathcal{P}$.

Using the relationship $(X - T) \cdot n = 0$, you can determine a linear equation which must be satisfied by (x, y, z) in order that $X \in \mathcal{P}$. For example, if **n** is the vector $(6, 4, 3)$ and **T** is the point $(1, 0, 2)$, then $X(x, y, z)$ belongs to the plane through **T** with normal vector **n** if and only if

$$[(x, y, z) - (1, 0, 2)] \cdot (6, 4, 3) = 0,$$
$$(x - 1, y, z - 2) \cdot (6, 4, 3) = 0,$$
$$6(x - 1) + 4y + 3(z - 2) = 0,$$
$$(1) \qquad\qquad\qquad 6x + 4y + 3z = 12$$

We call equation (1) a scalar equation of the plane. The triangular surface shown in Figure 14–9 pictures the portion of the plane lying in the first octant.

Notice that the coefficients of the variables in the left member of equation (1) are the entries of **n**, the normal vector to the plane, while the

Figure 14–9

right member, 12, is $\mathbf{T} \cdot \mathbf{n}$. This example suggests (Exercise 21, page 587) that $\mathbf{X}(x, y, z)$ is a point of the plane $\mathcal{O}$ through $\mathbf{T}(x_1, y_1, z_1)$ with normal vector $\mathbf{n} = (a, b, c)$ if and only if

$$ax + by + cz = d$$

where $d = ax_1 + by_1 + cz_1$. We call the equation $ax + by + cz = d$ a **scalar equation** of $\mathcal{P}$.

It is easy to prove that any nonzero vector parallel to $\mathbf{n}$ is also a normal vector of the plane $\mathcal{P}$. We use this fact in the next example.

EXAMPLE 1. Determine a unit vector normal to the plane with equation $3x - 2y + z = 7$.

Solution: By inspection $\mathbf{n} = (3, -2, 1)$ is a vector normal to the plane. (Why?) Hence a unit vector parallel to $\mathbf{n}$ is

$$\frac{(3, -2, 1)}{\|(3, -2, 1)\|} = \frac{1}{\sqrt{9 + 4 + 1}} (3, -2, 1)$$

$$= \left(\frac{3}{\sqrt{14}}, -\frac{2}{\sqrt{14}}, \frac{1}{\sqrt{14}} \right), \text{ **Answer.**}$$

Note: Another unit vector normal to the plane is

$$\left(-\frac{3}{\sqrt{14}}, \frac{2}{\sqrt{14}}, -\frac{1}{\sqrt{14}} \right),$$

which has direction opposite to the vector given in the answer to the problem.

You define planes to be **parallel (perpendicular)** if and only if their normal vectors are parallel (perpendicular).

EXAMPLE 2. Determine whether the planes with equations

$$3x + 4y - 2z + 5 = 0 \quad \text{and} \quad 7x + 9y - 5z + 7 = 0$$

are parallel, perpendicular, or neither.

Solution: By inspection, normals to the planes are $(3, 4, -2)$ and $(7, 9, -5)$.

$$(3, 4, -2) \times (7, 9, -5) = \left(\begin{vmatrix} 4 & -2 \\ 9 & -5 \end{vmatrix}, -\begin{vmatrix} 3 & -2 \\ 7 & -5 \end{vmatrix}, \begin{vmatrix} 3 & 4 \\ 7 & 9 \end{vmatrix} \right)$$

$$= (-2, 1, -1) \neq (0, 0, 0).$$

$$(3, 4, -2) \cdot (7, 9, -5) = 3(7) + 4(9) + (-2)(-5) = 67 \neq 0.$$

$\therefore$ the planes are neither parallel nor perpendicular, **Answer.**

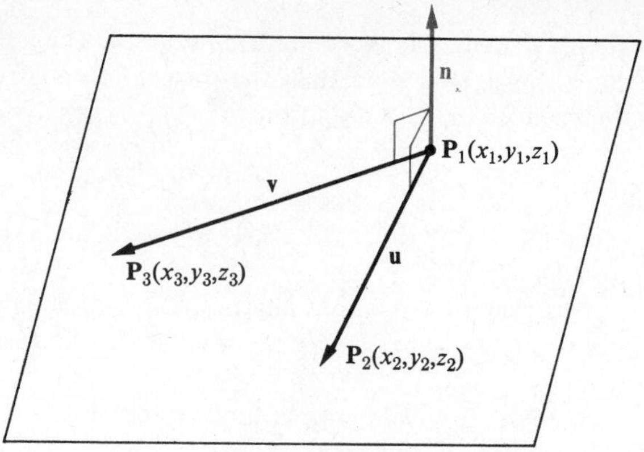

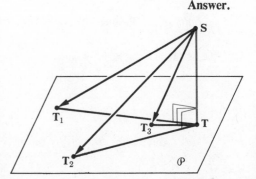

Figure 14-10

Three noncollinear points in $\mathcal{R}_3$ determine a plane (Figure 14-10). For if $\mathbf{u} = \mathbf{P}_2 - \mathbf{P}_1$ and $\mathbf{v} = \mathbf{P}_3 - \mathbf{P}_1$, then the vector $\mathbf{n} = \mathbf{v} \times \mathbf{u}$ is not the zero vector (Why?), and is perpendicular to both $\mathbf{u}$ and $\mathbf{v}$. Therefore,

$$(\mathbf{X} - \mathbf{P}_1) \cdot \mathbf{n} = 0$$

determines a plane containing $\mathbf{P}_1$, $\mathbf{P}_2$, and $\mathbf{P}_3$.

EXAMPLE 3. Find an equation of the plane containing $(2, 2, 2)$, $(3, 1, 1)$, and $(6, -4, -6)$.

Solution: Let $\mathbf{u} = (3, 1, 1) - (2, 2, 2) = (1, -1, -1)$ and
$\mathbf{v} = (6, -4, -6) - (2, 2, 2) = (4, -6, -8)$.

Then

$$\mathbf{n} = \mathbf{u} \times \mathbf{v} = \left(\begin{vmatrix} -1 & -1 \\ -6 & -8 \end{vmatrix}, - \begin{vmatrix} 1 & -1 \\ 4 & -8 \end{vmatrix}, \begin{vmatrix} 1 & -1 \\ 4 & -6 \end{vmatrix} \right) = (2, 4, -2).$$

Next, $\mathbf{X} - \mathbf{P}_1 = (x, y, z) - (2, 2, 2) = (x - 2, y - 2, z - 2)$.

Then $(\mathbf{X} - \mathbf{P}_1) \cdot \mathbf{n} = (x - 2, y - 2, z - 2) \cdot (2, 4, -2)$
$$= 2(x - 2) + 4(y - 2) - 2(z - 2)$$
$$= 2x + 4y - 2z - 8.$$

$\therefore 2x + 4y - 2z - 8 = 0$, or $x + 2y - z - 4 = 0$,
Answer.

The method used to define the distance from a point to a line in a plane (page 195) suggests a means of defining the distance from a point to a plane in space. Let $\mathbf{S}$ be a point in $\mathcal{R}_3$ and $\mathcal{P}$ a plane (Figure 14-11). Notice that if $\mathbf{T}$

Figure 14-11

is any point in $\mathcal{P}$, then the component of $S - T$ perpendicular to $\mathcal{P}$ is constant for all points T in $\mathcal{P}$. Thus if T_1 and T_2 are any two points in $\mathcal{P}$, then

$$\text{Comp}_n (S - T_1) = \text{Comp}_n (S - T_2).$$

Hence,

$$(S - T_1) \cdot n = (S - T_2) \cdot n.$$

For the same reasons stated on page 195, therefore, the distance $d(S, \mathcal{P})$ from the point S to the plane $\mathcal{P}$ is defined to be

$$d(S, \mathcal{P}) = \frac{|(S - T) \cdot n|}{\|n\|}.$$

EXAMPLE 4. Find the distance from the point $S(2, -1, 3)$ to the plane with equation $3x - 2y + z - 4 = 0$.

Solution: A point of the plane is $T(0, 0, 4)$. (Why?)
$S - T = (2, -1, 3) - (0, 0, 4) = (2, -1, -1).$
$n = (3, -2, 1).$
$(S - T) \cdot n = (2, -1, -1) \cdot (3, -2, 1) = 6 + 2 - 1 = 7.$
Also, $\|n\| = \sqrt{9 + 4 + 1} = \sqrt{14}.$

$$\therefore \frac{|(S - T) \cdot n|}{\|n\|} = \frac{|7|}{\sqrt{14}}, \text{ and } d(S, \mathcal{P}) = \frac{7}{\sqrt{14}}, \textbf{ Answer.}$$

By an argument similar to the one given on page 196, you can show that if the coordinates of S are (x^*, y^*, z^*), then

$$d(S, \mathcal{P}) = \frac{|ax^* + by^* + cz^* - d|}{\sqrt{a^2 + b^2 + c^2}}.$$

In particular, if S is the origin, you find (Why?) that

$$d(O, \mathcal{P}) = \frac{|d|}{\sqrt{a^2 + b^2 + c^2}} = d^*.$$

Using this fact, you can write the equation $ax + by + cz = d$ in the equivalent form

$$\frac{a}{\sqrt{a^2 + b^2 + c^2}} x + \frac{b}{\sqrt{a^2 + b^2 + c^2}} y + \frac{c}{\sqrt{a^2 + b^2 + c^2}} z = \pm d^*,$$

where the right member is d^* or $-d^*$, according as $d \geq 0$ or $d < 0$.

Do you see that the coefficients of x, y, and z in this equation are the direction cosines of (a, b, c), the normal to the plane? This fact permits you to rewrite the equation in the following form:

$$x \cos \alpha + y \cos \beta + z \cos \gamma = \pm d(O, \mathcal{P}),$$

which is called the **normal form** of the equation of the plane.

EXAMPLE 5. Find the distance from the origin to the plane

$$3x - 2y + 4z = 5.$$

Solution: Since $\mathbf{n} = (3, -2, 4)$, $\|\mathbf{n}\| = \sqrt{9 + 4 + 16} = \sqrt{29}$.

Dividing each member of the equation of the plane by $\sqrt{29}$, you have

$$\frac{3}{\sqrt{29}} x - \frac{2}{\sqrt{29}} y + \frac{4}{\sqrt{29}} z = \frac{5}{\sqrt{29}}.$$

Since this is the normal form of the equation of the plane, the distance from the origin to the plane is $\dfrac{5}{\sqrt{29}}$, **Answer.**

Exercises

In Exercises 1–8, find a scalar equation of the plane with the given characteristics.

 1. Containing $(4, 6, 2)$; normal vector $(3, -1, 4)$.
 2. Containing $(6, 5, 3)$; normal vector $(1, 1, 5)$.
 3. Containing $(-1, 5, 4)$; parallel to the plane with equation

$$3x - 2y + 6z - 6 = 0.$$

 4. Containing $(1, 5, -2)$; parallel to the plane with equation

$$3x - y + 4z + 3 = 0.$$

 5. Containing $(2, -1, 0)$ and $(3, 0, 5)$; perpendicular to the xy-plane.
 6. Containing $(1, 2, 3)$ and $(3, 2, -1)$; perpendicular to the plane with equation $3x + 2y + 6z + 4 = 0$.
 7. Containing $(3, 3, 1)$, $(-3, 2, -1)$, and $(8, 6, 3)$.
 8. Containing $(-3, 1, 0)$, $(5, 0, 1)$, and $(5, 7, 2)$.
 9. Find a unit vector normal to the plane with equation $3x + 2y - 3z + 6 = 0$.
10. Find a unit vector normal to the plane with equation $3y - 2x + 6 - 3z = 0$.
11. Write the normal form for $6x - 3y + 2z - 8 = 0$, and determine the distance from the origin to the associated plane.
12. Write the normal form for $x - y - 2z - 12 = 0$, and determine the distance from the origin to the associated plane.
13. Find the distance between the parallel planes with equations

$$9x - 6y + 2z - 11 = 0 \quad \text{and} \quad 18x - 12y + 4z - 55 = 0.$$

(*Hint:* Write the normal form for both equations.)

14. Find the distance between the parallel planes with equations

$$3x - y - z = 6 \quad \text{and} \quad 6x - 2y - 2z = 10.$$

(*Hint:* See Exercise 13.)

15. Find the distance from the point $(5, 2, 4)$ to the plane with equation

$$8x + 4y + z = 16.$$

16. Find the distance from the point $(1, 2, -2)$ to the plane with equation $x - y - z - 7 = 0$.

B **17.** Find an equation for the plane that contains $(1, -3, 2)$ and is perpendicular to the planes with equations $x + 2y + 3z = 4$ and $3x - 4y - 4z = 2$.

18. Find an equation for the plane that contains $(3, -1, 2)$ and is perpendicular to the planes with equations $x - 2y + 3z = 6$ and $4x - 3y - z = 4$.

19. Find an equation for the plane parallel to the plane with equation

$$x + 3y - z - 5 = 0$$

and situated so that $(-1, 1, 1)$ is midway between the planes.

20. Find an equation for the plane containing $(1, -1, 5)$, perpendicular to the plane $4x + 2y - 3z - 8 = 0$, and having y-intercept 3.

C **21.** Show that a scalar equation of the plane containing $P(x_1, y_1, z_1)$ and having normal vector (a, b, c) is

$$a(x - x_1) + b(y - y_1) + c(z - z_1) = 0$$

22. You define a line $\mathcal{L}$ to be **parallel** to a plane $\mathcal{P}$ if and only if a direction vector of $\mathcal{L}$ is perpendicular to a normal vector to $\mathcal{P}$. Find a vector equation for a line that is parallel to the planes with equations

$$a_1x + b_1y + c_1z + d_1 = 0 \quad \text{and} \quad a_2x + b_2y + c_2z + d_2 = 0$$

and contains the origin. (*Hint:* Consider the cross product of normal vectors to the planes.)

23. Find a vector equation of the line parallel to the planes with equations $4x - 3y - z - 1 = 0$ and $2x + 4y + z - 5 = 0$ and containing $(3, -1, -2)$. (*Hint:* See Exercise 22.)

24. Find a vector equation of the line parallel to the planes $3x - 2y + 3z + 3 = 0$ and $x + y - 2z = 4$ and containing $(2, -3, -2)$.

25. Prove that if $\mathcal{L}$ and $\mathfrak{M}$ are distinct intersecting lines in space, there is one and only one plane in space containing both $\mathcal{L}$ and $\mathfrak{M}$. (*Hint:* Consider the plane through the point of intersection of the lines and having normal vector perpendicular to the direction vectors of the lines.)

26. The theorem stated in Exercise 25 is an analogue for planes and lines of Theorem 5 (page 577) for lines and points. Try to state and prove corresponding analogues of the other theorems stated on pages 577 and 578.

27. An **angle between two planes** is defined to be an angle between a normal vector of one plane and a normal vector of the other. If ϕ is an angle between the planes with equations

$$3x + 2y + 5z = 4 \quad \text{and} \quad 5x - y + z = 7,$$

determine two possible values of $\cos \phi$.

28. Lines in space are called **skew** if they neither intersect nor are parallel. (a) Show that two skew lines cannot lie in the same plane. (b) Show that if $\mathcal{L} = \{P + tv\}$ and $\mathfrak{M} = \{R + sw\}$ are skew lines, then the length of the line segment perpendicular to both $\mathcal{L}$ and $\mathfrak{M}$ is given by

$$\frac{|(v \times w) \cdot (P - R)|}{\|v \times w\|}.$$

14–6 Intersections of Planes and Lines

The following example illustrates a useful fact.

EXAMPLE 1. Show that the planes $\mathcal{P}_1$ and $\mathcal{P}_2$ with equations

$$4x + 2y - 5z = 2 \quad \text{and} \quad x - y + 3z = -3$$

have at least one point in common.

Solution: *Plan:* Determine the point in the xy-plane which lies on $\mathcal{P}_1$ and also on $\mathcal{P}_2$.

In the xy-plane, $z = 0$. (Why?) Replacing z by 0 in the equation of each plane, you obtain the following system of equations in two variables:

$$4x + 2y = 2$$
$$x - y = -3$$

Since the coefficient determinant of this system is not zero, you can solve the system and find that $x = -\frac{2}{3}$ and $y = \frac{7}{3}$.

Hence, $(-\frac{2}{3}, \frac{7}{3}, 0)$ lies on both $\mathcal{P}_1$ and $\mathcal{P}_2$, **Answer.**

Notice that the normal vectors of the planes in Example 1 are *not* parallel. You can generalize the argument in the solution of Example 1 to show that every pair of planes with nonparallel normal vectors have at least one point in common.

Figure 14–12 pictures two planes $\mathcal{P}_1$ and $\mathcal{P}_2$ having normal vectors n_1 and n_2 and each containing the point T. The figure suggests that the set of all points common to the planes is the line through T with direction vector perpendicular to both n_1 and n_2. We are thus led to the following assertion.

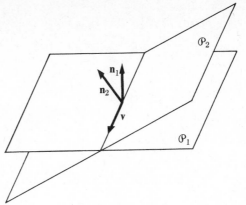

Figure 14–12

| **THEOREM** | Two planes whose normal vectors are not parallel intersect in a line. |

Proof: Let $\mathbf{n}_1$ and $\mathbf{n}_2$ be normal vectors of the planes. You know that the planes have at least one point $\mathbf{T}$ in common. Hence, one plane, call it $\mathcal{P}_1$, is the plane through $\mathbf{T}$ with normal vector $\mathbf{n}_1$, and the other is the plane $\mathcal{P}_2$ through $\mathbf{T}$ with normal vector $\mathbf{n}_2$.

Since $\mathbf{n}_1$ and $\mathbf{n}_2$ are not parallel, $\mathbf{n}_1 \times \mathbf{n}_2 \neq \mathbf{0}$. (Why?). Therefore, $\mathbf{n}_1 \times \mathbf{n}_2$ can be used as the direction vector of a line. Let $\mathcal{L}$ be the line through $\mathbf{T}$ with $\mathbf{n}_1 \times \mathbf{n}_2$ as direction vector. Then $\mathcal{L}$ consists of the points $\mathbf{T} + s(\mathbf{n}_1 \times \mathbf{n}_2)$, $s \in \mathcal{R}$. Now a point of $\mathcal{L}$ belongs to $\mathcal{P}_1$ provided it satisfies the equation

$$(\mathbf{X} - \mathbf{T}) \cdot \mathbf{n}_1 = \mathbf{0}.$$

Replacing $\mathbf{X}$ by $\mathbf{T} + s(\mathbf{n}_1 \times \mathbf{n}_2)$, you find

$$[\mathbf{T} + s(\mathbf{n}_1 \times \mathbf{n}_2) - \mathbf{T}] \cdot \mathbf{n}_1 = s(\mathbf{n}_1 \times \mathbf{n}_2) \cdot \mathbf{n}_1 = 0,$$

because $\mathbf{n}_1 \times \mathbf{n}_2$ is perpendicular to $\mathbf{n}_1$. Hence, each point of $\mathcal{L}$ belongs to $\mathcal{P}_1$.

Similarly, you can show that each point of $\mathcal{L}$ lies in $\mathcal{P}_2$.

To complete the proof, you must show that any point $\mathbf{R}$ in both $\mathcal{P}_1$ and $\mathcal{P}_2$ belongs to $\mathcal{L}$. By the corollary to Theorem 1, page 577, $\mathbf{R} \in \mathcal{L}$ if and only if

$$(\mathbf{R} - \mathbf{T}) \times (\mathbf{n}_1 \times \mathbf{n}_2) = \mathbf{0}.$$

Using the first vector triple-product property, page 573, you find

$$(\mathbf{R} - \mathbf{T}) \times (\mathbf{n}_1 \times \mathbf{n}_2) = [(\mathbf{R} - \mathbf{T}) \cdot \mathbf{n}_2]\mathbf{n}_1 - [(\mathbf{R} - \mathbf{T}) \cdot \mathbf{n}_1]\mathbf{n}_2.$$

But $(\mathbf{R} - \mathbf{T}) \cdot \mathbf{n}_1 = 0$ because $\mathbf{R} \in \mathcal{P}_1$, and

$(\mathbf{R} - \mathbf{T}) \cdot \mathbf{n}_2 = 0$ because $\mathbf{R} \in \mathcal{P}_2$. Hence,

$(\mathbf{R} - \mathbf{T}) \times (\mathbf{n}_1 \times \mathbf{n}_2) = 0\,\mathbf{n}_1 - 0\,\mathbf{n}_2 = \mathbf{0}$, and $(\mathbf{R} - \mathbf{T}) \in \mathcal{L}$. This completes the argument.

We call the line $\mathcal{L}$ described in the theorem the **line of intersection** of the planes.

EXAMPLE 2. Find vector and parametric equations of $\mathcal{L}$, the line of intersection of the planes with equations

$$4x + 2y - 5z = 2 \quad \text{and} \quad x - y + 3z = -3.$$

Solution: By inspection of the equations, you see that normal vectors of the planes are $\mathbf{n}_1 = (4, 2, -5)$ and $\mathbf{n}_2 = (1, -1, 3)$. Therefore, a direction vector of $\mathcal{L}$ is $\mathbf{n}_1 \times \mathbf{n}_2$;

$$\mathbf{n}_1 \times \mathbf{n}_2 = \left(\begin{vmatrix} 2 & -5 \\ -1 & 3 \end{vmatrix}, -\begin{vmatrix} 4 & -5 \\ 1 & 3 \end{vmatrix}, \begin{vmatrix} 4 & 2 \\ 1 & -1 \end{vmatrix} \right)$$

$$= (1, -17, -6).$$

From Example 1, page 588, $\mathbf{T}(-\tfrac{2}{3}, \tfrac{7}{3}, 0) \in \mathcal{L}$.

$\therefore \mathcal{L} = \{(x, y, z): (x, y, z) = (-\tfrac{2}{3}, \tfrac{7}{3}, 0) + t(1, -17, -6)\}$

or

$$\mathcal{L} = \{(x, y, z): (x, y, z) = (-\tfrac{2}{3} + t, \tfrac{7}{3} - 17t, -6t)\},$$

from which you have the parametric equations

$$x = -\tfrac{2}{3} + t, y = \tfrac{7}{3} - 17t, z = -6t, \textbf{ Answer.}$$

Relationships between three planes are of various kinds, and can be examined through systems of three equations in three variables. Perhaps you recall from your earlier study of mathematics the method of finding solutions for such systems by addition of equations.

EXAMPLE 3. Find the solution set of the system

$$2x - y + z = 3,$$
$$x + 2y - z = 3,$$
$$3x - 4y + 2z = -1,$$

Solution: Adding left- and right-hand members of the first two equations, you obtain $3x + y = 6$, while the sum of twice the

members of the second equation and the corresponding
members of the third is $5x = 5$. Therefore, the given system
is equivalent to the system

$$2x - y + z = 3,$$
$$3x + y \quad\;\; = 6,$$
$$5x \qquad\;\; = 5.$$

From the last equation in this system, $x = 1$. Replacing x
in the second equation with 1, you obtain $y = 3$, while
replacement of x with 1 and y with 3 in the first equation
yields $z = 4$. $\therefore$ $\{(1, 3, 4)\}$, **Answer.**

One of the planes determined by the equations in Example 3 is shown in
Figure 14–13, together with the point
$(1, 3, 4)$ at which the three planes intersect. Can you sketch the graphs of
the other two planes?

Not all sets of three planes in $\Re_3$
intersect in a point. Figure 14–14 shows
the graphs of the equations in the
system

$$x + y + z = 4$$
$$x + y + z = 8$$
$$x - y \quad\;\; = 0$$

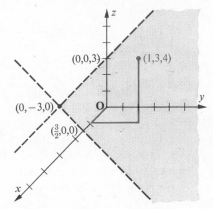

Figure 14–13

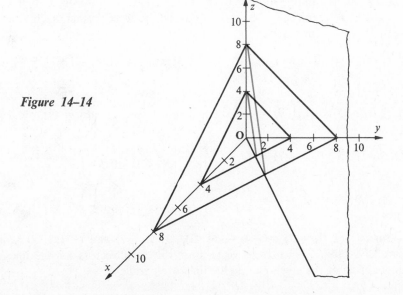

Figure 14–14

As you can see, the plane with equation $x - y = 0$ intersects the other two planes in parallel lines. Analytically, you would anticipate this by observing that normal vectors to the planes with equations $x + y + z = 4$ and $x + y + z = 8$ are parallel, and hence the planes are parallel and have an empty intersection since they do not coincide.

Figure 14–15

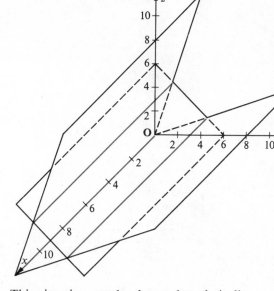

Figure 14–15 shows still another possibility. The graphs of $y - 3z = 0$, $3y - z = 0$, and $y + z = 6$ intersect, in pairs, in parallel lines. This situation can be detected analytically by observing that the cross-product vectors of normal vectors to each pair of planes are parallel vectors.

EXAMPLE 4. Show that the line of intersection of any pair of planes from among those with equations $x + 3y - z = 6$, $x + y = 4$, and $2y - z = 0$ is parallel to every other such line of intersection.

Solution: Normal vectors to the planes are $(1, 3, -1)$, $(1, 1, 0)$ and $(0, 2, -1)$. Then

$$(1, 3, -1) \times (1, 1, 0) = \left(\begin{vmatrix} 3 & -1 \\ 1 & 0 \end{vmatrix}, -\begin{vmatrix} 1 & -1 \\ 1 & 0 \end{vmatrix}, \begin{vmatrix} 1 & 3 \\ 1 & 1 \end{vmatrix} \right) = (1, -1, -2),$$

$$(1, 3, -1) \times (0, 2, -1) = \left(\begin{vmatrix} 3 & -1 \\ 2 & -1 \end{vmatrix}, -\begin{vmatrix} 1 & -1 \\ 0 & -1 \end{vmatrix}, \begin{vmatrix} 1 & 3 \\ 0 & 2 \end{vmatrix} \right) = (-1, 1, 2),$$

$$(1, 1, 0) \times (0, 2, -1) = \left(\begin{vmatrix} 1 & 0 \\ 2 & -1 \end{vmatrix}, -\begin{vmatrix} 1 & 0 \\ 0 & -1 \end{vmatrix}, \begin{vmatrix} 1 & 1 \\ 0 & 2 \end{vmatrix} \right) = (-1, 1, 2).$$

Since $(1, 1, -2) = -1(-1, 1, 2)$, $(1, 1, -2)$ and $(-1, 1, 2)$ are parallel vectors. Since these vectors are direction vectors for the lines of intersection of the given planes, the lines are parallel.

Still other situations involve three planes that are mutually parallel and have no intersection points, or three planes of which two or three are coincident.

Can you determine whether or not a line $\mathcal{L}$ intersects a plane $\mathcal{P}$? Figure 14–16 indicates that if the direction vector of $\mathcal{L}$ is perpendicular to the normal vector of $\mathcal{P}$, either $\mathcal{L}$ lies wholly in $\mathcal{P}$ or $\mathcal{L}$ has no point in common with $\mathcal{P}$. Figure 14–17, on the other hand, suggests that if the direction vector of $\mathcal{L}$ is not perpendicular to the normal vector of $\mathcal{P}$, then $\mathcal{L}$ and $\mathcal{P}$ have a single point **T** in common.

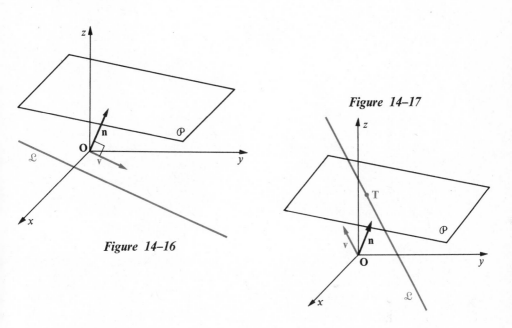

Figure 14–17

Figure 14–16

Proving the theorems which these observations suggest are left as exercises for you (page 594).

Exercises

Find vector and parametric equations of the lines of intersection of the planes whose equations are given.

A

1. $x + 2y + 2z = 10, x + 3y + z = 9$
2. $x - 6y + 6z + 35 = 0, 2x - 2y - 3z = 0$
3. $x + 2y + 3z = 2, 3x - y + 2z = 0$
4. $4x + 2y - 5z = 0, 2x - y + 3z + 3 = 0$
5. $2x + 3y + 4z - 5 = 0, x - 2y + 3z - 4 = 0$
6. $x + 2y - z - 6 = 0, x - 2y - 2z - 2 = 0$

In Exercises 7–12, determine the nature of the intersections of the planes with equations as given. If the intersection is a point, give its coordinates; if the intersection is one or more lines, give direction vector(s) for the line(s).

7.
$$x + y + 4z = 1$$
$$-2x - y + z = 2$$
$$3x - 2y + 3z = 5$$

10.
$$2x + y - 3z = 1$$
$$3y - z = 2$$
$$4x + 5y - 7z = 4$$

8.
$$x - y + z = 3$$
$$3x + 2y - z = 1$$
$$4x - 2y - 3z = 2$$

11.
$$2x - 3y + z = 1$$
$$-4x + 6y - 2z = -2$$
$$6x - 9y + 3z = 3$$

9.
$$3x - y + z = 2$$
$$x - 2y + z = 3$$
$$7x - 4y + 3z = 7$$

12.
$$3x - 6y + 15z = 2$$
$$2x - 4y + 10z = 4$$
$$5x - 10y + 25z = 6$$

B

13. Show that if $a_1x + b_1y + c_1z + d_1 = 0$ and $a_2x + b_2y + c_2z + d_2 = 0$ are the equations of distinct nonparallel planes, then the graph of

$$s(a_1x + b_1y + c_1z + d_1) + t(a_2x + b_2y + c_2z + d_2) = 0$$

contains every point in the intersection of the two planes. This equation is called a **linear combination** of the given equations.

14. Use the results of Exercise 13 to find an equation of another plane containing the line of intersection of the planes with equations $x - 2y + z = 3$ and $3x - 2y + 2z = 1$.

15. Use the results of Exercise 13 to find an equation of the plane which contains the line of intersection of the planes with equations $x - 2y + z = 3$ and $3x - 2y + 2z = 1$ and also contains the origin.

16. Use the results of Exercise 13 to find an equation of the plane which contains the line of intersection of the planes with equations $2x - 3y + z - 4 = 0$ and $x + y + 2z - 3 = 0$ and also contains the origin.

C

17. Find an equation for the plane containing the line

$$\mathcal{L} = \{X: X = (t, t, t + 2)\}$$

and the point $(2, 1, 3)$.

18. Find an equation for the plane containing the line

$$\mathcal{L} = \{X: X = (2t, 1 - t, t + 3)\}$$

and the point $(-1, 1, 2)$.

19. Prove that a line whose direction vector is perpendicular to the normal vector of a plane either lies wholly in the plane or has no point in common with the plane.

20. Prove that a line whose direction vector is not perpendicular to the normal vector of a plane intersects the plane in exactly one point.

Chapter Summary

1. A (three-dimensional) **vector** is an ordered triple in $\mathfrak{R} \times \mathfrak{R} \times \mathfrak{R} = \mathfrak{R}_3$. A **scalar** is a number belonging to $\mathfrak{R}$. **Sums, scalar products,** and **inner products** of vectors in $\mathfrak{R}_3$ are defined by extensions of the corresponding definitions for vectors in $\mathfrak{R} \times \mathfrak{R}$. The **cross product** of the vectors $\mathbf{u} = (x_1, y_1, z_1)$ and $\mathbf{v} = (x_2, y_2, z_2)$ is the vector

$$\mathbf{u} \times \mathbf{v} = (y_1 z_2 - z_1 y_2, z_1 x_2 - x_1 z_2, x_1 y_2 - y_1 x_2).$$

Note that $\mathbf{u} \times \mathbf{v} = -(\mathbf{v} \times \mathbf{u})$.

2. The vectors $\mathbf{u}$ and $\mathbf{v}$ are **parallel** if and only if $\mathbf{u} \times \mathbf{v} = \mathbf{0}$, and are **perpendicular** if and only if $\mathbf{u} \cdot \mathbf{v} = 0$.

3. A vector equation for the line in $\mathfrak{R}_3$, containing point $\mathbf{P}$ and having direction vector $\mathbf{v}$ is $\mathbf{X} = \mathbf{P} + t\mathbf{v}$. Direction cosines for the line through $\mathbf{P}(x_1, y_1, z_1)$ and $\mathbf{Q}(x_2, y_2, z_2)$ are

$$\cos \alpha = \frac{x_2 - x_1}{\|\mathbf{P} - \mathbf{Q}\|}, \cos \beta = \frac{y_2 - y_1}{\|\mathbf{P} - \mathbf{Q}\|}, \cos \gamma = \frac{z_2 - z_1}{\|\mathbf{P} - \mathbf{Q}\|}.$$

4. A scalar equation of a plane through the point (x_1, y_1, z_1) with normal vector (a, b, c) is $a(x - x_1) + b(y - y_1) + c(z - z_1) = 0$. A vector equation of the same plane is $[\mathbf{X} - (x_1, y_1, z_1)] \cdot (a, b, c) = 0$. Planes are parallel or perpendicular if and only if their normal vectors are parallel or perpendicular, respectively. The distance from a point $\mathbf{S}$ to a plane $\mathcal{P}$ is

$$d(\mathbf{S}, \mathcal{P}) = \frac{|(\mathbf{S} - \mathbf{T}) \cdot \mathbf{n}|}{\|\mathbf{n}\|},$$

where $\mathbf{T}$ is any point in $\mathcal{P}$ and $\mathbf{n}$ is a normal vector to $\mathcal{P}$. The **normal form** for the equation of a plane is

$$x \cos \alpha + y \cos \beta + z \cos \gamma - d = 0,$$

where α, β, and γ are direction cosines for a normal vector to $\mathcal{P}$ and $|d|$ is the distance from the origin to $\mathcal{P}$.

5. Systems of planes in $\mathfrak{R}_3$ may have points, lines, or planes for intersections. You can investigate these intersections analytically by studying Cartesian equations for the planes.

Chapter Test

14–1　**1.** Find the cosine of the angle determined by the vectors $(2, -1, 3)$ and $(5, -3, 6)$.

　　2. Prove that if $\mathbf{u}$ and $\mathbf{v}$ are vectors in $\Re_3$, then $\mathbf{u} + (\mathbf{v} - \mathbf{u}) = \mathbf{v}$.

14–2　**3.** Find the distance between the points $(3, -1, 4)$ and $(6, 1, 2)$.

　　4. Find the center and radius of the sphere whose equation is

$$x^2 + y^2 + z^2 - 8x + 4y - 4z - 1 = 0.$$

14–3　**5.** If $\mathbf{u} = (4, -3, 1)$ and $\mathbf{v} = (-1, 2, 6)$, find $\mathbf{u} \times \mathbf{v}$.

　　6. Find a unit vector perpendicular to each of the vectors $(3, -1, 0)$, $(2, 1, 1)$.

14–4　**7.** Find the equation and direction cosines of the line containing $(4, 2, 1)$ and $(-3, -2, 0)$.

　　8. Find the distance from the point $(2, -1, 3)$ to the line containing $(-2, 1, -3)$ and $(1, 1, 1)$.

14–5　**9.** Find a normal vector to the plane with equation

$$3x - 4y + 5z - 6 = 0,$$

and determine the distance from the origin to the plane.

　　10. Find a scalar equation for the plane containing the point $(2, -1, 1)$ and parallel to the plane with equation $2x - 3y + z - 3 = 0$.

14–6　**11.** State the nature of the intersection of the planes with equations

$$2x - y + z - 3 = 0,$$
$$x + 3y - z - 2 = 0,$$
$$5x + y + z - 8 = 0.$$

Reading List

CARMAN, ROBERT A. *A Programmed Introduction to Vectors,* New York: John Wiley and Sons, Inc., 1963.

FULTON, CURTIS M. *Vector Space Axioms for Geometry.* Mathematics Magazine, vol. 36, pp. 299–301, 1963.

GLICKSMAN, ABRAHAM M. *Vectors in Three-Dimensional Geometry.* Washington, D.C.: National Council of Teachers of Mathematics, 1961.

KELLEY, JOHN L. *Introduction to Modern Algebra.* Princeton, N.J.: D. Van Nostrand Company, Inc., 1960.

SCHUSTER, SEYMOUR. *Elementary Vector Geometry.* New York: John Wiley and Sons, Inc., 1962.

TELLER, EDWARD. *The Geometry of Space and Time.* The Mathematics Teacher, vol. 54, pp. 505–514, 1961.

Henri Poincaré

Imagine for a moment a spherical universe two feet in diameter. In this universe the temperature at any point is determined by the distance of the point from the center. As the distance increases, the temperature decreases, approaching absolute zero near the boundary. In addition, all things expand with the heat and contract with the cold at the same rate. This is the universe which the French mathematician Henri Poincaré (1854–1912) created to demonstrate the relationship between geometry and the physical world.

For Poincaré, the postulates of a geometrical system are not statements of physical law; they are conventions. Any postulate system which does not lead to contradictions is as "true" as any other system. But only a system which gives an accurate description of the physical universe can be considered useful. Thus, in Euclid's geometry, it is no accident that lines are straight and figures can be moved rigidly, for experiments carried out by the scientists of that period indicated that in our world light rays travel in straight lines and solids can be displaced without distortion. In the world described above, however, light rays travel in circular arcs and bodies change size and shape with a change in position, so it is reasonable to conclude that its inhabitants would develop a geometry entirely unlike Euclidean geometry. Strange as it may seem, though, they could never discover this difference by experiment, because as bodies changed with a change in position, so would the instruments of measurement. Moreover, to them their universe would appear infinite, for as one of them traveled away from the center, he would grow smaller and smaller, his speed would become slower and slower, and he would never reach the boundary.

Poincaré's work covered many fields of pure and applied mathematics, from topology to celestial mechanics. He wrote a number of books for the layman on the foundations of science and mathematics. In analysis his work on automorphic functions, infinite determinants, and asymptotic series was particularly important. He came in conflict with other leading mathematicians of his day by insisting on the need for intuition in mathematics and doubting the validity of some of the newly developed methods of mathematical logic and set theory.

597

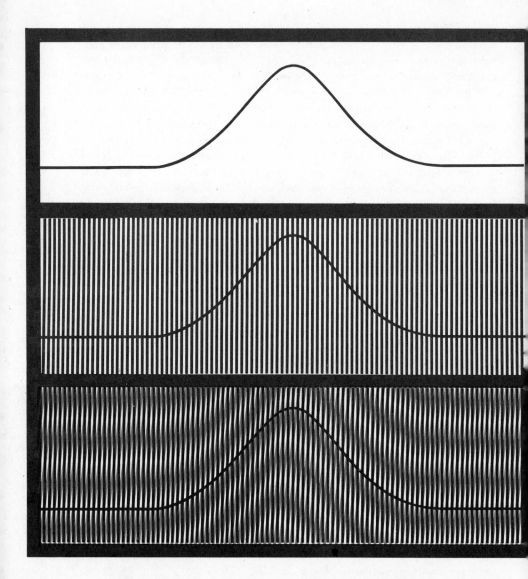

Many times the elements of a set of measurements are normally distributed, that is, they can be arranged to fit the normal probability distribution curve $y = \dfrac{1}{\sqrt{2\pi}}\, e^{-\frac{x^2}{2}}$ (top diagram). If parallel lines are drawn through the intersection of uniformly spaced lines and the normal curve, a moiré pattern of normal curves results (bottom diagram).

Probability

The modern theory of mathematical probability, arising out of interest in games of chance, is a little over 300 years old. During the 18th century much attention was given to studies of population statistics and to the rapidly growing life-insurance business. By the end of the 18th century the use of probability in the analysis of errors in physical and astronomical measurements had been introduced. Through the 19th and 20th centuries right up to the present time developments in the theory and application of probability have been extensive and spectacular. They have included deep studies of the foundations of the subject and ever-broadening applications in such fields as economics, genetics, physical science, and engineering.

RANDOM EXPERIMENTS AND PROBABILITIES

15–1 Sample Spaces and Events

In games of chance and in other situations there are many familiar experimental procedures that have the characteristic property that, when they are repeated time after time under apparently similar conditions, they yield results that vary in an unpredictable way. We will call such procedures *random experiments*. Consider the following examples:

EXAMPLE 1. A coin is tossed twice. If H and T stand for heads and tails, the set of outcomes is {HH, HT, TH, TT}.

EXAMPLE 2. A pair of dice, a white one and a green one, are rolled. The set of outcomes is tabulated below. (Each number pair in the table indicates a reading of the white die and the green die in that order.)

1, 1	1, 2	1, 3	1, 4	1, 5	1, 6
2, 1	2, 2	2, 3	2, 4	2, 5	2, 6
3, 1	3, 2	3, 3	3, 4	3, 5	3, 6
4, 1	4, 2	4, 3	4, 4	4, 5	4, 6
5, 1	5, 2	5, 3	5, 4	5, 5	5, 6
6, 1	6, 2	6, 3	6, 4	6, 5	6, 6

For such sets of outcomes of random experiments we introduce some definitions.

> The set of all possible outcomes of a random experiment is called the **sample space** of the experiment.
>
> Each individual outcome is called an **element** of the sample space. A subset of a sample space is called an **event**.

In the above tabulation of the elements of the sample space for the two-dice experiment, for example, the statement "The sum of the numbers of dots shown is 7" describes the event consisting of the elements in the diagonal running from the lower left to the upper right. The statement "The green die shows 3" describes the event represented by the third column. "The sum of the numbers is ≥ 11" describes the event consisting of the triangular array of three elements in the lower right-hand corner.

We next assign what we will call a **probability** to each element of a sample space. These probabilities are real numbers and are required to satisfy two conditions:

1. Each probability is a positive number or zero.
2. The sum of the probabilities assigned to all the elements of any sample space equals 1.

We will occasionally refer to these assigned numbers as *elemental probabilities*.

The numbers assigned as probabilities may be based on previous studies of observed frequency ratios or they may be simply assumed hypothetically. One hypothetical method of assignment that will frequently be employed will be that of assigning the number $1/n$ to each element of a sample space, where n is the number of elements contained in the space. This, of course, is the formal way of characterizing the imprecise notion of "equally likely" outcomes. If you do this in the 2-dice example, you will assign the number $\frac{1}{36}$ to each of the 36 elements. In doing this, however, you are not saying that you know the dice are perfect. You are merely constructing a mathematical model which will enable you to make probability statements about what the behavior of the dice might be like if they were perfect. Such hypothetical models have been found in many situations to approximate reality very closely.

We denote the set of all elements in a given sample space by U; the subset comprising an event in U, by A; the event complementary to A, by A'; and the probability of the event A, by $P(A)$.

> $P(A)$ is defined as the sum of the elemental probabilities assigned to the elements of A.

EXAMPLE 3. In the sample space of Example 2, let A be the event that the sum of the number of dots shown face up on the dice is 7. Determine $P(A)$ if equal elemental probabilities are assigned.

Solution: A contains 6 elements (Why?), each having the assigned probability $\frac{1}{36}$ (Why?)

$$\therefore P(A) = 6 \cdot \tfrac{1}{36} = \tfrac{1}{6}, \textbf{ Answer.}$$

Three simple results follow at once from our basic definitions, namely,

1. $P(U) = 1$ and $P(U') = P(\emptyset) = 0$

2. $0 \le P(A) \le 1$

3. $P(A) + P(A') = 1$

The proofs of these statements are very easy and they are left for you to supply.

Exercises

A

1. Set up a sample space for the experiment of tossing a coin three times.

2. If equal elemental probabilities are assigned to the sample space of Exercise 1, find the probability that 3 tosses of a coin will produce at least 2 heads.

3. If equal probabilities are assigned to 36 elements in the space of our 2-dice experiment, find the probabilities of the following events. (w = the number of dots shown on the white die and g the number on the green one.)

   a. $w + g = 5$ **c.** $w + g \ge 8$

   b. $w > 4$ **d.** $g \le 3$

4. Let two regular tetrahedra, each with faces numbered from 1 to 4, be used as dice, with the "down" face being the one counted. Let there also be one white and one green, and set up the sample space for the experiment of rolling them.

5. Assign equal probabilities to the elements of the sample space of Exercise 4 and find **(a)** $P(w + g < 6)$, **(b)** $P(w + g = 5)$, **(c)** $P(w < 2)$.

6. Let an integer be chosen at random from the first 10 positive even integers. Specify the sample space and the event that the chosen integer is not divisible by 3 or 5.

7. Three horses are to be assigned at random to four single stalls in a line. Specify a sample space, and the event that the first stall in the line is not occupied.

8. In Exercise 7, specify the event that **(a)** three adjacent stalls are occupied, **(b)** no more than two consecutive stalls are occupied.

9. Four draftees, Privates Jones, Brown, Smith, and Doe are to be assigned at random to either the artillery or the infantry. Specify a sample space and the event that Privates Brown and Smith are assigned to the same service.

10. In Exercise 9, specify the event that (a) three of the men are assigned to the infantry and one to the artillery; (b) at least three men are assigned to the infantry.

B 11. From 6 cards bearing the letters a, b, c, d, e, and f, 2 cards are drawn. Give in roster form the sample space and the event that at least one of the cards drawn bears a vowel.

12. A bag contains a large number of red, green, blue, yellow, and black marbles. Two marbles are drawn. List the elements in the sample space. List also the event that the marbles drawn are of different colors.

Many probabilistic situations can be depicted in terms of assigning balls to cells. For example, a single flip of a coin is equivalent to the random assignment of a single ball to one of two cells. For another example, Exercise 1 in this set of exercises corresponds to the random assignments of three balls to two cells.

13. To what ball-cell model does the experiment in Exercise 3 in this set correspond?

14. To what ball-cell model does the experiment in Exercise 4 in this set correspond?

15. To what ball-cell model does the experiment in Exercise 11 in this set correspond?

16. To what ball-cell model does the experiment in Exercise 12 in this set correspond?

C 17. A die is rolled, and a coin is tossed twice. Set up the sample space for this experiment. Specify the event that the die shows an even number and the coin comes up heads at least once.

18. A poker hand of 5 cards is dealt from a 52-card pack. Describe the sample space. Describe also the event that the hand is a "full house" (2 of one denomination and 3 of another). List a few elements of the sample space and of the event.

19. To what ball-cell model does the experiment in Exercise 17 in this set correspond?

20. To what ball-cell model does the experiment in Exercise 18 in this set correspond?

15–2 Addition of Probabilities

In connection with the sample space of the 2-dice experiment described in Example 2 in the previous section let us consider the following events: $A(w > 4)$, $B(g \leq 2)$, $C(w + g \geq 10)$, and $D(w + g < 6)$. If you assign equal probabilities of $\frac{1}{36}$ to the elements of U, you can ask and answer a number of questions about certain combinations of these events. We will list a few such questions.

1. What is the probability of A or B (or both)?
2. What is the probability of C or D?
3. What is the probability of both A and B?
4. What is the probability of both C and D?
5. What is the probability of C, given the occurrence of A?

If you represent the set U by a square array of 36 points, the events A, B, C, and D can be graphically illustrated as indicated in Figure 15–1.

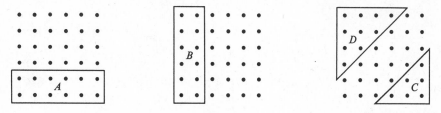

Figure 15–1

If you next recall the definitions of the union and intersection of sets, you see that the above questions can be neatly restated as follows:

1. What is $P(A \cup B)$?　　(*Answer*, $\frac{5}{9}$)
2. What is $P(C \cup D)$?　　(*Answer*, $\frac{4}{9}$)
3. What is $P(A \cap B)$?　　(*Answer*, $\frac{1}{9}$)
4. What is $P(C \cap D)$?　　(*Answer*, 0)
5. In the reduced sample space consisting of the set A, what is $P(A \cap C)$? (*Answer*, $\frac{5}{12}$)

With the aid of Figure 15–1, you should find it easy to interpret these questions and to verify the given answers. They will be found to illustrate and clarify a number of ideas which we are about to consider. Note that $P(C \cup D) = P(C) + P(D)$ but that $P(A \cup B) \neq P(A) + P(B)$. Note also how the set A' was ignored in question 5 when it was given that the event A had actually occurred. Finally, note that in Figure 15–1 we have, in effect, introduced the Venn diagram as a convenient device for representing sample spaces and events.

Consider two events A and B such as those illustrated in Figure 15–2 on the following page. Using the definition of probability of an event, you see that $P(A) + P(B)$ is equal to the sum of the elemental probabilities assigned to the elements of A added to the similar sum for the elements of B. Thus the elemental probabilities assigned to the event $A \cap B$ contribute twice to $P(A) + P(B)$. Hence, by the definitions of $A \cup B$ and $P(A \cup B)$, you have the following important result.

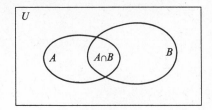

Figure 15-2   **Figure 15-3**

THEOREM 1 $P(A \cup B) = P(A) + P(B) - P(A \cap B)$.

EXAMPLE 1. In Figure 15-1, $P(A) = P(B) = \frac{12}{36}, P(A \cap B) = \frac{4}{36}$. Hence $P(A \cup B) = \frac{12}{36} + \frac{12}{36} - \frac{4}{36} = \frac{5}{9}$.

In the situation illustrated in Figure 15-3, where $A \cap B = \emptyset$, you describe the events A and B as **mutually exclusive**. For such events $P(A \cap B) = 0$, and Theorem 1 becomes:

THEOREM 2 If A and B are mutually exclusive events, then

$$P(A \cup B) = P(A) + P(B).$$

EXAMPLE 2. In Figure 15-1, $C \cap D = \emptyset$.

Hence $P(C \cup D) = \frac{6}{36} + \frac{10}{36} = \frac{4}{9}$.

Theorems 1 and 2 are known as the *additive rules for probabilities*.

It is an easy matter to extend Theorem 2 to cases involving more than 2 events. For n events this leads to the following assertion:

THEOREM 3 If events $A_1, A_2, \ldots, A_n$ are such that $A_i \cap A_j = \emptyset$ for every pair $i, j, (i \neq j)$, then

$$P(A_1 \cup A_2 \cup \cdots \cup A_n)$$
$$= P(A_1) + P(A_2) + \cdots + P(A_n).$$

The proof of this theorem, which is left for you to complete, can readily be given by mathematical induction. (See Exercises 21 and 22, page 606.)

EXAMPLE 3. A number is selected at random from the set $\{1, 2, 3, 4, 5, 6, 7, 8, 9\}$. If equal elemental probabilities are assigned, what is the probability that the number chosen is either less than 4 or is odd?

Solution: Let A be the event that the number selected is less than 4.

Then, $A = \{1, 2, 3\}$ and $P(A) = \frac{3}{9} = \frac{1}{3}$.

Let B be the event that the number selected is odd.

Then $B = \{1, 3, 5, 7, 9\}$ and $P(B) = \frac{5}{9}$.

Also $A \cap B = \{1, 3\}$ and $P(A \cap B) = \frac{2}{9}$.

$\therefore P(A \cup B) = P(A) + P(B) - P(A \cap B) = \frac{1}{3} + \frac{5}{9} - \frac{2}{9} = \frac{2}{3}$,

Answer.

Exercises

In the following exercises assume that equal elemental probabilities are assigned.

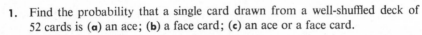

1. Find the probability that a single card drawn from a well-shuffled deck of 52 cards is (**a**) an ace; (**b**) a face card; (**c**) an ace or a face card.

2. In Exercise 1, what is the probability that the card is (**a**) not an ace; (**b**) not a face card; (**c**) neither an ace nor a face card.

3. A bag contains 7 red, 4 white, 5 blue, and 4 black marbles. If one marble is taken from the bag, find the probability that it is (**a**) not black; (**b**) red or blue.

4. In Exercise 3, what is the probability that the marble is (**a**) either white or black; (**b**) neither white nor black?

5. From 6 cards bearing the letters a, b, c, d, e, and f, 2 cards are drawn. Find the probability that they are either both vowels or both consonants.

6. A number is chosen at random from the first 50 positive integers. Find the probability that it is (**a**) either prime or a perfect square; (**b**) either even or a perfect square.

7. Let the 8 kings and queens be removed from a pack of cards. If 2 cards are drawn from these 8, find the probability that they are either both red or both queens.

8. Two letters are chosen at random from the word B E T T E R. Find the probability that either they are the same or at least one of them is a vowel.

9. In an experiment in psychology, subjects (students) are assigned to one of four experimental groups by two flips of a coin. If the first flip results in a head, the subject is assigned to group 1 or 2, and if a tail results, to group 3 or 4. The second flip then determines precisely which of the remaining two groups receives the subject. Thus, HH is group 1, HT is group 2, TH is group 3, and TT is group 4. What is the probability that Mary and Jane are both assigned to group 1? to the same group?

10. In Exercise 9, what is the probability that either Mary is assigned to group 2 or else both Mary and Jane are assigned to group 4?

In Exercises 11–20, use Venn diagrams to help you find an answer to the question.

11. In a group of 100 persons, 85 had Rh positive blood (Rh factor present), 45 had Type O blood, and 38 had both type O and Rh positive blood. If one person was selected at random from the group, what is the probability that:

   a. his blood type was not O?

   b. his blood type was Rh negative?

   c. his blood type was O and Rh negative?

   d. his blood type was not O or else was Rh positive?

12. In a mathematics class of thirty students, fifteen are also taking chemistry, eighteen are taking physics, and eight are taking both chemistry and physics. If a student is selected at random from the class, what is the probability that he is taking either chemistry or physics? What is the probability that he is taking physics but not chemistry?

13. In Exercise 12, what is the probability that a student selected at random is taking neither chemistry nor physics? What is the probability that he is taking chemistry but not physics?

14. Find the probability that all coins turn up heads when:

   a. one coin is flipped,   **c.** four coins are flipped,

   b. two coins are flipped,   **d.** six coins are flipped.

15. Deduce from the results of Exercise 14 the probability that if n coins are flipped, all of them will show heads.

16. Deduce from the results of Exercise 15 and Formula 3 on page 601 the probability that, if n coins are flipped, at least one of them shows a tail.

17. If A and B are events in a sample space S, $P(A) = n \neq 0$, and $P(A \cap B) = 0$, what is $P(A')$? Explain why $P(B) \leq P(A')$.

18. If A and B are events in a sample space S, if $P(A) + P(B) < 1$, and if $P(A \cap B) = n \neq 0$, show that $P(A \cup B) < 1 - n$.

19. Show that if A and B are events in a sample space S, then

$$P(A \cap B) \leq P(A) \leq P(A \cup B) \leq P(A) + P(B).$$

20. Show that if A and B are events in a sample space S, then

$$P(A' \cup B') = 1 - P(A \cap B).$$

21. By constructing a suitable Venn diagram, verify the following generalization of Theorem 1 for three events A, B, and C:

$$P(A \cup B \cup C) = P(A) + P(B) + P(C) - P(A \cap B) - P(A \cap C) \\ - P(B \cap C) + P(A \cap B \cap C).$$

22. Use mathematical induction to prove Theorem 3, page 604.

15-3 Multiplication of Probabilities

Let A and B be events such that $P(A) \neq 0$. (Figure 15-2, page 604.) We introduce the symbol $P(B|A)$ to denote the **conditional** probability of B, given that A has occurred, and we define $P(B|A)$ by

$$P(B|A) = \frac{P(A \cap B)}{P(A)} \cdot \text{ If } P(A) = 0, P(B|A) = 0.$$

In order to see that this is a reasonable definition, let us examine it together with a simple example. Let one die be rolled, and let us assign elemental probabilities of $\frac{1}{6}$. Let event A be "The number rolled is even" and event B be "The number is 6." Then $P(A) = \frac{1}{2}$ and $P(B) = \frac{1}{6}$. If, however, it is given that the number rolled is even and then the probability of a 6 is sought, the problem is in effect to be re-worked after dropping A' (the set of odd-number outcomes) from the sample space. The set A becomes the new sample space, and the probabilities assigned to the elements of A must be adjusted so that their sum is 1 instead of $P(A)$. This will be accomplished if these numbers are all divided by $P(A)$. (Why?)

In our example they would be divided by $\frac{1}{2}$ and thus changed from $\frac{1}{6}$ to $\frac{1}{3}$. Furthermore, in the example, $P(A \cap B) = P(B)$, so $P(B|A)$ becomes $\frac{P(A \cap B)}{P(A)} = \frac{\frac{1}{6}}{\frac{1}{2}} = \frac{1}{3}$. This result is consistent with the fact that $A = \{2, 4, 6\}$, so that under the assumption that the elements of A are assigned equal probabilities, the probability of selecting 6 from A is $\frac{1}{3}$.

Thus, the expression $\dfrac{P(A \cap B)}{P(A)}$ represents the sum of the probabilities assigned to the elements of $B \cap A$ after the elemental probabilities in A have been adjusted proportionally so that A becomes the sample space. Observe that if $P(A) \neq 0$, then $P(A \cap B) = P(A) \cdot P(B|A)$. (Why?) On the other hand, if $P(A) = 0$, then $P(A \cap B) = 0$. (Why?), and again, $P(A \cap B) = P(A) \cdot P(B|A)$. Hence, whether $P(A) \neq 0$ or $P(A) = 0$, you have the following result.

THEOREM 4 $P(A \cap B) = P(A) \cdot P(B|A)$.

Stated in words instead of symbols, Theorem 4 says that the probability of the joint occurrence of two events A and B is equal to the probability that one of them occurs, multiplied by the probability that after the one has occurred then the other one also occurs.

In some situations the events A and B may be such that $P(A|B) = P(A)$ and $P(B|A) = P(B)$. (See Exercise 3, page 609.) When this happens the events A and B are said to be **independent**, and as a corollary of Theorem 4, you obtain the following assertion.

THEOREM 5 For independent events A and B

$$P(A \cap B) = P(A) \cdot P(B).$$

Theorems 4 and 5 are known as the *multiplicative rules for probabilities*.

As an illustration of the notion of independence let us consider an experiment in which we simultaneously toss a coin and roll a die. The sample space contains the following 12 elements:

H 1   H 2   H 3   H 4   H 5   H 6
T 1   T 2   T 3   T 4   T 5   T 6

Let A be the event of tossing a head, and B the event of rolling a 6. Also, let equal probabilities of $\frac{1}{12}$ be assigned to each of the above elements. Clearly, $P(A) = \frac{6}{12}$, or $\frac{1}{2}$, and $P(B) = \frac{2}{12}$, or $\frac{1}{6}$.

The set $A \cap B$ contains just 1 element, H 6, so $P(A \cap B) = \frac{1}{12}$. We see that $P(A) \cdot P(B)$ also is $\frac{1}{12}$. You can verify that A and B are independent by noting that

$$P(B|A) = \frac{P(A \cap B)}{P(A)} = \frac{\frac{1}{12}}{\frac{1}{2}} = \frac{1}{6} = P(B).$$

Common sense would certainly anticipate the independence of these events A and B. One would expect that the probability of rolling a 6 with a die would not be affected by the way a coin might happen to fall.

Two events that are not independent are said to be **dependent**.

EXAMPLE 1. Two dice are thrown. Event A is the throwing of at least one 2. Event B is the throwing of two numbers whose sum is 5. Graph the sample space and indicate both events on the graph. Show that the events are dependent.

Solution: Graph A and B on the sample space, and compute $P(A)$, $P(B)$, and $P(A \cap B)$.

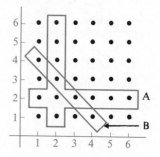

$$P(A) = \frac{11}{36} \qquad P(B) = \frac{4}{36} = \frac{1}{9}$$

$$P(A \cap B) = \frac{2}{36} = \frac{1}{18}$$

Is $\frac{11}{36} \times \frac{1}{9} = \frac{1}{18}$? No.

A and B are dependent, **Answer.**

Exercises

1. A coin is tossed twice and a pair of dice are rolled. Assuming independence for the coin and dice and equal elemental probabilities, find the probability of tossing 2 heads and rolling a 5 with at least one of the dice.

2. A 4-faced tetrahedral die is rolled twice, the down faces being the ones counted. Let event A be "The sum of the down numbers is ≥ 6." Let event B be "The first down number is 4." Assuming equal elemental probabilities for the sample space, find $P(A|B)$.

B

3. If $P(A) \neq 0$ and $P(B) \neq 0$, show that $P(A|B) = P(A)$ implies that $P(A \cap B) \neq 0$ and $P(B|A) = P(B)$.

4. A pair of dice, one white and one green, are thrown. Let A be the event that the sum of the numbers is 7. Let B be the event that the sum is 5. Let C be the event that the green die shows 4. (**a**) Are A and C independent? (**b**) Are B and C independent?

5. The probability that Tom will solve a certain problem is $\frac{1}{2}$, that Dick will solve it is $\frac{2}{3}$, and that Harry will solve it is $\frac{3}{5}$. If all try it independently, find (**a**) the probability that the problem will be solved and (**b**) the probability that at least two people solve it.

6. In Exercise 5, what is the probability that Dick will solve it but Harry and Tom will not?

7. If a coin is tossed 10 times, what is the probability that it comes up (**a**) heads every time? (**b**) alternately heads and tails?

8. One bag contains 3 red and 5 green marbles. A second bag contains 6 red and 2 green marbles. If two marbles are drawn, one from each bag, find the probability that they will be of the same color.

9. Three urns contain red marbles and black ones. The first urn contains 2 red and 3 black, the second urn contains 9 red and 11 black, and the third urn 3 red and 7 black. If a marble is drawn from each urn, what is the probability that they are (**a**) all red; (**b**) all the same color?

10. A pair of dice are thrown twice. What is the probability that (**a**) the sum of the numbers on the first throw is 5 and the sum on the second throw is also 5; (**b**) the sum of the numbers on the first throw is 6 and the sum on the second throw is 6; (**c**) the sum of the numbers on the first throw is the same as the sum of the numbers on the second throw?

11. A card is drawn from a standard deck of 52 cards. Let A be the event that the card is black, B be the event that the card is an ace, and C be the event that the card is either an ace or a king. Which of the following are independent events?

(**a**) A and B (**b**) A and C (**c**) B and C

12. Two dice are thrown. Let A be the event that the sum of the numbers is 7, B be the event that at least one of the numbers is a 5, and C be the event that the number on one dice is the same as that on the other. Which of the following are independent events?

(**a**) A and B (**b**) A and C (**c**) B and C

In Exercises 13–16, let A and B be events in a sample space S.

13. Show that $P(A|A) = 1$.

14. Show that $P(A'|B) = 1 - P(A|B)$.

15. Show that $P(A'|A) = 0$.

16. Show that if $P(B) > 0$ and A and B are mutually exclusive events, then $P(A|B) = 0$.

C **17.** Prove that if A and B are events in a sample space S with probabilities such that $P(A) \cdot P(B) \neq 0$, and if A and B are mutually exclusive, then they cannot be independent.

18. Prove that if the events A and B in Exercise 17 are independent, then they cannot be mutually exclusive.

SYSTEMATIC COUNTING

15–4 Permutations

Can you answer a question like "What is the probability that a bridge hand of 13 cards will contain 8 or more spades including the ace, king, and queen?" Assuming that equal probabilities are assigned to all possible hands, you merely need to list the elements in the sample space, count them, count also the elements in the appropriate subset, and divide the numbers obtained to compute the answer. Your chief problem is living long enough to complete the listing and counting because the sample space contains 635,013,559,600 elements! You have to learn counting procedures to deal with practical problems in which the sample spaces contain large numbers of elements.

You will have frequent occasion to use the following *multiplication principle*.

> If two finite sets contain, respectively, *m* elements and *n* elements, then their Cartesian product contains *mn* elements.

In less technical language, this principle can be restated as follows:

> If a certain act can be performed in *m* different ways and if, for each of these ways, a second act can be performed in *n* different ways, then the two acts can be performed successively in *mn* different ways.

Using the latter version, we may add that if for each of the *mn* ways of performing the two acts there are *p* ways of performing a third act, then there are *mnp* ways of performing the three acts successively, and similarly for a fourth act, and so on.

For example, if 5 airlines offer service from Chicago to New York and 3 offer service from New York to Paris, then a flight from Chicago to Paris by way of New York can be arranged in 15 different ways.

Next consider a set of 3 objects, represented by the letters a, b, and c and arranged in all possible orders. The list of arrangements is

$$abc, acb, bac, bca, cab, cba,$$

the number of arrangements being 6.

You can also arrive at this number by the following line of reasoning. Suppose you have 3 blank spaces in a row such as ⬜⬜⬜ or — — — , and that each space is to be filled by one of the letters a, b, c. The first space can then be filled in any of three ways. For any of these ways the next can be filled in two ways. Finally, the third space will be filled by the one remaining letter. By the multiplication principle the number of ways in which the three spaces can be filled is $3 \times 2 \times 1 = 6$.

An arrangement of a set of objects in a particular order is called a **permutation** of those objects. The symbol $_nP_n$ will be used to denote the number of possible permutations of a set of n different objects. We have shown above that $_3P_3 = 6 = 3!$ By extending the argument, you can show that

$$_nP_n = n!$$

Now suppose you are asked to find the number of permutations of 5 objects taken only 3 at a time. In the diagram ⬜⬜⬜ , the first space can be filled in 5 ways, the second in 4 ways, and the last in 3. Thus $\boxed{5 \mid 4 \mid 3}$ represents the situation. Therefore, by the multiplication principle there are $5 \cdot 4 \cdot 3 = 60$ permutations of the 5 objects taken 3 at a time.

For $r \leq n$ we will use the symbol $_nP_r$ to denote the number of permutations of n different objects taken r at a time. Thus, $_5P_3 = 60$.

To obtain a formula for $_nP_r$, notice that the diagram representing the situation contains r spaces to be filled as shown:

$$\boxed{n \mid n-1 \mid n-2 \mid \ldots \mid n-(r-1)}$$

Thus, $_nP_r = n(n-1)(n-2)\ldots[n-(r-1)]$.

Note also that

$$_nP_r = \frac{n(n-1)\cdots(n-r+1)(n-r)(n-r-1)\cdots 1}{(n-r)(n-r-1)\cdots 1},$$

or

$$_nP_r = \frac{n!}{(n-r)!}$$

EXAMPLE. With 8 flags of different colors the number of possible vertical arrangements of 3 flags on a staff is $8 \cdot 7 \cdot 6 = 336$.

Let us now consider the number of possible arrangements of the five letters a, a, a, b, and c. If we replaced the 3 a's by x, y, z, we would have 5 different letters and the answer would be 5!. However, in any arrangement such as *xbyzc* the letters x, y, z could be arranged in 3! ways, whereas if those spaces were occupied by 3 a's there would be only one *distinguishable* arrangement. Thus there are 3! times as many distinguishable permutations when the a's are replaced by x, y, z; hence the permutations of the 5 letters of which 3 are identical is $\dfrac{5!}{3!} = 20$.

By similar reasoning, the permutations of n objects of which n_1 are alike, n_2 others are alike, and so on, is $\dfrac{n!}{n_1!n_2! \ldots}$. A time-honored example which illustrates the use of this formula is the question of the number of possible arrangements of the letters of the word Mississippi. The answer is $\dfrac{11!}{4!4!2!}$.

Exercises

A

1. A certain make of car is available in 4 body types, 5 colors, and 3 kinds of upholstery. How many cars would a dealer have to keep in stock in order to be able to show his complete line to prospective customers?

2. How many three-digit numerals can be formed using the digits 2, 3, 5, 7 and 8 (**a**) if repetition of digits is not permitted, and (**b**) if repetition of digits is permitted?

3. The Greek alphabet contains 24 letters. How many Greek-letter fraternity names can be formed, each containing either 2 or 3 letters, a repetition of letters being permitted?

4. **a.** From the digits 0, 1, 2, ..., 9, how many numbers between 4000 and 6000 can be denoted if repetition of digits is not allowed?

   b. How many of these are divisible by 5?

5. In how many different distinguishable orders can the letters of the word Tennessee be arranged?

6. If 3 books have red covers, 3 have green covers, and 4 have brown covers, find the number of ways in which the 10 books can be arranged on a shelf so that books of the same color are kept together.

7. If $_nP_5 = 42_nP_3$, find n.

8. The dial of a combination lock has the 26 letters of the alphabet on it. A combination is formed by dialing 3 different letters in a particular order. If the owner of the lock forgets the combination, how many trials may be needed to open the lock?

9. How many different characters can be transmitted by Morse code if each character is represented by not more than 5 dots and/or dashes?

10. How many positive integers less than 100,000 have decimal numerals containing the digits 4, 5, and 6 in the order given?

B **11.** How many decimal numerals for positive even integers less than 500 can be formed using the digits 1, 2, 3, 4, 5, 6, **(a)** if no digit is repeated; **(b)** if any digit can be used at the most twice; **(c)** if any digit can be used once, twice, or three times?

12. In Exercise 11, answer the same questions relative to numerals for odd numbers less than 400, using the same digits.

13. The ten cards from ace to ten, inclusive, in the spade suit are removed from a bridge deck, shuffled, and laid out in a row. Then the cards from ace to ten in the heart suit are removed, shuffled, and laid out in a row just below the spades. How many ways can distinct pairings (of ten cards) occur?

14. In Exercise 13, how many ways can such pairings be made so that the cards in the third position have the same value?

15. In Exercise 13, how many ways can such pairings be made so that exactly one of the pairs in the same position have the same value?

16. In Exercise 13, how many ways can such pairings be made so that at least one of the pairs in the same position have the same value?

C **17.** Show that $_nP_r - {_nP_{r-1}} = (n - r)_nP_{r-1}$.

18. Solve $_nP_r = K(_{n-1}P_{r-1})$ for n.

15–5 Combinations

Let us next examine the complete list of the 24 permutations of 4 letters a, b, c, and d taken 3 at a time. One way to make up the list is as follows:

abc	abd	acd	bcd
acb	adb	adc	bdc
bac	bad	cad	cbd
bca	bda	cda	cdb
cab	dab	dac	dbc
cba	dba	dca	dcb

You will observe at once that in each column are found the 3!, or 6 permutations of the 3 letters at the head of the column. The list makes it clear that if you are interested only in the question of how many different groups of 3 letters can be selected from the given set of 4 letters, the matter of order being unimportant, the answer would be simply the number of columns, or 4. Groups selected without regard to the order of the objects within the group are called **combinations**. We adopt the symbol $_nC_r$ to represent the number of combinations of n objects taken r at a time. The meaning of the symbol $_nC_r$ can also be indicated by stating that $_nC_r$ is equal to the number of subsets of r elements that can be formed from a set of n objects.

The above listing for 4 objects taken 3 at a time suggests a simple way to obtain a formula for $_nC_r$. If you were to list and count all the possible combinations of n objects taken r at a time, and then multiply the resulting number by $r!$, which is the number of permutations of each combination, the answer would have to be $_nP_r$. (Why?) In symbols,

$$_nC_r \cdot r! = {}_nP_r.$$

Hence $_nC_r = \dfrac{_nP_r}{r!} = \dfrac{n!}{r!(n-r)!} = \dfrac{n(n-1)\cdots(n-r+1)}{r!}.$

EXAMPLE 1. In a club with 10 members,

 a. In how many ways can a committee of 3 be selected?

 b. In how many ways can the offices of president, secretary, and treasurer be filled?

Solution: **a.** The order of selection is immaterial, so you have $_{10}C_3 = \dfrac{10!}{7!3!} = 120.$

 b. The order in which the 3 persons chosen are assigned to the offices is significant, so you have $_{10}P_3 = \dfrac{10!}{7!} = 720.$

The formula $_nC_r = \dfrac{n(n-1)\cdots(n-r+1)}{r!}$ may have reminded you of the formula for the binomial coefficient $\dbinom{n}{r}$ (page 89). The fact that $_nC_r = \dbinom{n}{r}$ suggests an alternative way of deriving the binomial theorem. Consider the following expansion:

$(a + b)^3 = (a + b)(a + b)(a + b)$
$= aaa + baa + aab + aba + bba + bab + abb + bbb.$

You obtain each product shown in the expansion by multiplying three variables, one from each of the binomial factors of $(a + b)^3$. The term *baa*, for example, is the result of choosing b from the first binomial factor, a from the second, and a from the third. Do you see that the products *baa*, and *aab*, and *aba* are the ones occurring when you select b from one factor and a from both of the other factors? Thus, if you combine similar terms in the expansion to obtain

$$(a + b)^3 = a^3 + 3a^2b + 3ab^2 + b^3,$$

then 3, the coefficient of a^2b, is the number of ways of selecting one b from the three factors; that is, $_3C_1$. Similarly, because you obtain a^3 by choosing no b from the three factors, the coefficient of a^3 is 1, or $_3C_0$. In fact, you can rewrite the expansion as follows:

$$(a + b)^3 = {}_3C_0 a^3 + {}_3C_1 a^2 b + {}_3C_2 ab^2 + {}_3C_3 b^3$$

The reasoning used in determining the coefficients in the expansion of $(a + b)^3$ can be extended to determining the coefficients in the expansion of $(a + b)^n$. Thus,

$$(a + b)^n = {}_nC_0 a^n + {}_nC_1 a^{n-1} b + {}_nC_2 a^{n-2} b^2 + \cdots + {}_nC_n b^n$$

The following examples illustrate the way in which our counting procedures can be used in computing probabilities.

EXAMPLE 2. An urn contains 5 white and 7 black balls. If 4 balls are drawn, what is the probability that they will be **(a)** all black, **(b)** 2 of each color?

Solution: The sample space for this problem contains $\binom{12}{4}$ elements.

The subset corresponding to **(a)** contains $\binom{7}{4}$ elements. For **(b)**, using the multiplication principle, we obtain $\binom{5}{2} \cdot \binom{7}{2}$ elements. Hence, assuming that the $\binom{12}{4}$ elements are assigned equal probabilities, we have the answers

for **(a)** $\dfrac{\binom{7}{4}}{\binom{12}{4}} = \dfrac{7}{99}$ and for **(b)** $\dfrac{\binom{5}{2} \cdot \binom{7}{2}}{\binom{12}{4}} = \dfrac{14}{33}$.

EXAMPLE 3. Four cards are drawn one by one from a well-shuffled pack. What is the probability that the first 2 are aces and the other 2 are kings?

Solution: Denoting the two events by A and B, we have $P(A) = \dfrac{{}_4P_2}{{}_{52}P_2}$

and $P(B|A) = \dfrac{{}_4P_2}{{}_{50}P_2}$.

Then $P(A \cap B) = P(A) \cdot P(B|A) = \dfrac{4 \cdot 3}{52 \cdot 51} \cdot \dfrac{4 \cdot 3}{50 \cdot 49}$

$$= \frac{6}{270725}, \textbf{ Answer.}$$

Exercises

1. Prove that the number of permutations of n objects of which r are identical and the remaining $n - r$ are also identical is $\binom{n}{r}$.

2. If 10 persons are seated at random in a row of 10 chairs, what is the probability that 2 designated individuals will be seated together?

3. In Exercise 2 what is the probability if the 10 persons are seated around a circular table?

4. A committee of 4 is chosen by lot from a group consisting of 8 Republicans and 6 Democrats. Find the probability that there will be at least 1 Republican and 1 Democrat on the committee.

5. A bureau drawer contains 10 brown socks and 8 gray socks well mixed. A man goes to this drawer in the dark and takes out 2 socks. What is the probability that they will match?

6. A box contains tickets numbered $1, 2, \ldots, 20$. If 2 tickets are drawn, find the probability that the sum of their numbers is even.

7. Prove that $_nC_r + {_nC_{r-1}} = {_{n+1}C_r}$.

8. How many different sums of money can be formed with a penny, a nickel, a dime, a quarter, a half dollar, and a dollar?

9. Of a group of 15 football linemen, 3 can play only center and 5 can play only end. The others can play either guard or tackle. How many different 7 man lines can be formed?

10. Four cards are drawn one at a time from a well-shuffled pack.

    a. What is the probability that all 4 will be clubs?

    b. What is the probability that red and black cards will be drawn alternately?

11. One card is drawn from each of 4 separate well-shuffled packs.

    a. What is the probability that all 4 will be clubs?

    b. What is the probability that red and black cards will be drawn alternately?

12. One bag contains 7 white and 3 black balls. Another bag contains 2 white and 8 black balls. Two coins are tossed. If they show 2 heads, a ball is drawn from the first bag; otherwise it is drawn from the second. Find the probability that a white ball will be drawn.

13. In Exercise 12 two balls are transferred from the second bag to the first and then a ball is drawn from the first bag. Find the probability that a white ball will be drawn.

14. A set of 15 pool balls bearing the numbers 1 to 15 inclusive is placed in a bag. A man draws a ball. If its number is less than 8, he replaces it and draws again. Find the probability that he draws a total of 12 or more balls.

15. Dominos contain two sets of spots, one set on each half. If you consider the number of spots in each set, then, since the domino is symmetric, the number pair formed is not ordered. How many different dominos can be made using the numbers from 1 to 12, inclusive? Using the numbers 0–12, inclusive?

16. A table of random numbers is a long sequence of digits in which each successive digit is chosen (either mechanically or mathematically) at random. If you admit all of the digits 0-9, what is the probability that in a sequence of four random digits there occurs a repetition? Two pairs of repetitions?

17. In Exercise 16, what is the probability that, in a sequence of five random digits, there occurs at least one repetition?

18. Show that the probability of getting at least one five in a cast of four dice is greater than the probability of throwing a pair of fives in twenty-four throws of two dice.

C 19. Use logarithms to find an approximation to the number of possible bridge hands containing thirteen cards that can be dealt from a standard deck of fifty-two cards.

20. Show that $_nC_r = {}_nC_{n-r}$.

15-6 Random Variables and Probability Distributions

Let us consider an urn containing 7 white and 5 black balls well mixed. If 4 balls are taken from the urn all at once, we have an example of a random experiment with a sample space of $\binom{12}{4}$, or 495, elements. Let the 4 balls be described as consisting of x white and $4 - x$ black balls. Then x must have one of the values 0, 1, 2, 3, 4 and corresponding to each of these values an event is defined. These 5 events clearly are mutually exclusive each to each, and they represent nonoverlapping subsets of the sample space, which must exhaust it because one of these events must occur. Hence the sum of the probabilities of the 5 events must be equal to 1. Assuming that equal probabilities are assigned to the 495 elements, let us find the probabilities $P(x)$ of the events associated with the 5 values of x.

x	$P(x)$
0	$\binom{5}{4} \Big/ \binom{12}{4} = \dfrac{5}{495}$
1	$\binom{5}{3} \cdot \binom{7}{1} \Big/ \binom{12}{4} = \dfrac{70}{495}$
2	$\binom{5}{2} \cdot \binom{7}{2} \Big/ \binom{12}{4} = \dfrac{210}{495}$
3	$\binom{5}{1} \cdot \binom{7}{3} \Big/ \binom{12}{4} = \dfrac{175}{495}$
4	$\binom{7}{4} \Big/ \binom{12}{4} = \dfrac{35}{495}$

$$\text{Total} = \frac{495}{495} = 1$$

The numerators of the fractions in the column on the right (5, 70, 210, etc.) are, of course, the numbers of elements in the subsets which constitute the events $x = 0$, $x = 1$, etc., and you see that they do exhaust the 495 elements in the sample space, as they should.

A variable x of the sort that we have just illustrated, which is defined over a sample space, is called a **random variable**. Some writers have called such a variable a "variate." The set of probabilities associated with the several values in the domain of definition of the random variable are said to form its **probability distribution**.

Let us analyze another example which will involve a random variable and its probability distribution. We will suppose that 2 bad electric light bulbs have been put in a box with 8 good bulbs. The bulbs are taken out and tested one by one until the second bad one is found and removed. Let x equal the number of bulbs that have to be removed. Clearly x must equal one of the integers 2, 3, . . . , 10. The sample space for this experiment contains $\binom{10}{2}$, or 45, elements since, the bulbs being tested in some order, the 2 bad ones can occupy any 2 places in that order. The subset of the sample space corresponding to the event $x = k$ (where $2 \leq k \leq 10$) must contain $k - 1$ elements because x will equal k only if one bad bulb is the kth one tested and the other one is one of the previously tested $k - 1$ bulbs. The probability distribution of x is therefore:

x	2	3	4	5	6	7	8	9	10	Total
$P(x)$	$\frac{1}{45}$	$\frac{2}{45}$	$\frac{3}{45}$	$\frac{4}{45}$	$\frac{5}{45}$	$\frac{6}{45}$	$\frac{7}{45}$	$\frac{8}{45}$	$\frac{9}{45}$	$\frac{45}{45}$

Again we see that the sum of the probabilities of a set of mutually exclusive events which exhaust the sample space is 1. From the above table we can make various observations about the experiment, such as $P(x \leq 5) = \frac{2}{9}$ or $P(5 \leq x \leq 9) = \frac{2}{3}$.

Exercises

1. Let x be the number shown when 2 dice are rolled ($x = 2, 3, \ldots, 12$). Find the probability distribution of x. Find $P(5 \leq x \leq 9)$.

2. Let x be the number of heads obtained when a coin is tossed 3 times ($x = 0, 1, 2, 3$). Find the probability distribution of x.

3. A particle begins at the origin and moves in a "random walk" in the direction of the positive x-axis, each move being a diagonal of a unit square, either upward or downward. One possible path of three steps is shown at the right. Let Y be the y-coordinate of the particle after three steps. Find the probability distribution of Y. Find $P(-1 \leq Y \leq 1)$.

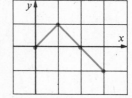

4. In Exercise 3, find a probability distribution for Y after the particle has moved four steps. Find $P(1 \leq Y \leq 3)$.

5. An urn contains two green and three white marbles. Let x denote the number of white marbles in a random drawing of three marbles. Find the probability distribution for x. What is $P(x = 0)$?

6. In Exercise 5, let x be the number of green marbles in a random drawing of three marbles. Find the probability distribution for x. What is $P(x \neq 0)$?

7. Let x be the number of spades in a drawing of 5 cards at random from a standard deck of 52 well-shuffled cards. Find the probability distribution for x. What is $P(1 \leq x \leq 3)$?

8. Let x be the number of red two's, three's, or four's in a drawing of six cards at random from a standard deck of 52 well-shuffled cards. Find the probability distribution for x. What is $P(0 \leq x \leq 3)$?

9. A box contains 20 transistors, of which four are defective. If x is the number of defective transistors in a random selection of four transistors from the box, find the probability distribution for x. What is $P(x = 0)$?

10. In Exercise 9, let x be the number of defective transistors in a random selection of five transistors from the box. Find the probability distribution for x. What is $P(x \leq 1)$?

15-7 Expected Value

In the light-bulb example of the previous section, while it is understood that in any trial of the experiment there is no way of knowing in advance what x will turn out to be, we might still wonder what the number of bulbs tested might be *on the average* if the experiment were repeated a fairly large number of times. The answer to this question is given by what is called the *expected value* of a random variable.

Let x be a random variable defined for a finite set of values, and let $P(x)$ denote its probability distribution. **Then the expected value of x, denoted by $E(x)$, is $\sum_x x \cdot P(x)$.** (Note: $\sum_x$ is read "the sum over the set of values of x.")

For the light-bulb example we have

$$E(x) = 2 \cdot \tfrac{1}{45} + 3 \cdot \tfrac{2}{45} + \cdots + 10 \cdot \tfrac{9}{45} = \tfrac{330}{45} = 7\tfrac{1}{3}.$$

This, then, on the average is the number of bulbs to be tested.

For the example of the 4 balls taken from the urn (page 617) you have

$$E(x) = \frac{0 \cdot 5 + 1 \cdot 70 + 2 \cdot 210 + 3 \cdot 175 + 4 \cdot 35}{495} = \frac{1155}{495} = \frac{7}{3},$$

where x denoted the number of white ones. Hence in a large number of repetitions of that experiment, $2\tfrac{1}{3}$ white balls should be expected on the average.

Suppose that a Mr. A has 1 ticket in a lottery for which 1000 tickets have been sold. There is one prize of $50.00 to be awarded. Let x be the amount of Mr. A's winning. The probability distribution of x is as follows:

x	$P(x)$
50.00	.001
0	.999
Total	1.000

Then $E(x) = 50.00 \cdot (.001) + 0 \cdot (.999) = .05$. In other words, if Mr. A paid more than a nickel for his ticket, he made a poor investment!

Exercises

A

1. If x denotes the number of tails resulting from three separate tossings of a coin, find the probability distribution of x. Find $E(x)$.

2. Two out of five light bulbs in a box are defective. Let x denote the number of bulbs tested and removed to locate both defective bulbs. Find the probability distribution of x. Find $E(x)$.

3. Show that if x is the number resulting from the roll of a single die, then $E(x) = 3\frac{1}{2}$. Note that $E(x)$ is not one of the values x.

4. Two cards are drawn at random from a well-shuffled standard deck of 52 cards. Let x denote the number of black cards in the pair. Find a probability distribution for x. What is $E(x)$?

B

5. The probability that Tom will solve a certain problem in mathematics is $\frac{2}{3}$, that Mary will solve it is $\frac{1}{2}$, and that Bill will solve it is $\frac{1}{4}$. Let x denote the number of people who solve the problem. Find a probability distribution for x. How many people can be "expected" to solve the problem?

6. A man wagers $10 on a football game, giving odds of 2 to 1. He feels confident that the odds* in favor of his team are really 4 to 1. Assuming his estimate to be correct, and letting x be the amount he will win, find the probability distribution of x and $E(x)$.

7. If x is the number shown when 2 dice are rolled, find $E(x)$. Can the answer be readily guessed in advance after inspecting the distribution?

8. Twenty identical envelopes are spread out on a table; 2 of them contain $10 bills, 3 contain $5 bills, 5 contain $1 bills, and the others contain blank pieces of paper. Two envelopes are chosen at random. Let $x =$ the amount they contain ($x = 0, 1, 2, 5, 6, \ldots, 20$). Find the probability distribution of x, and then find $E(x)$. Can the value of this $E(x)$ be guessed in advance?

C

9. Show that if $x \in \{1, 2, 3, \ldots n\}$, and if $P(x) = \dfrac{1}{n}$ for each x, then

$$E(x) = \frac{1}{n} \sum_{i=1}^{n} i.$$ Notice that $E(x)$ is the arithmetic mean of the values of x.

10. Define values for a variable y by $y = x - b$, where x is a random variable and b is a constant. Use the fact that y is a random variable with $P(y) = P(x)$ to prove that $E(y) = E(x) - b$.

15-8 The Binomial Distribution

In Section 15–6 we carried out a detailed study of an experiment in which a number of balls were drawn from an urn all at once. This experiment could just as well have been described by saying that the balls were drawn one by one but without replacement. We now wish to consider a similar experiment in which the drawings are made one by one but *with replacement*. That is, after each ball is drawn and its color noted it is replaced and the balls in the urn are well mixed before the next drawing is made. The effect of this is to produce a sequence of independent trials of an experiment such that each trial must have one of just two possible outcomes and such that the probability of a given outcome (the drawing of a white ball for example) remains constant throughout the experiment. We will let the urn contain 20 white and 10 black balls this time so that the probabilities of white and black in any one drawing will be respectively $\frac{2}{3}$ and $\frac{1}{3}$. Now let 5 balls be drawn of which x are white and $5 - x$ are black (again $x = 0$, 1, 2, ..., 5). For this random variable x let us compute the probability distribution $P(x)$.

We can find $P(0)$ very simply. The probability of drawing a black ball is $\frac{1}{3}$ for each trial and the trials are independent. Hence $P(0) = (\frac{1}{3})^5$.

The case $x = 1$ is somewhat more involved. The probability of obtaining 1 white ball followed by 4 black ones in independent drawings is $\frac{2}{3} \cdot \frac{1}{3} \cdot \frac{1}{3} \cdot \frac{1}{3} \cdot \frac{1}{3}$. There is no reason, however, why the white one must be the first one drawn. If it happened to be the fourth, say, then the probability of 1 white and 4 black in that particular order is $\frac{1}{3} \cdot \frac{1}{3} \cdot \frac{1}{3} \cdot \frac{2}{3} \cdot \frac{1}{3}$. There are clearly 5 possible orders which are mutually exclusive, and for each of these the probability of 1 white and 4 black is $(\frac{1}{3})^4 \cdot (\frac{2}{3})$. Hence $P(1) = 5(\frac{1}{3})^4(\frac{2}{3})$.

For $x = 2$ we can see that the probability of 2 white and 3 black, again in a particular order, would be $\frac{2}{3} \cdot \frac{2}{3} \cdot \frac{1}{3} \cdot \frac{1}{3} \cdot \frac{1}{3}$ or $\frac{1}{3} \cdot \frac{2}{3} \cdot \frac{1}{3} \cdot \frac{1}{3} \cdot \frac{2}{3}$. The various possible orders are mutually exclusive and there are $\binom{5}{2}$, or 10, such orders because the fraction $\frac{2}{3}$ can occupy any 2 of the 5 places. Thus $P(2) = 10(\frac{1}{3})^3(\frac{2}{3})^2$.

This line of reasoning applied to $x = 3$, $x = 4$, and $x = 5$ leads to similar results, and we can summarize what has been worked out by simply stating that $P(x) = \binom{5}{x}\left(\frac{1}{3}\right)^{5-x}\left(\frac{2}{3}\right)^{x}$. Written out in full the probability distribution of x looks like this:

For $x =$	0	1	2	3	4	5
$P(x) =$	$(\frac{1}{3})^5$	$5(\frac{1}{3})^4(\frac{2}{3})$	$10(\frac{1}{3})^3(\frac{2}{3})^2$	$10(\frac{1}{3})^2(\frac{2}{3})^3$	$5(\frac{1}{3})(\frac{2}{3})^4$	$(\frac{2}{3})^5$

---

* The **odds** that the event A will occur is $\dfrac{P(A)}{P(A')}$.

You will note that $P(0)$, $P(1)$, etc., in the preceding table are the six terms of the expansion of $(\frac{1}{3} + \frac{2}{3})^5$, so you can now see why this section was headed *The Binomial Distribution.*

Let us now put together a general formulation of the binomial distribution. We consider any experiment which in any one trial has two and only two possible outcomes, which we will call *success* and *failure.* In any trial of the experiment let p be the probability of success and $q = (1 - p)$ be the probability of failure, where p remains constant for all trials. Then, if n independent trials take place, the probability of obtaining x successes and $n - x$ failures is given by the formula

$$P(x) = \binom{n}{x} q^{n-x} p^x \quad (x = 0, 1, 2, \ldots, n).$$

This, we recognize, is the $(x + 1)$st term in the expansion of $(q + p)^n$.

The proof of this involves exactly the same reasoning as was used in the above example. The expression $q^{n-x} p^x$ gives the probability of x successes and $n - x$ failures in a particular order. $\binom{n}{x}$ gives the number of possible mutually exclusive orders. Hence the formula follows.

EXAMPLE 1. Let 2 coins be tossed simultaneously 6 times. Find the probability that double heads will appear 4 or more times.

Solution: In each toss the probability of double heads is $\frac{1}{4}$. The result is then given by the sum of the last 3 terms of $(\frac{3}{4} + \frac{1}{4})^6$, which is $15(\frac{3}{4})^2(\frac{1}{4})^4 + 6(\frac{3}{4})(\frac{1}{4})^5 + (\frac{1}{4})^6 = \dfrac{154}{4^6}$.

EXAMPLE 2. In a certain town Mr. A was elected mayor over Mr. B in the last election with a 3 to 2 majority. It is election time again and B is having another try at beating A. However, Mayor A has had an excellent administration and it appears to the local prognosticators that A may get even more than $\frac{3}{5}$ of the vote this time. To check this, they poll 25 votes chosen at random and learn that 21 intend to vote for Mayor A. What can they infer from this?

Solution: Assuming that the probability, P, that a voter picked at random will favor A is still $\frac{3}{5}$, consider the last several terms of the expansion of $(\frac{2}{5} + \frac{3}{5})^{25}$. They are very tedious to compute, but with the aid of logarithms the following probabilities can be verified. If x stands for the number who favor A in a sample of 25, it turns out that $P(x \geq 18) = .154$, $P(x \geq 19) = .074$, $P(x \geq 20) = .029$, $P(x \geq 21) = .009$. These are, of course, the sums of the last 8 terms, the last 7 terms, etc. of the above expansion. We are tempted to conclude that 21 in favor of A in a random sample of 25 makes it appear very likely that p is now $> \frac{3}{5}$. The probability of obtaining such a sample if $p = \frac{3}{5}$ is $< 1\%$. If even 20 out of 25 had favored A, this probability would still be $< 3\%$.

In the example just discussed, common sense would suggest that if $p = \frac{3}{5}$, then in a sample of 25 the number who were found to favor A should have been about $\frac{3}{5}$ of 25, or 15. As a matter of fact, it is easy to show that, in any binomial-type experiment in which x is the number of successes in n trials and p is the probability of success in one trial, the value of $E(x) = np$. Writing out part of the distribution, we have:

x	0	1	2	3	$\cdots$	n
$P(x)$	q^n	$nq^{n-1}p$	$\dfrac{n(n-1)}{1\cdot 2}q^{n-2}p^2$	$\dfrac{n(n-1)(n-2)}{1\cdot 2\cdot 3}q^{n-3}p^3$	$\cdots$	p^n

Hence

$$E(x) = 0 \cdot q^n + 1 \cdot nq^{n-1}p + \frac{2 \cdot n(n-1)}{1 \cdot 2} q^{n-2}p^2 + \cdots + np^n$$

$$= np(q^{n-1} + (n-1)q^{n-2}p^2 + \cdots + p^{n-1})$$

$$= np(q+p)^{n-1} = np.$$

In other words, common sense is mathematically correct in this instance. Similarly, the expected number of heads in 50 tosses of an ideal coin is 25, as we feel sure it should be.

We add two further comments regarding the election example.

The first has to do with computation procedures. The use of logarithms, which was suggested above, is usually unnecessary in practice. Extensive tables of binomial probabilities have been compiled and, for large values of n, there are available accurate methods of approximation.

The other comment is that the solution of the example was described in a way that was intended to illustrate informally the idea of a test of a hypothesis. We rejected the hypothesis $p = \frac{3}{5}$ because if it were true our sample would be highly improbable.

A detailed study of these matters belongs in a more advanced treatment of probability distribution theory and statistical inference.

Exercises

1. A coin is tossed 6 times. Find the probability of 2 or more heads.

2. The probability that a bridge hand will contain no aces is .3 (approximately). Find the probability that a player will be dealt hands with no aces 3 or more times in 4 deals.

B

3. On a package of seeds it is indicated that 98% of the seeds can be expected to germinate. Assuming this to be correct, find the probability that, if 50 seeds are planted, 49 or more will germinate. Use logarithms.

4. Hospital records show that $\frac{2}{5}$ of the cases of a certain disease are fatal. If 6 patients are admitted with this disease, find the probability that at least two will recover.

5. A multiple-choice test contains 8 questions with 4 possible answers listed for each question. Only one answer is correct in each case. Find the probability that a student who answers each question by guessing will have at least half of his answers correct.

6. In Exercise 5, what is the probability that a student who knows nothing about the subject matter of the test will have a perfect paper?

7. A baseball player has a batting average of .300. Assuming that this represents the probability of his hitting safely in any one time at bat, find the probability that, in his next 5 times at bat, he will get (**a**) at most one hit, and (**b**) exactly two hits.

8. A rifleman is able, on the average, to hit the bull's-eye 80% of the time when shooting from a certain distance. If he fires 8 shots at this range, what is the probability that he will get (**a**) 7 bull's-eyes or more; (**b**) 5 bull's-eyes or less?

C

9. Ten students are chosen at random from Mr. Lane's geometry class, and ten are chosen at random from Miss Smith's. The ten students from Mr. Lane's class are then randomly paired with those from Miss Smith's class. If the students are assumed to be equal in their knowledge of geometry, what is the probability that all but two of Mr. Lane's students scored higher on a geometry test than their partners from Miss Smith's class? In the event this occurred, what would you be willing to assume about the hypothesis that the students do not differ from each other in knowledge of geometry?

10. In Exercise 9, suppose all but one of the pairs of students showed an advantage over Mr. Lane's students. What is the probability of this occurring strictly by chance? How many times out of a hundred would you "expect" this to happen if no difference exists in the students' knowledge of geometry?

11. A "secret ingredient" is added to Brand X toothpaste, and 24 persons randomly selected from a school are paired. One member in each of the twelve pairs is then selected by flipping a coin. He uses the fortified Brand X toothpaste, while his partner uses the regular Brand X. After a suitable period of regular dental care on the part of all concerned, all but two of those using the toothpaste with the "secret ingredient" show a gain in the number of cavities exceeding the gain of those using regular Brand X. What is the probability that this result is a matter of pure chance? What would you advise the company to do about marketing the paste containing the "secret ingredient"?

12. In Exercise 9, let x be a random variable denoting the number of pairs of students in which Mr. Lane's students scored higher on the test than Miss Smith's students. Assuming none but chance differences between the students, what is $E(x)$?

13. In Exercise 11, let x be a random variable denoting the number of pairs of students in which the "secret ingredient" students exceeded the regular Brand X students in gain in cavities. Assuming none but chance differences in the paired students cavity gains, what is $E(x)$?

Chapter Summary

1. The set of all possible outcomes of a random experiment is called the **sample space** of the experiment. A subset of a sample space is an **event**. Probabilities are real nonnegative numbers assigned to the elements of a sample space. The probability $P(A)$ of an event A is the sum of the numbers assigned to the elements of A. $P(U) = 1$, where U is the sample space.

2. If A and B are events, the probability of occurrence of A or B (or both) is $P(A \cup B) = P(A) + P(B) - P(A \cap B)$. The probability of occurrence of both A and B is $P(A \cap B) = P(A) \cdot P(B|A)$. A and B are independent if and only if $P(A \cap B) = P(A) \cdot P(B)$.

3. If two finite sets contain m and n elements, respectively, then their Cartesian product contains mn elements. The number of permutations of n different things r at a time is given by $_nP_r = \dfrac{n!}{(n-r)!}$. The number of subsets of size r in a set of n elements is given by $\dbinom{n}{r} = \dfrac{n!}{r!(n-r)!}$.

4. If a random variable x defined for a sample space has a probability distribution $P(x)$, then the expected value of x is given by $\sum\limits_{x} x \cdot P(x)$.

5. If x denotes the number of successes in n independent trials of an event for which the probability of success, p, is the same in all trials, then the probability that exactly x successes will occur ($x = 0, 1, 2, \ldots, n$) in the n trials is given by $P(x) = \dbinom{n}{x} q^{n-x} p^x$, where $q = 1 - p$. The variable x is said to have a binomial distribution.

Chapter Test

15-1   1. The aces and kings are removed from a pack of cards and kept separate. One ace and one king are selected at random.

     a. Set up the sample space for this experiment.

     b. Assign equal elemental probabilities, and find the probability that both cards are spades.

     c. Find the probability that they are of different color.

15–2   **2.** An integer x is selected at random from the set $1, 2, \ldots, 25$. Find the probability that

     a. $7 \leq x \leq 15$;

     b. x is even and >10;

     c. x satisfies **(a)** or **(b)** or both.

15–3   **3.** If a white die and a green die are rolled, find the probability that the number shown on the white die is >4 if you are given that the total on both dice is >7.

15–4   **4.** A dinner menu offers a choice of 4 appetizers, 3 soups, 5 main courses, 2 salads, and 6 desserts. In how many different ways can one order a complete dinner?

     5. How many different license plates can be made up using two letters and four numerals? The letters O and I are not to be used and the first of the four numerals is not 0 but characters can be repeated.

15–5   **6.** There are 12 lines in a plane. No two are parallel and no three are concurrent. In how many points do they intersect?

     7. A bag contains 7 red, 10 white, and 5 blue marbles. If three marbles are taken from the bag, find the probability that they will all be of the same color.

15–6   **8.** A coin is tossed 6 times, resulting in x heads and $6 - x$ tails. Assuming that the coin is well-balanced, find the probability distribution of x.

15–7   **9.** A man has 3 tickets in a lottery in which 50 tickets have been sold. There are two prizes, one of \$100 and one of \$50. Find the expected value of the amount he may win.

15–8 **10.** A beats B at tennis $\frac{2}{3}$ of the time on the average. If they play 5 sets, find the probability that B will win 2 or more sets.

Reading List

CRAMER, HARALD. *The Elements of Probability Theory.* New York: John Wiley and Sons, Inc., 1955. First 6 or 7 chapters.

DILLEY, NORMAN R. *Some Probability Distributions and Their Associated Structures. Parts I, II.* Mathematics Magazine, vol. 36, pp. 175–179, 227–231, 1963.

HODGES and LEHMAN. *Basic Concepts of Probability and Statistics.* San Francisco: Holden-Day, Inc., 1964.

JOHNSON, D. *Probability and Chance.* St. Louis: Webster Publishing Co., 1963.

MOSTELLER, F., R. E. K. ROURKE, and G. B. THOMAS, JR. *Probability—A First Course.* Reading, Mass.: Addison-Wesley Publishing Co., Inc., 1961.

MYERS, DONALD E. *Irrationals, Area, and Probability.* The Mathematics Teacher, vol. 57, pp. 203–207, 1964.

NEYMAN, JERZY. *First Course in Probability and Statistics.* New York: Holt, Rinehart and Winston, Inc., 1950.

WEAVER, W. *Lady Luck; The Theory of Probability.* Garden City, N.Y.: Doubleday and Co., Inc., 1963.

TABLES

TABLE 1 VALUES OF CIRCULAR FUNCTIONS

Real Number x or $m^R \angle \theta$	$m° \angle \theta$	sin x or sin θ	csc x or csc θ	tan x or tan θ	cot x or cot θ	sec x or sec θ	cos x or cos θ
0.00	0° 00′	0.0000	Undefined	0.0000	Undefined	1.000	1.000
.01	0° 34′	.0100	100.0	.0100	100.0	1.000	1.000
.02	1° 09′	.0200	50.00	.0200	49.99	1.000	0.9998
.03	1° 43′	.0300	33.34	.0300	33.32	1.000	0.9996
.04	2° 18′	.0400	25.01	.0400	24.99	1.001	0.9992
0.05	2° 52′	0.0500	20.01	0.0500	19.98	1.001	0.9988
.06	3° 26′	.0600	16.68	.0601	16.65	1.002	.9982
.07	4° 01′	.0699	14.30	.0701	14.26	1.002	.9976
.08	4° 35′	.0799	12.51	.0802	12.47	1.003	.9968
.09	5° 09′	.0899	11.13	.0902	11.08	1.004	.9960
0.10	5° 44′	0.0998	10.02	0.1003	9.967	1.005	0.9950
.11	6° 18′	.1098	9.109	.1104	9.054	1.006	.9940
.12	6° 53′	.1197	8.353	.1206	8.293	1.007	.9928
.13	7° 27′	.1296	7.714	.1307	7.649	1.009	.9916
.14	8° 01′	.1395	7.166	.1409	7.096	1.010	.9902
0.15	8° 36′	0.1494	6.692	0.1511	6.617	1.011	0.9888
.16	9° 10′	.1593	6.277	.1614	6.197	1.013	.9872
.17	9° 44′	.1692	5.911	.1717	5.826	1.015	.9856
.18	10° 19′	.1790	5.586	.1820	5.495	1.016	.9838
.19	10° 53′	.1889	5.295	.1923	5.200	1.018	.9820
0.20	11° 28′	0.1987	5.033	0.2027	4.933	1.020	0.9801
.21	12° 02′	.2085	4.797	.2131	4.692	1.022	.9780
.22	12° 36′	.2182	4.582	.2236	4.472	1.025	.9759
.23	13° 11′	.2280	4.386	.2341	4.271	1.027	.9737
.24	13° 45′	.2377	4.207	.2447	4.086	1.030	.9713
0.25	14° 19′	0.2474	4.042	0.2553	3.916	1.032	0.9689
.26	14° 54′	.2571	3.890	.2660	3.759	1.035	.9664
.27	15° 28′	.2667	3.749	.2768	3.613	1.038	.9638
.28	16° 03′	.2764	3.619	.2876	3.478	1.041	.9611
.29	16° 37′	.2860	3.497	.2984	3.351	1.044	.9582
0.30	17° 11′	0.2955	3.384	0.3093	3.233	1.047	0.9553
.31	17° 46′	.3051	3.278	.3203	3.122	1.050	.9523
.32	18° 20′	.3146	3.179	.3314	3.018	1.053	.9492
.33	18° 55′	.3240	3.086	.3425	2.920	1.057	.9460
.34	19° 29′	.3335	2.999	.3537	2.827	1.061	.9428
0.35	20° 03′	0.3429	2.916	0.3650	2.740	1.065	0.9394
.36	20° 38′	.3523	2.839	.3764	2.657	1.068	.9359
.37	21° 12′	.3616	2.765	.3879	2.578	1.073	.9323
.38	21° 46′	.3709	2.696	.3994	2.504	1.077	.9287
.39	22° 21′	.3802	2.630	.4111	2.433	1.081	.9249
0.40	22° 55′	0.3894	2.568	0.4228	2.365	1.086	0.9211
.41	23° 30′	.3986	2.509	.4346	2.301	1.090	.9171
.42	24° 04′	.4078	2.452	.4466	2.239	1.095	.9131
.43	24° 38′	.4169	2.399	.4586	2.180	1.100	.9090
.44	25° 13′	.4259	2.348	.4708	2.124	1.105	.9048
0.45	25° 47′	0.4350	2.299	0.4831	2.070	1.111	0.9004
.46	26° 21′	.4439	2.253	.4954	2.018	1.116	.8961
.47	26° 56′	.4529	2.208	.5080	1.969	1.122	.8916
.48	27° 30′	.4618	2.166	.5206	1.921	1.127	.8870
.49	28° 05′	.4706	2.125	.5334	1.875	1.133	.8823

TABLE 1 VALUES OF CIRCULAR FUNCTIONS

Real Number x or $m^R \angle \theta$	$m° \angle \theta$	sin x or sin θ	csc x or csc θ	tan x or tan θ	cot x or cot θ	sec x or sec θ	cos x or cos θ
0.50	28° 39′	0.4794	2.086	0.5463	1.830	1.139	0.8776
.51	29° 13′	.4882	2.048	.5594	1.788	1.146	.8727
.52	29° 48′	.4969	2.013	.5726	1.747	1.152	.8678
.53	30° 22′	.5055	1.978	.5859	1.707	1.159	.8628
.54	30° 56′	.5141	1.945	.5994	1.668	1.166	.8577
0.55	31° 31′	0.5227	1.913	0.6131	1.631	1.173	0.8525
.56	32° 05′	.5312	1.883	.6269	1.595	1.180	.8473
.57	32° 40′	.5396	1.853	.6410	1.560	1.188	.8419
.58	33° 14′	.5480	1.825	.6552	1.526	1.196	.8365
.59	33° 48′	.5564	1.797	.6696	1.494	1.203	.8309
0.60	34° 23′	0.5646	1.771	0.6841	1.462	1.212	0.8253
.61	34° 57′	.5729	1.746	.6989	1.431	1.220	.8196
.62	35° 31′	.5810	1.721	.7139	1.401	1.229	.8139
.63	36° 06′	.5891	1.697	.7291	1.372	1.238	.8080
.64	36° 40′	.5972	1.674	.7445	1.343	1.247	.8021
0.65	37° 15′	0.6052	1.652	0.7602	1.315	1.256	0.7961
.66	37° 49′	.6131	1.631	.7761	1.288	1.266	.7900
.67	38° 23′	.6210	1.610	.7923	1.262	1.276	.7838
.68	38° 58′	.6288	1.590	.8087	1.237	1.286	.7776
.69	39° 32′	.6365	1.571	.8253	1.212	1.297	.7712
0.70	40° 06′	0.6442	1.552	0.8423	1.187	1.307	0.7648
.71	40° 41′	.6518	1.534	.8595	1.163	1.319	.7584
.72	41° 15′	.6594	1.517	.8771	1.140	1.330	.7518
.73	41° 50′	.6669	1.500	.8949	1.117	1.342	.7452
.74	42° 24′	.6743	1.483	.9131	1.095	1.354	.7385
0.75	42° 58′	0.6816	1.467	0.9316	1.073	1.367	0.7317
.76	43° 33′	.6889	1.452	.9505	1.052	1.380	.7248
.77	44° 07′	.6961	1.437	.9697	1.031	1.393	.7179
.78	44° 41′	.7033	1.422	.9893	1.011	1.407	.7109
.79	45° 16′	.7104	1.408	1.009	.9908	1.421	.7038
0.80	45° 50′	0.7174	1.394	1.030	0.9712	1.435	0.6967
.81	46° 25′	.7243	1.381	1.050	.9520	1.450	.6895
.82	46° 59′	.7311	1.368	1.072	.9331	1.466	.6822
.83	47° 33′	.7379	1.355	1.093	.9146	1.482	.6749
.84	48° 08′	.7446	1.343	1.116	.8964	1.498	.6675
0.85	48° 42′	0.7513	1.331	1.138	0.8785	1.515	0.6600
.86	49° 17′	.7578	1.320	1.162	.8609	1.533	.6524
.87	49° 51′	.7643	1.308	1.185	.8437	1.551	.6448
.88	50° 25′	.7707	1.297	1.210	.8267	1.569	.6372
.89	51° 00′	.7771	1.287	1.235	.8100	1.589	.6294
0.90	51° 34′	0.7833	1.277	1.260	0.7936	1.609	0.6216
.91	52° 08′	.7895	1.267	1.286	.7774	1.629	.6137
.92	52° 43′	.7956	1.257	1.313	.7615	1.651	.6058
.93	53° 17′	.8016	1.247	1.341	.7458	1.673	.5978
.94	53° 52′	.8076	1.238	1.369	.7303	1.696	.5898
0.95	54° 26′	0.8134	1.229	1.398	0.7151	1.719	0.5817
.96	55° 00′	.8192	1.221	1.428	.7001	1.744	.5735
.97	55° 35′	.8249	1.212	1.459	.6853	1.769	.5653
.98	56° 09′	.8305	1.204	1.491	.6707	1.795	.5570
.99	56° 43′	.8360	1.196	1.524	.6563	1.823	.5487

TABLE 1 VALUES OF CIRCULAR FUNCTIONS

Real Number x or $m^R \angle \theta$	$m° \angle \theta$	sin x or sin θ	csc x or csc θ	tan x or tan θ	cot x or cot θ	sec x or sec θ	cos x or cos θ
1.00	57° 18′	0.8415	1.188	1.557	0.6421	1.851	0.5403
1.01	57° 52′	.8468	1.181	1.592	.6281	1.880	.5319
1.02	58° 27′	.8521	1.174	1.628	.6142	1.911	.5234
1.03	59° 01′	.8573	1.166	1.665	.6005	1.942	.5148
1.04	59° 35′	.8624	1.160	1.704	.5870	1.975	.5062
1.05	60° 10′	0.8674	1.153	1.743	0.5736	2.010	0.4976
1.06	60° 44′	.8724	1.146	1.784	.5604	2.046	.4889
1.07	61° 18′	.8772	1.140	1.827	.5473	2.083	.4801
1.08	61° 53′	.8820	1.134	1.871	.5344	2.122	.4713
1.09	62° 27′	.8866	1.128	1.917	.5216	2.162	.4625
1.10	63° 02′	0.8912	1.122	1.965	0.5090	2.205	0.4536
1.11	63° 36′	.8957	1.116	2.014	.4964	2.249	.4447
1.12	64° 10′	.9001	1.111	2.066	.4840	2.295	.4357
1.13	64° 45′	.9044	1.106	2.120	.4718	2.344	.4267
1.14	65° 19′	.9086	1.101	2.176	.4596	2.395	.4176
1.15	65° 53′	0.9128	1.096	2.234	0.4475	2.448	0.4085
1.16	66° 28′	.9168	1.091	2.296	.4356	2.504	.3993
1.17	67° 02′	.9208	1.086	2.360	.4237	2.563	.3902
1.18	67° 37′	.9246	1.082	2.428	.4120	2.625	.3809
1.19	68° 11′	.9284	1.077	2.498	.4003	2.691	.3717
1.20	68° 45′	0.9320	1.073	2.572	0.3888	2.760	0.3624
1.21	69° 20′	.9356	1.069	2.650	.3773	2.833	.3530
1.22	69° 54′	.9391	1.065	2.733	.3659	2.910	.3436
1.23	70° 28′	.9425	1.061	2.820	.3546	2.992	.3342
1.24	71° 03′	.9458	1.057	2.912	.3434	3.079	.3248
1.25	71° 37′	0.9490	1.054	3.010	0.3323	3.171	0.3153
1.26	72° 12′	.9521	1.050	3.113	.3212	3.270	.3058
1.27	72° 46′	.9551	1.047	3.224	.3102	3.375	.2963
1.28	73° 20′	.9580	1.044	3.341	.2993	3.488	.2867
1.29	73° 55′	.9608	1.041	3.467	.2884	3.609	.2771
1.30	74° 29′	0.9636	1.038	3.602	0.2776	3.738	0.2675
1.31	75° 03′	.9662	1.035	3.747	.2669	3.878	.2579
1.32	75° 38′	.9687	1.032	3.903	.2562	4.029	.2482
1.33	76° 12′	.9711	1.030	4.072	.2456	4.193	.2385
1.34	76° 47′	.9735	1.027	4.256	.2350	4.372	.2288
1.35	77° 21′	0.9757	1.025	4.455	0.2245	4.566	0.2190
1.36	77° 55′	.9779	1.023	4.673	.2140	4.779	.2092
1.37	78° 30′	.9799	1.021	4.913	.2035	5.014	.1994
1.38	79° 04′	.9819	1.018	5.177	.1931	5.273	.1896
1.39	79° 39′	.9837	1.017	5.471	.1828	5.561	.1798
1.40	80° 13′	0.9854	1.015	5.798	0.1725	5.883	0.1700
1.41	80° 47′	.9871	1.013	6.165	.1622	6.246	.1601
1.42	81° 22′	.9887	1.011	6.581	.1519	6.657	.1502
1.43	81° 56′	.9901	1.010	7.055	.1417	7.126	.1403
1.44	82° 30′	.9915	1.009	7.602	.1315	7.667	.1304
1.45	83° 05′	0.9927	1.007	8.238	0.1214	8.299	0.1205
1.46	83° 39′	.9939	1.006	8.989	.1113	9.044	.1106
1.47	84° 14′	.9949	1.005	9.887	.1011	9.938	.1006
1.48	84° 48′	.9959	1.004	10.98	.0911	11.03	.0907
1.49	85° 22′	.9967	1.003	12.35	.0810	12.39	.0807

TABLE 1 VALUES OF CIRCULAR FUNCTIONS

Real Number x or $m^R \angle \theta$	$m° \angle \theta$	sin x or sin θ	csc x or csc θ	tan x or tan θ	cot x or cot θ	sec x or sec θ	cos x or cos θ
1.50	85° 57′	0.9975	1.003	14.10	0.0709	14.14	0.0707
1.51	86° 31′	.9982	1.002	16.43	.0609	16.46	.0608
1.52	87° 05′	.9987	1.001	19.67	.0508	19.70	.0508
1.53	87° 40′	.9992	1.001	24.50	.0408	24.52	.0408
1.54	88° 14′	.9995	1.000	32.46	.0308	32.48	.0308
1.55	88° 49′	0.9998	1.000	48.08	0.0208	48.09	0.0208
1.56	89° 23′	.9999	1.000	92.62	.0108	92.63	.0108
1.57	89° 57′	1.000	1.000	1256	.0008	1256	.0008

TABLE 2 VALUES OF TRIGONOMETRIC FUNCTIONS

m∠θ Degrees	Radians	sin θ	csc θ	tan θ	cot θ	sec θ	cos θ		
0° 00′	.0000	.0000	Undefined	.0000	Undefined	1.000	1.0000	1.5708	90° 00′
10′	.0029	.0029	343.8	.0029	343.8	1.000	1.0000	1.5679	50′
20′	.0058	.0058	171.9	.0058	171.9	1.000	1.0000	1.5650	40′
30′	.0087	.0087	114.6	.0087	114.6	1.000	1.0000	1.5621	30′
40′	.0116	.0116	85.95	.0116	85.94	1.000	.9999	1.5592	20′
50′	.0145	.0145	68.76	.0145	68.75	1.000	.9999	1.5563	10′
1° 00′	.0175	.0175	57.30	.0175	57.29	1.000	.9998	1.5533	89° 00′
10′	.0204	.0204	49.11	.0204	49.10	1.000	.9998	1.5504	50′
20′	.0233	.0233	42.98	.0233	42.96	1.000	.9997	1.5475	40′
30′	.0262	.0262	38.20	.0262	38.19	1.000	.9997	1.5446	30′
40′	.0291	.0291	34.38	.0291	34.37	1.000	.9996	1.5417	20′
50′	.0320	.0320	31.26	.0320	31.24	1.001	.9995	1.5388	10′
2° 00′	.0349	.0349	28.65	.0349	28.64	1.001	.9994	1.5359	88° 00′
10′	.0378	.0378	26.45	.0378	26.43	1.001	.9993	1.5330	50′
20′	.0407	.0407	24.56	.0407	24.54	1.001	.9992	1.5301	40′
30′	.0436	.0436	22.93	.0437	22.90	1.001	.9990	1.5272	30′
40′	.0465	.0465	21.49	.0466	21.47	1.001	.9989	1.5243	20′
50′	.0495	.0494	20.23	.0495	20.21	1.001	.9988	1.5213	10′
3° 00′	.0524	.0523	19.11	.0524	19.08	1.001	.9986	1.5184	87° 00′
10′	.0553	.0552	18.10	.0553	18.07	1.002	.9985	1.5155	50′
20′	.0582	.0581	17.20	.0582	17.17	1.002	.9983	1.5126	40′
30′	.0611	.0610	16.38	.0612	16.35	1.002	.9981	1.5097	30′
40′	.0640	.0640	15.64	.0641	15.60	1.002	.9980	1.5068	20′
50′	.0669	.0669	14.96	.0670	14.92	1.002	.9978	1.5039	10′
4° 00′	.0698	.0698	14.34	.0699	14.30	1.002	.9976	1.5010	86° 00′
10′	.0727	.0727	13.76	.0729	13.73	1.003	.9974	1.4981	50′
20′	.0756	.0756	13.23	.0758	13.20	1.003	.9971	1.4952	40′
30′	.0785	.0785	12.75	.0787	12.71	1.003	.9969	1.4923	30′
40′	.0814	.0814	12.29	.0816	12.25	1.003	.9967	1.4893	20′
50′	.0844	.0843	11.87	.0846	11.83	1.004	.9964	1.4864	10′
5° 00′	.0873	.0872	11.47	.0875	11.43	1.004	.9962	1.4835	85° 00′
10′	.0902	.0901	11.10	.0904	11.06	1.004	.9959	1.4806	50′
20′	.0931	.0929	10.76	.0934	10.71	1.004	.9957	1.4777	40′
30′	.0960	.0958	10.43	.0963	10.39	1.005	.9954	1.4748	30′
40′	.0989	.0987	10.13	.0992	10.08	1.005	.9951	1.4719	20′
50′	.1018	.1016	9.839	.1022	9.788	1.005	.9948	1.4690	10′
6° 00′	.1047	.1045	9.567	.1051	9.514	1.006	.9945	1.4661	84° 00′
10′	.1076	.1074	9.309	.1080	9.255	1.006	.9942	1.4632	50′
20′	.1105	.1103	9.065	.1110	9.010	1.006	.9939	1.4603	40′
30′	.1134	.1132	8.834	.1139	8.777	1.006	.9936	1.4573	30′
40′	.1164	.1161	8.614	.1169	8.556	1.007	.9932	1.4544	20′
50′	.1193	.1190	8.405	.1198	8.345	1.007	.9929	1.4515	10′
7° 00′	.1222	.1219	8.206	.1228	8.144	1.008	.9925	1.4486	83° 00′
10′	.1251	.1248	8.016	.1257	7.953	1.008	.9922	1.4457	50′
20′	.1280	.1276	7.834	.1287	7.770	1.008	.9918	1.4428	40′
30′	.1309	.1305	7.661	.1317	7.596	1.009	.9914	1.4399	30′
40′	.1338	.1334	7.496	.1346	7.429	1.009	.9911	1.4370	20′
50′	.1367	.1363	7.337	.1376	7.269	1.009	.9907	1.4341	10′
8° 00′	.1396	.1392	7.185	.1405	7.115	1.010	.9903	1.4312	82° 00′
10′	.1425	.1421	7.040	.1435	6.968	1.010	.9899	1.4283	50′
20′	.1454	.1449	6.900	.1465	6.827	1.011	.9894	1.4254	40′
30′	.1484	.1478	6.765	.1495	6.691	1.011	.9890	1.4224	30′
40′	.1513	.1507	6.636	.1524	6.561	1.012	.9886	1.4195	20′
50′	.1542	.1536	6.512	.1554	6.435	1.012	.9881	1.4166	10′
9° 00′	.1571	.1564	6.392	.1584	6.314	1.012	.9877	1.4137	81° 00′
		cos θ	sec θ	cot θ	tan θ	csc θ	sin θ	Radians	Degrees m∠θ

TABLE 2 VALUES OF TRIGONOMETRIC FUNCTIONS

m∠θ Degrees	Radians	sin θ	csc θ	tan θ	cot θ	sec θ	cos θ		
9° 00′	.1571	.1564	6.392	.1584	6.314	1.012	.9877	1.4137	81° 00′
10′	.1600	.1593	6.277	.1614	6.197	1.013	.9872	1.4108	50′
20′	.1629	.1622	6.166	.1644	6.084	1.013	.9868	1.4079	40′
30′	.1658	.1650	6.059	.1673	5.976	1.014	.9863	1.4050	30′
40′	.1687	.1679	5.955	.1703	5.871	1.014	.9858	1.4021	20′
50′	.1716	.1708	5.855	.1733	5.769	1.015	.9853	1.3992	10′
10° 00′	.1745	.1736	5.759	.1763	5.671	1.015	.9848	1.3963	80° 00′
10′	.1774	.1765	5.665	.1793	5.576	1.016	.9843	1.3934	50′
20′	.1804	.1794	5.575	.1823	5.485	1.016	.9838	1.3904	40′
30′	.1833	.1822	5.487	.1853	5.396	1.017	.9833	1.3875	30′
40′	.1862	.1851	5.403	.1883	5.309	1.018	.9827	1.3846	20′
50′	.1891	.1880	5.320	.1914	5.226	1.018	.9822	1.3817	10′
11° 00′	.1920	.1908	5.241	.1944	5.145	1.019	.9816	1.3788	79° 00′
10′	.1949	.1937	5.164	.1974	5.066	1.019	.9811	1.3759	50′
20′	.1978	.1965	5.089	.2004	4.989	1.020	.9805	1.3730	40′
30′	.2007	.1994	5.016	.2035	4.915	1.020	.9799	1.3701	30′
40′	.2036	.2022	4.945	.2065	4.843	1.021	.9793	1.3672	20′
50′	.2065	.2051	4.876	.2095	4.773	1.022	.9787	1.3643	10′
12° 00′	.2094	.2079	4.810	.2126	4.705	1.022	.9781	1.3614	78° 00′
10′	.2123	.2108	4.745	.2156	4.638	1.023	.9775	1.3584	50′
20′	.2153	.2136	4.682	.2186	4.574	1.024	.9769	1.3555	40′
30′	.2182	.2164	4.620	.2217	4.511	1.024	.9763	1.3526	30′
40′	.2211	.2193	4.560	.2247	4.449	1.025	.9757	1.3497	20′
50′	.2240	.2221	4.502	.2278	4.390	1.026	.9750	1.3468	10′
13° 00′	.2269	.2250	4.445	.2309	4.331	1.026	.9744	1.3439	77° 00′
10′	.2298	.2278	4.390	.2339	4.275	1.027	.9737	1.3410	50′
20′	.2327	.2306	4.336	.2370	4.219	1.028	.9730	1.3381	40′
30′	.2356	.2334	4.284	.2401	4.165	1.028	.9724	1.3352	30′
40′	.2385	.2363	4.232	.2432	4.113	1.029	.9717	1.3323	20′
50′	.2414	.2391	4.182	.2462	4.061	1.030	.9710	1.3294	10′
14° 00′	.2443	.2419	4.134	.2493	4.011	1.031	.9703	1.3265	76° 00′
10′	.2473	.2447	4.086	.2524	3.962	1.031	.9696	1.3235	50′
20′	.2502	.2476	4.039	.2555	3.914	1.032	.9689	1.3206	40′
30′	.2531	.2504	3.994	.2586	3.867	1.033	.9681	1.3177	30′
40′	.2560	.2532	3.950	.2617	3.821	1.034	.9674	1.3148	20′
50′	.2589	.2560	3.906	.2648	3.776	1.034	.9667	1.3119	10′
15° 00′	.2618	.2588	3.864	.2679	3.732	1.035	.9659	1.3090	75° 00′
10′	.2647	.2616	3.822	.2711	3.689	1.036	.9652	1.3061	50′
20′	.2676	.2644	3.782	.2742	3.647	1.037	.9644	1.3032	40′
30′	.2705	.2672	3.742	.2773	3.606	1.038	.9636	1.3003	30′
40′	.2734	.2700	3.703	.2805	3.566	1.039	.9628	1.2974	20′
50′	.2763	.2728	3.665	.2836	3.526	1.039	.9621	1.2945	10′
16° 00′	.2793	.2756	3.628	.2867	3.487	1.040	.9613	1.2915	74° 00′
10′	.2822	.2784	3.592	.2899	3.450	1.041	.9605	1.2886	50′
20′	.2851	.2812	3.556	.2931	3.412	1.042	.9596	1.2857	40′
30′	.2880	.2840	3.521	.2962	3.376	1.043	.9588	1.2828	30′
40′	.2909	.2868	3.487	.2994	3.340	1.044	.9580	1.2799	20′
50′	.2938	.2896	3.453	.3026	3.305	1.045	.9572	1.2770	10′
17° 00′	.2967	.2924	3.420	.3057	3.271	1.046	.9563	1.2741	73° 00′
10′	.2996	.2952	3.388	.3089	3.237	1.047	.9555	1.2712	50′
20′	.3025	.2979	3.357	.3121	3.204	1.048	.9546	1.2683	40′
30′	.3054	.3007	3.326	.3153	3.172	1.049	.9537	1.2654	30′
40′	.3083	.3035	3.295	.3185	3.140	1.049	.9528	1.2625	20′
50′	.3113	.3062	3.265	.3217	3.108	1.050	.9520	1.2595	10′
18° 00′	.3142	.3090	3.236	.3249	3.078	1.051	.9511	1.2566	72° 00′
		cos θ	sec θ	cot θ	tan θ	csc θ	sin θ	Radians	Degrees m∠θ

TABLE 2 VALUES OF TRIGONOMETRIC FUNCTIONS

$m \angle \theta$ Degrees	Radians	$\sin \theta$	$\csc \theta$	$\tan \theta$	$\cot \theta$	$\sec \theta$	$\cos \theta$		
18° 00′	.3142	.3090	3.236	.3249	3.078	1.051	.9511	1.2566	72° 00′
10′	.3171	.3118	3.207	.3281	3.047	1.052	.9502	1.2537	50′
20′	.3200	.3145	3.179	.3314	3.018	1.053	.9492	1.2508	40′
30′	.3229	.3173	3.152	.3346	2.989	1.054	.9483	1.2479	30′
40′	.3258	.3201	3.124	.3378	2.960	1.056	.9474	1.2450	20′
50′	.3287	.3228	3.098	.3411	2.932	1.057	.9465	1.2421	10′
19° 00′	.3316	.3256	3.072	.3443	2.904	1.058	.9455	1.2392	71° 00′
10′	.3345	.3283	3.046	.3476	2.877	1.059	.9446	1.2363	50′
20′	.3374	.3311	3.021	.3508	2.850	1.060	.9436	1.2334	40′
30′	.3403	.3338	2.996	.3541	2.824	1.061	.9426	1.2305	30′
40′	.3432	.3365	2.971	.3574	2.798	1.062	.9417	1.2275	20′
50′	.3462	.3393	2.947	.3607	2.773	1.063	.9407	1.2246	10′
20° 00′	.3491	.3420	2.924	.3640	2.747	1.064	.9397	1.2217	70° 00′
10′	.3520	.3448	2.901	.3673	2.723	1.065	.9387	1.2188	50′
20′	.3549	.3475	2.878	.3706	2.699	1.066	.9377	1.2159	40′
30′	.3578	.3502	2.855	.3739	2.675	1.068	.9367	1.2130	30′
40′	.3607	.3529	2.833	.3772	2.651	1.069	.9356	1.2101	20′
50′	.3636	.3557	2.812	.3805	2.628	1.070	.9346	1.2072	10′
21° 00′	.3665	.3584	2.790	.3839	2.605	1.071	.9336	1.2043	69° 00′
10′	.3694	.3611	2.769	.3872	2.583	1.072	.9325	1.2014	50′
20′	.3723	.3638	2.749	.3906	2.560	1.074	.9315	1.1985	40′
30′	.3752	.3665	2.729	.3939	2.539	1.075	.9304	1.1956	30′
40′	.3782	.3692	2.709	.3973	2.517	1.076	.9293	1.1926	20′
50′	.3811	.3719	2.689	.4006	2.496	1.077	.9283	1.1897	10′
22° 00′	.3840	.3746	2.669	.4040	2.475	1.079	.9272	1.1868	68° 00′
10′	.3869	.3773	2.650	.4074	2.455	1.080	.9261	1.1839	50′
20′	.3898	.3800	2.632	.4108	2.434	1.081	.9250	1.1810	40′
30′	.3927	.3827	2.613	.4142	2.414	1.082	.9239	1.1781	30′
40′	.3956	.3854	2.595	.4176	2.394	1.084	.9228	1.1752	20′
50′	.3985	.3881	2.577	.4210	2.375	1.085	.9216	1.1723	10′
23° 00′	.4014	.3907	2.559	.4245	2.356	1.086	.9205	1.1694	67° 00′
10′	.4043	.3934	2.542	.4279	2.337	1.088	.9194	1.1665	50′
20′	.4072	.3961	2.525	.4314	2.318	1.089	.9182	1.1636	40′
30′	.4102	.3987	2.508	.4348	2.300	1.090	.9171	1.1606	30′
40′	.4131	.4014	2.491	.4383	2.282	1.092	.9159	1.1577	20′
50′	.4160	.4041	2.475	.4417	2.264	1.093	.9147	1.1548	10′
24° 00′	.4189	.4067	2.459	.4452	2.246	1.095	.9135	1.1519	66° 00′
10′	.4218	.4094	2.443	.4487	2.229	1.096	.9124	1.1490	50′
20′	.4247	.4120	2.427	.4522	2.211	1.097	.9112	1.1461	40′
30′	.4276	.4147	2.411	.4557	2.194	1.099	.9100	1.1432	30′
40′	.4305	.4173	2.396	.4592	2.177	1.100	.9088	1.1403	20′
50′	.4334	.4200	2.381	.4628	2.161	1.102	.9075	1.1374	10′
25° 00′	.4363	.4226	2.366	.4663	2.145	1.103	.9063	1.1345	65° 00′
10′	.4392	.4253	2.352	.4699	2.128	1.105	.9051	1.1316	50′
20′	.4422	.4279	2.337	.4734	2.112	1.106	.9038	1.1286	40′
30′	.4451	.4305	2.323	.4770	2.097	1.108	.9026	1.1257	30′
40′	.4480	.4331	2.309	.4806	2.081	1.109	.9013	1.1228	20′
50′	.4509	.4358	2.295	.4841	2.066	1.111	.9001	1.1199	10′
26° 00′	.4538	.4384	2.281	.4877	2.050	1.113	.8988	1.1170	64° 00′
10′	.4567	.4410	2.268	.4913	2.035	1.114	.8975	1.1141	50′
20′	.4596	.4436	2.254	.4950	2.020	1.116	.8962	1.1112	40′
30′	.4625	.4462	2.241	.4986	2.006	1.117	.8949	1.1083	30′
40′	.4654	.4488	2.228	.5022	1.991	1.119	.8936	1.1054	20′
50′	.4683	.4514	2.215	.5059	1.977	1.121	.8923	1.1025	10′
27° 00′	.4712	.4540	2.203	.5095	1.963	1.122	.8910	1.0996	63° 00′
		$\cos \theta$	$\sec \theta$	$\cot \theta$	$\tan \theta$	$\csc \theta$	$\sin \theta$	Radians	Degrees $m \angle \theta$

TABLE 2   VALUES OF TRIGONOMETRIC FUNCTIONS

m∠θ Degrees	Radians	sin θ	csc θ	tan θ	cot θ	sec θ	cos θ		
27° 00′	.4712	.4540	2.203	.5095	1.963	1.122	.8910	1.0996	63° 00′
10′	.4741	.4566	2.190	.5132	1.949	1.124	.8897	1.0966	50′
20′	.4771	.4592	2.178	.5169	1.935	1.126	.8884	1.0937	40′
30′	.4800	.4617	2.166	.5206	1.921	1.127	.8870	1.0908	30′
40′	.4829	.4643	2.154	.5243	1.907	1.129	.8857	1.0879	20′
50′	.4858	.4669	2.142	.5280	1.894	1.131	.8843	1.0850	10′
28° 00′	.4887	.4695	2.130	.5317	1.881	1.133	.8829	1.0821	62° 00′
10′	.4916	.4720	2.118	.5354	1.868	1.134	.8816	1.0792	50′
20′	.4945	.4746	2.107	.5392	1.855	1.136	.8802	1.0763	40′
30′	.4974	.4772	2.096	.5430	1.842	1.138	.8788	1.0734	30′
40′	.5003	.4797	2.085	.5467	1.829	1.140	.8774	1.0705	20′
50′	.5032	.4823	2.074	.5505	1.816	1.142	.8760	1.0676	10′
29° 00′	.5061	.4848	2.063	.5543	1.804	1.143	.8746	1.0647	61° 00′
10′	.5091	.4874	2.052	.5581	1.792	1.145	.8732	1.0617	50′
20′	.5120	.4899	2.041	.5619	1.780	1.147	.8718	1.0588	40′
30′	.5149	.4924	2.031	.5658	1.767	1.149	.8704	1.0559	30′
40′	.5178	.4950	2.020	.5696	1.756	1.151	.8689	1.0530	20′
50′	.5207	.4975	2.010	.5735	1.744	1.153	.8675	1.0501	10′
30° 00′	.5236	.5000	2.000	.5774	1.732	1.155	.8660	1.0472	60° 00′
10′	.5265	.5025	1.990	.5812	1.720	1.157	.8646	1.0443	50′
20′	.5294	.5050	1.980	.5851	1.709	1.159	.8631	1.0414	40′
30′	.5323	.5075	1.970	.5890	1.698	1.161	.8616	1.0385	30′
40′	.5352	.5100	1.961	.5930	1.686	1.163	.8601	1.0356	20′
50′	.5381	.5125	1.951	.5969	1.675	1.165	.8587	1.0327	10′
31° 00′	.5411	.5150	1.942	.6009	1.664	1.167	.8572	1.0297	59° 00′
10′	.5440	.5175	1.932	.6048	1.653	1.169	.8557	1.0268	50′
20′	.5469	.5200	1.923	.6088	1.643	1.171	.8542	1.0239	40′
30′	.5498	.5225	1.914	.6128	1.632	1.173	.8526	1.0210	30′
40′	.5527	.5250	1.905	.6168	1.621	1.175	.8511	1.0181	20′
50′	.5556	.5275	1.896	.6208	1.611	1.177	.8496	1.0152	10′
32° 00′	.5585	.5299	1.887	.6249	1.600	1.179	.8480	1.0123	58° 00′
10′	.5614	.5324	1.878	.6289	1.590	1.181	.8465	1.0094	50′
20′	.5643	.5348	1.870	.6330	1.580	1.184	.8450	1.0065	40′
30′	.5672	.5373	1.861	.6371	1.570	1.186	.8434	1.0036	30′
40′	.5701	.5398	1.853	.6412	1.560	1.188	.8418	1.0007	20′
50′	.5730	.5422	1.844	.6453	1.550	1.190	.8403	.9977	10′
33° 00′	.5760	.5446	1.836	.6494	1.540	1.192	.8387	.9948	57° 00′
10′	.5789	.5471	1.828	.6536	1.530	1.195	.8371	.9919	50′
20′	.5818	.5495	1.820	.6577	1.520	1.197	.8355	.9890	40′
30′	.5847	.5519	1.812	.6619	1.511	1.199	.8339	.9861	30′
40′	.5876	.5544	1.804	.6661	1.501	1.202	.8323	.9832	20′
50′	.5905	.5568	1.796	.6703	1.492	1.204	.8307	.9803	10′
34° 00′	.5934	.5592	1.788	.6745	1.483	1.206	.8290	.9774	56° 00′
10′	.5963	.5616	1.781	.6787	1.473	1.209	.8274	.9745	50′
20′	.5992	.5640	1.773	.6830	1.464	1.211	.8258	.9716	40′
30′	.6021	.5664	1.766	.6873	1.455	1.213	.8241	.9687	30′
40′	.6050	.5688	1.758	.6916	1.446	1.216	.8225	.9657	20′
50′	.6080	.5712	1.751	.6959	1.437	1.218	.8208	.9628	10′
35° 00′	.6109	.5736	1.743	.7002	1.428	1.221	.8192	.9599	55° 00′
10′	.6138	.5760	1.736	.7046	1.419	1.223	.8175	.9570	50′
20′	.6167	.5783	1.729	.7089	1.411	1.226	.8158	.9541	40′
30′	.6196	.5807	1.722	.7133	1.402	1.228	.8141	.9512	30′
40′	.6225	.5831	1.715	.7177	1.393	1.231	.8124	.9483	20′
50′	.6254	.5854	1.708	.7221	1.385	1.233	.8107	.9454	10′
36° 00′	.6283	.5878	1.701	.7265	1.376	1.236	.8090	.9425	54° 00′
		cos θ	sec θ	cot θ	tan θ	csc θ	sin θ	Radians	Degrees m∠θ

TABLE 2 VALUES OF TRIGONOMETRIC FUNCTIONS

m∠θ Degrees	Radians	sin θ	csc θ	tan θ	cot θ	sec θ	cos θ	
36° 00′	.6283	.5878	1.701	.7265	1.376	1.236	.8090	.9425	54° 00′
10′	.6312	.5901	1.695	.7310	1.368	1.239	.8073	.9396	50′
20′	.6341	.5925	1.688	.7355	1.360	1.241	.8056	.9367	40′
30′	.6370	.5948	1.681	.7400	1.351	1.244	.8039	.9338	30′
40′	.6400	.5972	1.675	.7445	1.343	1.247	.8021	.9308	20′
50′	.6429	.5995	1.668	.7490	1.335	1.249	.8004	.9279	10′
37° 00′	.6458	.6018	1.662	.7536	1.327	1.252	.7986	.9250	53° 00′
10′	.6487	.6041	1.655	.7581	1.319	1.255	.7969	.9221	50′
20′	.6516	.6065	1.649	.7627	1.311	1.258	.7951	.9192	40′
30′	.6545	.6088	1.643	.7673	1.303	1.260	.7934	.9163	30′
40′	.6574	.6111	1.636	.7720	1.295	1.263	.7916	.9134	20′
50′	.6603	.6134	1.630	.7766	1.288	1.266	.7898	.9105	10′
38° 00′	.6632	.6157	1.624	.7813	1.280	1.269	.7880	.9076	52° 00′
10′	.6661	.6180	1.618	.7860	1.272	1.272	.7862	.9047	50′
20′	.6690	.6202	1.612	.7907	1.265	1.275	.7844	.9018	40′
30′	.6720	.6225	1.606	.7954	1.257	1.278	.7826	.8988	30′
40′	.6749	.6248	1.601	.8002	1.250	1.281	.7808	.8959	20′
50′	.6778	.6271	1.595	.8050	1.242	1.284	.7790	.8930	10′
39° 00′	.6807	.6293	1.589	.8098	1.235	1.287	.7771	.8901	51° 00′
10′	.6836	.6316	1.583	.8146	1.228	1.290	.7753	.8872	50′
20′	.6865	.6338	1.578	.8195	1.220	1.293	.7735	.8843	40′
30′	.6894	.6361	1.572	.8243	1.213	1.296	.7716	.8814	30′
40′	.6923	.6383	1.567	.8292	1.206	1.299	.7698	.8785	20′
50′	.6952	.6406	1.561	.8342	1.199	1.302	.7679	.8756	10′
40° 00′	.6981	.6428	1.556	.8391	1.192	1.305	.7660	.8727	50° 00′
10′	.7010	.6450	1.550	.8441	1.185	1.309	.7642	.8698	50′
20′	.7039	.6472	1.545	.8491	1.178	1.312	.7623	.8668	40′
30′	.7069	.6494	1.540	.8541	1.171	1.315	.7604	.8639	30′
40′	.7098	.6517	1.535	.8591	1.164	1.318	.7585	.8610	20′
50′	.7127	.6539	1.529	.8642	1.157	1.322	.7566	.8581	10′
41° 00′	.7156	.6561	1.524	.8693	1.150	1.325	.7547	.8552	49° 00′
10′	.7185	.6583	1.519	.8744	1.144	1.328	.7528	.8523	50′
20′	.7214	.6604	1.514	.8796	1.137	1.332	.7509	.8494	40′
30′	.7243	.6626	1.509	.8847	1.130	1.335	.7490	.8465	30′
40′	.7272	.6648	1.504	.8899	1.124	1.339	.7470	.8436	20′
50′	.7301	.6670	1.499	.8952	1.117	1.342	.7451	.8407	10′
42° 00′	.7330	.6691	1.494	.9004	1.111	1.346	.7431	.8378	48° 00′
10′	.7359	.6713	1.490	.9057	1.104	1.349	.7412	.8348	50′
20′	.7389	.6734	1.485	.9110	1.098	1.353	.7392	.8319	40′
30′	.7418	.6756	1.480	.9163	1.091	1.356	.7373	.8290	30′
40′	.7447	.6777	1.476	.9217	1.085	1.360	.7353	.8261	20′
50′	.7476	.6799	1.471	.9271	1.079	1.364	.7333	.8232	10′
43° 00′	.7505	.6820	1.466	.9325	1.072	1.367	.7314	.8203	47° 00′
10′	.7534	.6841	1.462	.9380	1.066	1.371	.7294	.8174	50′
20′	.7563	.6862	1.457	.9435	1.060	1.375	.7274	.8145	40′
30′	.7592	.6884	1.453	.9490	1.054	1.379	.7254	.8116	30′
40′	.7621	.6905	1.448	.9545	1.048	1.382	.7234	.8087	20′
50′	.7650	.6926	1.444	.9601	1.042	1.386	.7214	.8058	10′
44° 00′	.7679	.6947	1.440	.9657	1.036	1.390	.7193	.8029	46° 00′
10′	.7709	.6967	1.435	.9713	1.030	1.394	.7173	.7999	50′
20′	.7738	.6988	1.431	.9770	1.024	1.398	.7153	.7970	40′
30′	.7767	.7009	1.427	.9827	1.018	1.402	.7133	.7941	30′
40′	.7796	.7030	1.423	.9884	1.012	1.406	.7112	.7912	20′
50′	.7825	.7050	1.418	.9942	1.006	1.410	.7092	.7883	10′
45° 00′	.7854	.7071	1.414	1.000	1.000	1.414	.7071	.7854	45° 00′
		cos θ	sec θ	cot θ	tan θ	csc θ	sin θ	Radians	Degrees m∠θ

TABLE 3 SQUARES AND SQUARE ROOTS

N	N^2	$\sqrt{N}$	$\sqrt{10N}$	N	N^2	$\sqrt{N}$	$\sqrt{10N}$
1.0	1.00	1.000	3.162	5.5	30.25	2.345	7.416
1.1	1.21	1.049	3.317	5.6	31.36	2.366	7.483
1.2	1.44	1.095	3.464	5.7	32.49	2.387	7.550
1.3	1.69	1.140	3.606	5.8	33.64	2.408	7.616
1.4	1.96	1.183	3.742	5.9	34.81	2.429	7.681
1.5	2.25	1.225	3.873	6.0	36.00	2.449	7.746
1.6	2.56	1.265	4.000	6.1	37.21	2.470	7.810
1.7	2.89	1.304	4.123	6.2	38.44	2.490	7.874
1.8	3.24	1.342	4.243	6.3	39.69	2.510	7.937
1.9	3.61	1.378	4.359	6.4	40.96	2.530	8.000
2.0	4.00	1.414	4.472	6.5	42.25	2.550	8.062
2.1	4.41	1.449	4.583	6.6	43.56	2.569	8.124
2.2	4.84	1.483	4.690	6.7	44.89	2.588	8.185
2.3	5.29	1.517	4.796	6.8	46.24	2.608	8.246
2.4	5.76	1.549	4.899	6.9	47.61	2.627	8.307
2.5	6.25	1.581	5.000	7.0	49.00	2.646	8.367
2.6	6.76	1.612	5.099	7.1	50.41	2.665	8.426
2.7	7.29	1.643	5.196	7.2	51.84	2.683	8.485
2.8	7.84	1.673	5.292	7.3	53.29	2.702	8.544
2.9	8.41	1.703	5.385	7.4	54.76	2.720	8.602
3.0	9.00	1.732	5.477	7.5	56.25	2.739	8.660
3.1	9.61	1.761	5.568	7.6	57.76	2.757	8.718
3.2	10.24	1.789	5.657	7.7	59.29	2.775	8.775
3.3	10.89	1.817	5.745	7.8	60.84	2.793	8.832
3.4	11.56	1.844	5.831	7.9	62.41	2.811	8.888
3.5	12.25	1.871	5.916	8.0	64.00	2.828	8.944
3.6	12.96	1.897	6.000	8.1	65.61	2.846	9.000
3.7	13.69	1.924	6.083	8.2	67.24	2.864	9.055
3.8	14.44	1.949	6.164	8.3	68.89	2.881	9.110
3.9	15.21	1.975	6.245	8.4	70.56	2.898	9.165
4.0	16.00	2.000	6.325	8.5	72.25	2.915	9.220
4.1	16.81	2.025	6.403	8.6	73.96	2.933	9.274
4.2	17.64	2.049	6.481	8.7	75.69	2.950	9.327
4.3	18.49	2.074	6.557	8.8	77.44	2.966	9.381
4.4	19.36	2.098	6.633	8.9	79.21	2.983	9.434
4.5	20.25	2.121	6.708	9.0	81.00	3.000	9.487
4.6	21.16	2.145	6.782	9.1	82.81	3.017	9.539
4.7	22.09	2.168	6.856	9.2	84.64	3.033	9.592
4.8	23.04	2.191	6.928	9.3	86.49	3.050	9.644
4.9	24.01	2.214	7.000	9.4	88.36	3.066	9.695
5.0	25.00	2.236	7.071	9.5	90.25	3.082	9.747
5.1	26.01	2.258	7.141	9.6	92.16	3.098	9.798
5.2	27.04	2.280	7.211	9.7	94.09	3.114	9.849
5.3	28.09	2.302	7.280	9.8	96.04	3.130	9.899
5.4	29.16	2.324	7.348	9.9	98.01	3.146	9.950
5.5	30.25	2.345	7.416	10.0	100.00	3.162	10.000

TABLE 4 COMMON LOGARITHMS OF NUMBERS *

N	0	1	2	3	4	5	6	7	8	9
10	0000	0043	0086	0128	0170	0212	0253	0294	0334	0374
11	0414	0453	0492	0531	0569	0607	0645	0682	0719	0755
12	0792	0828	0864	0899	0934	0969	1004	1038	1072	1106
13	1139	1173	1206	1239	1271	1303	1335	1367	1399	1430
14	1461	1492	1523	1553	1584	1614	1644	1673	1703	1732
15	1761	1790	1818	1847	1875	1903	1931	1959	1987	2014
16	2041	2068	2095	2122	2148	2175	2201	2227	2253	2279
17	2304	2330	2355	2380	2405	2430	2455	2480	2504	2529
18	2553	2577	2601	2625	2648	2672	2695	2718	2742	2765
19	2788	2810	2833	2856	2878	2900	2923	2945	2967	2989
20	3010	3032	3054	3075	3096	3118	3139	3160	3181	3201
21	3222	3243	3263	3284	3304	3324	3345	3365	3385	3404
22	3424	3444	3464	3483	3502	3522	3541	3560	3579	3598
23	3617	3636	3655	3674	3692	3711	3729	3747	3766	3784
24	3802	3820	3838	3856	3874	3892	3909	3927	3945	3962
25	3979	3997	4014	4031	4048	4065	4082	4099	4116	4133
26	4150	4166	4183	4200	4216	4232	4249	4265	4281	4298
27	4314	4330	4346	4362	4378	4393	4409	4425	4440	4456
28	4472	4487	4502	4518	4533	4548	4564	4579	4594	4609
29	4624	4639	4654	4669	4683	4698	4713	4728	4742	4757
30	4771	4786	4800	4814	4829	4843	4857	4871	4886	4900
31	4914	4928	4942	4955	4969	4983	4997	5011	5024	5038
32	5051	5065	5079	5092	5105	5119	5132	5145	5159	5172
33	5185	5198	5211	5224	5237	5250	5263	5276	5289	5302
34	5315	5328	5340	5353	5366	5378	5391	5403	5416	5428
35	5441	5453	5465	5478	5490	5502	5514	5527	5539	5551
36	5563	5575	5587	5599	5611	5623	5635	5647	5658	5670
37	5682	5694	5705	5717	5729	5740	5752	5763	5775	5786
38	5798	5809	5821	5832	5843	5855	5866	5877	5888	5899
39	5911	5922	5933	5944	5955	5966	5977	5988	5999	6010
40	6021	6031	6042	6053	6064	6075	6085	6096	6107	6117
41	6128	6138	6149	6160	6170	6180	6191	6201	6212	6222
42	6232	6243	6253	6263	6274	6284	6294	6304	6314	6325
43	6335	6345	6355	6365	6375	6385	6395	6405	6415	6425
44	6435	6444	6454	6464	6474	6484	6493	6503	6513	6522
45	6532	6542	6551	6561	6571	6580	6590	6599	6609	6618
46	6628	6637	6646	6656	6665	6675	6684	6693	6702	6712
47	6721	6730	6739	6749	6758	6767	6776	6785	6794	6803
48	6812	6821	6830	6839	6848	6857	6866	6875	6884	6893
49	6902	6911	6920	6928	6937	6946	6955	6964	6972	6981
50	6990	6998	7007	7016	7024	7033	7042	7050	7059	7067
51	7076	7084	7093	7101	7110	7118	7126	7135	7143	7152
52	7160	7168	7177	7185	7193	7202	7210	7218	7226	7235
53	7243	7251	7259	7267	7275	7284	7292	7300	7308	7316
54	7324	7332	7340	7348	7356	7364	7372	7380	7388	7396

*Mantissas; decimal points omitted. Characteristics are found by inspection.

TABLE 4 COMMON LOGARITHMS OF NUMBERS

N	0	1	2	3	4	5	6	7	8	9
55	7404	7412	7419	7427	7435	7443	7451	7459	7466	7474
56	7482	7490	7497	7505	7513	7520	7528	7536	7543	7551
57	7559	7566	7574	7582	7589	7597	7604	7612	7619	7627
58	7634	7642	7649	7657	7664	7672	7679	7686	7694	7701
59	7709	7716	7723	7731	7738	7745	7752	7760	7767	7774
60	7782	7789	7796	7803	7810	7818	7825	7832	7839	7846
61	7853	7860	7868	7875	7882	7889	7896	7903	7910	7917
62	7924	7931	7938	7945	7952	7959	7966	7973	7980	7987
63	7993	8000	8007	8014	8021	8028	8035	8041	8048	8055
64	8062	8069	8075	8082	8089	8096	8102	8109	8116	8122
65	8129	8136	8142	8149	8156	8162	8169	8176	8182	8189
66	8195	8202	8209	8215	8222	8228	8235	8241	8248	8254
67	8261	8267	8274	8280	8287	8293	8299	8306	8312	8319
68	8325	8331	8338	8344	8351	8357	8363	8370	8376	8382
69	8388	8395	8401	8407	8414	8420	8426	8432	8439	8445
70	8451	8457	8463	8470	8476	8482	8488	8494	8500	8506
71	8513	8519	8525	8531	8537	8543	8549	8555	8561	8567
72	8573	8579	8585	8591	8597	8603	8609	8615	8621	8627
73	8633	8639	8645	8651	8657	8663	8669	8675	8681	8686
74	8692	8698	8704	8710	8716	8722	8727	8733	8739	8745
75	8751	8756	8762	8768	8774	8779	8785	8791	8797	8802
76	8808	8814	8820	8825	8831	8837	8842	8848	8854	8859
77	8865	8871	8876	8882	8887	8893	8899	8904	8910	8915
78	8921	8927	8932	8938	8943	8949	8954	8960	8965	8971
79	8976	8982	8987	8993	8998	9004	9009	9015	9020	9025
80	9031	9036	9042	9047	9053	9058	9063	9069	9074	9079
81	9085	9090	9096	9101	9106	9112	9117	9122	9128	9133
82	9138	9143	9149	9154	9159	9165	9170	9175	9180	9186
83	9191	9196	9201	9206	9212	9217	9222	9227	9232	9238
84	9243	9248	9253	9258	9263	9269	9274	9279	9284	9289
85	9294	9299	9304	9309	9315	9320	9325	9330	9335	9340
86	9345	9350	9355	9360	9365	9370	9375	9380	9385	9390
87	9395	9400	9405	9410	9415	9420	9425	9430	9435	9440
88	9445	9450	9455	9460	9465	9469	9474	9479	9484	9489
89	9494	9499	9504	9509	9513	9518	9523	9528	9533	9538
90	9542	9547	9552	9557	9562	9566	9571	9576	9581	9586
91	9590	9595	9600	9605	9609	9614	9619	9624	9628	9633
92	9638	9643	9647	9652	9657	9661	9666	9671	9675	9680
93	9685	9689	9694	9699	9703	9708	9713	9717	9722	9727
94	9731	9736	9741	9745	9750	9754	9759	9763	9768	9773
95	9777	9782	9786	9791	9795	9800	9805	9809	9814	9818
96	9823	9827	9832	9836	9841	9845	9850	9854	9859	9863
97	9868	9872	9877	9881	9886	9890	9894	9899	9903	9908
98	9912	9917	9921	9926	9930	9934	9939	9943	9948	9952
99	9956	9961	9965	9969	9974	9978	9983	9987	9991	9996

TABLE 5 VALUES OF THE EXPONENTIAL FUNCTION

x	e^x	e^{-x}	x	e^x	e^{-x}
0.00	1.0000	1.0000	2.5	12.182	0.0821
0.05	1.0513	0.9512	2.6	13.464	0.0743
0.10	1.1052	0.9048	2.7	14.880	0.0672
0.15	1.1618	0.8607	2.8	16.445	0.0608
0.20	1.2214	0.8187	2.9	18.174	0.0550
0.25	1.2840	0.7788	3.0	20.086	0.0498
0.30	1.3499	0.7408	3.1	22.198	0.0450
0.35	1.4191	0.7047	3.2	24.533	0.0408
0.40	1.4918	0.6703	3.3	27.113	0.0369
0.45	1.5683	0.6376	3.4	29.964	0.0334
0.50	1.6487	0.6065	3.5	33.115	0.0302
0.55	1.7333	0.5769	3.6	36.598	0.0273
0.60	1.8221	0.5488	3.7	40.447	0.0247
0.65	1.9155	0.5220	3.8	44.701	0.0224
0.70	2.0138	0.4966	3.9	49.402	0.0202
0.75	2.1170	0.4724	4.0	54.598	0.0183
0.80	2.2255	0.4493	4.1	60.340	0.0166
0.85	2.3396	0.4274	4.2	66.686	0.0150
0.90	2.4596	0.4066	4.3	73.700	0.0136
0.95	2.5857	0.3867	4.4	81.451	0.0123
1.0	2.7183	0.3679	4.5	90.017	0.0111
1.1	3.0042	0.3329	4.6	99.484	0.0101
1.2	3.3201	0.3012	4.7	109.95	0.0091
1.3	3.6693	0.2725	4.8	121.51	0.0082
1.4	4.0552	0.2466	4.9	134.29	0.0074
1.5	4.4817	0.2231	5.0	148.41	0.0067
1.6	4.9530	0.2019	5.5	244.69	0.0041
1.7	5.4739	0.1827	6.0	403.43	0.0025
1.8	6.0496	0.1653	6.5	665.14	0.0015
1.9	6.6859	0.1496	7.0	1096.6	0.0009
2.0	7.3891	0.1353	7.5	1808.0	0.0006
2.1	8.1662	0.1225	8.0	2981.0	0.0003
2.2	9.0250	0.1108	8.5	4914.8	0.0002
2.3	9.9742	0.1003	9.0	8103.1	0.0001
2.4	11.023	0.0907	10.0	22026	0.00005

APPENDIX

Area Under a Curve

In a study of calculus, methods are developed for finding areas of regions bounded partially or wholly by curves. The purpose at present is to introduce you to a basic method for determining the areas of certain regions.

First, for a and b any two real numbers with $a < b$, define $[a, b]$ to be the following set of real numbers: $\{x : a \le x \le b\}$. This set is called a **closed interval**; the same name is used to denote its graph on a number line, the line segment having a and b as end points.

Next, consider carefully a region R described as follows: Let $[a, b]$ be a closed interval on the x-axis and f a function such that, for all numbers x in $[a, b]$, $f(x) \ge 0$ and f is continuous. Then R is the region of the coordinate plane bounded by the x-axis, the graph of f, and the vertical lines $x = a$ and $x = b$. If the graph of f intercepts the x-axis at $(a, 0)$ or $(b, 0)$, there will be no vertical side boundary at this point. Examples of such regions are the shaded regions in Figure 1. A region like R will be referred to as either "the region under the graph of f from $x = a$ to $x = b$," or "the region under the graph of f over the interval $[a, b]$."

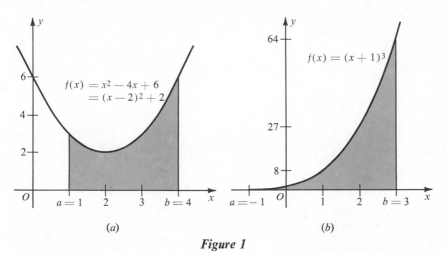

(a)   *(b)*

Figure 1

You know that the area of a rectangular region is the product of the lengths of any two consecutive sides. Using this assumption, it follows at once that if R is a rectangular region — i.e., f is a constant function, $f(x) = c$, $c > 0$ — then the area of R is $c(b - a)$. If R is not a rectangular region, then the area of R can be found by using, in addition to the formula for the area of a rectangle, the limit concept studied in Chapter 3.

Subsequent examples and generalizations will be concerned with areas of such regions R. You will find in later courses that areas of more complex regions are often found by partitioning them into subregions with the characteristics of R.

641

In the following example, the area of a triangular region will be found. Although the area of this region can easily be found without the use of limits, the present method demonstrates the principle involved in finding areas of other regions of type R.

EXAMPLE 1.   If f is the function such that $f(x) = x$, find the area of the region of the plane under the graph of f from $x = 0$ to $x = 1$. (See Figure 2.)

Solution: Construct a sequence U_n whose limit is the desired area.

Let U_1, the first term of the sequence, be the area of the rectangle whose base is the interval $[0, 1]$ on the x-axis and whose height is the number $f(1) = 1$. Then $U_1 = 1 \cdot 1 = 1$.

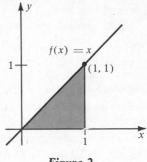

Figure 2

Divide the interval $[0, 1]$ on the x-axis into two congruent subintervals, each of length $\frac{1}{2}$. Using these subintervals as bases, construct on each a rectangle whose height is the value of the function at the right end point. Then the heights of the rectangles are $f(\frac{1}{2}) = \frac{1}{2}$ and $f(1) = 1$. Let U_2 be the sum of the areas of these two rectangles. Then $U_2 = \frac{1}{2} \cdot \frac{1}{2} + \frac{1}{2} \cdot 1 = \frac{3}{4}$.

Continuing this process, for every natural number n, let U_n be the sum of the areas of the n rectangles formed as follows: Divide the interval $[0, 1]$ into n congruent subintervals, each of length $\dfrac{1}{n}$. Using these subintervals as bases, construct on each a rectangle whose height is the value of the function at the right end point. (See Figure 3 on the opposite page.)

Then

$$U_n = \frac{1}{n} f\left(\frac{1}{n}\right) + \frac{1}{n} f\left(\frac{2}{n}\right) + \frac{1}{n} f\left(\frac{3}{n}\right) + \cdots + \frac{1}{n} f\left(\frac{n}{n}\right)$$

$$= \frac{1}{n}\left(\frac{1}{n}\right) + \frac{1}{n}\left(\frac{2}{n}\right) + \frac{1}{n}\left(\frac{3}{n}\right) + \cdots + \frac{1}{n}\left(\frac{n}{n}\right)$$

$$= \frac{1}{n^2}[1 + 2 + 3 + \cdots + n].$$

In Exercise 14 of Chapter 3 (page 73), it was shown that $1 + 2 + 3 + \cdots + n = \dfrac{n(n + 1)}{2}$, for every natural number n.

Thus

$$U_n = \frac{1}{n^2}\left[\frac{n(n+1)}{2}\right] = \frac{1}{2}\left(\frac{n}{n}\right)\left(\frac{n+1}{n}\right) = \frac{1}{2}\left(1 + \frac{1}{n}\right).$$

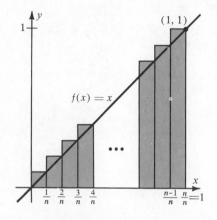

Figure 3

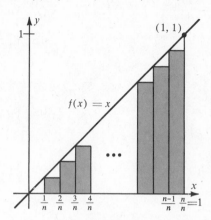

Figure 4

Using the expression $\frac{1}{2}\left(1 + \frac{1}{n}\right)$ for U_n, notice that some particular terms of the sequence are

$$U_1 = 1, \; U_2 = \frac{3}{4}, \; U_3 = \frac{2}{3}, \; U_8 = \frac{9}{16}, \text{ and } U_{1000} = \frac{1001}{2000}.$$

Note also that $U_1 > U_2 > U_3 > \cdots$; in fact, the terms of the sequence get smaller and smaller as n increases. However, since $\frac{1}{2}\left(1 + \frac{1}{n}\right) > \frac{1}{2}$ for every natural number n, each $U_n > \frac{1}{2}$.

By the theorems on sums and products of limits (which you may need to review, on page 97 of Chapter 3),

$$\lim_{n\to\infty} U_n = \lim_{n\to\infty} \frac{1}{2}\left(1 + \frac{1}{n}\right) = \left[\lim_{n\to\infty}\frac{1}{2}\right]\cdot\left[\lim_{n\to\infty}\left(1 + \frac{1}{n}\right)\right]$$

$$= \tfrac{1}{2}(1 + 0) = \tfrac{1}{2}.$$

Leaving this limit briefly, consider now another sequence, L_n, as follows:

Divide the interval $[0, 1]$ on the x-axis into n congruent subintervals, each of length $1/n$. On each of these subintervals (except the first one) construct a rectangle whose base has length $1/n$ and whose height is the value of the function at the *left* end point. (See Figure 4 above.)

Let L_n be the sum of the areas of the $n - 1$ rectangles formed. Then

$$L_n = \frac{1}{n} f\left(\frac{1}{n}\right) + \frac{1}{n} f\left(\frac{2}{n}\right) + \frac{1}{n} f\left(\frac{3}{n}\right) + \cdots + \frac{1}{n} f\left(\frac{n-1}{n}\right)$$

$$= \frac{1}{n}\left(\frac{1}{n}\right) + \frac{1}{n}\left(\frac{2}{n}\right) + \frac{1}{n}\left(\frac{3}{n}\right) + \cdots + \frac{1}{n}\left(\frac{n-1}{n}\right)$$

$$= \frac{1}{n^2}[1 + 2 + 3 + \cdots + (n-1)]$$

$$= \frac{1}{n^2}\left[\frac{(n-1)(n)}{2}\right] \quad \text{(using } 1 + 2 + 3 + \cdots + n = \frac{n(n+1)}{2}, \text{ with } n \text{ replaced by } n - 1\text{)}$$

$$= \frac{1}{2}\left(\frac{n-1}{n}\right)\left(\frac{n}{n}\right) = \frac{1}{2}\left(1 - \frac{1}{n}\right).$$

Using this expression for L_n, notice that

$$L_1 = 0, L_2 = \frac{1}{4}, L_3 = \frac{1}{3}, \text{ and } L_{1000} = \frac{999}{2000}.$$

Note also that $L_1 < L_2 < L_3 < \cdots$; in fact, the terms of the sequence get larger and larger as n increases. However, since $\frac{1}{2}\left(1 - \frac{1}{n}\right) < \frac{1}{2}$ for every natural number n, each $L_n < \frac{1}{2}$. But, of course,

$$\lim_{n \to \infty} L_n = \lim_{n \to \infty} \frac{1}{2}\left(1 - \frac{1}{n}\right) = \left[\lim_{n \to \infty} \frac{1}{2}\right] \cdot \left[\lim_{n \to \infty} \left(1 - \frac{1}{n}\right)\right]$$

$$= \frac{1}{2}(1 - 0) = \frac{1}{2}.$$

Now every term of the sequence L_n is less that $\frac{1}{2}$, and every term of the sequence U_n is greater than $\frac{1}{2}$. Since the values of L_n get larger and larger and approach $\frac{1}{2}$ as a limit, and since the values of U_n get smaller and smaller and approach $\frac{1}{2}$ as a limit, then $\frac{1}{2}$ is the only real number r meeting the two conditions

$$L_n < r \text{ for all natural numbers } n, \text{ and}$$
$$r < U_n \text{ for all natural numbers } n.$$

Geometric intuition suggests the following fact: area A of the region under consideration is greater than every term of L_n and is less than every term of U_n. That is,

$$L_n < A \text{ for all natural numbers } n, \text{ and}$$
$$A < U_n \text{ for all natural numbers } n.$$

Hence A must be the number $\frac{1}{2}$.

REMARK. In the preceding example, two sequences were constructed, L_n and U_n, both of which have limit $\frac{1}{2}$, and this common limit was seen to be the area of the given triangular region. Since it is true in general that both the sequence of *lower sums* $(L_1, L_2, L_3, \ldots)$ and the sequence of *upper sums* $(U_1, U_2, U_3, \ldots)$ have the same limit, it will be unnecessary to consider both sequences in subsequent area problems.

The method demonstrated in Example 1 can be used to find areas of other regions of the coordinate plane.

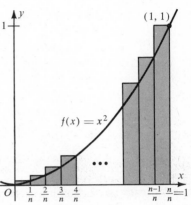

Figure 5

EXAMPLE 2. If f is the function such that $f(x) = x^2$, find the area of the region under the graph of f from $x = 0$ to $x = 1$.

Solution: Divide the interval $[0, 1]$ on the x-axis into n congruent subintervals, where n is any natural number. The right end points of the n subintervals are

$$\frac{1}{n}, \frac{2}{n}, \frac{3}{n}, \ldots, \frac{n}{n}.$$

Using these subintervals as bases, construct on each a rectangle whose height is the value of the function at the right end point. (See Figure 5.)

Construct a sequence U_n whose nth term is the sum of the areas of the n rectangles. Then

$$U_n = \frac{1}{n}f\left(\frac{1}{n}\right) + \frac{1}{n}f\left(\frac{2}{n}\right) + \frac{1}{n}f\left(\frac{3}{n}\right) + \cdots + \frac{1}{n}f\left(\frac{n}{n}\right)$$

$$= \frac{1}{n}\left(\frac{1}{n}\right)^2 + \frac{1}{n}\left(\frac{2}{n}\right)^2 + \frac{1}{n}\left(\frac{3}{n}\right)^2 + \cdots + \frac{1}{n}\left(\frac{n}{n}\right)^2$$

$$= \frac{1}{n^3}[1^2 + 2^2 + 3^2 + \cdots + n^2].$$

In Exercise 45 of Chapter 3 (p. 78), it was shown that, for all natural numbers n,

$$1^2 + 2^2 + 3^2 + \cdots + n^2 = \frac{n(n + 1)(2n + 1)}{6}.$$

Then

$$U_n = \frac{1}{n^3}\left[\frac{n(n + 1)(2n + 1)}{6}\right] = \frac{1}{6}\left(\frac{n}{n}\right)\left(\frac{n + 1}{n}\right)\left(\frac{2n + 1}{n}\right)$$

$$= \frac{1}{6}\left(1 + \frac{1}{n}\right)\left(2 + \frac{1}{n}\right),$$

so that

$$\lim_{n \to \infty} U_n = \left[\lim_{n \to \infty} \frac{1}{6} \right] \cdot \left[\lim_{n \to \infty} \left(1 + \frac{1}{n} \right) \right] \cdot \left[\lim_{n \to \infty} \left(2 + \frac{1}{n} \right) \right]$$

$$= \tfrac{1}{6}(1 + 0)(2 + 0) = \tfrac{1}{3}.$$

Thus the area of the region under the graph of f from $x = 0$ to $x = 1$ is $\tfrac{1}{3}$ square unit.

In the two preceding examples, areas over the interval $[0, 1]$ were considered. The technique used for finding those areas can now be extended to apply to areas over intervals in general on the x-axis.

Let $[a, b]$ be any closed interval on the x-axis and f a function such that, for all numbers x in $[a, b]$, $f(x) \geq 0$ and f is continuous. A sequence S_n is constructed as follows:

For every natural number n, divide the interval $[a, b]$ into n congruent subintervals, each of length $\dfrac{b - a}{n}$. Let a and b be labeled x_0 and x_n, respectively. Let the points of subdivision be labeled $x_1, x_2, x_3, \ldots, x_{n-1}$, so that $x_0 < x_1 < x_2 < x_3 < \cdots < x_{n-1} < x_n$.

For each subinterval $[x_{i-1}, x_i]$, where $i = 1, 2, 3, \ldots, n$, choose *any* point c_i such that $x_{i-1} \leq c_i \leq x_i$. Let the nth term of S_n be the number

$$S_n = (x_1 - x_0)f(c_1) + (x_2 - x_1)f(c_2) + (x_3 - x_2)f(c_3) + \cdots +$$
$$(x_n - x_{n-1})f(c_n).$$

Since all subintervals $[x_{i-1}, x_i]$ have the same length, $\dfrac{b - a}{n}$, then

$$S_n = \left(\frac{b - a}{n} \right) f(c_1) + \left(\frac{b - a}{n} \right) f(c_2)$$

$$+ \left(\frac{b - a}{n} \right) f(c_3) + \cdots + \left(\frac{b - a}{n} \right) f(c_n)$$

$$= \frac{b - a}{n} [f(c_1) + f(c_2) + f(c_3) + \cdots + f(c_n)].$$

The sequences L_n and U_n which were devised in Examples 1 and 2 are particular instances of this type of sequence.

Although the sequences considered in this Appendix use either the left end points or the right end points of the subintervals, the points c_i may be chosen arbitrarily within their respective subintervals. Thus there will be an *infinite* number of different sequences S_n for a given nonconstant function f and a given interval $[a, b]$. It can be proved that each such sequence S_n will have a limit and that these limits will all be the same number. If you study calculus, you will see that the assumption of continuity of the function is necessary to a proof of this statement. Without it, there may or may not exist a number which is the limit of all possible sequences S_n.

The **area of the region under the graph of f from $x = a$ to $x = b$** is now defined to be the limit of the sequences S_n described above.

EXAMPLE 3. In Example 2 it was shown that $\frac{1}{3}$ is the area of the region under the graph of f, where $f(x) = x^2$, from $x = 0$ to $x = 1$. Now prove that if $[a, b]$ is any interval of real numbers, then $\dfrac{b^3 - a^3}{3}$ is the area of the region under the graph of f, where $f(x) = x^2$, from $x = a$ to $x = b$.

Solution: Divide the interval $[a, b]$ into n congruent subintervals, each of length $\dfrac{b - a}{n}$. For each subinterval $[x_{i-1}, x_i]$, where $i = 1, 2, 3, \ldots, n$, choose c_i to be the right end point; that is, $c_i = a + i \cdot \dfrac{b - a}{n}$. (See Figure 6.)

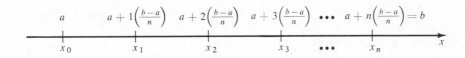

Figure 6

Let S_n be the sum of the areas of the n rectangles. Then for each natural number n,

$$S_n = \frac{b - a}{n}[f(c_1) + f(c_2) + f(c_3) + \cdots + f(c_n)]$$

$$= \frac{b - a}{n}\left[f\left(a + 1 \cdot \frac{b - a}{n}\right) + f\left(a + 2 \cdot \frac{b - a}{n}\right)\right.$$

$$\left. + f\left(a + 3 \cdot \frac{b - a}{n}\right) + \cdots + f\left(a + n \cdot \frac{b - a}{n}\right)\right)$$

$$= \frac{b - a}{n}\left[\left(a + 1 \cdot \frac{b - a}{n}\right)^2 + \left(a + 2 \cdot \frac{b - a}{n}\right)^2\right.$$

$$\left. + \left(a + 3 \cdot \frac{b - a}{n}\right)^2 + \cdots + \left(a + n \cdot \frac{b - a}{n}\right)^2\right].$$

Carrying out the computations as before gives

$$S_n = (b - a)(a^2) + a(b - a)^2\left(1 + \frac{1}{n}\right)$$

$$+ \frac{(b - a)^3}{6}\left(1 + \frac{1}{n}\right)\left(2 + \frac{1}{n}\right).$$

Then

$$\lim_{n \to \infty} S_n = (b - a)(a^2) + a(b - a)^2 + \frac{(b - a)^3}{3}$$

$$= \frac{b^3 - a^3}{3}.$$

By proceeding in the same fashion as in Example 3, the following statement can be proved: If $[a, b]$ is any interval with $0 \le a < b$, then $\dfrac{b^4 - a^4}{4}$ is the area of the region under the graph of f, where $f(x) = x^3$, from $x = a$ to $x = b$.

The results of the preceding examples in this investigation of area can be generalized as follows:

> Let p be any real number except -1, and let $[a, b]$ be any interval in which the function f, where $f(x) = x^p$, is everywhere defined and non-negative. Then $\dfrac{b^{p+1} - a^{p+1}}{p + 1}$ is the area of the region under the graph of f from $x = a$ to $x = b$.

A proof of this generalization cannot be presented easily at this point.

In the special case when $a = 0$, the expression $\dfrac{b^{p+1} - a^{p+1}}{p + 1}$ reduces to $\dfrac{b^{p+1}}{p + 1}$.   Thus the area under the graph of f, where $f(x) = x^p$, over the interval $[0, b]$ is $\dfrac{b^{p+1}}{p + 1}$.   In particular, over $[0, 1]$, the area under the graph of f, where $f(x) = x^p$, is simply $\dfrac{1}{p + 1}$.   Recall that, in Examples 1 and 2, the area under f, where $f(x) = x^1$, over $[0, 1]$ was shown to be $\frac{1}{2}$ and the area under f, where $f(x) = x^2$, over $[0, 1]$ was shown to be $\frac{1}{3}$.

EXAMPLE 4.   Find the areas of the shaded regions in Figures 7(a) and 7(b) on the opposite page.

Solution: The region in Figure 7(a) has area

$$\frac{4^5 - (-2)^5}{5} = 211\tfrac{1}{5} \text{ square units.}$$

The region in Figure 7(b) has area

$$\frac{25^{\frac{3}{2}} - 4^{\frac{3}{2}}}{\frac{3}{2}} = \frac{5^3 - 2^3}{\frac{3}{2}} = 78 \text{ square units.}$$

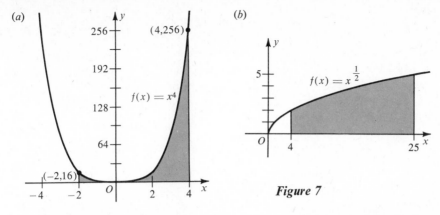

Figure 7

In this investigation of area, a method has been demonstrated for finding the area under the graph of any function f for which $f(x) = x^p (p \neq -1)$ over an interval in which the function is everywhere defined and non-negative. In the next section of this Appendix, you will develop rapid techniques for finding areas of other regions, but the techniques you will use all grow from the techniques discussed in this section.

Exercises

1. By following the procedure used in Example 2, find the area of the region under the graph of f, where $f(x) = x^3$:

   a. over $[0, 1]$ **b.** over $[0, b]$, $b > 0$

   (Use the identity $1^3 + 2^3 + 3^3 + \cdots + n^3 = \left[\dfrac{n(n + 1)}{2} \right]^2$, which is true for all natural numbers n.)

2. By following the procedure used in Example 2, find the area of the region under the graph of f, where $f(x) = cx^2$ and c is any positive real number, over the interval $[0, b]$, $b > 0$.

3. Make a conjecture regarding the area of the region under the graph of f, where $f(x) = cx^p (p \neq -1, c$ any positive real number), over any interval $[a, b]$ on which f is everywhere defined and nonnegative.

4. Find the area of the regions in Figures 1(a) and 1(b). Use any method.

5. Find the area of the region of the coordinate plane which is bounded by the graphs of f and g, where $f(x) = x^2$ and $g(x) = x^3$, and the vertical lines $x = 1$ and $x = 3$.

6. Devise a sequence whose limit is the area of the region in the first quadrant bounded by the x-axis, the y-axis, and the ellipse $\dfrac{x^2}{9} + \dfrac{y^2}{4} = 1$. Find the first three terms of this sequence. You need not attempt to find the limit of this sequence.

Integration

In the preceding section of this Appendix you saw, for a continuous function f such that $f(x) \geq 0$ for all x in $[a, b]$, how to use a limiting process to find the area of the region R under the graph of f from $x = a$ to $x = b$.

This limiting process is called **integration** and the area (or the limit) is denoted by the symbol

$$\int_a^b f(x)\, dx$$

(read "the integral from a to b of f of x with respect to x"). Thus (see Example 3, page 647),

$$\int_a^b x^2\, dx = \frac{b^3}{3} - \frac{a^3}{3}.$$

The symbolism $\int_a^b f(x)\, dx$, which was introduced by the German mathematician Gottfried Wilhelm von Leibniz (1646–1716), is suggested when you use the summation sign (page 76) to write the formula on page 646,

$$S_n = f(c_1)\left(\frac{b-a}{n}\right) + f(c_2)\left(\frac{b-a}{n}\right)$$
$$+ f(c_3)\left(\frac{b-a}{n}\right) + \cdots + f(c_n)\left(\frac{b-a}{n}\right)$$

as

$$S_n = \sum_{j=1}^{n} f(c_j)\Delta x,$$

where Δx (read "delta x" or "change in x") denotes $\dfrac{b-a}{n}$. You then make slight notational alterations to indicate the limiting process:

$$\lim_{n \to \infty} \sum_{j=1}^{n} f(c_j)\Delta x = \int_a^b f(x)\, dx. \tag{1}$$

Thus the **integral sign** $\int$, which is an elongated Old English S, corresponds to the summation sign $\sum$, which is the Greek letter sigma.

The symbol $\int_a^b f(x)\, dx$ is particularly useful in applying computational algorithms, as you will see as we look further into the notion of an integral.

The integral of a continuous function f is defined by Equation (1) as the limit of a sum even when f does not satisfy $f(x) \geq 0$ throughout $[a, b]$. Further, the integral can be interpreted geometrically in terms of area as an *algebraic sum* of areas, with areas *below* the x-axis counted as being *negative*.

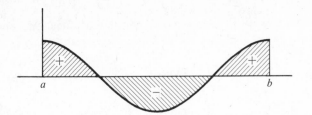

Figure 8

On page 648 it was pointed out that if p is any real number except -1 and if the function f defined by $f(x) = x^p$ is nonnegative on $[a, b]$, then the area of the region under the graph of f from $x = a$ to $x = b$ is equal to

$$\frac{b^{p+1}}{p+1} - \frac{a^{p+1}}{p+1};$$

that is,

$$\int_a^b x^p \, dx = \frac{b^{p+1}}{p+1} - \frac{a^{p+1}}{p+1}, \, p \neq -1.$$

This formula also holds if $f(x) < 0$ on all or part of $[a, b]$.

EXAMPLE 1. Evaluate $\int_{-1}^1 x^3 \, dx$.

Solution: $\quad\int_{-1}^1 x^3 \, dx = \dfrac{1^4}{4} - \dfrac{(-1)^4}{4} = \dfrac{1}{4} - \dfrac{1}{4} = 0,$ **Answer.**

You will understand why the answer in Example 1 should be 0 when you examine Figure 9.

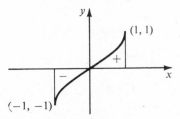

Figure 9

From Equation (1) and the properties of limits given in the theorem on page 97, you can establish some basic properties of integrals. In particular, you can define the integral not only for $b > a$ but also for $b \leq a$. However, if $b < a$ then $\Delta x = \dfrac{b - a}{n}$ is negative; you can use this fact to prove property (1) on page 652. Also, it is not necessary that the subintervals of $[a, b]$ be of equal length for each division, but only that the maximum length approaches 0 as $n \to \infty$; you can use this fact to prove property (2).

THEOREM   If f and g are continuous functions on the given intervals, and k is a real constant, then:

(1) $\displaystyle\int_a^b f(x)dx = -\int_b^a f(x)dx$

(2) $\displaystyle\int_a^b f(x)dx + \int_b^c f(x)dx = \int_a^c f(x)dx$

(3) $\displaystyle\int_a^b kf(x)dx = k\int_a^b f(x)dx$

(4) $\displaystyle\int_a^b [f(x) + g(x)]dx = \int_a^b f(x)dx + \int_a^b g(x)dx$

Proof of Property (3):

$$\int_a^b kf(x)dx = \lim_{n\to\infty} \sum_{j=1}^n kf(c_j)\Delta x = \lim_{n\to\infty} k \sum_{j=1}^n f(c_j)\Delta x$$

$$= k \lim_{n\to\infty} \sum_{j=1}^n f(c_j)\Delta x$$

$$= k \int_a^b f(x)dx$$

Supplying a reason for each step in this proof, and a proof of each of the other properties, is left to you (Exercises 3–6, below).

You can use properties (3) and (4) of the theorem to integrate any polynomial function.

EXAMPLE 2. Evaluate $\int_2^5 (x^2 - 4x + 3)dx$.

Solution: By properties (3) and (4),

$$\int_2^5 (x^2 - 4x + 3)dx = \int_2^5 x^2\,dx - 4\int_2^5 x\,dx + 3\int_2^5 dx$$

$$= \left(\frac{5^3}{3} - \frac{2^3}{3}\right) - 4\left(\frac{5^2}{2} - \frac{2^2}{2}\right) + 3(5-2) = 6,$$

Answer.

Exercises

Evaluate:

1. $\int_{-2}^3 (x^3 + 2x)dx$ **2.** $\int_0^4 (x^4 - 4x^3 + 1)dx$

3. Give a reason for each step in the proof of property (3) of this section.

Give a proof of the stated property in the theorem of this section.

4. Property (1)   **5.** Property (2)   **6.** Property (4)

7. Show that if the function f is continuous on $[a, b]$ and satisfies $m \leq f(x) \leq M$ for all x in $[a, b]$, then $m(b - a) \leq \int_a^b f(x)dx \leq M(b - a)$ for $b > a$.

The Indefinite Integral

In the preceding section of the Appendix we considered integrals with *fixed* **limits of integration** a and b. Such an integral is sometimes called a **definite integral**. Let us now consider **indefinite integrals**, or integrals with a fixed *lower* limit of integration a and a variable *upper* limit of integration x:

$$F(x) = \int_a^x f(u)du. \tag{2}$$

Notice that we have here used u as the **variable of integration** to avoid using x for two purposes. Any other letter not otherwise being used would have served as well in place of u; for example,

$$F(x) = \int_a^x f(t)\,dt.$$

Notice also that, as indicated in Equation (2), the indefinite integral of a given function f is a function F of the upper limit of integration x (see Figure 10).

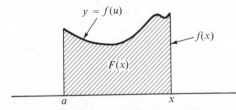

Figure 10

The processes of integration and differentiation are related through the following **fundamental theorem of calculus:**

THEOREM   If f is a continuous function on $[a, b]$, and

$$F(x) = \int_a^x f(u)du,$$

then for $a < x < b$,

$$F'(x) = f(x).$$

Proof: For any c between a and b, we must show that $F'(c) = f(c)$. Recalling from page 301 that, by definition,

$$F'(c) = \lim_{x \to c} \frac{F(x) - F(c)}{x - c},$$

we first observe that $F(x) - F(c)$ is the shaded area in Figure 11.

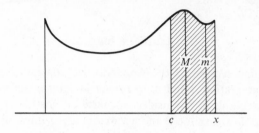

Figure 11

Next, we see that this area lies between $(x - c)m$ and $(x - c)M$, where m is the least, and M is the greatest, value of $f(u)$ in the interval $c \le u \le x$. Thus:

$$(x - c)m \le F(x) - F(c) \le (x - c)M$$

$$m \le \frac{F(x) - F(c)}{x - c} \le M.$$

Since f is continuous,

$$\lim_{x \to c} m = f(c) \text{ and also } \lim_{x \to c} M = f(c).$$

Therefore

$$F'(c) = \lim_{x \to c} \frac{F(x) - F(c)}{x - c} = f(c),$$

as desired.

Because $F'(x) = f(x)$, we say that F is a **primitive function** of f. Notice that if G is also a primitive function of f, that is, if $G'(x) = f(x)$, then

$$[F(x) - G(x)]' = F'(x) - G'(x) = f(x) - f(x) = 0;$$

that is, the derivative of the function $F - G$ is 0. Thus the tangent to the graph of $F - G$ is everywhere horizontal. Then it is intuitively clear (and can be proved) that $F - G$ must be a constant function,

$$F(x) - G(x) = k, \text{ or } F(x) = G(x) + k,$$

where k is a constant.

The relationship between F and G yields a useful rule for evaluating definite integrals. Since $\int_a^a f(u)du = 0$, it follows that $F(a) = 0$. Therefore

$$F(a) = G(a) + k = 0, \text{ or } k = -G(a),$$

and so

$$F(x) = G(x) + k = G(x) - G(a).$$

Consequently,

$$F(b) = \int_a^b f(x)dx = G(b) - G(a).$$

Thus, *to evaluate the definite integral $\int_a^b f(x)dx$, you need only to find a primitive function of f, that is, a function G such that $G' = f$, and evaluate $G(b) - G(a)$.*

EXAMPLE.   Find the area under one arch of the graph of the sine curve $y = \sin x$; that is, evaluate $\int_0^\pi \sin x \, dx$.

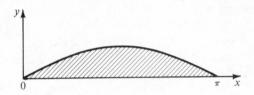

Figure 12

Solution: From page 451 you know that if $G(x) = -\cos x$, then $G'(x) = \sin x$. Accordingly,

$$\int_0^\pi \sin x \, dx = -\cos \pi - (-\cos 0)$$
$$= -(-1) - (-1) = 1 + 1 = 2.$$

$$\therefore \int_0^\pi \sin x \, dx = 2, \quad \textbf{Answer.}$$

Exercises

Evaluate, and interpret the answer graphically by means of areas.

1. $\int_0^\pi \cos x \, dx$

2. $\int_0^{\pi/2} 3 \sin x \, dx$

3. $\int_{-\pi/2}^{\pi/2} 2 \sin x \, dx$

4. $\int_{-\pi/2}^{\pi/2} \cos x \, dx$

5. $\int_1^e \frac{1}{x} dx$

6. $\int_0^1 e^x \, dx$

Chapter 3

1. Write a program that will print out the values of:
$$1!, 2!, 3!, 4!, 5!, 6!, 7!, 8!, 9!, 10!$$
2. Write a program to find the sum of the first six terms of:

   (a) $1 - \frac{1}{2!} + \frac{1}{4!} - \frac{1}{6!} + \cdots$

   (b) $1 - \frac{1}{3!} + \frac{1}{5!} - \frac{1}{7!} + \cdots$

3. Write a program that will print out the coefficients of $(a + b)^n$ when a value of n (a positive integer) is INPUT.
★ 4. Print out the polynomial $(X + Y)^N$ when a value of N (a positive integer) is INPUT.

Chapter 4

1. Write a program that will print out the sum (resultant) and inner product of two vectors when their ordered pairs are INPUT.
2. Write a program that will find the components of vector **v** parallel and perpendicular to vector **w**.

Chapter 5

1. Write a program that will find the distance between two points (the norm of the difference between two vectors).
2. Print out a scalar equation of the line through point (P1, P2) having (N1, N2) as normal vector. Also print out its direction vector.
3. Write a program to find the solution of a system of two linear equations in two variables, using the formulas given on page 200.

Chapter 6

1. Using the sequence of steps at the bottom of page 231, write a program that will find values of a polynomial when you INPUT the degree, the coefficients, and a given value of x.
2. Extend the preceding program to allow you to INPUT several values of x in succession.

Chapter 7

1. Write a program to find the sum and product of two imaginary numbers.
2. Using the formulas of Exercise 33 on page 266, write a program that will find a square root of an imaginary number.

Chapter 8

1. Write a program that will locate real roots of a polynomial equation as integers or between integers.
★ 2. Extend the preceding program so that you can find values of the nonintegral real roots to hundredths.

★ indicates the more difficult exercises.

656

Chapter 11

1. Given that $\sin 18° = \dfrac{-1 + \sqrt{5}}{4}$, find sin 3° to six decimal places. (This can be done on a calculator.)
2. Using the value of sin 3° found in the preceding exercise, write a program that will compute the sine values of angles from 0° to 90° in multiples of 3°. Round the values to four decimal places.

Chapter 12

1. Using the formula in Exercise 21 on page 476, write a program that will find the measures of the angles of a triangle when the measures of the sides are given.
2. Write a program that will find the measures of the remaining parts of a triangle, given the measures of two angles and the included side.
3. Modify the program in the preceding exercise to take care of the case when the side is not included between the angles.
4. Write a program that will find the measures of the remaining parts of a triangle, given the measures of two sides and the included angle.
★ 5. Write a program that will find the measures of the remaining parts of a triangle, given the measures of two sides and an angle *not* included between them (the ambiguous case).
6. Write a program that will print out the rectangular form for an imaginary number, given the polar form.
7. Write a program that will print out the polar form for an imaginary number, given the rectangular form.

Chapter 15

1. Using your computer's random-number-generating function, write a program that will simulate the tossing of a coin. Compute the ratio of the number of heads to the total number of tosses.
2. Write a program that will simulate tossing a pair of dice, noting the sum on each toss. (Try tossing the pair thirty times.)
★ 3. Extend the preceding program to find the ratio of the occurrence of each sum to the total number of tosses. Simulate 100 tosses, omitting the print-out of each sum.

LIST OF SYMBOLS

PAGE

cos	the cosine function over $\mathcal{R}$	376
sin	the sine function over $\mathcal{R}$	377
tan	the tangent function over $\mathcal{R}$	391
cot	the cotangent function over $\mathcal{R}$	391
sec	the secant function over $\mathcal{R}$	391
csc	the cosecant function over $\mathcal{R}$	391
$1°$	1 degree	401
$1'$	1 minute	401
$1''$	1 second	401
1^R	1 radian	401
$m° \angle AOC$	degree measure of angle AOC	402
$m^R \angle AOC$	radian measure of angle AOC	402
$l(\overset{\frown}{ED})$	length of arc ED	403
Arcsin x	the principal value of arc sin x	434
$(r, m\angle\theta)$ or (r, θ)	polar coodinates of a point	485
τ	translation	526
τ^{-1}	inverse of translation	526
ρ	rotation	532
$\begin{bmatrix} a_1\,a_2 \\ b_1\,b_2 \end{bmatrix}$ matrix		547

PAGE

A^T	A transpose	548
A^{-1}	inverse of the matrix A	556
$\delta(A)$	determinant of the matrix A	556–557
$K \times L \times M$	Cartesian product of three sets K, L, and M	565
$\mathcal{R}_3$	$\mathcal{R} \times \mathcal{R} \times \mathcal{R}$	565
$\mathbf{t} \times \mathbf{v}$	the cross product of vectors $\mathbf{t}$ and $\mathbf{v}$ in $\mathcal{R}_3$	572
U	set of all elements in a sample space	600
A	an event	600
$P(A)$	the probability of event A	600
A'	the event complementary to A	600
$P(B|A)$	conditional probability of B, given that A has occurred	607
$_nP_n$	number of permutations of a set of n different objects	611
$_nP_r$	number of permutations of a set of n different objects taken r at a time	611
$_nC_r$	number of combinations of n objects taken r at a time	613
$E(x)$	expected value of x	619

GREEK ALPHABET

Letters		Names	Letters		Names	Letters		Names
A	α	Alpha	I	ι	Iota	P	ρ	Rho
B	β	Beta	K	κ	Kappa	Σ	$\sigma\,s$	Sigma
Γ	γ	Gamma	Λ	λ	Lambda	T	τ	Tau
Δ	δ	Delta	M	μ	Mu	γ	υ	Upsilon
E	ϵ	Epsilon	N	ν	Nu	Φ	ϕ	Phi
Z	ζ	Zeta	Ξ	ξ	Xi	X	χ	Chi
H	η	Eta	O	o	Omicron	Ψ	ψ	Psi
Θ	θ	Theta	Π	π	Pi	Ω	ω	Omega

SCRIPT ALPHABET

$\mathcal{A}$	$\mathcal{E}$	$\mathcal{I}$	$\mathcal{M}$	$\mathcal{Q}$	$\mathcal{U}$	$\mathcal{X}$
$\mathcal{B}$	$\mathcal{F}$	$\mathcal{J}$	$\mathcal{N}$	$\mathcal{R}$	$\mathcal{V}$	$\mathcal{Y}$
$\mathcal{C}$	$\mathcal{G}$	$\mathcal{K}$	$\mathcal{O}$	$\mathcal{S}$	$\mathcal{W}$	$\mathcal{Z}$
$\mathcal{D}$	$\mathcal{H}$	$\mathcal{L}$	$\mathcal{P}$	$\mathcal{J}$		

GLOSSARY

Abscissa of a point. The first coordinate of the ordered pair associated with the point. (p. 123)

Absolute value. For every nonzero real number x, its **absolute value,** denoted by $|x|$, is the positive real number of the pair x and $-x$. $|0| = 0$. (p. 56)

Absolute value of a complex number. The nonnegative real number $\sqrt{a^2 + b^2}$ is called the **absolute value** of $a + bi$ (in symbols, $|a + bi|$). (p. 258)

Additive inverse. For each a in $\Re$, there exists a unique element $-a$ in $\Re$, called the **additive inverse** of a, such that $a + (-a) = 0$ (p. 35)

Algebraically complete. A field F over which *every* nonconstant polynomial is the product of a number and one or more prime *linear* polynomials over F is said to be **algebraically complete.** (p. 255)

Amplitude of a periodic function. When a periodic function attains a maximum value M and a minimum value m, the function has **amplitude** $\dfrac{M - m}{2}$. (p. 385)

Angle of depression. The angle between the line of sight to an object (below the observer) and a horizontal ray through the observer. (p. 470)

Angle of elevation. The angle between a horizontal ray through the observer and the line of sight to an object (above the observer). (p. 470)

Angle of inclination. The angle from the horizontal axis to a line in the plane. (p. 466)

Antilogarithm. If $\log_{10} k = x$, then k is called the **antilogarithm** of x, abbreviated **antilog**$_{10} x$. (p. 358)

Arithmetic means. The terms between any two given terms in an arithmetic progression. A single arithmetic mean between two numbers is the **average** or *the* **arithmetic mean.** (p. 80)

Arithmetic progression (A.P.). A sequence in which each term after the first is the sum of a given constant (called the **common difference**) and the preceding term. (p. 79)

Arithmetic series. A series whose terms are in arithmetic progression. (p. 81)

Axes. In a plane (or in space), two (or three) reference lines intersecting at right angles at a point O, called the **origin.** (pp. 123, 569)

Axiom. Statement assumed to be true. (p. 23)

Base. In r^n, r is called the **base.** (p. 70)

Between. Each point of a line segment that is not an endpoint is said to be **between** the endpoints. (p. 183)

Bounded sequence. Whenever there exists a number which equals or exceeds the absolute value of every term of a sequence, the sequence is said to be **bounded** by that number. (p. 108)

Cartesian product. The set of all ordered pairs of the elements of two sets, K and M, where the first element is from K and the second from M, denoted by $K \times M$. (p. 121)

Characteristic. The integral part of a logarithm; the exponent of 10 when the number is expressed in scientific notation. (p. 357)

Circular function. A function which involves the unit circle in its definition. See also *Sine, Cosine, Tangent, Cotangent, Secant,* and *Cosecant.* (p. 377)

Coincident. Lines that consist of the same set of points are said to **coincide,** or to be **coincident.** (p. 175)

Collinear points. A set of points all of which lie on the same line. (p. 180)

Combination. An r-element subset of a set with n elements is called a **combination** of n elements taken r at a time. (p. 613)

Common factor. If a, b, and c are integers and c is a factor cf both a and b, then c is a **common factor** or **common divisor** of a and b. The greatest such factor is called the **greatest common factor** of a and b. (G.C.F.). (p. 61)

Complement of a set A. The set of all elements in the universal set that do not belong to A (in symbols, A'). (p. 17)

Complete. A subset of real numbers is called **complete** if it contains the limit of every convergent sequence of its elements. (p. 110)

Complex number. Ordered pair of real numbers (a, b) belonging to the complex number system, written in standard form as $a + bi$. (p. 256)

Composite number. Any integer greater than 1 which is not a prime. (p. 62)

Composition of functions. The **composition** of f and g (in symbols, $f \circ g$) is a function which maps x into $f[g(x)]$. (p. 346)

Conditional. For statements p and q, the statement "If p, then q" is called the **conditional** of p and q (in symbols, $p \rightarrow q$). (p. 11)

Conditional probability. The probability that event B will occur, given that event A has occurred (in symbols, $P(B \mid A)$). (p. 607)

Conic section. The graph in $\Re \times \Re$ of an equation of the form $Ax^2 + Bxy + Cy^2 + Dx + Ey + F = 0$, where A, B, and C are not all 0. (p. 540)

Conjugate. Complex numbers of standard form $a + bi$ and $a - bi$ are called **conjugates** of each other (in symbols, $\overline{a + bi} = a - bi$). (p. 261)

Conjunction. A new statement formed by placing the word *and* between two statements p, q (in symbols, $p \wedge q$). (p. 8)

Constant function. A function whose range contains just one element. (p. 228)

Continuous. A function is said to be **continuous at c** if and only if $\lim_{x \to c} f(x) = f(c)$. A function is said to be **continuous** if it is continuous at each element of its domain. (p. 287)

Contrapositive of a conditional. If $p \rightarrow q$ is any conditional, the logically equivalent conditional $q' \rightarrow p'$ is called the **contrapositive** of the original conditional. (p. 23)

Convergent. An infinite sequence which has a limit is said to be *convergent.* (p. 96)

Converse of a conditional. When the statements p and q are interchanged in the conditional "If p, then q," the new conditional "If q, then p" is called the **converse** of the original conditional. (p. 13)

Corollary. A theorem which can be deduced quickly from another closely related theorem. (p. 40)

Cosecant function. The function whose value at x is the reciprocal of the value of the sine function at x. (p. 391)

Cosine function. The function whose domain is $\Re$ and whose range is the set of all first coordinates of the ordered pairs corresponding to the points on the unit circle. (p. 376)

Cotangent function. The function whose value at x is the ratio of the value of the cosine function to the value of the sine function at x. (p. 391)

Counterexample. A value of the variable for which the statement is false. (p. 14)

Critical points. Points on a graph of a function where the derivative equals zero. (p. 304)

Degree. The measure of the central angle subtended by an arc whose length is $\frac{1}{360}$ of the circumference of the circle (in symbols, 1°). (p. 401)

Dependent events. Two events A and B are **dependent** if and only if $P(A \cap B) \neq P(A) \cdot P(B)$. (p. 608)

Derivative. The function whose value at c is the slope of the graph of f at $[c, f(c)]$ is called the **derivative** of f (in symbols, f'). (p. 301)

Dimensions of a matrix. The number of rows (m) followed by the number of columns (n) in a matrix (in symbols, $m \times n$). (p. 547)

Direction vector. For the vector equation of a line $\{X : X = P + sv\}$, v is the **direction vector.** (pp. 144, 170)

Discriminant. $a_1^2 - 4a_0a_2$ is called the **discriminant** of $a_0x^2 + a_1x + a_2$. (p. 276)

Disjunction. A new statement formed by placing the word *or* between two statements p, q (in symbols, $p \vee q$). (p. 9)

Displacement. A change of position along a geometric line associated with each real number, or a change of position in the coordinate plane associated with each ordered pair of real numbers. (p. 125)

Divergent. An infinite sequence which does not have a limit is said to be **divergent.** (p. 98)

Divisible. If a and b are integers and $b \neq 0$, then a is said to be **divisible** by b if and only if there exists an integer q such that $a = bq$. (p. 61)

Domain. The set of all first coordinates of the ordered pairs in a relation. (p. 215)

Ellipse. The set of points in the plane such that the sum of the distance from each point in the set to two fixed points, called the **foci** of the ellipse, is a constant. (p. 515)

Empty set. The set which contains no members (in symbols, $\emptyset$). (p. 3)

Entries of a matrix. The numbers that make up the matrix. If all the entries are zeros, the matrix is a **zero matrix.** (p. 547)

Equal functions. Two functions f and g with the same domain D, and for which $f(x) = g(x)$ for each $x \in D$. (p. 226)

Equivalence statement. A statement asserting that p and q are equivalent (in symbols, $p \leftrightarrow q$). (p. 13)

Equivalent statements. When the conditional $p \rightarrow q$ and its converse $q \rightarrow p$ are both true, p and q are said to be **equivalent statements.** (p. 13)

Exponent. In r^n, n is called the **exponent** of the base r. (p. 70)

Factor. If a and b are integers, $b \neq 0$, and the equation $bx = a$ is solvable over the integers, then b is a **factor** or **divisor** of a (in symbols, $b \mid a$). (p. 61)

Factorial. If n is any positive integer, n **factorial** $(n!)$ is the product of all the positive integers from 1 to n inclusive (in symbols, $n! = 1 \cdot 2 \cdot 3 \cdots n$). $0! = 1$. (p. 89)

Factorization. If an integer is the product of other integers, say $a = bcd$, then the expression bcd is called a **factorization** of a. (p. 61)

Field. A set of numbers, together with operations of addition and multiplication, satisfying all the axioms of equality, addition, and multiplication, and the distributive axiom, is said to be a **number field,** or simply a **field.** (p. 36)

Function. A relation in which no two different ordered pairs have the same first coordinate. (p. 222)

Geometric means. The terms between any two given terms in a geometric progression. A single geometric mean between two numbers is *the* **geometric mean,** or **mean proportional,** of the numbers. (p. 84)

Geometric progression (G. P.). A sequence in which each term after the first is the product of a given constant (called the **common ratio**) and the preceding term. (p. 83)

Geometric series. A series whose terms are in geometric progression. (p. 85)

Group. Any set of elements together with a binary operation satisfying the axioms of closure, associativity, existence of identity, and existence of inverses is called a **group** with respect to the given operation. If the axiom of commutativity is also satisfied, the set is called a **commutative group.** (p. 35)

Half-plane. The line whose equation is $ax + by = c$ separates the plane into two **open half-planes:** $\{(x, y): ax + by > c\}$, and $\{(x, y): ax + by < c\}$. The line is the **boundary** of each half-plane. The union of an open half-plane and its boundary is a **closed half-plane.** (p. 219)

Hyperbola. The set of points in the plane such that the absolute value of the difference of the distances from each of two given points, called **foci,** is a constant. (p. 520)

Hypotheses. See *Premises.*

Identity. Any equation which is true for every element in the replacement sets of the variables involved. (p. 395)

Identity function. For any domain, the function which pairs each element in the domain with itself. (p. 228)

Independent events. Two events A and B are **independent** if and only if $P(A \cap B) = P(A) \cdot P(B)$. (p. 607)

Inflection point. A point **P** on a curve such that the curve is concave upward in an interval on one side of **P** and concave downward in an interval on the other side of **P**. (p. 306)

Inner product. For any two vectors, **v** and **t**, the expression $v_1t_1 + v_2t_2$ (in symbols, $\mathbf{v} \cdot \mathbf{t}$) is called the **inner product** of **v** and **t**. (p. 149)

Intersection. The **intersection** of two sets R and S (in symbols, $R \cap S$) is the set consisting of the elements belonging to *both* R and S. (p. 8)

Intersection point. A point common to two lines is called an **intersection point** of the lines. (p. 198)

Inverse of function. If f is a one-to-one function, then the **inverse** of f (in symbols f^{-1}) is the function whose domain $D_{f^{-1}}$ is the range of f and whose values are, defined by $f^{-1}(b) = a$ where $b \in R_f$ and $f(a) = b$. (p. 349)

Irreducible polynomial. A polynomial which is not reducible. (p. 253)

Lemma. A proposition introduced to help prove another theorem. (p. 187)

Limit of a function. A function $f(x)$ has a limit ℓ at c (in symbols, $\lim\limits_{x \to c} f(x) = \ell$) provided that the sequence $f(x_n)$ approaches ℓ whenever the sequence x_n approaches c. (p. 286)

Limit of a sequence. Any infinite sequence $a_1, a_2, \ldots, a_n, \ldots$ has a limit A (in symbols, $\lim\limits_{n \to \infty} a_n = A$) provided that for each positive number h there exists a positive integer M such that $|a_n - A| < h$ if $n \geq M$. (p. 96)

Linear equation. Any equation of the form $ax + by = c$, where a, b, and c denote real constants and $(a, b) \neq 0$, is called a **linear equation** in the variables x and y. (p. 190)

Linear relation. A relation defined by an open sentence in which one member is an expression of the form $ax + by$ (a and b constants and not both zero), and the other member is a constant. (p. 219)

Locus. The set containing all points that satisfy a certain condition and containing no points that do not satisfy that condition. (p. 508)

Logically equivalent. Any two compound statements whose truth values are the same for each particular assignment of truth values to the original statements are said to be **logically equivalent.** (p. 20)

Mantissa. The decimal fractional part of a logarithm. (p. 357)

Matrix. A rectangular array of numbers. (p. 547)

Members of a set. Objects in a set, which are said to *belong to* or to *be contained in* the set. (p. 2)

***m*-fold factor.** If $P(x)$ and $Q(x)$ are polynomials, $P(x) = (x - a)^m Q(x)$, and $x - a$ is not a factor of $Q(x)$, then $x - a$ is called an ***m*-fold factor** of $P(x)$, or a factor of **multiplicity *m*.** (p. 239)

Minute. $\frac{1}{60}$ of a degree (in symbols, $1'$). (p. 401)

Modulus. See *Absolute value of complex numbers.*

Multiplicative inverse. For each a except 0 in $\Re$, there exists a unique element $\frac{1}{a}$ in $\Re$, called the **multiplicative inverse** of a, such that $a \cdot \frac{1}{a} = 1$ and $\frac{1}{a} \cdot a = 1$. (p. 35)

Mutually exclusive. The events A and B are **mutually exclusive** if $A \cap B = \emptyset$. (p. 604)

Negation of a statement. If p represents any statement, then *not p* (in symbols p') is the denial of p and is called the **negation** of p. (p. 15)

Negative number. A real number c for which the statement "$c < 0$" is true. (p. 50)

Norm of a vector. A real number (in symbols $\|v\|$) giving the length of an arrow representing the vector. (p. 138)

Normal vector. Any nonzero vector perpendicular to a direction vector of a line is called a **normal vector** to the line. (p. 189)

Octant. Each of the eight regions into which space is separated by a set of coordinate planes. (p. 570)

One-to-one function. A function which pairs distinct elements of the domain with distinct elements of the range. (p. 346)

Open sentence. A sentence containing a variable. (p. 5)

Ordinate of a point. The second coordinate of the ordered pair associated with the point. (p. 123)

Orthogonal vectors. See *Perpendicular vectors.*

Parabola. The set of points equidistant from a fixed line and a fixed point not on the line. The fixed line is called the **directrix,** and the fixed point, the **focus** of the parabola. (p. 513)

Parameter. A variable such as the variable t in the vector equation for a line, $L = \{X : X = P + tv, t \in \Re\}$. (p. 171)

Periodic function. A function whose values recur at regular intervals. Its **period** is the length of the shortest such interval. (p. 383)

Permutation. An arrangement of a set of objects in a particular order. (p. 611)

Perpendicular components of a vector. Two perpendicular vectors **w** and **t** whose sum is **v** are called **perpendicular components** of **v**. (p. 157)

Perpendicular lines. Two lines are said to be **perpendicular** to each other if a direction vector of one is perpendicular to a direction vector of the other. Line segments are **perpendicular** provided that the lines containing them are perpendicular lines. (p. 191)

Perpendicular vectors. Two vectors whose inner product is zero. (p. 149)

Phase shift. The graphs of the equations $y = A \sin (Bx + C)$ and $y = A \cos (Bx + C)$, $B \neq 0$, are sinusoids with **phase shift** equal to $\dfrac{-C}{B}$. (p. 389)

Polar coordinates. The components of the ordered pair (r, θ) specifying the location of a point in the plane in terms of the distance from a fixed point, called the **pole,** and the direction from a fixed line, called the **polar axis,** through the pole. (p. 486)

Polynomial. An expression of the form $a_0 x^n + a_1 x^{n-1} + \cdots + a_{n-2} x^2 + a_{n-1} x + a_n$, where n denotes a nonnegative integer. The numbers $a_0, a_1, \ldots, a_{n-1}, a_n$ are the **coefficients** of the polynomial. The exponents $n, n - 1, \ldots 2, 1$ of x are the **degrees** of the terms in which they appear. (p. 230)

Polynomial equation. An equation of the form $P(x) = 0$, where $P(x)$ is a polynomial. The roots of the equation are called the **zeros** of P. (p. 238)

Polynomial function. A function defined by an equation of the form $y = P(x)$, where $P(x)$ is a polynomial. (p. 231)

Positive number. A real number c for which the statement "$0 < c$" is true. (p. 50)

Postulate. See *Axiom.*

Premises. Statements which are given as true. (p. 22)

Prime polynomial. An irreducible polynomial whose leading coefficient is 1. (p. 253)

Prime number. If an integer greater than 1 has only a trivial factorization ($a = 1 \cdot a$), then the integer is called a **prime number,** or simply a **prime.** (p. 62)

Proposition. See *Statement.*

Quadrantal angle. An angle whose terminal ray lies on one of the coordinate axes. (p. 408)

Quadrant. Each of the four regions into which the plane is separated by a set of coordinate axes. (p. 123)

Quantifier. Word(s) involving the idea of *how many* or *quantity*, such as *all, every, some, there exists,* and so on, used in combination with a variable in an open sentence. (p. 6)

Radian. The measure of the central angle subtended by an arc of length 1 on the unit circle (in symbols, 1^R). (p. 401)

Radical. The symbol $\sqrt[n]{a}$ is called a **radical** and is read "the nonnegative **nth root** of a." (p. 113)

Range. The set of all second coordinates of the ordered pairs in a relation. (p. 215)

Reciprocal. See *Multiplicative inverse.*

Recursion formula. A formula that states the relationship between each term and its successor in a sequence. (p. 75)

Reducible polynomial. A polynomial over a field F is **reducible** over F if it is the product of two or more polynomials over F, none of which is a constant. (p. 253)

Reduction formulas. Formulas used to reduce the problem of finding a function value of a given number (or angle with given measure) in Quadrants II, III, and IV to one of finding a function value on Quadrant I. (p. 417)

Relation. A set of ordered pairs. (p. 215)

Relative maximum [minimum]. $f(c)$ is a **relative maximum [minimum]** of a function f provided that there exist distinct real numbers a and b, $a < c < b$, such that if x is between a and b, then $f(c) \geq f(x)$ $[f(c) \leq f(x)]$. (p. 306)

Relatively prime. If the greatest common integer factor of two integers is 1, then they are said to be **relatively prime.** (p. 61)

Resolving a vector. Expressing a vector as a sum of perpendicular components, one of which has a specified direction. (p. 157)

Resultant. The sum of two vectors. (p. 138)

Rotation. A function which maps each point (x, y) into the point $(x \cos \emptyset - y \sin \emptyset, x \sin \emptyset + y \cos \emptyset)$, where $\emptyset$ denotes a real constant (or the radian or degree measure of an angle). (p. 533)

Sample space. The set of all possible outcomes of a random experiment. (p. 600)

Scalar. Any real number. (p. 131)

Scalar equation of a line. An equation for the line of the form $ax + by = c$. (p. 190)

Secant function. The function whose value at x is the reciprocal of the values of the cosine function at x. (p. 391)

Second. $\frac{1}{60}$ of a minute (in symbols, $1''$). (p. 401)

Second derivative. The derivative of the derivative (in symbols, f''). (p. 302)

Sequence. A set of elements in one-to-one correspondence with the set of positive integers (an infinite sequence) or with a subset $\{1, 2, 3, \ldots, m\}$ of the positive integers (a finite sequence). (p. 75)

Series. An expression consisting of the terms of a sequence alternating with the symbol $+$. (p. 76)

Sigma. Sigma ($\sum$) is called the **summation sign** and is used to abbreviate the writing of a series. (p. 76)

Sine function. The function whose domain is $\Re$ and whose range is the set of all second coordinates of the ordered pairs corresponding to the points on the unit circle. (p. 377)

Sinusoid. Graph of the sine function, also called a **sine wave.** (p. 383)

Slope. If $\mathbf{v} = (v_1, v_2)$ is a direction vector for the line $\mathcal{L}$, and $v_1 \neq 0$, then the ratio $\frac{v_2}{v_1}$ is called the **slope** of $\mathcal{L}$. (p. 203)

Solution set. The subset of the domain of an open sentence consisting of the values of the variable for which the sentence is true. (p. 5)

Solving two linear equations simultaneously. Determining coordinates of the intersection of the two lines specified by the linear equations. (p. 199)

Standard form. Every complex number (a, b) can be written in **standard form** $a + bi$, where a is called the **real part** and b the **imaginary part** of $a + bi$. (p. 256)

Standard position. In a Cartesian coordinate system, angles having the origin as vertex and the positive ray of the horizontal axis as initial side are said to be in **standard position.** (p. 400)

Standard representation. An arrow which has its initial point at the origin is said to be in **standard position** and to be the **standard representation** of the ordered pair giving the coordinates of its terminal point. (p. 127)

Statement. In logic, a set of symbols which forms a meaningful assertion that is either true or false, but not both true and false. (p. 1)

Subset. When two sets R and S are such that every element of R is an element of S, R is said to be a **subset** of S (in symbols $R \subset S$). Each set is said to be the **improper subset** of itself; every other subset is called a **proper subset** of the set. (p. 3)

Tangent. The **tangent** to the graph of f at $P[c, f(c)]$ is the line through P with slope equal to $\lim\limits_{x \to c} \dfrac{f(x) - f(c)}{x - c}$ if this limit exists. (p. 294)

Tangent function. The function whose value at x is the ratio of the value of the sine function to the value of the cosine function at x. (p. 391)

Tautology. A combination of statements which is always true, regardless of the truth value assigned to the original statements. (p. 20)

Theorem. A statement which can be proved from other statements accepted or previously proved to be true. (p. 21)

Translation. A function which maps each point (x, y) into the point $(x + r, y + s)$, where (r, s) is a given vector. (p. 526)

Transpose. If the rows of a matrix A are the same as the columns of a matrix B, then each is called the **transpose** of the other (in symbols, $A = B^{\mathsf{T}}$). (p. 548)

Truth set. See *Solution set*.

Union. The **union** of two sets R and S (in symbols, $R \cup S$) is the set consisting of the elements belonging to *at least one* of the given sets. (p. 8)

Unit circle. A circle whose radius is one unit. (p. 373)

Unit vector. A vector whose length is one unit. (p. 146)

Value of a function at x. For any ordered pair (x, y) of a function A, the second element y is called the **value of the function at x** (in symbols $A(x)$). (p. 222)

Variable. A symbol used to represent any element of a specified set. (p. 4)

Vector. Any ordered pair of real numbers (x, y). The sum of two ordered pairs is a **vector sum,** and the operation associated with the sum is **vector addition.** (p. 131)

Venn diagram. A drawing used to picture set relationships. (p. 3)

x-intercept. The x-coordinate of the point in which a line intersects the x-axis is called the x-intercept of the line. (p. 206)

y-intercept. The y-coordinate of the point in which a line intersects the y-axis is called the y-intercept of the line; the constant d in the equation of a line, $y = mx + d$. (p. 205)

Answers for

Odd-Numbered Exercises

Modern Introductory Analysis

MARY P. DOLCIANI

EDWIN F. BECKENBACH

ALFRED J. DONNELLY

RAY C. JURGENSEN

WILLIAM WOOTON

HOUGHTON MIFFLIN COMPANY · BOSTON

ATLANTA · DALLAS · GENEVA, ILL. · HOPEWELL, NEW JERSEY · PALO ALTO